⁕⟨ VOLUME 3 ⟩⁕

THE PAPERS OF JOSEPH HENRY

January 1836–December 1837

The Princeton Years

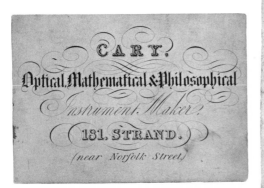

Souvenirs from Henry's European trip. Courtesy of the Smithsonian Archives.

Henry, Joseph

The Papers of
JOSEPH HENRY

Editor: Nathan Reingold
Associate Editor: Arthur P. Molella
Assistant Editor: Marc Rothenberg
Staff Historian: Kathleen Waldenfels
Research Assistant: Joel N. Bodansky

 VOLUME 3

January 1836–December 1837
The Princeton Years

SMITHSONIAN INSTITUTION PRESS
CITY OF WASHINGTON
1979

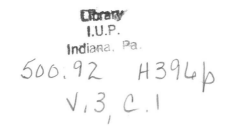
The preparation of this volume of The Papers of Joseph Henry *was made possible in part through a grant from the Editing Program of the National Endowment for the Humanities, an independent Federal agency.*

Published in the United States by the Smithsonian Institution Press. Designed by Crimilda Pontes. Produced in the United States by Heritage Printers, Inc.

ENDPAPERS: *A modern view of Nassau Hall—in Henry's day the center of college activities. Courtesy of the Princeton University Archives.*

Library of Congress Cataloging in Publication Data

Henry, Joseph, 1797–1878
The papers of Joseph Henry.

Includes bibliographical references and index.

CONTENTS: *v. 1. December 1797–October 1832: the Albany years.*
    v. 2. November 1832–December 1835: the Princeton years.
    v. 3. January 1836–December 1837: the Princeton years.

1. Science—Collected works.
2. Science—History—United States—Collected works.
3. Smithsonian Institution—Collected works.
  I. Reingold, Nathan, ed.
Q113.H43   537'.092'4   72–2005
ISBN 0–87474–123–8 (v. 1)

ISBN 0–87474–174–2 (v. 3)

⁓{ CONTENTS }⁓

Contents

philosophy course (ca. November 11)—Refereeing for the American Philosophical Society: Emmet's theory of colors (December 4)—The continuing controversy in meteorology.

❧ ILLUSTRATIONS ❧

Frontispiece: Souvenirs
from Henry's European Trip

Although the time span of this volume is only two years, the period covered was extraordinarily eventful. It is filled with beginnings, foreshadowings, and accomplishments, as Henry becomes more and more involved in both the national and international scientific communities. He was one of a number of scientists whose advice was solicited in regard to the United States Exploring Expedition, which sailed, after many delays, in 1838. The effects of that expedition preoccupied an entire generation of American scientists. Henry was also a participant in the international effort to elucidate the phenomena of terrestrial magnetism, an effort expanded in 1838 with the organization of Edward Sabine's "magnetic crusade." Such events, however, were overshadowed in Henry's life by his first trip to Europe, a formative interlude in his early career. Henry's tour of Britain, France, and Belgium, which occupied most of 1837, supplies the core of this volume's documentation. The routine of academic and family life was upset by preparations for the voyage and eight months of travel. Henry's research program was interrupted; his teaching schedule was accelerated; Harriet prepared to move the family to the Albany-Schenectady area for the duration of Henry's absence.

Henry's experience abroad was not unique. Many of his professional colleagues went to Europe in the early decades of the century, part of a general European-American tourist boom[1] that took hold in this era as the transatlantic cultures sought to become reacquainted after the turmoil of revolution and the Napoleonic Wars. When Benjamin Silliman traveled in the first decade of the century the threat of war was a major feature of the European scene.[2] No such hindrances, save for the disputes which made crossing the border into Holland a prohibiting inconvenience,[3] confronted Henry and his traveling companions. And the trip was not considered overly expensive: Henry estimated that (with his family staying with friends) the entire cost of the trip would not amount to much more

[1] For our general descriptions of American travel abroad, we are indebted to Foster Rhea Dulles, *Americans Abroad: Two Centuries of European Travel* (Ann Arbor, Michigan, 1964).

[2] John F. Fulton and Elizabeth H. Thomson, *Benjamin Silliman, Pathfinder in American Science* (New York, 1947), Chapter III.

[3] See his comments in his letter to Harriet of July 26–31, 1837, printed in this volume.

than the costs of remaining home. Even the Panic of 1837,[4] which worsened during Henry's tour and worried some travelers, failed to curtail Henry's itinerary. Transportation developments were a major factor in the growth of the tourist trade. The inauguration of regularly scheduled packet service in 1818 was a signal event. In his printed travel journal *Sketches of Europe* (1833),[5] the inventor Zachariah Allen made a point of this convenience in advising the "practical tourist." The regular sailings were an accepted but appreciated feature of Henry's travels. Just after Henry's return to the United States another upturn in tourism occurred when the great steamers began to ply oceanic routes. Between 1820 and 1860, an estimated two to eight thousand Americans visited Europe annually, depending upon political and economic conditions.[6] The itinerary of the general traveler was well established by the middle third of the nineteenth century.[7] Great Britain, France, and Italy were considered essential. The Low Countries, Germany, and Switzerland were thought optional. Tourist attractions then were pretty much the same as now: museums, cathedrals, palaces, shopping promenades, and the theater. Side visits to ancestral homes, such as Henry's visit to Ayrshire, Scotland, were common. The popularity of Sir Walter Scott made a visit to the sites of his works almost obligatory. If Belgium was included, then it was quite likely that an excursion would be made to the battlefield of Waterloo.

The European tour was especially attractive to the intellectual and artistic communities—painters, sculptors, scientists, literary figures, and scholars—who viewed their tours as a necessity for their personal and professional growth. For them, the European journey represented a strengthening of the links between Old and New World cultures—links temporarily weakened by republican upheaval. There was even a sense of pilgrimage. Yet, while feelings of heritage and participation were strong in these travelers, they went also to measure themselves against older cultures—a competitive attitude manifested by most American visitors.

As deeply imbued with a sense of European heritage as their artistic and literary countrymen, Henry and his scientific colleagues harbored an enormous curiosity about the European scientific world, a world known through the literature but still tantalizingly distant. Scientists went abroad to meet great figures, to pay homage to historic personages, to immerse themselves in cultural wellsprings. The travel diaries of Henry and his contemporaries

---

[4] Henry had always been interested in economics, but the magnitude of the depression led him to reexamine the American economy. He concluded that speculation was the root of the problem and came down in favor of hard money (a stand which will be further documented in the next volume).

[5] 2 vols. (Boston), *1*:13.

[6] Dulles, op. cit., p. 27.

[7] Ibid., pp. 68–85.

convey the thrill of these encounters. Reinforcing these reverent feelings were traditional ideologies of scientific internationalism and of the cumulative and progressive nature of the scientific enterprise. And yet, the visitors were far from overawed. Conflicting with filial piety was the competitive spirit of science, prizing novelty and priority of discovery. National rivalries heightened these competitive instincts. The European trip was both a badge of participation and a self-advertisement for the American scientist.

A youthful Benjamin Silliman was something of a pioneer with his year-long stay in England in 1805 and 1806. But by the time of Henry's visit, the trip abroad was all the fashion among scientists. John Torrey, Henry Darwin Rogers, Asa Gray, Elias Loomis, and Alexander Dallas Bache, to name only some of the notables, all traveled abroad for varying lengths of time in the 1830s.[8] And, as Henry was to discover in his travels, a multitude of lesser known figures from his country's scientific, medical, and technical communities were crisscrossing Europe at the same time.

Scientists often had institutional backing for the European trip. American colleges of the early nineteenth century were eager to upgrade their science curricula and their laboratory facilities; the recognized superiority of the European, especially the French, instrument makers made buying trips a pleasurable necessity for many professors of natural philosophy. They also embraced the opportunity to observe research methods in European laboratories. Henry's natural history colleagues received support for related activities: to fill out their collections, to exchange specimens, to see North American type specimens which were often found in European cabinets[9] and, in general, to make comparisons of Old and New World phenomena. The European sojourns were an opportunity to take care of other necessities: to obtain books not readily available in the United States for personal or academic libraries, to participate in meetings of general and specialized societies, to attend lectures, and to obtain information and data best gained through personal contact. American colleges realized that the value of sending their leading scientific faculty members to Europe went beyond anticipated improvements to the laboratories, collections, and libraries. A successful trip was a point of institutional pride and symbolic of the college's aspirations.

---

[8] A comparison of the experiences of some of these travelers in the fourth decade is made by Bruce Sinclair, "Americans Abroad: The Class of '37 Tours Britain," in Nathan Reingold, ed., *The Sciences in the American Context: New Perspectives* (in press).

[9] When Asa Gray traveled abroad in 1838 and 1839 one of his chief aims was to examine North American materials owned by European botanists. A. Hunter Dupree, *Asa Gray* (New York, 1968), pp. 74–92.

Eager to establish its reputation, Princeton shared these aspirations and commissioned Henry to buy apparatus for the outmoded laboratories of Philosophical Hall. Unfortunately, the college's good intentions were thwarted by the economic downturn of 1837. While continuing Henry's salary (which he had earned anyway through double teaching in the months before departure), their initial pledge of $5000 for philosophical apparatus dwindled to a mere $600. Nevertheless, Henry purchased a respectable collection of both research and demonstration apparatus, while seriously pursuing the professional goals he had set for himself:

> 1st. The formation of personal acquaintance with men of science which may be the basis of future correspondence on scientific subjects. 2nd. The study of the modes of instruction in science. 3rd. The methods of making original researches in the different branches of science. In short, to make such attainments as may be useful either in the way of my duties as an instructor or in reference to my own researches and which cannot be obtained from books.[10]

Henry was an avid sightseer and, in many respects, the typical scientific tourist. The scientific traveler, like any other, needs his landmarks, institutional and personal. The great names and venerable institutions fill Henry's diary as one might expect with an impressionable first-time traveler. They are the royalty of his European chronicles (the other royalty also received attention but considerably less respect). Armed with letters of introduction, Henry met most of the leading figures of British science and saw several eminent French investigators as well. He viewed historic implements and manuscripts: Newton's reflector, Boyle's air pump, and a manuscript *Principia* at the Royal Society of London; letters of famous scientists gathered by David Brewster and by Faraday. He heard popular lectures at the Royal Institution and attended sessions at the Paris Academy of Sciences.

Travel diaries, like the slides of modern-day tourists, tend to look alike and Henry's written impressions are sharply reminiscent of earlier printed diaries like Benjamin Silliman's and Zachariah Allen's. Indeed, previous diarists provided Henry with a guidebook of sorts for his European tour. Yet there are important differences hinging on Henry's scientific interests and position. His was not just a general tour of science abroad, but one shaped by professional and special concerns.

Astronomical observatories were an obligatory tourist stop for most scientific travelers, but Henry had an additional motivation for visiting observatories. Detailed descriptions of the Edinburgh and Cambridge Ob-

---

[10] See below, Henry to Anonymous, February 6, 1837.

servatories have survived in Henry's diary. He wanted information on astronomical techniques and apparatus both for himself and his brother-in-law Stephen Alexander, whose deep interest in astronomy was already evident and who would exploit the opportunity presented by Henry's absence (with Henry's cooperation and encouragement) to begin his own career as an astronomer at Princeton. The observatories were great centers of scientific discovery whose equivalent did not exist in the United States. Modern research observatories were in many ways the marvels of Henry's scientific world. They represented the coming together of skilled technologists, tremendous financial support for science, and the concept of cooperative scientific investigation. The problems being studied were inherently interesting; astronomy, after all, was the queen of the sciences.

The hospitality shown Henry at observatories exceeded that usually accorded scientific visitors. Perhaps the most eminent American scientist to visit Europe since Benjamin Franklin, Henry had no difficulty in making professional contacts. As he confided to Harriet mid-way through his journey:

> I believe . . . I could furnish more material for sketches in the line of English and French science than anyone who has of late years visited Europe since I have been usually fortunate in gaining admission to intimacy with most of the men actually engaged in science in London and Paris.[11]

This was especially true in his field of expertise. An active and respected research scientist, Henry's range of associations with workers in electricity and magnetism was extensive, reflecting a lively and well-populated community in this field. Most of the eminent names in electromagnetism appear in his journal, including Faraday, Wheatstone, and Sturgeon. Not only was he admitted to their laboratories, but he was even invited to participate with them in experimentation. An indication of the high regard for Henry was an invitation into Faraday's home.

Another notable feature of his travel diary is the presence of many not-so-familiar European scientific figures. Included are electromagnetic investigators like Snow Harris and S. Hunter Christie, and makers of electrical instruments like E. M. Clarke. Despite their subsequent historical obscurity, they were once active participants in the research community.

Henry was also an assiduous notetaker at lectures delivered by illustrious figures like Gay-Lussac and Michael Faraday. His extensive contacts with working and teaching scientists left him impressed but often gave him a

---

[11] Quoted from his first letter to Harriet of July 5, 1837, printed below.

more realistic view of living monuments, resulting in some candid portraits.[12] Perhaps memories of a recent rivalry tinctured these impressions of Faraday:

> Mr F is deservedly a very popular lecture[r] but does not surprise or strike one with the depth of his remarkes or the power of a profound mind but more by his vivacity of manner & his hapy illustrations as well as inimitable tact of experimenting.[13]

Faraday was notorious for a deceptively simple demeanor. Other examples of Henry's skepticism were perhaps closer to the mark, as, for example, his impressions of a distinguished and historic Paris institution, the Academy of Sciences. After attending one of the meetings of that body, Henry was more impressed by the open boredom of the attending savants than by the quality of the proceedings, correctly sensing that the action in French science had passed elsewhere.

In fact, many of Henry's opinions of France would provide ammunition for recent historiography arguing the decline of French science in the nineteenth century. He felt that the French scientific elite was preoccupied with political and economic considerations rather than original research. Compared to the openness and friendliness of the English scientific community, Henry thought the French aloof and uninterested in his work. Not until he met younger less established French scientists did he develop relationships comparable to those he had in London. Henry's evaluation of French and British science must, however, be qualified. At least some of Henry's problems with French science can be traced to differences in perception and reception. The language and cultural differences made France appear alien to Henry, predisposing him to be critical, while British institutions and attitudes, if sometimes new, were understandable.

While Henry was busy evaluating European science, Europeans were just as concerned with the progress of the Americans. As one of the active participants in efforts to raise American science to the level of Europe, Henry was very sensitive to European evaluations. He knew first hand of the charlatans and incompetents, their ability to obtain undeserved publicity and praise, and their success in discrediting American science in the eyes of Europeans who represented the standard for science. When John Edward Gray of the British Museum pointed out certain deficiencies of American

---

[12] Henry took some satisfaction in telling Asa Gray that those "we have long considered almost more than human" are "but men inferior perhaps in some respects to ourselves."

Quoted in Dupree, op. cit., p. 74.

[13] From Henry's second diary entry of April 8, 1837, printed below.

naturalists, Henry quietly agreed. But again, as one of the participants in reform, he appreciated the importance of separating in European minds the competent from the incompetent. He vigorously fought the possibility that American would become simply an epithet for incompetence and enjoyed every sign of European acceptance of American activity. He was naturally gratified by the enthusiastic response to his own work.

While anxious for his country's scientific reputation, Henry resisted the intrusion of partisan considerations into scientific and technological questions. He responded angrily to the practice of evaluating scientific output or technological results according to the nationality of the scientist or inventor. Each publication or innovation should, in Henry's view, be judged upon its own merits. Both patriotic pride and scientific sensibilities were severely hurt on those occasions when Americans came under what Henry felt were prejudicial attacks. In May 1837 he became involved in the controversy surrounding the Franklin Institute's report on steam boiler explosions. The editor of the *Magazine of Popular Science and Useful Knowledge* had used the opportunity of reviewing the report to make cutting attacks upon American science which revealed little but the editor's own bad taste and ignorance of the subject. When Henry, at the editor's request, wrote an analysis of the Institute's work, the editor mutilated Henry's article, twisting it into another attack on America. Another difficult incident occurred at the 1837 meeting of the British Association, just a few weeks prior to Henry's return to the United States. The encyclopedist Dionysius Lardner, displaying a combination of ignorance and chauvinism, called Henry a liar when Henry claimed that Hudson River steamboats reached velocities exceeding those in England. Even some of Lardner's countrymen were embarrassed by his obvious bias. Henry's rapid vindication just underlined the problems created when partisanship invaded scientific and technological discussions.

One unfortunate but understandable American response to English sneers was to wave the flag whenever an American did obtain recognition from the European community. One such incident involving Henry took place during his visit to England: Henry's success in producing self-induction from thermoelectricity after Faraday had failed. Adding to Henry's triumph was his acknowledged superior understanding of the phenomenon. The story became more involved and more a triumph of America over England with each telling, as native talent bested the leading lights of English science on their home ground.

European physics at the time of Henry's visit was undergoing theoretical ferment. Early in the century a vigorous debate had revived over the atomic versus the wave conception of nature. Although a shift to undulatory modes first appeared in optics, its effect soon extended to electricity, magnetism, and heat theory. These stirrings were an important part of what Henry saw overseas. David Brewster, a noted holdout for a corpuscularian optics, entertained Henry in his laboratory near Melrose Abbey with a series of demonstrations designed to refute the wave model. In Paris, Henry received subtle indoctrination to the opposite effect from Babinet, an instrument maker and physicist devoted to Fresnel's wave conception. Paris was also the scene for a fruitful encounter between Henry and the brilliant Italian émigré Melloni, a pioneer in the wave theory of heat. On occasion, Henry was even treated to doses of history calculated to advance one or the other of the conflicting arguments. Curiously, the issue of physical models apparently did not arise at all between Henry and Faraday in their discussions of electricity. In 1838, Henry would opt for the idea of an electrical plenum and would soon emerge as an adherent of wave and plenist theories. However, these commitments, to our knowledge, had no visible effect on his basic (non-field) approach to electricity and magnetism. Nor did the theoretical nuances of the corpuscular-wave debates appeal to him in general, even when in the presence of able polemicists like Brewster. What counted for him were the tangible manifestations in the laboratory of the hypothetical models. If the theoretical issues did not seem to register strongly with him in Europe, the experimental ingenuity demonstrated in the debates made a profound impression. Henry took meticulous notes, for instance, on the ultrasensitive thermoelectric devices invented by Melloni for the study of heat radiation. Babinet's superb optical laboratory received equal attention. He showed great curiosity in Wheatstone's revolving-mirror apparatus for determining electrical velocity, a device that would soon be applied to optics in a decisive test between the wave and corpuscular alternatives.

The 1830s were also a time of philosophical ferment in Britain: Whewell and Babbage clashed over the role of miracles in natural theological arguments; Brewster attacked Whewell's idealist philosophy of science; many questioned the validity of Bacon as a model for scientific research. Henry encountered but generally stayed aloof from the controversies. Aware of the differing philosophical views, he rarely, at this stage, took sides. Babbage's *Ninth Bridgewater Treatise* was a case in point. Henry knew of Babbage's defense of miracles as manifestations of the Divine Order and therefore not violations of the tenets of natural theology. Since natural theology was part of the basic intellectual fabric of American science, he was also aware of the significance of such a defense. Yet his comment on Babbage's view, recorded in his diary entry of April 22, 1837, was limited to a noncommittal indication of interest. He neither condemned nor defended.

The only important philosophical stand taken by Henry in his European diary was one more likely to attract the attention of the experimentalist than the theorist. Speaking, as it were, for an entire generation of American scientists who were subsequently libeled as "Baconians," Henry recorded his feelings while visiting Brewster at his manor in Scotland: "No working man of science advocates Bacons method."[14] Henry's position, more fully expounded later in his career, was to accept Bacon as an important symbol of the inductive method, but to deny him practical significance. Since he had interpreted Bacon's method as naive empiricism, a method which could not lead to scientific discovery, he argued for what he thought was the contrary position: carefully tested hypotheses were essential if mankind was to further its understanding of the natural world; data without organizing theories was not science.

For all the scientific and intellectual excitement of the European scene, it is noteworthy that Henry's diary begins not with a visit to a scientific laboratory or lecture hall, but with a day-long tour of the great naval shipyards of Plymouth harbor, where he disembarked. His technological observations were not limited to the celebrated achievements of British shipbuilding. Major portions of the European journal are devoted to lighthouses, harborworks, railroads, gas establishments, and even London breweries. He attended lectures at technical societies on subjects from chronometers to paper making.

Applied topics were prominent for several reasons. To begin with, technical feats were notable, often picturesque features of the European landscape; Henry was as impressed by the spectacle as any tourist. The famous Eddystone Lighthouse at Plymouth, designed by the architect-engineer John Smeaton, was a landmark, and the Thames Tunnel, in the final stages of construction under the superintendence of the famed M. I. Brunel, was already on the way to becoming one. The Northern Lights, the magnificent Scottish lighthouse system which Henry visited in August 1837, had been immortalized by the celebrated tour of Sir Walter Scott. The British railway system, in its first decade of construction, impressed visitors with its elaborate and, as some Americans felt, extravagant engineering.

But technological developments were more than mere tourist attractions to Henry. To the extent that they embodied scientific principles they were matters of professional interest to him. The Scottish lighthouses were a dramatic example. In the year of Henry's visit, they were undergoing a technological revolution with the introduction of dioptric lights developed

---

[14] Henry expressed his opinion in "Visit to Melrose Abbey to Dr Brewster," August 19–21, 1837, printed below.

by the brothers Fresnel (the engineer Léonor and the optical physicist Augustin Jean). Henry's visit to these establishments centered on the scientific principles underlying the revolution, particularly the optical geometry of what came to be known as the Fresnel lens. At the London gas works, Henry took special note of the self-registering devices used to measure gas flow, with the thought of applying the devices to scientific areas such as meteorology.

Henry's contemplation of science in applied contexts may puzzle some historians expecting a neat dichotomy between pure and applied. The technological detail may seem to them to be only a diversion from the real science being done in European laboratories. Actually, Henry sought out technological situations in large part because his European scientific colleagues were there as well—conducting research, consulting, instructing, or otherwise earning a living. The people he saw in England and, to a lesser extent, in France moved easily between the worlds of science and high technology. Actually it was all one world in the nineteenth century. Take the case of the Plymouth shipyard. Snow Harris, that city's resident scientific genius, regularly visited the dockyards to take readings of temperature and rainfall for a series of articles presented to the British Association. Harris had a more intimate nautical connection through his effort to sell the Admiralty his controversial scientific method of mounting lightning rods on ships. British shipyards provide another important example of such interpenetrations. Some of the ship designs Henry described at Plymouth harbor were due to the eminent shipwright Robert Seppings, not a scientist but certainly a mathematical practitioner. The controversy (in 1810) over the acceptance of Seppings's novel engineering methods in British shipyards lured the great classical scholar and optical theoretician Thomas Young from his study. It was Young's report (1814) on Seppings's techniques that induced the Admiralty to accept the designs that Henry later saw implemented at the Plymouth docks.[15] This was but one instance of many—going back to Newton—of the interest of British scientists in nautical engineering.

Other fields also showed the involvement of scientists. The mathematician and physicist Peter Barlow was a Royal consultant on British railways. Barlow and several other scientists, including Olinthus Gregory, taught principles of gunnery and other applied subjects to cadets at the Royal Military establishment at Woolwich Arsenal. When Henry visited Charles Wheatstone, the British natural philosopher was taking out a patent for an electrical telegraph.

One aspect of English technology that does not appear in Henry's ac-

---

[15] George Peacock, *Life of Thomas Young* (London, 1855), pp. 345–350.

counts is the social effect of industrialization. The infamous Coketown of Charles Dickens's *Hard Times* is never evident in his surviving descriptions of English cities. Technology, to Henry, was a test of human ingenuity, a form of puzzle-solving for the improvement of life. Such a positive view left no room for the darker side of technology. He wanted to know how machinery operated, not the living conditions of mill workers.

What degraded mankind, in Henry's view, was not the machine, but oppressive political and social mechanisms. As a good republican, Henry took self-righteous exception to the militaristic and aristocratic class structure of France (and to a lesser extent, England). The poverty and ignorance of the European peasant compared to the well-being of the American yeoman was one indication of the failure of the European way of life. Another was the deference which titles brought.

Henry was shocked by French attitudes and morals, as were most American visitors.[16] To the usual list of strange French customs—the dress, the art, the sidewalk cafes, disrespect for the Sabbath and casual hedonism—Henry added the number of working women, especially those doing physical, menial labor. The American middle class in the ante-bellum era, of which Henry was a conservative, tradition-minded member, tended to elevate its women. There was no cursing in the presence of women; men gave up their seats on crowded trains. In Henry's perception of America, a woman might work hard, but only in the home or around the farmyard, never on the street or in the fields (with the exception of slaves).[17] They never worked in what were traditionally male occupations. To find large numbers of women working in the fields, carrying heavy burdens, sweeping streets, or making shoes was very alien. Actually, there is historical evidence that American urban women did engage in what might be called male or public occupations, but the numbers were relatively small and these women might have escaped Henry's notice.[18]

The abolitionist sentiment of the English was another European social attitude which seemed alien to Henry. Although by contemporary American standards a racial moderate, Henry was a strong proponent of the hier-

---

[16] Dulles presents a number of examples of this shock; see especially pp. 22–23, 38–39, 75–76.

[17] America's treatment of its women drew comments from Englishwomen visiting the United States. Two examples are Isabella Lucy Bird, *The Englishwoman in America* (Madison, 1966), pp. 151–152, 160–161, and Harriet Martineau, *Retrospect of Western Travel*, 2 vols. (1838; reprint ed., New York, 1969), *1*: 218. Bird described an incident in her account when the only man to refuse to give up his seat was an Englishman, leading the American men on board the train to physically eject him from the car amid cries of "A regular John Bull trick! just like them!" Martineau remarked that she did "not share in the horror of the Americans at the idea of women being employed in outdoor labour."

[18] See below, Henry to Harriet Henry, July 5, 1837 (first letter), especially footnote 9.

archical system of races. While opposed to the concept of slavery, he felt the differences between the races too great to allow for a fully integrated society.

Whatever his opinion of the shortcomings of European society, its cultural achievements were undeniable. Henry was an enthusiastic tourist who frequently responded emotionally when faced with beauty or history. The Tower of London, St. Paul's, the London theater, Scott's Melrose Abbey, Edinburgh Castle, the gardens and boulevards of Paris, and the fields of Waterloo were all noted.

Henry came away from his European experience with a new cultural understanding, but most importantly with a sense of acceptance in the international scientific community. What this international spirit meant, however, for concrete issues of transatlantic influence is problematic. Although one of Henry's original objectives was to learn research methods, there is no outstanding evidence that his presence in European laboratories altered his method or line of investigation. Henry's correspondence network expanded as a result of the trip, but his chief source of knowledge of European developments continued to be the literature. Where the effects of the trip seem most visible is in the area of scientific organization. Henry was shortly to enter the institution-building phase of his career. What he learned of scientific organizations in Europe through personal observation could not be learned from books. For example, the pitfalls of amateur participation in the British Association were obvious to him and influenced his views on the American Association for the Advancement of Science. On the other hand, he greatly admired the British Association's program of research grants and hoped to implement comparable research support at home. The Smithsonian Institution embodied some of those aspirations. European social attitudes toward science also made strong impressions on Henry, who felt that Europeans in general treated their scientists relatively well. He would come back with different standards by which to judge his own society's attitudes toward science.

But the trip was at the cost of time lost in the laboratory. The bulk of the original research documented in this volume was accomplished during just a few months of 1836. It was devoted to the phenomenon of lateral discharge. He worked up a brief publication on the subject while he was in Europe and presented it to the British Association in 1837. The lateral discharge experiments were a preliminary to the work on mutual induction from static discharges that formed the core of his forthcoming article "Contributions to Electricity and Magnetism. No. III. On Electro-Dynamic Induction." At the first break in his teaching schedule after his return from Europe Henry immersed himself in the laboratory to do the research necessary for this lengthy publication. Henry's renewed preoccupation with research will be a major theme of the next installment of the *Henry Papers.*

*   *   *   *   *

The editorial work on this volume of *The Papers of Joseph Henry* was supported by the Smithsonian Institution, supplemented by a generous grant from the National Endowment for the Humanities. The Peter C. Cornell Trust provided matching funds for part of the grant. The National Historical Publications and Records Commission provided welcome support for the expenses of the editorial office. Additional financial aid came from the National Academy of Sciences. The staff of the Henry Papers is most grateful for this financial assistance. Once again we wish to acknowledge the enlightened concern of the Joint Committee of our sponsoring institutions.

At early stages, Michele L. Aldrich and James M. Hobbins, two former staff members, contributed to the contents of this volume, as did Christopher Beam, a fellow of the National Historical Publications and Records Commission. Over the years we have benefitted from the assistance of graduate and undergraduate interns. Three were especially important for this volume: James Berkman, Daniel Preston, and Elizabeth Schmidt.

Beverly Jo Lepley, Administrative Officer of the project, not only managed the daily activities of the office, but prepared the typescript of this volume. We are especially grateful for her care and expertise in both areas.

As in our previous efforts, the aid of an enormous number of librarians, archivists, and specialists of all kinds has contributed to the virtues of what follows. We are greatly indebted to our colleagues at the Smithsonian, particularly at the Smithsonian Archives and the Smithsonian Library. Understandably, the Henry Papers staff is especially conscious of the assistance and kindness of the individuals at the institutions from which our documents come. We thank these organizations for making them available. In addition to the Smithsonian Archives, they are:

American Philosophical Society Library
Barrett Library, University of Virginia Library
Beinecke Library, Yale University
Duke University Library
Firestone Library, Princeton University
Historical Society of Pennsylvania
Huntington Library and Art Gallery
Library of Congress
National Archives and Records Service
New York Botanical Garden Library

Princeton University Archives
St. Andrew's University Library, Scotland
South Caroliniana Library, University of South Carolina
Sterling Library, Yale University

No volume of this endeavor can pass into print without mention of our very great indebtedness to the volunteers who transcribed the original manuscripts.

Our practices are generally similar to those of other editorial projects, particularly to those of the Adams Papers. The nature of our documents and our personal inclinations have resulted in a few departures from the style of that great project, and these are noted below. In preparing this volume we followed an expanded and revised version of the style manual prepared prior to the editing of volume one. Copies of the revised manual are available to scholars interested in the editing of historical documents. Here a few points necessary for the reader's understanding are presented.

Organization

Documents are given in chronological order. If a specific date is not given or is not ascribable, the document is placed at the end of the dated documents from the nearest unit of time to which it can be tied. For example, if only the year can be determined, the document will appear at the end of all the items of that year. If the month and year are available but not the day, the document will appear after the fully dated documents of that month and year. Where the year is in doubt, the item will normally appear in an appendix.

Preliminaries to the Documents

Preliminaries to the documents are title, provenance note, and (sometimes) an introductory headnote.

The title briefly signals what is to come. In the case of correspondence, if Henry is the author of the letter, we simply indicate to whom he is writing:

TO BENJAMIN SILLIMAN, SR.

or we note the name of the person writing to Joseph Henry:

FROM BENJAMIN SILLIMAN, SR.

If Henry is neither the author nor the recipient, both parties are specified:

BENJAMIN SILLIMAN, SR., TO ROBERT HARE

In the case of noncorrespondence items, we prefer using the titles given on the originals. If the title is lacking or if the given title is noncommunicative, the editors will devise a suitable title, usually with an explanatory footnote. "RECORD OF EXPERIMENTS" will be used for entries from Henry's three-volume laboratory notebook. Entries from his various reading and lecture notebooks will be titled HENRY NOTEBOOK ENTRY.

The provenance note, immediately following the title, briefly gives the location of the original and, if necessary, the nature of the document being published (i.e., "draft," "retained copy," etc.). If these matters are too complicated for the provenance note, we normally provide additional pertinent details in a footnote. In the provenance note and in footnotes, we will refer to Henry's lecture and reading notebooks by the numbers (enclosed in brackets) which were assigned when they were entered into the project's control system (e.g., notebook [7171]). The use of such traditional abbreviations as "ALS" and the like are avoided. When the particulars of authorship or handwriting are historically significant, these are elaborated in a footnote if not clear from the title and provenance note.

In a few instances an explanatory headnote, immediately after the provenance note, will introduce a document. Where important items are not suitable for publication in a work of this nature, the headnote, often expanded in size, stands in their stead.

Date and Place

Date and place are usually placed at the top, right-hand side preceding the body of the text, regardless of location in the original. Missing dates are supplied in brackets as an editorial insertion. If the place is lacking, it is only supplied or discussed in a footnote if of some historical significance. Where the dating is not obvious or hinges on a matter of moment, this too becomes the subject of a footnote.

Texts

Our general practice is to hew as close to the original as possible, so long as the meaning is reasonably clear to a modern reader. A few revisions, mostly specified below, are made silently in the interest of clarity. We prefer to retain the original and to aid the modern reader in this respect by means of our annotations: only rarely do we make changes or insertions indicated by using square brackets, [ ]. "Sic" does not appear in our texts; barring human error, a reader must assume that any strange usage in print is a faithful transcription of the original.

Mary Henry, our subject's daughter, bequeathed a nasty problem to this project. Shortly after her father's death Mary Henry began working toward the preparation of a biography. In her possession were most of Joseph Henry's personal papers. To this she added items gathered from friends and relatives, as well as documents culled from the official archives of the

Smithsonian Institution. Mary Henry's efforts eventually progressed to the point where she had prepared a partial text which included original documents and transcriptions done by herself and her cohorts. Her text and its associated materials were largely the basis upon which Coulson based his biography of Joseph Henry. Although posterity owes Mary Henry thanks for efforts to preserve her father's literary remains, many of her actions resulted in irreparable damage to many Joseph Henry manuscripts. For example, in a number of cases she removed part of a book or transcribed a few pages, carelessly losing the entire volume. A neat trick of Mary's was to remove items from groups of documents and, in the process, to lose some and hopelessly disorder and scatter the remainder. The transcriptions she prepared for the contemplated biography are another vexation she inflicted on posterity. Almost invariably they omit an undisclosed amount of text, frequently passages of great interest. The transcribing is inaccurate at times and often corrects the language to conform with later standards, sometimes changing meanings. Unfortunately, many of the originals were lost, because, we think, of careless handling by Mary Henry and her aides. Many of these faulty, unique copies are quite important. We have decided to use them in our edition, signaling their nature by the expression "Mary Henry Copy" in the provenance note. From the numerous instances where both the copy and the original survive, we are convinced these are not fabrications, that the omissions were short-sighted but not acts of suppression, and that the surviving texts are reliable enough for use. Here and here alone, in the absence of any evidence to the contrary, we resolve textual uncertainties by opting for modern usage. There seems little point in trying to recapture Henry's archaisms.

Only in the few cases where the original paragraphing causes confusion in modern print have we made changes. Grammatical usage, punctuation, and spelling are usually faithfully preserved. The biggest exception is our decision to start each sentence with a capital letter and to end with appropriate punctuation. Punctuation that is obviously intrusive is removed; ubiquitous dashes are converted to modern commas and periods, and a few commas and periods are inserted silently where absolutely necessary for clear understanding. Only in a few egregious cases do we silently correct slips of the pen. Where the reading is doubtful or where meaning is otherwise unclear, we give an editorial insertion in square brackets, [ ]. Where these insertions are offered tentatively, we indicate our uncertainty by placing a question mark within the bracket. If the entire insertion is tentative, the question mark is placed immediately after the opening bracket, [? March 6, 1832]; if only one element is uncertain, the question mark is placed immediately afterward to indicate our doubt, [March 6?, 1832].

When the insertions arise from matters of moment, they will receive amplification in footnotes. A special case are entries from Henry's "Record of Experiments." The unique format of these entries called for special treatment which is explained in the headnote to the entry of August 15, 1834, in volume two.

In a number of documents there are interlineations, canceled matter, variant texts, marginalia, and even footnotes by the original author. The first are silently brought into line unless there is some point in their position. In that event we generally use a footnote to elucidate the significance, retaining the original position only in exceptional cases. If canceled matter or variant versions of expressions have historical, psychological, or stylistic significance, we place them immediately preceding the text in question in italics within angled brackets:

celebrated <*mathematical*> philosophical school at Alexandria.

Marginalia of significance are inserted into the text at the proper points with suitable comments in footnotes. Author's footnotes are given symbols other than arabic numerals which are reserved for editorial annotations.

Where one or two words are illegible or missing, we have so indicated by inserting suspension points enclosed in square brackets, [. . .]; if more than two words, we will, in addition, give an explanatory footnote, estimating, where possible, the number missing. Where a reasonable reconstruction is possible, we do so as an editorial insertion within square brackets.

Abbreviations occur frequently in the documents. If clear to the modern reader, they are retained. Otherwise the term is spelled out. The ampersand is used in place of the many variant forms occurring during Henry's lifetime. A particular problem to many readers unfamiliar with past usages is abbreviations involving raised letters, a practice quite common in Henry's generation and at least as far back as the seventeenth century. The writer would retain the first letter or letters of a word, giving the last letter or letters of the word in a raised position with or without a marking underneath:

Jany or Jan^{ry} for January

A reader aware of this practice should have no trouble understanding such abbreviations which we leave unchanged. Some raised letter abbreviations are likely to cause trouble. Sch^{dy} for Schenectady is not exactly obvious. In such cases we simply spell out the word without comment.

Signatures or initials at the close are given as in the original, usually without any commentary. Draft or retained copies generally lack these, as will our printed versions without any further notice. Where the recipient's name appears at the bottom left of the last page of an original letter, this is silently omitted as repeating information already given in the title. Dates at the end are also suppressed as redundant unless we silently shift their position to supply the missing dating at the start. We have retained closing matter of this nature only where meaning is conveyed. In the love letters exchanged by Joseph Henry and his wife Harriet, the closing salutations tell us something about the sentiments of the correspondents and are, therefore, given.

Editorial footnotes are numbered consecutively within each entry. We follow the citation form of the 12th edition of the *Manual of Style* of the University of Chicago Press with one important exception. We prefer the ISIS form in citing the periodical literature. Of less moment, perhaps, are two other preferences. The Editor does not relish the current tendency to suppress capitalization and to use the lower case in titles of officials, names of institutions, and publications. We capitalize. There is also an antipathy here against the tendency to run abbreviation-wild. We think readers should not have to approach each footnote as an exercise in decoding. Except for a few standard usages (e.g., n.d., ibid., etc.), everything is given in full or nearly so. The principal exceptions are the items below for which we consistently use short titles or standard abbreviations.

Academy Seventy-fifth Anniversary	*The Celebration of the Seventy-fifth Anniversary of the Founding of the Albany Academy, October 25, 1888* (Albany, 1889).
"Alexander Genealogy"	Unpublished Alexander Family Genealogy by Robert Gaylord Lester in the Henry Papers files.
Biographical Directory of the American Congress	*Biographical Directory of the American Congress, 1774–1949* (Washington, 1950).
Burke's Index	Edmund Burke, compiler, *List of Patents for Inventions and Designs Issued by the United States from 1790–1847, with the Patent Laws and Notes of Decisions of the Courts of the United States for the Same Period* (Washington, 1847).
Columbia Alumni	M. Halsey Thomas, compiler, *Columbia University Officers and Alumni, 1754–1857* (New York, 1936).
"Contributions I: Battery"	Joseph Henry, "Contributions to Electricity and Magnetism. No. I.—Description of a Galvanic Battery for Producing Electricity of Different Intensities," *Transactions of the American Philosophical Society*, 1837, n.s., 5:217–222.
"Contributions II: Spiral Conductor"	Joseph Henry, "Contributions to Electricity and Magnetism. No. II.—On the Influence of a Spiral Conductor in Increasing the Intensity of Electricity from a Galvanic Arrangement of a Single Pair, &c.," *Transactions of the American Philosophical Society*, 1837, n.s., 5:223–231.
"Contributions III: Electro-Dynamic Induction"	Joseph Henry, "Contributions to Electricity and Magnetism. No. III.—On Electro-Dynamic Induction," *Transactions of the American Philosophical Society*, 1839, n.s., 6:303–337.
"Contributions IV: Electro-Dynamic Induction"	Joseph Henry, "Contributions to Electricity and Magnetism. No. IV.—On Electro-Dynamic Induction," *Transactions of the American Philosophical Society*, 1843, n.s., 8:1–35.

"Contributions V: Induction from Ordinary Electricity; Oscillatory Discharge"	Joseph Henry, "Contributions to Electricity and Magnetism. No. V.—On Induction from Ordinary Electricity; And on the Oscillatory Discharge," *Proceedings of the American Philosophical Society*, January 1841–June 1843, 2:193–196.
Coulson	Thomas Coulson, *Joseph Henry: His Life and Work* (Princeton, 1950).
Cullum	G. W. Cullum, *Biographical Register of the Officers and Graduates of the United States Military Academy, at West Point, New York*, rev. ed., 2 vols. (New York, 1879).
DAB	*Dictionary of American Biography*
DNB	*Dictionary of National Biography*
DSB	*Dictionary of Scientific Biography*
Hageman	John F. Hageman, *History of Princeton and its Institutions*, 2d ed., 2 vols. (Philadelphia, 1879).
Henry Papers	Nathan Reingold, editor, *The Papers of Joseph Henry* (Washington, 1972–).
Herringshaw	Thomas William Herringshaw, *Encyclopedia of American Biography of the Nineteenth Century* (Chicago, 1905).
Howell and Tenney	George Rogers Howell and Jonathan Tenney, editors, *History of the County of Albany, N.Y., from 1609 to 1886* (New York, 1886).
Hun, "Albany Academy"	Henry Hun, "A Survey of the Activity of the Albany Academy" (unpublished manuscript, 1922–1935, Manuscript Division, New York State Library and Archives of the Albany Academy).
King	W. James King, "The Development of Electrical Technology in the 19th Century: 1. The Electrochemical Cell and the Electromagnet; 2. The Telegraph and the Telephone; 3. The Early Arc Light and Generator," *United States Museum Bulletin No. 228* (Washington, 1962), pp. 231–271, 273–332, 333–407.
Maclean	John Maclean, *History of the College of New Jersey, 1746–1854*, 2 vols. in 1 vol. (1877; reprint ed., New York, 1969).
Munsell, *Ann. Alb.*	Joel Munsell, compiler, *Annals of Albany*, 10 vols. (Albany, 1850–1859).

Munsell, *Coll. Alb.* — Joel Munsell, compiler, *Collections on the History of Albany, from Its Discovery to the Present Time, with Notices of Its Public Institutions and Biographical Sketches of Citizens Deceased,* 4 vols. (Albany, 1865–1871).

Nason — Henry B. Nason, editor, *Biographical Record of the Officers and Graduates of the Rensselaer Polytechnic Institute, 1824–1886* (Troy, 1887).

Phil. Mag. — The well-known London journal which began as *The Philosophical Magazine* in 1798 and appeared under various titles throughout Henry's life. See Henry Carrington Bolton, *A Catalogue of Scientific and Technical Periodicals, 1665–1895. . . ,* 2d ed. (Washington, 1897), pp. 445–446.

Phil. Trans. — *Philosophical Transactions of the Royal Society of London.*

Poggendorff — J. C. Poggendorff, compiler, *Biographisch-Literarisches Handwörterbuch Zur Geschichte Der Exacten Wissenschaften.*

Princeton Annual Catalogue — *Catalogue of the Officers and Students of the College of New-Jersey* (Princeton).

Princeton Catalogue — *General Catalogue of Princeton University, 1746–1906* (Princeton, 1908).

Reynolds, *Alb. Chron.* — Cuyler Reynolds, compiler, *Albany Chronicles: A History of the City Arranged Chronologically* (Albany, 1906).

Roberts — Edward Howell Roberts, compiler, *Biographical Catalogue of the Princeton Theological Seminary, 1815–1932* (Princeton, 1933).

Silliman's Journal — Benjamin Silliman, editor, *American Journal of Science and Arts* (New Haven, 1818–   ).

Sprague, *Annals* — William Buell Sprague, *Annals of the American Pulpit,* 9 vols. (New York, 1857–1869).

Union Catalog — *Union University: Centennial Catalog, 1795–1895, of the Officers and Alumni of Union College in . . . Schenectady, N.Y.* (Troy, 1895).

Weiner, "Joseph Henry's Lectures" — Charles Irwin Weiner, "Joseph Henry's Lectures on Natural Philosophy: Teaching and Research in Physics, 1832–1847" (Ph.D. dissertation, Case Institute of Technology, 1965).

Wertenbaker — Thomas Jefferson Wertenbaker, *Princeton, 1746–1896* (Princeton, 1946).

THE PAPERS OF JOSEPH HENRY

FROM BENJAMIN SILLIMAN, SR.
Henry Papers, Smithsonian Archives

New Haven Jan 4, 1836

Dear Sir

On the 5ᵗʰ I go to New York & remain until the 19 or 20.[1] A letter addressed care of B D Silliman Esqr[2] Wall Street will find me & I will ask the favor of you to inform me within that time whether it is likely you will be able to furnish me with the magnetic apparatus which you were so kind as to say you would have fitted up for me; and also whether you obtained the information in Philᵃ respecting the most improved form of the revolving galvanic magnet for sparks, decompositions &c—as it was I believe in the hands of Prof Green.[3]

I do not wish to be troublesome to you or to have you take any inconvenient trouble—but if I could know rather early after my arrival at N York I might consult with Chilton[4] if you should not find it quite convenient to attend to these matters. In about two months I shall need to use them in Boston. My kind regards to Mr Alexander.[5]

as ever
Yours very truly
B Silliman

[1] For a course of popular lectures.

[2] His nephew Benjamin Douglas Silliman (1805–1901), B.A. Yale 1824, M.A. He received an honorary LL.D. from Yale in 1874 and from Columbia in 1873. After assisting his uncle in chemistry at Yale, B. D. Silliman went into law, became a New York State legislator and a U.S. Attorney in the New York Eastern District. John F. Fulton and Elizabeth H. Thomson, *Benjamin Silliman: Pathfinder in American Science* (New York, 1947), pp. 148, 156. *Herringshaw*, p. 849. *Catalogue of the Officers and Graduates of Yale University in New Haven, Connecticut, 1701–1910* (New Haven, 1910), p. 96.

[3] Silliman inquired about the magnetic apparatus as early as October 31, 1835. Henry's friend Jacob Green possessed one of the magnetoelectric generators constructed by the Philadelphia mechanics Isaiah Lukens and Joseph Saxton (see *Henry Papers*, 2:474, 158–161).

[4] Henry had instructed the New York instrument maker James Chilton in many of the details of his electrical apparatus. See *Henry Papers*, 2:316–317.

[5] Stephen Alexander.

FROM TITUS W. POWERS[1]

Henry Papers, Smithsonian Archives

New York January 14ᵗʰ 1836
177 Grand St.

My dear Henry,

Your card, left at Francis' book-store,[2] did not reach me until Tuesday of last week; and upon enquiring for you the same day at Dᴿ Torrey's, I learned that you had departed for home that morning. I regret extremely that I did not sooner learn of your being in town, as I was, for many reasons, particularly desirous of seeing you & conversing with you.

I thought, certainly, that nothing would have prevented me from making you a short visit last season as I promised; but, so engrossing have been my engagements here & elsewhere for the last six months, that I have positively not yet found it convenient or possible, to appropriate the time for a journey to Princeton. I am determined, however, that, should I not be able to visit you this winter, to let nothing prevent my doing so in the course of the spring. My friend Mᴿ Codman[3] also, has been long desirous of fulfilling his promise to Mr. Alexander[4] of visiting him, & he will, probably, accompany me.

You may have noticed, in the newspapers, that the remarkable *Aurora*, seen in different parts of this country on the evening of the 18ᵗʰ Novᴿ last, was also seen in great brilliancy in London, Liverpool, and other places in England. Mr. Ehlers,[5] a friend of mine, who arrived here the 18ᵗʰ Decᴿ in the ship Ontario from London, informs me, that its appearance at sea on the evenings of the 17ᵗʰ & 18ᵗʰ Novᴿ was splendid in the extreme, far beyond any previous exhibition of it that he had seen; and he had often witnessed it in great splendor in Sweden & Russia. His description of it, as he observed it, Novᴿ 17ᵗʰ 6 to 7 P.M.* Lat: 48°, Long: W. 39° 30′, and on the 18ᵗʰ 7 to 8 P.M.* supposed latitude 47° (no observation that day), Long: 41°, corre-

* The time you will perceive corresponds nearly to the time it was seen here in its greatest brilliancy, allowing for the difference in longitude.

---

[1] Titus William Powers (?–1863) was a physician and sometime merchant in New York City (*Henry Papers, 1:331*).

[2] Charles Stephen Francis (1805–1887) located his bookstore under Peale's Museum as of this date. Francis, the son of an eminent early Boston printer, had made his concern a congenial social and literary gathering place in New York. He published and imported books and maintained a circulating library.

DAB.

[3] A merchant in New York City, William Codman lived at 179 Grand Street in 1835–1836 and thus was Powers's neighbor (New York City Directory).

[4] Stephen Alexander.

[5] Not identified, unless Powers misspelled the name of Abraham Ehle, a dry goods merchant in the New York City Directory for 1835–1836.

sponds exactly with the different descriptions of it as seen in this country. My friend Capt Johnston[6] of the Havre packet-ship Albany, states, that in Havre, no signs of Aurora (as far as he noticed) were visible on the 17th, 18th, or 19th Novr last. This is rather singular as it was seen here in much lower latitudes than Havre; at Wheeling Va. for example, where its appearance was very brilliant. Did you observe any effect produced upon the needle during its appearance or any disturbance for the 24 hours previous?[7]

The Troughton Theodolite, ordered for the Albany Academy has arrived, and is now at Megarey's.[8] I am of course incompetent to judge of its excellence; but it is apparently a most complete, as it is truly a most splendid instrument. Cost $.300. without duty. Does the Fraunhofer telescope operate to your satisfaction? I have recently, for Dr Ten Eyck, requested Mr Werckmeister to import a telescope, from the manufactory of Fraunhofer, of the size marked *No. 12*, in M^r W's catalogue.[9] *Price $320.* Mr W. stated, on receiving this order, that he would also write for No. 13, together with some other astronomical & optical apparatus. I procured for Dr. Ten Eyck, some time since, of Werckmeister, a most superb double prism, made by Fraunhofer, consisting of two short triangular prisms of different kinds of glass joined together at their summits. It most beautifully illustrates the different degrees of dispersive & refractive powers possessed by the two sorts of glass (crown & flint) of which it is composed. Price $.15.00. I think you would find such a one admirable for experimental illustration in your lectures.

I suppose you have seen the North American Review for this month. The

[6] Perhaps William Johnston, who appears in the New York City Directory for 1835–1836 as a mariner.

[7] The problem of the origin of auroras especially fascinated physical scientists of Powers's era. The aurora's influence on a vibrating magnetized needle led to speculation that the aurora was an electrical or magnetic phenomenon; the time and location of an aurora's appearance could be used to calculate its extent. Joseph Henry's work on the subject is documented in the previous two volumes of the *Henry Papers*. For Henry's observations of this particular aurora, see *Henry Papers*, 2: 477.

[8] Edward Troughton (1753–1835) apprenticed as a mechanic in London and gradually acquired skill as a scientific instrument maker. Troughton specialized in astronomical, marine, and surveying instruments. He created a new method for dividing circles and invented or improved several scientific devices. Ferdinand Hassler bought one of Troughton's superb theodolites for the United States Coast Survey in 1815. After Troughton's death on June 12, 1835, his partner William Simms (1793–1860) continued the business. *DNB*.

Alexander Megary (1790–1850) was born in Ireland but had arrived in New York City by 1823, where he made scientific instruments, notably telescopes and surveying devices. He published a brief work on navigation methods in 1849. M. V. Brewington, *The Peabody Museum of Navigating Instruments with Notes on Their Makers* (Salem, Massachusetts, 1963), p. 135.

[9] Joseph Fraunhofer (1787–1826), an instrument maker in Germany who contributed to the science of optics, is identified in *Henry Papers*, 2:273. Princeton had acquired a used Fraunhofer telescope from the New York businessman Michael Werckmeister (1766–1844; *Henry Papers*, 2:273, 284). Philip Ten Eyck (1802–1892) taught mathematics and science at the Albany Academy from 1832 until 1848 (*Henry Papers*, 1:214).

notice of Prof: Hassler's papers on the Coast Survey is written in a liberal spirit,[10] and the review of M. Arago's works on Comets shews considerable science on the part of the reviewer.[11]

I have just bestowed a hasty glance upon the London quarterly for Dec.ʳ just arrived. It contains among other articles, two of particular interest to you—one a notice of a biography of Flamsteed, the other an article on Comets.[12] I have transcribed some portions of the latter, & shall send them to morrow to M.ʳ Alexander, knowing that he will be much interested in reading them, & presuming that a week or two at least will elapse before he will have access to the Journal.

Please present my regards to Mrs. Henry, & believe me

Yours Sincerely
T. W. Powers.

P.S. When shall you exhibit to your class the action of your great magnet? I am desirous of knowing on M.ʳ Codman's account, as he is very anxious to see its operation, and to hear an exposition of the principles of Electromagnetism. *Ceteris paribus*, we would prefer making a visit to Princeton when you were upon that branch of your course. Let me hear from you soon if your avocations will permit.

---

[10] James Ferguson (*Henry Papers*, 2:15–16), a Coast Survey employee, wrote "Survey of the Coast" for the *North American Review*, 1836, *42*:75–94. He summarized the early years of the survey under Ferdinand Hassler (1770–1843, *DAB, DSB; Henry Papers, 1*:297), pleaded for civilian rather than military control of federal scientific projects, and complained of the government's reluctance to publish Coast Survey research papers.

[11] John Farrar used his essay "Arago on Comets" (*North American Review*, 1836, *42*: 196–216) to comment on the astronomical findings prompted by the return of Halley's Comet.

[12] One article was a review of Francis Baily's *An Account of the Rev. John Flamsteed . . .*; the other reviewed K. L. von Littrow's *Ueber den Halleyschen Cometen* and J. F. Encke's work of the same name. *Quarterly Review*, 1835, *55*:96–128, 195–233. Baily had attempted to tell the side of Flamsteed (1646–1719) in the quarrel with Isaac Newton over publishing Flamsteed's astronomical data. The second piece was a general essay on comets occasioned by recent German publications; the author (Mary Somerville) included an assessment of the theory of etherial matter outside the atmosphere.

TO ALEXANDER DALLAS BACHE

Mary Henry Copy, Henry Papers, Smithsonian Archives

Princeton, Jan. 18, 1836.

My dear Sir: . . . I intended to write in my last letter that I was on the eve of going to New York.[1] I saw our friend, Dr. Torrey. He is the same good man

---

[1] The earlier letter had mistakenly said Philadelphia (*Henry Papers*, 2:481).

as ever. I had a very pleasant time with him, and almost promised to return and give a lecture before his class on electro-magnetism. . . . On due reflection however, I cannot reconcile with my feelings of scientific pride, the thought of appearing unnecessarily before a New York audience in the character of a lecturer.[2]

I will visit your city as soon as possible. This session has been one of more labor to me than any other since my connection with the college. I hope however soon to find leisure to prepare a paper for the society in continuance of my series.[3] I can say nothing about the shooting stars this evening except that Mr. Alexander and an assistant kept watch on Friday, Jan. 1, from 11 to 12, but did not observe a single meteor during the time.[4] Have you noticed in the papers that the grand aurora of November was seen in London and Liverpool? Did you make observations on the magnetic needle that night?[5] I have received a number of letters in reference to it, and one which informs me that it was seen on the Atlantic ocean, between this and London.[6] In haste, As ever Yours, Joseph Henry.

I have just finished my course of lectures on hydraulics,[7] and tried, as I promised, Mr. Espy's experiment of water flowing freely from a vessel and falling into another vessel placed immediately under. The time of emptying was the same (68 deg.) three times in succession, as measured by the astronomical clock, with and without the receiving vessel. The effect, however, is different. The water from a long tube projecting from the bottom of the vessel.[8] J. H.

---

[2] Torrey had extended the invitation in December (*Henry Papers*, 2:487), perhaps meaning his medical classes. Why Henry felt this particular exercise demeaning is not entirely clear to us—or to Bache, who expressed puzzlement in his reply to Henry, below. It may be that Henry doubted the effectiveness or seriousness of delivering a single physics lecture to medical students. In any case, the operative word here seems to be "unnecessarily." Henry certainly recognized the value of popular scientific lecturing, for the public good and the cause of science. But, as a spokesman for a developing research ethic, Henry opposed vulgarizing for public consumption. He willingly undertook popularizing responsibilities on occasion, but insisted on choosing his subjects and his forums carefully. He also supported the popularizing activities of others such as Silliman (see his letter to Silliman, below, of March 2, 1836) as long as the lectures and demonstrations communicated accurate and meaningful information.

[3] "Contributions to Electricity and Magnetism."

[4] Henry had been helping Bache with the observations throughout the winter. See his correspondence with Bache in November and December, 1835, in volume 2 of the *Henry Papers*.

[5] Bache responded on January 22–28, 1836, below.

[6] The sighting reports came from Powers's letter of January 14, 1836, above.

[7] Henry's hydraulics lectures were an early segment of his natural philosophy course. Hydraulics he defined as the practical application of hydrodynamics. The lectures covered both pure and applied topics, including the motion of fluids through the sides and bottoms of vessels, through short and long pipes, in river beds, and in the generation of water power. See the contemporary student lectures of Aaron B. Belknap, Princeton University Library.

[8] As given, the experiment is not meaning-

ful. No clues to it exist in Henry's lecture notes or those of his students. Either Bache already knew the details from Espy or Mary Henry gives an incomplete text. Espy's concern with hydraulics probably dates from his prior service on a Franklin Institute committee for water power. Bruce Sinclair, *Philadelphia's Philosopher Mechanics: A History of the Franklin Institute, 1824–1865* (Baltimore, 1974), pp. 144, 150.

FROM JOHN VAUGHAN[1]
Henry Papers, Smithsonian Archives

Phil. 21 Jany 1836

My dear Sir

I was much pleased with your friend *Ferguson*[2] & with pleasure put him at home in our Library; he & others connected in the Coast Survey, are about re-publishing Hasslers Communication to our Soc^y published in our Transactions,[3] & I procured a permission from the Society to let him take as many impressions as he might want from our plates.

We have published N° 2 of V. Vol. & are now ready to commence the 3^d, & shall be much pleased for a Communication from you which could go soon to press as we have got over our pecuniary difficulties, & have nothing to stop us.[4] Prof. Bache told me he should write you on the subject. Do attend to it.[5] We should not to publish enough to close the Vol. If value[d] com^s offer to make only 100 pages we should not wait, being desirous of giving an early publication.[6]

[1] Vaughan (1756–1841) managed the day-to-day affairs of the American Philosophical Society (*Henry Papers*, 2:107–108, 351). At this time his formal titles were Librarian and Treasurer.

[2] James Ferguson.

[3] Ferdinand Hassler, director of the United States Coast and Geodetic Survey from 1807 until 1818 and 1832 to his death, habitually reprinted material on his survey work in compilations such as *Principal Documents Relating to the Survey of the Coast of the United States, Since 1816*, 3 vols. (New York, 1834–1836). To our knowledge he did not succeed in republishing the article referred to here, "Papers on Various Subjects Connected with the Survey of the Coast of the United States," American Philosophical Society *Transactions*, 1825, n.s. 2:232–420, a heavily illustrated piece describing Hassler's improvements in design and use of complicated scientific instruments. Neither the *National Union Catalog* nor standard bibliographies list such a reprinted edition.

[4] Vaughan was referring to the money shortage of the Publications Committee, which had experienced cost overruns on the fourth volume and the early parts of the fifth volume of the Society's *Transactions*. Printing continued after the Society appropriated additional funds to the Committee. Annual Report of the Publications Committee, December 5, 1834, Archives, American Philosophical Society.

[5] No articles by Henry appeared in addition to "Contributions I and II" in volume five; those two items had already been printed by the date of Vaughan's letter.

[6] Our reading of these two sentences is conjectural. Vaughan's handwriting and diction are not clear at this point in the letter. We assume he meant to say that they did not have enough articles to complete the volume, but that they would publish it as a relatively short one if an additional one hundred pages of

I have got Mr Biddles Oration delivered at your Commencement—but I cannot get *the other* delivered at same period.[7] I wish to get one. They are not for sale here as far as I can learn.

I remain Yours
Jn Vaughan

---

good material were to arrive. In fact, volume five did not appear until the third part (pp. 348–482) was printed in 1837.

[7] William Gaston spoke at the invitation of the Princeton literary societies on September 29, 1835, and Nicholas Biddle was the graduation speaker the next day (*Henry Papers*, 2: 463).

TO JAMES HENRY

Family Correspondence, Henry Papers, Smithsonian Archives

Princeton Jany 22nd 1836

My Dear James

Why have you not written for more than a month past? Your letters must have miscarried. I can account for our not hearing from you for so long a time only on this supposition. I commenced a letter to you on Monday last but was not able to finish it before the closing of the mail and have not found leasure to resume my pen until now. Since then Mrs H. has received a budget of news from Charlotte & Luisa Meads.

We are all as usual at Princeton. Few things occur here to break the monotony of a village residence in the winter. The college continues as flourishing as ever notwithstanding the denunciations on account of Biddles address.[1] The children are now both well. The boy is making some progress in the way of his letters &c. The girl begins to speak quite plainly and is very quick in catching an *idea*. I spent New Years day in travelling between this and New York. I arrived in the city about 4 O'clock P.M. and slept the same night at Mr. McMullens. All well there. Lucinda complained a little on account of the fatigue of New Year visiting. I returned on Tuesday following. You are I suppose very busily engaged in the store at this time since the Legislature are now in session. What think you in Albany of the *War message*. Will we yet come to blows with the French.[2] I hope not as I wish to purchase a collection of Philosophical apparatus for the college

[1] Nicholas Biddle's address at the 1835 Princeton commencement had drawn criticism from his political enemies. See *Henry Papers*, 2:490.

[2] The crisis with France over payment for damages to American property during the Napoleonic Wars had eased considerably by this time and was finally resolved in January 1836 through Lord Palmerston's mediation. See *Henry Papers*, 2:354.

9

in Paris in the course [of] an other year.[3] I know not how the *Judge* whom you mention in your last may feel towards me. He has always expressed himself friendly; if not warm towards me he is probably indifferent. It is however a matter of small moment one way or the other except that I would rather have the good will of any respectable man than his indifference or dislike.[4] Has Nancy returned from Galway? She must be snowed under at this time if she did not return before the late storm. The snow has not been as deep as at present since we came to Princeton. It was nearly two feet on a level. It has made fine sleighing and the students have all been mad to enjoy it particularly the southern ones many of them having never before rode in a sleigh. William Bullions[5] is with me and renders me considerable assistance in the preparation of my lectures.

I received yesterday from the author a copy of an address by Mr Barnard before the Young Men's Association of Troy.[6] I have not as yet given it a perusal. I suppose you received the copies of the addresses sent you. I saw Foster[7] the writing master in N.Y. He has a large writing class in a second floor room in Broadway, appears to be doing very well; he is married to a Boston Lady. I did not find time to read the message of Governor Marcy[8] but have laid aside the paper for future perusal. We have now a considerable number of Albanians in Princeton. Besides our family, Bullions, Newland[9] and McIntyre,[10] there are in the Seminary (Theological) Henry James,[11] young Fowler[12] and a Mr Goodrich[13] formerly Teacher in the new academy at Albany and to these I must not forget to add the Widow Hand and her son.[14] Also Mr Winkoop[15] formerly Teacher in the female academy.

[3] In a February 1835 letter to his brother, Henry had mentioned the crisis with France and his fears that a war would prevent him from ordering apparatus from Paris (*Henry Papers*, 2:354). In this 1836 letter it is unclear whether he is repeating that statement or announcing his intention of actually going to Paris himself. The first explicit mention of a European trip is in a letter from John Maclean to Henry of July 25, 1836, printed below.

[4] We have no idea what this refers to.

[5] See *Henry Papers*, 2:274n.

[6] A copy of Daniel D. Barnard's *Introductory Lecture Delivered before the Young Men's Association for Mutual Improvement in the City of Troy* (Troy, 1835) is in the Henry Library. Barnard spoke on the value and history of "mental cultivation."

[7] Benjamin Franklin Foster (*Henry Papers*, 1:399).

[8] Marcy delivered his annual message to the New York legislature on January 5. Included with the usual topics was an endorsement of John A. Dix's plan for the New York Natural History Survey. *Messages from the Governors* (Albany, 1909), 3:534-584.

[9] John Newland (*Henry Papers*, 2:467n) was a junior at Princeton.

[10] James McIntyre, son of Archibald and Eliza McIntyre, entered Princeton as a junior. He proved to be a disciplinary problem and left Princeton at the end of the school year.

[11] Henry James (*Henry Papers*, 2:35n) never finished at the Seminary. In 1837 he joined Henry in London.

[12] Philemon Halsted Fowler (1814–1879) was ordained later in the year. He served as a pastor in Washington, D.C., and later in New York state. *Roberts*, p. 81.

[13] Butler Goodrich (*Henry Papers*, 2:278), who had taught at the Albany Female Academy before entering the Seminary, died within a month. Charles E. West, *An Address on the Fiftieth Anniversary of the [Union College] Class of 1832* (Brooklyn, 1882), pp. 3–7.

[14] Aaron Hicks Hand (1811–1880), son of

I will send with this letter a package of Pamphlets for B. Van Renselaer[16] to be transmitted to Thomas Hunn in Paris. I suppose the prospect of war will induce Hunn[17] and young Townsend[18] to return home.

How are all our Friends in and about Albany? If you have heard any news from Nancy let us have it in your next. I am very much engaged this winter in College duties; give 4 lectures a week which with my recitations occupy nearly all my time. James Ferguson was in Princeton before New Year on his way to Washington. He will probably make this place a point in the Survey and will be in our neighbourhood a good part of next summer. He left his wagon and horses with an Irishman, the attendant, in my care. I received a letter from him a few days since requesting the team to be sent to New York but the deep snow has rendered the roads impassible for a wagon so that it must remain until a thaw comes.

Give my respects to Mrs Platt,[19] Mr William & Anthony Goold,[20] Dean,[21] Mead,[22] B Van Rensselaer, F. Wendell,[23] Shankland[24] and should you see him old Mr Fisher[25] also Mr Platt. Love to Caroline and Nancy when she returns from Galway. Are not provisions very dear in Albany this winter. Butter with us is 2/– per *lb*. Coal $7½—in the fall we could purchase it for 5 dollars. Has Dr Wing and yourself done anything about Frank's note. I would not consider the debt as due to the Dr from Mother but from Frank and request him to settle as he has promised with Frank. The Dr ought to make some discount on the ammount of his bill as he has probably put down his charging not his taking prices. I have just got a statement of our Dr's bill for the whole family during the 3½ years nearly that we have been in

---

Aaron and Tamar Platt Hand, was a graduate of Williams College. Leaving the Seminary in 1837, he spent his ministry in Georgia, New Jersey, and New York. *Roberts*, p. 86. Alfred Nevin, ed., *Encyclopedia of the Presbyterian Church in the United States of America* (Philadelphia, 1884), p. 300.

[15] Stephen Rose Wynkoop (*Henry Papers*, 2:473).

[16] Bernard S. Van Rensselaer (*Henry Papers*, 1:250–251) worked in the Surveyor General's Office.

[17] Thomas Hun (*Henry Papers*, 2:63n) studied in Europe from 1833 to 1839. Henry visited him in Paris in 1837.

[18] Not identified.

[19] Three Platts appear throughout the Family Correspondence. They seem to be close friends of James Henry's family and may be relatives of Caroline Henry. We think Mr. and Mrs. Platt are Ananias Platt (1762–1842) and his wife Lydia Jacobs Platt (1766–1847). Aunty Platt, not mentioned in this document, may be

Mary Platt (ca. 1770–1856), widow of John Platt (d. 1828).

Caroline and James Henry named their first child John Platt Henry. Mary Platt lived at the same address as James Henry's family. Following the death of Ananias, his widow is also listed at the same address as James Henry. *Proceedings of the Common Council and the Various Religious Organizations of the City of Albany Relative to the State Street Burial Grounds* (Albany, 1867), pp. 47 and 48. Munsell, *Ann. Alb.*, 1:159, 8:352, 9:172, 10:326. Albany City Directories, 1828–1846.

[20] The Goulds were James Henry's employers (*Henry Papers*, 1:446n).

[21] Amos Dean (*Henry Papers*, 1:26–27).

[22] Probably Orlando Meads (*Henry Papers*, 2:71n).

[23] Not identified.

[24] Peter V. Shankland (*Henry Papers*, 1:284n).

[25] *Henry Papers*, 2:72n.

Princeton. The ammount is 51 dollars. Dr Ws charges for the same would have been at least 200.[26]

Your Brother

[26] Henry had written earlier about the problem of Francis N. Selkirk's debt to Joel Wing (*Henry Papers*, 2:432) and also complained about Wing's charges (*Henry Papers*, 2:346).

FROM ALEXANDER DALLAS BACHE
Mary Henry Copy, Henry Papers, Smithsonian Archives

Philadelphia, Jan. [22–28,][1] 1836.

My dear friend: ... About the stars. Prithee send on your times before Espy and self forget all about our observations. There is nothing like being fresh. Just read my letter again and if you can find time do what I said in it about the meteors.[2]

The sooner you send *that paper* for our transactions the better chance of seeing daylight early will it have.

I do not perfectly enter into your scruples about lecturing at New York, but suppose you have a reason, though I do not see it.

You must positively lend your help to the Physical Science Department of our Journal.[3]

The Aurora? An aurora was seen as far west as Jefferson Barracks,[4] on the 16th of Nov. The lights of the *same* aurora seen from London, and 180 deg w. long. from Greenwich, what would it be?[5] You see I *sneer*. At any rate,

[1] Mary Henry's typescript lacks the specific date. Our conjectural dating assumes that Bache penned this response to Henry's letter of January 18 soon after its receipt. Bache had just promised John Vaughan that he would promptly urge Henry to submit another article for the American Philosophical Society's *Transactions*.

[2] During the winter of 1835–1836 Henry watched for meteor showers on Friday nights, helping Bache and James P. Espy gather observations to challenge Denison Olmsted's theory (see *Henry Papers*, 2, especially pp. 117n, 302, 477–481). For Henry's most recent observations, see *Henry Papers*, 2:478–482. No manuscript record of Henry's subsequent observations has been found. Likewise, neither Bache nor Espy appears to have published any data from 1836 relating to the frequency of shooting stars.

[3] Bache's plea, quoted in Bruce Sinclair's *Philadelphia's Philosopher Mechanics* (Baltimore, 1974), p. 210, illustrates his efforts to make the Franklin Institute's *Journal* into a first-rate periodical in the world of science. Bache was motivated by both strong national pride and his own designs for a more scientific Institute (see *Henry Papers*, 2:207n).

[4] An active Army post from 1826 until 1946, about twelve miles south of St. Louis along the Mississippi River. Bache, a West Point graduate who maintained close ties with military personnel, relied upon Army sentinels for gathering celestial observations. See *Henry Papers*, 2:479n.

[5] Henry was interested in the extent of the aurora's appearance because he felt it was a celestial or global phenomenon, not an aspect of local weather. He suspected that auroras appeared simultaneously throughout most of

if you were at my elbow you would see. The horizontal needle was violently affected early in the evening; and again after [?midnight] [6] so strongly that I was sure there was an aurora in full blast. On going out all was overcast.

The club seems dispersed.[7] It ought not to be so. Do we tire of each other?

Faraday's discovery of the non-conducting power of ice for electricity was known to Franklin and his assistants.[8] To ramble once more before stopping, why do you not send on the Forbes needle?[9] It will grow stale if you keep it too long.

Allow yourself to be betrayed into a return letter, as I have been into writing this most discursive. Goodbye, A. D. Bache.

---

the northern hemisphere. See *Henry Papers*, 2:77, 489.

[6] Mary Henry's typescript has a blank here.

[7] The club, centered in Philadelphia, was a small, casual association of like-minded scientists, including both Henry and Bache. For its background and significance, see *Henry Papers*, 2:290n–291n. Because its activities were informal and irregularly scheduled, the club's decline is particularly hard to trace. Nonetheless, the club met less frequently in the first half of 1836 than in the previous year. In the spring of 1836 Henry, for one, hoped for renewed club activity (see below, Henry to Bache, May 10, 1836). Thereafter, however, mentions of the club virtually disappear, probably owing initially to Bache's and Henry's absence during their European trips. By 1840 the club had been inactive for "a few years," according to Bache's letter to Henry, February 13, 1840, Henry Papers, Smithsonian Archives.

[8] Benjamin Franklin's assistants, really his associates in his early electrical experiments, were Ebenezer Kinnersley (1711–1778), Thomas Hopkinson (1709–1751), and Phillip Syng (1703–1789). I. Bernard Cohen, ed., *Benjamin Franklin's Experiments* (Cambridge, Massachusetts, 1941), pp. 77–85.

On January 15, 1836, Bache addressed the American Philosophical Society on the discovery of ice as a non-conductor, and soon thereafter he published the talk, "Historical Note on the Discovery of the Non-conducting Power of Ice," in the *Journal of the Franklin Institute*, March 1836, n.s. *17*:182–184. He based his "Historical Note" primarily on Benjamin Franklin's *Experiments and Observations on Electricity* . . . (London, 1751), which had gone through five editions by 1774, and

Michael Faraday's "Experimental Researches in Electricity, Fourth Series. 9. On a new law of electric conduction. 10. On conducting power generally," *Phil. Trans.*, 1833, pp. 507–522.

Bache in this instance was campaigning for due recognition of American science generally, and more specifically on behalf of his distinguished great grandfather Benjamin Franklin. Bache's pride in his nation's science is alluded to above in footnote 3. His claim on behalf of Franklin was essentially correct. Announced in his first publication on electrical experiments and disseminated widely in succeeding editions published in London and elsewhere, Franklin's discovery was well known in the literature by the 1830s. For instance, ice at −13°F is listed as a non-conductor in George John Singer, *Elements of Electricity and Electro-Chemistry* (London, 1814), p. 39, and is discussed in P. M. Roget, *Treatises on Electricity, Galvanism, Magnetism, and Electromagnetism* (London, 1832), "Electricity," pp. 5–6. It is curious, then, that Michael Faraday was "extremely surprised to discover that an electric current would not pass through a thin sheet of ice." L. P. Williams, *Michael Faraday* (New York, 1965), p. 246. Nonetheless, Faraday did not explicitly claim to be the sole discoverer of the non-conducting power of ice. He merely derived inspiration from the phenomenon which led to an important series of experiments on the relationship between conduction and decomposition (Williams, pp. 246–257).

[9] Although we have not found his response, Henry clearly did send the needle to Bache promptly. See below, Henry to Forbes, June 7, 1836.

TO BENJAMIN SILLIMAN, SR.

Silliman Family Papers, Sterling Library, Yale University[1]

Princeton March 2nd 1836

My Dear Sir

I have been prevented by ill health from sending before this the account of the experiments which I promised.[2] I have been afflicted for several weeks with a slow feaver and pain in the head which although not confining me to my room have prevented my applica[tion] to any thing of a mental kind. Want of exercise during the long continuance of snow and too close attention to the business of my lectures have produced the attack. I am now however much better and hope soon to recover my usual health and spirits.

I intended before sending the account to have made some experiments for the express purpose of adding to the number and interest of those I send as these have been exhibited with scarcely any previous trial or preparation on the spur of the moment before the meeting of my class.

If my health will permit I will probably do something in this way at the time I am lecturing on the subject of electro magnetism which will be in about two weeks from this time. I regret that I did not meet with you in New York as I could have exhibited some of the experiments then and thus saved you the trouble of working out some of the minutia by your own experience. I have given as detailed an account as I think is necessary to the comprehension of the arrangements and I trust you will find but little difficulty in producing the results described.

I was much pleased with the accounts I received from New York of the unheard of success of your course of lectures in that city not only because the result must have been highly gratifying to you but because I believe that it will have a very favourable influence on the cause of science itself not only in that city but throuought our country.

Davey was doing nearly as much for the cause of English science when attracting by his eloquence to the Theatre of the Royal Institution the

---

[1] This is Henry's outgoing letter. The first part, through the paragraph after Henry's signature, is in Henry's handwriting. The second part, a description of experiments, is in Harriet Henry's handwriting, with corrections made by Henry. Henry may have drawn the sketches himself, although they are unusually neat for him.

A partial draft of the section on experiments, in Harriet Henry's hand with corrections by Henry, is in the Henry Papers, Smithsonian Archives. The recopying of the draft for this outgoing letter suggests Henry was trying to produce a very neat and accurate copy. Also in the Henry Papers, Smithsonian Archives, is a copy of the partial draft. This is in the handwriting of W. L. Nicholson who was working with Henry's papers in the 1880s.

[2] Silliman had originally asked for this information in a letter of October 31, 1835 (*Henry Papers*, 2:474).

Wealthy and Fashionable of the Metropolis as when engaged in the profound researches of his laboratory and much undoubtedly of the present popularity of the British Association is due to the taste for science which at that time began to be diffused among the higher classes of the English Nation.[3]

[3] Henry's praise for Silliman's lecturing and for the activities of contemporary British scientific societies again raises the issue of scientific popularization, this time from a comparative perspective. Aristocratic and fashionable clientele had been a conspicuous feature of the Royal Institution in London since its earliest years. The Institution was originally established in 1799 to diffuse science, useful knowledge, and news of the latest improvements among working-class mechanics as well as among England's upper classes. In 1802 the idea of a practical mechanics' school was dropped, leaving what Thomas Carlyle called "a kind of sublime *Mechanics' Institute* for the upper classes" (quoted on p. 7 of Foote's article, cited below).

Silliman himself was struck by the visible presence of London's elite at Royal Institution lectures on visits early in the century. His travel diary recorded the allure of the Institution's lecture hall for London high society, evidenced most visibly by the number of fashionable ladies in attendance. Silliman applauded the popularization effort, noting that "there can be no danger that the dignity of science will be degraded so long as this duty is committed to able hands"—an observation Henry would have endorsed. Aside from enhancing the image of science among groups that were potential sources of support, the popular discourses had for Silliman the added social benefit of diverting aristocratic London from more frivolous or cruder amusements. Silliman, *A Journal of Travels in England, Holland and Scotland, and of Two Passages over the Atlantic, in the Years 1805 and 1806* (New York, 1810), 2:219.

The socially prominent audience was catered to by an eminent staff of science professors that over the years gave the Institution the highest scientific reputation. Envisioning aristocrats yawning through learned discourses, skeptical contemporaries questioned the value of placing research scientists before such audiences. Yet, professors such as Davy, Faraday, and Thomas Young excelled at their public function as in research, Davy most of all. Brilliantly intermixing technical material, spectacular demonstration, and sheer entertainment, Davy gave lectures of substance that engaged the attention of his aristocratic following. Audiences were most impressed with lectures on the applications of science to the useful arts and human welfare. But doses of basic science were also successfully administered, especially in chemistry which enjoyed the advantage of spectacular experiments. Celebrated in London for his performances in the lecture hall, Davy both tapped and enhanced the prevalent amateur interest in science in England. The high quality of research conducted at the Royal Institution depended on the fortunate choice of professors but also on the support it won among well-placed members of society. George A. Foote, "Sir Humphry Davy and his Audience at the Royal Institution," *Isis*, 1952, *43*:6–12. For an alternative interpretation of Davy's popular lecturing as fulfilling the agricultural concerns of the Institution's landed founders, see Morris Berman, "The Early Years of the Royal Institution, 1799–1810: A Re-evaluation," *Science Studies*, 1972, *2*:205–240.

No doubt, as Henry suggests, other British scientific organizations benefited from the conspicuous social success of the Royal Institution. More accurately, societies like the British Association for the Advancement of Science, founded in 1831, drew upon the same widespread enthusiasm for science that underpinned the Royal Institution. Yet, the social and geographic setting of the British Association was quite different from the London society. The former was a migratory organization catering to commercial and industrializing provincial centers, not to upper-class groups in London. Popularization was an avowed primary goal of the Royal Institution. While the British Association also purported to diffuse knowledge, it functioned chiefly as a vehicle for scientific communication among professional scientists and lay cultivators participating directly in its activities. The itinerant BAAS knit together existing learned societies outside of London founded in the late eighteenth and early nineteenth centuries. According to recent research, the most active elements in the provincial network were scientists allied with middle-class entrepreneurs and

You mention in your last letter that you can have the use of a magneto-electrical machine. I am glad of this since Professor Bache informs me that Mr Lukens has not yet returned to Philadelphia and may be absent for some months to come.[4]

In the experiments with the coil the battery may be placed at the distance of two or three yards from the table on which the coil rests and this will render the effect more surprising.

In order to exhibit the effects of a spiral conductor in increasing the intensity of a galvanic battery of a single element as explained in my last paper in your journal[5] it is necessary that the coil should be formed into a close spiral that is, with no opening in the center. When you break the communication of the coil with the poles of the battery as you will be required to do, a spark and perhaps a loud snap will be perceived. This is caused by the induction of the spiral conductor.

With the highest respect Yours
Jos. Henry

In this apparatus Fig 7 the zinc cylender alone revolves when the iron is not employed. When it is required that the zinc cylender alone should revolve then the other parts of the apparatus may be made much stouter and the moveable part of the apparatus alone of thin materials.

The following is a description of the Electro-magnetic experiments which

---

professional men with serious intellectual aspirations. See A. D. Orange, "The British Association for the Advancement of Science: The Provincial Background," *Science Studies*, 1971, *1*:315–329.

From his experience in Albany, an American provincial center, Henry was accustomed to cultivating lay support for science. Although ambivalent about his own suitability for scientific popularization, his praise for Silliman, Davy, and other gifted popularizers was genuine. At the Albany Institute and in other contexts, Henry worked easily with concerned amateurs and willingly courted political influence and moneyed interests. When called upon, he was able to summon forceful public remarks designed to impress as well as edify. Although in dealing with lay groups Henry was probably most comfortable addressing those with serious interests in learning, the lessons of the Royal Institution were not lost on him. He recognized the pragmatic value of reaching fashionable and influential audiences, regardless of their scientific sophistication. Even after years of dealing with obstructionist amateurs, Henry remained impressed by the accomplishment of the Royal Institution in supporting science of the first rank. Urging the British physicist John Tyndall to go ahead with plans for a Baltimore lecture, Henry invoked the example of the Royal Institution in reiterating the importance of communicating physical principles to the wealthy and refined members of that community. Henry to Tyndall, October 6, 1876, letterpress copy, Henry Papers, Smithsonian Archives.

On his trip to Europe in the following year, Henry attended Royal Institution lectures, including Faraday's. Diary entries on these occasions appear below.

[4] The Philadelphia mechanic Isaiah Lukens (*Henry Papers*, 2:158–159) was the principal maker and purveyor of Joseph Saxton's magnetoelectric machines in America.

[5] "Facts in Reference to the Spark, &c. from a Long Conductor Uniting the Poles of a Galvanic Battery," *Silliman's Journal*, 1835, *28*: 327–331, containing an abstract of "Contributions II: Spiral Conductor" as well as an appendix with new material.

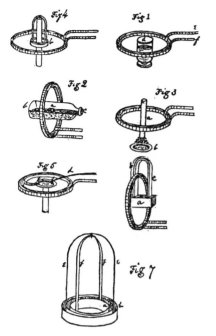

I mentioned to you as having been exhibited before my class with a large coil of copper ribbon.[6]

The ribbon is formed of slips of sheet copper, one inch wide and soldered together end to end so as to make an entire length of from one to two hundred feet. The whole is covered with strips of silk and wound on itself so as to form a circular coil of from 12 to 24 inches in diameter according to the size of the battery employed. The length of the ribbon forming the coil depends on the *intensity* of the Electricity used: if the battery employed be one of a single element the length of ribbon must not exceed one hundred feet, but if the battery be composed of several elements the electricity will have a greater projectile force and the coil in order to produce the same magnetic effects should have a corresponding increase of length. The length of ribbon proper to produce the maximum effect can only be determined by actual experiment in a given case with battery of a given force. The connection of the coil with the battery should be formed by dipping the ends well amalgamated into cups of mercury in order that the current may be passed through the coil at once with its full energy.

Exp. 1st.[7] To *exhibit the action of the coil in producing motion* in a *floating magnet.*[8]

Fig. 1st. represents the coil in a horizontal position *e f* are the ends which form the connection with the battery, *d* is a glass vessel (the article used in my experiments is a common air pump receiver inverted on a wooden foot) placed in the centre of the coil and

---

[6] Background for Henry's unique "ribbon coils" and his accompanying explanation of their effects are provided in the second volume of the *Henry Papers*, as well as in "Contributions II: Spiral Conductor."

[7] The following is a rather simple set of experiments chosen for their potential impact on a general audience. Characteristically, Henry emphasized strength or largeness of effect and

the action of invisible forces at a distance. For some experiments, the principles involved were elementary. Others reflected fairly recent research interests of Henry.

[8] In 1834, using similar apparatus, Henry began a series of experiments on the patterns of magnetic force in and around coils. *Henry Papers*, 2:225–227. Experiments 2 and 3 below illustrate similar electromagnetic effects.

nearly filled with water, on which is placed a floating magnet formed of a piece of rat tail file about 5 inches long and passed through a cork just sufficient in size to render the whole lighter than water.

When a galvanic current is transmitted through the coil, the magnet starts from its quiescent horizontal position and dives end foremost beneath the water so as to place its centre in the plane of the coil and its axes at right angles to the same. The North end of the magnet may be distinguished by a coat of white paint; when the current is in one direction, this end will descend first; when the current is reversed, the other end will be foremost.

Exp. 2nd. *Another method of exhibiting motion in a floating magnet.*

Fig. 2nd. In this arrangement the coil is placed in a vertical position and a glass jar *b, c* about 6 inches in diameter and 14 or 15 inches long, supported so that its axis coincides with the axes of the coil and its middle with the plane of the same; this jar is nearly half filled with water and thus serves as a trough in which to float the magnet *a* described in the last experiment. Perhaps, it would add to the interest of the experiment, if, a large (toy) magnetic fish were used in place of the magnet.

When a current is transmitted through the coil, the magnet if it be near one end of the jar, suddenly darts to the middle and after a few oscillations settles in this place; if, the current be now reversed it darts towards the end, turns half round and again takes up its position in the middle of the jar, with its north end in an opposite direction to that which it had in its first position. The action of the coil in these experiments is much more energetic, if the circle be made smaller, but the effect is not as striking in reference to these motions being produced by an invisible cause.

Exp. 3^{d} *To exhibit the action of the coil in developing magnetism in soft iron.*

Fig 3^{d} In this experiment, the coil is placed horizontally and a cylender of soft iron *a* about 10 inches long and 1½ or 1¾ inches in diameter held vertically in the centre. When the galvanic current is transmitted, this becomes so magnetic that it will support from its lower end another iron cylender of equal dimensions. The developement of magnetism is also strikingly shown by placing under the cylender a plate *b* containing a quantity of clean iron filings mixed with pieces of fine iron wire of about an inch in length. When the coil is in action the filings and wire adhere to the end of the cylender so as to form a large bunch which instantly falls off when the galvanic action ceases, or when the cylender is withdrawn from the magic circle.

Another variation of this experiment is to place the cylender perpendicularly on the table and the plate with filings on the top of this. At each contact of the ends of the coil with the poles of the battery the filings and pieces of wire bristle up on the surface of the plate as if suddenly animated.

Exp. 4th. To *shew the revolution of a large Ampere's cylender by means of the coil.*[9]

Fig 4th. The coil remains in its horizontal position and a large Ampere's cylender or bucket *b* is placed in the centre. When the bucket is charged with a strong solution of acid (Nitric) and the current transmitted through the coil, the moveable part of the apparatus begins to revolve with considerable velocity; when the direction of the current is reversed, the motion stops and then recommences in an opposite direction. The motion will be a little more rapid, if the bucket be supported as shewn in the figure, on the end of the iron cylender described in the last exp, this becoming magnetic reacts on the revolving apparatus and increases the effect. The experiment however is more pleasant without the use of the iron, although the motion is less rapid.

This is a highly interesting experiment when the motion is properly produced. The bucket I have used is nearly 6 inches in external diameter. The space between (*a* & b Fig 7)* the internal and external cylinder for the reception of the acid and the moveable zinc cylinder is about ¾ of an inch wide and about an inch deep. The two metalic arches *e, f* are made of thin sheet copper nearly ¼ of an inch wide and painted white so that their motion may be distinctly seen at a distance. The whole height of the apparatus is between 8 and 9 inches. Every part should be made as light as possible, the bucket of very thin copper and the zinc

* Fig 7 represents the revolving bucket of Ampere on a larger scale.

[9] For the operation of this popular piece of demonstration apparatus see *Henry Papers, 1*:317.

cylender of thin zinc plate which can be easily renewed. The one employed by me is so light that it makes several revolutions when strong acid is first poured in by the action of the magnetism of the earth, alone.

Exp. 5th. To *exhibit the revolutions of mercury with the coil*[10]

Fig. 5th. Place a plate of mercury in the centre of the coil on the top of the iron cylender mentioned in Exp. 3d. Also, place an end of the coil in the mercury at the side of the plate at *e*; the other end of the coil being in connection with one pole of the battery and the current completed by means of the wire *d*, which also dips into the plate of mercury on the oposit side at f. When the battery is put in action the mercury begins to revolve in a whirlpool around the point of its surface which is immediately above the end of the iron cylender on which the plate rests. When the current is reversed, the motion of the mercury is changed. The revolutions may be shown at a distance by throwing on the surface of the metal some pieces of light substance which will partake of its motion and render it more perceptible.

Exp. 6th. *To exhibit powerful magnetic induction with the coil.*

Fig. 6th. represents the coil placed vertically with a large piece of iron *a* (the lifter of my large magnet weighs 27 lbs.) in the centre. *b, c* represents a piece of bar iron about 3½ feet long bent into the form of a horse shoe and placed over the sides of the coil so as to support the weight in the centre by the magnetism developed when a current is transmitted through the coil. The face of the horse shoe and the iron should be ground to each other. The great power may be shown by suspending weights to the lifter from below.

NB The results will be more energetic with a large battery than a small one. I have ex[ecuted] these experiments with a battery of a single element exposing about 50 feet of zinc surface to the action of the acid.

[10] Henry touched on this effect in prior laboratory research. *Henry Papers,* 2:246–247.

FROM TITUS W. POWERS
Henry Papers, Smithsonian Archives

New York March 13, 1836
177 Grand St.

My dear Henry,

Absence from the city, and a multitude of engagements have prevented me from acknowledging your very kind & interesting letter[1] until this late period.

I regret extremely that I shall not be able to visit you this term as I had anticipated; I am determined, however, to let nothing prevent my doing so in the course of the next term.

Mͬ Codman desires me to present his acknowledgments to you & Mͬ Alexander for your polite invitation to visit Princeton during the present term, and to express his regrets that the urgent nature of his engagements will not admit of his leaving the City for several weeks. He trusts however that he shall be able in the course of the ensuing term to accompany me on a visit to you.

In regard to the Aurora of Novͬ last, I have not been able to procure any additional facts that would be of interest to you. A German gentleman[2] informs me that in a letter which he received from Hamburg dated Novͬ 28, 1835, it was stated, "that a splendid Aurora was seen there on the 19th & 20th Novͬ followed by a terrible storm causing the water to rise 19 feet."

I suppose before this time you have seen a copy of Mͬ Baily's "notice of the life & writings of Flamstead."[3] I perceive that the Lords Commissioners of the Admiralty have sent out a copy to Mͬ Hassler.[4]

In Fraser's magazine for February 1836, a notice of Mͬ Faraday with a portrait is given. As the journal may not be immediately accessible to you, I will transcribe some portions of this sketch for your amusement.[5]

"Here standeth, anno aetatis 42, at the head of one of the noblest of the

---

[1] Not found.

[2] Not identified; possibly the "Mr. Ehlers" mentioned by Powers in his letter to Henry of January 14, 1836.

[3] Francis Baily, *An Account of the Reverend John Flamsteed, the First Astronomer Royal; Compiled from His Own Manuscripts, and Other Authentic Documents, Never Before Published. To Which Is Added His British Catalogue of Stars, Corrected and Enlarged* (London, 1835). Baily is identified below in note 16 of Henry's diary entry for April 21, 1837.

[4] The Lords Commissioners of the Admiralty had published Baily's massive book (745 pages of text and tables). Ferdinand Hassler probably would have found the star catalog useful for his work as Superintendent of the United States Coast Survey.

[5] "Michael Faraday, F. R. S., Hon. D. C. L. Oxon, Etc. Etc.," *Fraser's Magazine*, 1836, *13*: 224. Powers excerpted the milder statements about Faraday. The brief sketch poked fun at Faraday's religion and newly awarded pension, but Powers omitted most of the derogatory passages.

sciences, honored as the compeer of Cuvier, Laplace & Buckland,[6] the son of a poor blacksmith, who was apprenticed at 9 years of age to an obscure bookbinder in Brandford Street[7] and earned his bread by that humble calling until he was 22. These are the spectacles on which, of all that history presents, we dwell with the highest exultation."

"Ned Magrath now Secr[y] to the Athenaeum[8] happening five & twenty years ago to enter the shop of Ribeau, observed one of the bucks of the paper bonnet sedulously studying a book he ought to have been binding. He approached—it was a vol: of the old Britannica open at Electricity. He entered into talk with the greasy journeyman, and was astonished to find in him a self taught chemist of no slender attainments. He presented him with a set of tickets for Davy's lectures at the Royal Institution,[9] and daily thereafter might the nondescript be seen perched, pen in hand, and his eyes starting out of his head, just over the clock opposite the chair. At last the course terminated, but Faraday's spirits had received a new impulse, which nothing but dire necessity could have restrained: and from that time he was saved by the promptitude with which, on his forwarding a modest outline of his history with the notes he had made of his lectures to Davy, that great & good man (so abominably caricatured by that *ass, Paris*)[10] rushed to the rescue of kindred genius. Sir Humphry immediately appointed him an assistant in his laboratory, and after 2 or 3 years had passed, he found Faraday qualified to act as his Sec[ry]. The steps of his subsequent progress are well

[6] Georges Cuvier (1769–1832), Pierre Simon Laplace (1749–1827), and William Buckland (1784–1856), known respectively for their contributions to zoology, astronomy, and geology.

[7] Faraday apprenticed to George Riebau (or Ribeau) at 13, not 9 years old. Riebau, an emigré from the French Revolution, lent newspapers and sold books as well as maintained the binding shop on Blandford Street (mistranscribed as Brandford by Powers). According to L. Pearce Williams, Riebau tolerated and even encouraged Faraday's scientific interests (*DSB; Michael Faraday: A Biography* [New York, 1965], pp. 8, 10–11, 22, and 25).

[8] Edward Magrath (d. 1855) was an assistant at the Royal Institution before becoming Secretary of the Athenaeum Club of London in 1824, a position he held until his death. Magrath's duties as Secretary were similar to those of a general manager, paralleling the work of John Vaughan for the American Philosophical Society. Magrath and Faraday were both in several informal, scientifically oriented associations; Magrath tutored the young Faraday on style and grammar in prose writing. Thomas Humphry Ward, *History of the*

Athenaeum, 1824–1925 (London, 1926), pp. 25 and 63; Williams, *Faraday*, pp. 20–21 and 328.

Clubs had begun to replace coffeehouses as the gathering places for gentlemen of London in the early nineteenth century. By the time of the founding of the Athenaeum in 1823–1824, clubs already existed for travellers, university alumni, politicians, military officers, and "men of fashion." The Athenaeum dedicated itself to scientific and literary pursuits; the heart of its activities was the library, which numbered 10,000 volumes by 1832. Ward, *Athenaeum*, pp. 1–13, 39, and 98. Alexander Dallas Bache described the organization graphically in his diary entry for April 7, 1837, printed below.

[9] Williams, *Faraday*, p. 26, using an account written by Riebau, credits the gift of the tickets to a Mr. Dance, presumably George Dance, architect and city surveyor of London (1741–1825; *DNB*).

[10] John Ayrton Paris (1785–1856), a physician known for his medical publications (*DNB*) and for the invention of the thaumatrope (*Henry Papers, 1*:207), wrote the hagiographical *Life of Sir Humphry Davy*, 2 vols. (London, 1831).

known. He travelled on the continent with Sir H. & Lady Davy, and he is now what Davy was, when he first saw Davy, in all but money: and money too, now that he has a nest egg, will accumulate."[11]

"Aye, Aye," quoth Hill,[12] playing for once Paul Pry, "aye, aye," quoth the sage peeping over our shoulders, *"Far a day,* I suppose means being interpreted, *near a Knight."*

"The *future Baronet* is a very good little fellow—we know few things more agreeable than a segar and a bowl of punch (which he mixes admirably) in the society of the *unpretending bookbinder."*

Please present my thanks to M⸰ Alexander for his interesting postscript in your letter. The following extract from a letter from Dr. Ten Eyck to me dated Jan⸶ 31⸲⸳ 1836, may be of interest to him & you. "On referring to my notes I find that on the 29⸲ᵗʰ Sept⸲ I observed with power of 80 a small star in the circle of light. At this time the comet appeared like a round nebula without a tail. As near as I recollect, the Star was near the edge of the circle. I saw the comet again on the 3⸲ʳᵈ & 10⸲ᵗʰ Oct⸲ with the large telescope. On the 11⸲ᵗʰ with my small Fraunhofer only. On the 12⸲ᵗʰ I first observed the curved pencil of rays, with all the powers of the large one—thus as seen inverted. The next evenings were very hazy. On the 16⸲ᵗʰ this appendage had assumed the form of a sector, the rays appearing straight, but the position nearly the same. The succeeding evenings were rather unfavorable until the time you looked with me, when I think it had disappeared."

There is a very favorable notice in the last No. (March) of the American Quarterly, of a work on Navigation, with a very high sounding title, by M⸰ Maury, Midshipman in the U.S. Navy. Do you know him? I am told he is a young man of great industry, ability & promise.[13] I suppose you have heard of the infamous & cowardly personal assault upon Dr. Jno. B. Beck of this

[11] A reference to the pension awarded by the government in 1835, despite initial opposition from Lord Melbourne (Williams, *Faraday,* p. 353).

[12] Not identified. Referred to in the article as *"alias* Hull, *alias* Hobbleday" and "the old bore."

[13] With startling prescience, the author in the *American Quarterly Review,* 1836, *19*:87–101, remarked "there are stations and duties, apart from the ordinary business of a midshipman, for which Mr. Maury must be peculiarly fitted. . . . The establishment of a national observatory will, it is believed, soon afford the department this opportunity [to reward Maury]" (p. 101). The book under review was Maury's *A New Theoretical and Practical Treatise on Navigation* (Philadelphia, 1836).

The professional career and scientific work of Matthew Fontaine Maury (1806–1873) intertwined closely with Joseph Henry's, especially in the fifteen years between 1846 and the Civil War when they were both in Washington. Maury joined the Navy after graduating from Harpeth Academy in 1825. He served at sea until an accident lamed him in 1839, forcing a shift to land-based operations. From 1844 until he resigned in 1861 to join the Confederate Navy, Maury directed the Naval Observatory. He thus headed one of the major scientific institutions in Washington during the crucial early years of Henry's leadership of the Smithsonian. After the Civil War, Maury worked briefly in Mexico, wrote geography texts in England, and then taught physics at the Virginia Military Institute from

city. If you have not heard of it, and if you desire the particulars I will furnish them to you.[14]

Yours Sincerely
Titus W. Powers.

P.S. I had nearly omitted to thank you for your very interesting paper upon Magnetic Electricity which you sent me together with the addresses of M[r] Biddle & M[r] Gaston.[15]

N.B. It is my intention to depart for Pittsburg the 22nd of this month to be absent 2 weeks, so if you have any commands, make them known before that time.

1868 until his death.

Despite his affiliation with the Observatory, Maury published relatively few papers in astronomy, all observational in approach. His scientific interests were earth-bound rather than heavenly: Maury concentrated on navigation, oceanography, and meteorology. His theories, data-gathering, and administrative ambitions in the latter two fields led to controversy with Henry and Bache, conflicts which will be documented in later volumes of the *Henry Papers*. In navigation and oceanography, Maury issued a series of *Wind and Sea Charts* based on ships' logs and indicating ocean currents and surface winds. He used the charts to recommend time-saving sailing directions for oceanic transport of passengers and goods. Maury also gathered soundings from the Naval fleet that he used to plot the contours of the ocean floor. His experience in these empirical undertakings made Maury a leader in efforts to standardize oceanographic observations on a worldwide scale, culminating in his report for an international con-ference on the subject in Brussels in 1853. Maury's interpretive work, best known from his popular *Physical Geography of the Sea* (1855), stirred considerable antagonism at the time. Ultimately his monistic ideas on the causes of the circulation of ocean waters and of winds were replaced by more complicated explanations depending on several factors, not just one phenomenon such as salinity differentials or paramagnetism. *DSB*.

[14] The biographers of physician John Brodhead Beck (1794–1851; *Henry Papers*, 1:284) and the newspapers of that day are silent on this incident. No other mention of the assault occurs in Joseph Henry's correspondence during this period.

[15] A reference to Henry's "Contributions I and II" and to the Princeton commencement addresses of Nicholas Biddle and William Gaston. For the distribution of Henry's articles see *Henry Papers*, 2:432–438; the commencement addresses are described on pages 463 and 490 of the same volume.

FROM BENJAMIN SILLIMAN, SR.[1]

Henry Papers, Smithsonian Archives

Boston March 15, 1836

My dear Sir

Your very kind letter of the 2 has been forwarded to me by my family & I thank you very sincerely for it:[2] it is exactly what I wished & I now write

---

[1] Also printed in Nathan Reingold, ed., *Science in Nineteenth-Century America: A Documentary History* (New York, 1964), p. 76. At the top of the letter are editorial comments by Mary Henry.

[2] See above. Silliman was lecturing in Boston.

to say that if you have any additional facts derived or soon to be derived from your lectures which I trust you are now about reforming there may be time to forward them to me before I come to that part of my course. I expect to give a lecture on electro magnetism in the last of this or the first of next month. Your drawings are excellent & enable me perfectly to understand you & if necessary I will thank you to sketch any additional experiments.

For Ampere's revolving apparatus I shall this morning send home for those which you formerly furnished me with for your great magnet, although I fear they may be too heavy. I should like your opinion on this point taking into view my battery which is 450 pairs of 10 inches by 4—in copper cases—all plunging at once; they are in six troughs & are also fitted as a calorimotor of any number of members between 6 & 18. Will this be powerful enough to produce the results?

I grieve to hear that you have been ill but trust in God that you are restored & I pray that your important life may be long preserved, as I think you are destined to a brilliant career in the science of this country.

It will give me the most sincere pleasure to promulgate your discoveries & I am not a little gratified that you think I am promoting a taste for science by my popular lectures.

I am now lecturing to an evening class of 1000 & to a day class—chiefly persons who cannot go out in the evening of 3 to 400 & there is great enthusiasm excited.

Hitherto every experiment has been successful. I am to go (by particular invitation) to New York on finishing here to give a full course of geology from April 19 to May 25.[3]

Hoping to hear from you soon at least as regards your health I remain my dear Sir

yours very truly
B Silliman

No. 21 Somerset Street at
Mrs Jackson's[4]

[3] Silliman's public course on "The Structure of the Earth" was to be given at Clinton Hall and to include twelve lectures. According to advertisements, its starting date was the eighteenth, not the nineteenth of April. *New York* *Daily Advertiser*, April 5, 1836, p. 2.
[4] Silliman was boarding with Lydia Jackson, widow of Captain Joseph Jackson. Boston City Directory.

HENRY NOTEBOOK ENTRY

Notebook [23894],[1] page [123], Henry Papers, Smithsonian Archives

March 15th 1836   This evening with Mr Alexander observed the light of the electrical spark through the prism. Observed several white or brilliant lines passing through the spectrum at right angles to the length of the spectrum. These lines are fixed and appear nearly the same with different balls[2] and different angles of the *prism.*

J.H.

[1] This notebook was used primarily to record experiments illustrating Henry's lectures. It is described in *Henry Papers,* 2:370.

[2] Although Henry was unaware of it, his interpretation of this experiment contradicted that of Charles Wheatstone. In a paper delivered before the British Association in 1835, Wheatstone announced that he had found that changing the balls on the electrical machine resulted in lines which differed both in number and position. For a detailed discussion of the light from the electric spark, see below,

Henry's European Diary, April 1, 1837, footnote 4.

With only a sketchy description of the experiment provided by Henry, we can only speculate why Henry obtained different results from Wheatstone. Perhaps the dispersion of the prism was insufficient. Perhaps Henry wasn't really concerned with the distribution of the lines, but was only looking for a classroom experiment. In any case, he would later accept Wheatstone's conclusions without fuss.

HENRY NOTEBOOK ENTRY

Notebook [23894], page [25], Henry Papers, Smithsonian Archives

March 15th, 1836

This evening suceded in producing electricity from the freezing of water by ether under the air pump. The gold leaf electrometer was used with a condenser. The leaves diverged so as to strike the sides.[1]

[1] This experiment on the production of static electricity was prompted by a reading of C. Despretz, *Traité élémentaire de physique,* 3d ed. (Paris, 1832), pp. 360–361: "D'une autre part, M. Grothus, en fondant de la glace ou en congelant de l'eau dans une bouteille de Leyden, a fourni à cet instrument une faible charge électrique." The same experiment is suggested below in "Record of Experiments," December 29, 1837.

"RECORD OF EXPERIMENTS"
Henry Papers, Smithsonian Archives

March 16th 1836

Since the last date I have made no experiments excep some in Philadelphia. The building of a new college edifice for the Phil Department[1] and other circumstances have prevented

This day repeated the experiments or some of those made by Nobili.[2] The poles of one of the *mercer* troughs were tipped with platina wire and then placed on a plate of silver over which a solution of the acetate of lead was poured just sufficient to cover the surface; one of the poles (the + one) was placed at about the 1/20 of an inch from the plate. When the current was transmitted the rings described by Nobili were formed. Various other metals were used and different solutions. The only singular circumstance

---

[1] Since the last entry of May 18, 1835, Henry had managed to perform some miscellaneous experiments—work not entered in the "Record of Experiments" (see preceding documents). The renovations to Philosophical Hall are documented in volume 2 of the *Henry Papers*.

[2] Henry is investigating a well-known electrolytic effect involving the motions of mercury under the influence of galvanism. It was a phenomenon that had greatly puzzled electrochemists in the 1820s and 1830s when the mechanisms underlying electrolytic action were not yet well understood. First reported by Davy, the motions occurred when a globule of mercury was covered by a layer of conducting saline or acid solution into which were placed the electrodes of a voltaic battery. When electricity passed through the solution, vigorous currents developed in the mercury which tended to elongate or radiate toward the negative pole. A smaller globule would move as a whole toward that electrode. Electrochemists immediately distinguished this effect from the electromagnetic rotations which occur in mercury when it is subjected to a magnet in conjunction with an electric current. At first it was believed that chemical forces were not involved and that the motions were purely mechanical, but they were soon seen to be more complex. It was not known to what extent forces like chemical affinity, cohesion, or direct action at a distance were involved. The precise role of the electric current was unknown as well. John Herschel, one of the earliest investigators of the motions of mercury, connected them to certain electrochemical phenomena. It was Leopoldo Nobili

who showed the motions were indeed a result of electrochemical decomposition by relating the effects to his earlier studies of iridescent electrochemical deposits known as Nobili's rings. Henry's first experiment reproduces these rings. The mercury was found to absorb the active agents of electrochemical decomposition and to share their motions and interactions. Once shown to be merely a special instance of electrolytic decomposition, the phenomenon of the motions of mercury rapidly lost the interest of scientists.

See John Herschel, "On Certain Motions Produced in Fluid Conductors When Transmitting the Electric Current," *Phil. Trans.*, 1824, pp. 162–196, and "On the Mechanical Effects Produced When a Conducting Liquid is Electrified in Connexion with Mercury," *Edinburgh Journal of Science*, 1825, 2:193–199. Nobili's articles appeared in several issues of the *Bibliothèque Universelle, Sciences et Arts*: "Sur une nouvelle classe de phénomènes électrochimiques," 1826, 33:302–314; "Sur les apparences et les mouvemens électrochimiques du mercure," 1827, 35:261–284; "Nouvelles observations sur les apparences électro-chimiques, les lois électro-dynamiques, et le mécanisme intérieur de la pile," 1834, 56: 150–168. A complete discussion of the subject can be found in A. A. De LaRive, *A Treatise on Electricity*, trans. C. V. Walker, 3 vols. (London, 1856), 2:424–434.

Henry intended publishing on the topic. See his letter to Silliman, below, of March 22, 1836. But to our knowledge, he conducted no systematic experiments beyond these. Nor did any results appear in print.

noticed was that when the pole (+) was placed near a plate of copper the other pole resting on it and a solution of the muriate of iron poured over the plate, the rings were formed but at the same time a deflagration took place at the point which was not visible when any other solution was used

Exp 2 The experiment of the rings was attempted with mercury; when the + pole was plunged in the mercury and the negative pole placed a little above the rings were formed on the surface as on the copper but when the + pole was withdrawn and the negative pole plunged in, the rings disappeared and the oxide or coating of the mercury was instantly transmitted to the other side and the metal made perfectly clean. (the + pole not withdrawn from the acid)

This effect appears to me to be produced by [the] circumstance of the — pole when the other is withd[rawn] being at the further extremity of the mercury. Thus when the — pole is in the acid at *d* then the wire forms the pole; when in the mercury then the poles may be considered as at *c* on the oposite side of the mercury nearest the + pole. If mercury be placed in a bent tube into which the wires of a trough dip and if a quantity of acid solution be poured on the negative side it will pass through between the glass and the mercury—is this not the same phenominon as the preceding

HENRY NOTEBOOK ENTRY
Notebook [23894], page [109], Henry Papers, Smithsonian Archives

March 18th 1836[1]

Neg and *Pos* spark may be distinguished by receiving them on the tongue. The + tastes acid, the — alkaline or caustic. Decomposition of the saliva (Berzelius) (Annals 1824 p 239 sept)[2]

Both appear acid to my taste. J H

---

[1] On the original, the date follows Henry's initials.

[2] The observation is from the scientific miscellany section of *The Annals of Philosophy*, September 1824, n.s. *8*:236. Henry added the reference to decomposition of the saliva.

In 1803 Berzelius and William Hisinger discovered that decomposition of salts by electrolysis resulted in acids at the positive pole and bases at the negative; hence acids are electronegative and bases electropositive. On such evidence, Berzelius later developed his dualistic theory, an electrochemical theory of chemical affinity. Although flawed, "as long as chemists dealt mostly with acids, bases, and salts . . . the theory served well enough, and, in a modified form, it is still essentially a part of our explanation of the nature of polar compounds." Henry M. Leicester, *The Historical Background of Chemistry* (New York, 1956), pp. 156–166, 168–169.

"RECORD OF EXPERIMENTS"
Henry Papers, Smithsonian Archives

March 19th 1836

This afternoon made a few experiments on the magnetization of steel by electricity.

Exp 1st Needle placed in coil described May 1835 containing about 500 feet fine wire,[1] discharge from largest jar—no signs of magnetism. Needle placed on outside of coil, no effect except that part of the cement of the side of the coil was thrown off.

Exp 2. Flat rasp 7 inches long ½ an inch wide ⅛ [inch] thick placed in same coil, no effect

Exp 3 Same rasp placed in coil formed of copper ribbon 37 feet long ½ inch wide, very thin—discharge from same jar considerable magnetism produced. Needles placed in same coil also became magnetic

Exp When the same discharge was passed through spiral formed of copper wire about 18 feet long, 1/10 of an inch in diameter, the spires being about an inch in diameter, the rasp surrounded with silk, much greater degree of magnetism was produced than by any other process. From *these experiments it would appear that to develope magnetism in steel a short passage is required through a good conductor*

A phenomenon was observed relative to the lateral action in these experiments which may lead to some knowledge of the law of action of currents on currents. It was observed that a spark passed from the end of the magnet to one of the spires of the spiral. It was concluded that this was produced by the inductive action of the electric current and this was proved by placing a glass tube[2] in the axis of the spiral and a copper wire in this; when the discharge was made a vivid spark passed from the end of the wire to a piece of tin foil which formed the connection with the outside of the jar. This effect was produced when a small jar was used. The arrangement was thus

---

[1] See the May 14–15 entry of Henry's laboratory notebook, printed in *Henry Papers*, 2:398. Having previously investigated magnetization by galvanism, Henry now seeks comparative data using "ordinary electricity." On May 18, 1835 (*Henry Papers*, 2:403), Henry found that the same coil, energized by a twenty-five-plate galvanic battery, strongly magnetized a soft iron cylinder. Comparisons between induction from voltaic and static electricity were central to Henry's next series of researches.

[2] Insulation to prevent the direct conduction of the discharge. For more on "lateral action," see other "Record of Experiments" entries, below.

 These experiments on the magnetism of steel with ordinary electricity were made with a jar 13.4 inches high, and 2 feet 2.5 in diameter that is the coated part about 2¼ square feet.

"RECORD OF EXPERIMENTS"
Henry Papers, Smithsonian Archives

March 19th 1836[1]

Exp to be tried. Put a drop of mercu[ry ...][2] capsule and with it a piece of zinc. [No] motion will be observed if these met[als are] covered with nitric acid but if the [pro]tonitrate of mercury be poured on the mercury rises and falls until the zinc intirely disappears. Other metals produce no motion, even iron is inefficient although it produces action in mercury covered with nitric acid

Buletin[3] 1831 T16

p 22

Exp 2 Send current through coil from single battery the coil having a cylender of soft iron in its center through which the current also must pass.[4] Will not this arrangement increase the intensity[5]

---

[1] These six suggested experiments are recorded on the last page of the first volume of Henry's three-volume laboratory notebook, after an entry on May 10, 1838. "March 1836" appears at the top of the page. The second experiment is dated "March 19th 1836."

[2] The right-hand corner of this page of the "Record of Experiments" has been torn off, causing this and subsequent gaps in the manuscript. However, we have reconstructed most of the missing material from a reading of the original paper from which Henry obtained his information. The only exception is this gap.

[3] Henry is referring to an abstract of a paper by F. F. Runge published in the *Bulletin des sciences mathématiques, physiques et chimiques*, 1831, *16*:22. The original paper appeared under the title "Ueber Bewegungen, welche eine Zink-Quecksilberkette in Berührung mit salpetersaurem Quecksilberoxydul zeigt," *Annalen der Physik und Chemie*, 1829, *16*:304–305. In a further discussion of this phenomenon, published as "Ueber die Bedingungen, unter welchen das Quecksilber durch Zink in rotirende Bewegungen gesetzt wird," *Annalen*

der Physik und Chemie, 1829, *17*:472–479, Runge argued that the rotation was accompanied by the formation of a zinc amalgam and would continue as long as there was zinc and protonitrate of mercury (in contemporary notation $HgNO_6$) available.

[4] This experimental suggestion and the three that follow appear to be the preliminary steps in the research which resulted in Henry's "Contributions III: Electro-Dynamic Induction." Here Henry is considering retesting Faraday's contention that inserting a soft iron core into the helix appreciably increased the intensity. Henry had earlier rejected this contention (*Henry Papers*, 2:400).

Because of the press of other business, his European trip and his desire to conduct other experiments, it was over two years before Henry got around to completing the preliminary experiments described in this entry. His results led him to reject Faraday's apparatus and instead use coils and helices without cores. "Contributions III: Electro-Dynamic Induction," pp. 304–308.

[5] Henry added the following note: "It does

Exp 3 Send current generated by the battery and coil through magnet. Note if the intensity is increased[6]

Exp 4 Place soft iron cylender in axis of coil make the current pass through the iron. See if intensity is increased.[7]

Exp 5 Surround cylender of iron with broad short coil, transmit current from thermo-electric pile. Note the effect. Current transmitted through iron—

Exp 6 Coulomb asserts that iron may be made to retain its magnetism by twisting it.[8] Try this and if so note the effect with Electro-magnetism.

1838." Evidently by the time Henry was ready to publish, he reversed himself or decided to omit the cores in any case.

[6] Another later notation is inserted here: "no 1838."

[7] Again Henry added "no 1838."

[8] In his torsion memoir of 1784, Coulomb compared the magnetic force in twisted and untwisted wire. He found that the former retained nine times the force of the latter when measured with the torsion balance. Such a result, when interpreted in light of Coulomb's theory of cohesion, indicated that the magnetic forces of molecules in the state of maximum contact (which was the situation when a wire was twisted to the point of rupture) were mutually reinforcing. In the normal state, which Coulomb's theory equated with little contact between molecules, the forces tended to cancel each other. Seven years later, Coulomb published his Seventh Memoir of Electricity and Magnetism. There he further explored the effect of the elastic history of a metal on its magnetic properties. C. Stewart Gillmor, *Coulomb and the Evolution of Physics and Engineering in Eighteenth-Century France* (Princeton, 1971), pp. 159–160, 210–219.

We have no evidence of Henry ever trying this with an electromagnet.

"RECORD OF EXPERIMENTS"
Henry Papers, Smithsonian Archives

March 20th [1836]

Mr Mason[1] of Phil[a] informed me that on discharging a jar by means of a rod with a glass handle there appeared a remarkable attraction of the ball of the rod in connection with the *<lower>* outer coating. In attempting to repeat this exp. this morning, holding the rod by the glass handle and accidentally touching the table with my right side the discharge aud[ib]ly took place along the moist handle through my right side and right hand and arm. This was the *<most intense>* largest discharge which has ever passed through any part of my body, the large jar just described being the one employed. It produced an involuntary shout, the fingers of the right hand

[1] See *Henry Papers*, 2:269n.

which grasped the glass were violently cramped and for the space of half an hour, felt as if they were immersed in cold water. A sensation of fainting came over me, the blood left my face, and the pulse sunk to 38. My arm and fingers on the side through which the charge passed now feel an hour after as if they had been [. . .] by lifting a heavy article. The discharge was thus produced by my accidentally touching a brass rod which in turned touched a piece of tin foil connected with the out side of the jar. The glass handle at the same time hapening to be wet and the charge very intense

On examining my leg at the place where the discharge passed out to the wire I found it marked with two lines as if produced by a hot iron; considerable pain was felt at the spot for some time after (several hours)[2]

[2] This was certainly one of the strongest jolts Henry sustained in his electrical research. In a potentially fatal laboratory accident, Henry found scientific interest, both as to the strength of certain electrical effects and to the connections between electricity and physiology, important concerns of early electrical physicists (see *Henry Papers*, 2:90n). Henry welcomed the hazards of his vocation. As he unflinchingly proclaimed in 1832, in the pursuit of science "as much heroism has been often desplayed as that exhibited in the field of battle or on the stormy deep. . . . A lost eye, a dismembered limb, or a scorched and crisped visage, bore frequent testimony of the conflicts they carried on with the powers of darkness." *Henry Papers*, 1:395.

"RECORD OF EXPERIMENTS"
Henry Papers, Smithsonian Archives

March 22nd [1836][1]

Ex 1 Placed a piece of amalgamated zinc at the bottom of a cylindrical jar and on this poured strong solution of sul. acid. No action was observed in the zinc as described by Mr Sturgeon.[2] Over the amalgamated zinc a plate of copper was placed the under side of which was covered with cement and a piece of glass passed through the centre. Into this a piece of thick copper wire was placed and bent so that one end touched the zinc and the other the copper plate. With this arrangement bubbles of hydrogen gas were given off in abundance—from the perpendicular part of the wire and also a few small bubles appeared on the upper part of the plate.

[1] This entry is out of sequence in the "Record of Experiments," being located between the entries of March 16 and March 19.

[2] Henry's interest in amalgamated zinc dates back to at least August of 1835 (*Henry Papers*, 2:439–440). From Henry's letter to Silliman of the same date as this entry it appears that Henry's goal in this case was to prepare a demonstration experiment for the classroom which would illustrate Sturgeon's observations. The specific reference is to William Sturgeon, *Recent Experimental Researches in Electro-Magnetism and Galvanism* (London, 1830), p. 74.

The plate was cemented to the sides of the jar but possibly some liquid communication was formed between the upper and the lower side

Exp 2 A copper bucket was placed in the jar with the acid touching the amalgamated zince. The bucket was partially filled with acid and in this arrangement there was no liquid communication between the outside & inside of the copper and hence no bubbles were seen to rise from the interior of the copper

TO BENJAMIN SILLIMAN, SR.

Silliman Family Papers, Sterling Library, Yale University

Princeton March 22nd 1836

My Dear sir

I have not yet commenced my lectures on Electro magnetism but will reach that part of my course on thursday next. I have therefore as yet nothing more to communicate on that subject.[1]

I do not think the revolving apparatus which was sent to you with the large magnet will answer the purpose of exhibition with the coil. If I recollect aright it is too small and the copper bucket too deep to succeed well. You can doubtless have one made at a very short notice in Boston as the article is easily constructed and that you may have the less difficulty in this I send you on the 4th page of this letter a projection in full size of an article which I constructed last week for my lectures. The zinc cylender is alone intended to revolve and therefore the other parts of the apparatus is made of not very thin copper. The zinc cylender is constructed of thin plate zinc. In using the apparatus, to insure success, be careful to amalgamate with the nitrate of mercury the point on which the bucket revol[v]es, also the pivot *hole* into which this point fits;[2] this hole should be filled with a small globule of mercury which will adhere by cappillary attraction although inverted.

Your galvanic apparatus will make a most splendid display of the deflagrating powers of galvanism but is not quite so well fitted for the development of magnetism which as you know requires great quantity with low intensity or small "projectile force"; if however the length of the coil be increased in proportion to the projectile force of the battery the same effects will be produced.[3]

---

[1] This is a response to Silliman's request of March 15, 1836, above.

[2] To ensure electrical contact.

[3] Silliman's galvanic apparatus is described

My health has much improved since I last wrote and while lecturing on the subjects of electricity and galvanism I was able to devote all my leisure time to the repetition of some of the more unusual experiments in these branches. Some of these have interested me much and have opened new subjects of investigation.[4] The following experiment will probably interest you as it illustrates one of the principles of galvanism in a pleasing way and may be exhibited to a large class with good effect.[5] On the bottom of a cylindrical jar *a* (Fig in margin) place a circular piece of amalgamated zinc *b* which is formed by removing a piece of thick plate zinc from a solution of sulphuric acid and immediately rubbing it with clean mercury. The metal will adhere and render the surface of the zinc uniformly bright. On the zinc pour a solution of sulphuric acid so as nearly to fill the jar. The zinc will remain at the bottom unacted on by the acid and the solution will continue perfectly transparent. If however we place in the same jar a copper article *d* consisting of a circular copper plate through which a copper wire is soldered, the under part of the plate and also the wire except the lower point being covered with wax or cement, as soon as the lower end of the wire *e* touches the zinc an intense action takes place and bubbles of gas are given off from the wire and the plate so rapidly that the upper part of the vessel or that above the copper plate becomes nearly white with the mixture of bubbles, while that portion beneath the copper plate remains perfectly transparent, as is represented in the 3rd figure. The experiment should be made in a large jar. The circular plate should be nearly of the same diameter as the jar and should be pierced with a number of holes to permit the bubbles of gas to pass up. The effect is very striking since the cloudiness of the upper part is so quickly produced by merely pushing down the copper into contact with the zinc. The upper wire serves as a handle for this purpose. Amalgamated zinc as you know is not acted on by sulphuric acid until a galvanic circle is formed. Then the action goes on with rapidity. This property is highly important in many galvanic experiments. The discovery was I believe made by Mr Sturgeon and has been applied by Mr Faraday in some of his late researches.[6]

---

in his March 15 letter. In numerous prior experiments, documented in volume 2 of the *Henry Papers*, Henry had worked out the interdependencies of battery type, conductor length, electrical intensity, and magnetizing power.

[4] Concurrent entries from Henry's "Record of Experiments" show he was giving Silliman fresh results from the laboratory. Although, as Henry states below, he was considering writing up some of his results, his descriptions for Silliman emphasized visual demonstration rather than theoretical aspects of his work.

[5] In the following Henry describes the galvanic action of amalgamated zinc, which he was currently investigating in the laboratory. See the "Record of Experiments" entry for this date.

[6] See *Henry Papers*, 2:440n.

I am of the opinion that with your large apparatus the mechanical (or chemico-mechanical) motions of mercury would be a very interesting exhibition. I would be pleased if you would repeat it and inform me of the result as I intend writing something on the subject.[7] It has been investigated by Herschel and Nobili.[8] You may have seen an article in the last No of the Franklin journal by Mr Draper on the same phenomenon but he appears to be interely ignorant of what has been done by others in the investigation of this subject.[9] The following is the method of exhibiting these motions according to my own experience.

Place on a common plate or a Wedgewoods basin[10] 2 or three pounds of mercury and over this pour a strong solution of *sulphuric* acid. If now the + pole be dipped into one side of the mercury and the negative pole held directly over the middle of the surface of the mercury in the acid but not touching the metal the surface will almost instantly be covered with a series of rings of the precipitate or metal which the acid has taken up from the mercury. The whole surface from perfect brightness will in some cases, become almost instantly black. If the + pole be now withdrawn from the

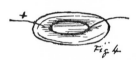

mercury and into the acid, see fig 4, while the *negative* pole is placed in the mercury at the opposite side the scum is suddenly driven from the negative to the + pole and the surface becomes perfectly clear. The acid at the same time will be observed in rapid motion which may be rendered more visible by a small quantity of saw dust thrown into the acid. This experiment is apparently somewhat capricious and does not always exhibit itself in the same form.

Again draw on the table a streak of acid by dipping the end of a glass rod into the solution; place in the middle of this a globule of mercury. The + pole at one extremity of the acid and the negative at the other. The globule of mercury will be seen to jump from its quiescent position towards the negative pole.

The streak of acid should contain as much liquid as possible without

[7] Although Henry had begun an extensive investigation of this effect (see "Record of Experiments" for March 16, 1836, above), he apparently never committed his results to print.

[8] See above, "Record of Experiments," March 16, 1836, footnote 2.

[9] John W. Draper, "Of the Tidal Motions of Conductors, Free to Move," *Journal of the Franklin Institute*, 1836, *17*:27–33. Draper did point out some of the early publications on the motions of mercury, including Herschel's, but failed to mention the latest literature known to Henry. A chemist, Draper attributed the fluid motions to forces exerted by the poles of the voltaic battery on the atomic forces of the mercury. Following Berzelius, Draper identified the forces of chemical affinity with electricity. The poles of the battery were centers of attraction acting analogously to gravitational centers in the solar system, producing tidelike motions in the globule of mercury.

[10] Wedgwood vessels of various types were common pieces of chemical apparatus.

spreading. It may be 5 or 6 inches long; with a trough of 48 plates 4 inches square, on the surface of a painted table, I have caused the globule to move from the + to neg. pole a distance of from 3 to 4 inches. Acid placed on a glass plate does not answer as well; the surface should be some what rough.

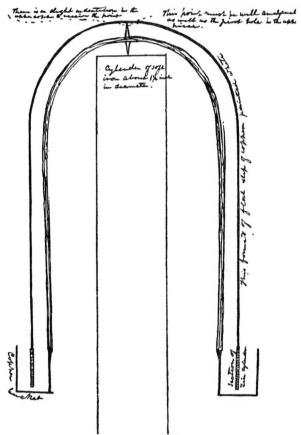

I place this apparatus on a small stand with three legs and a hole in the bottom of the same size of the opening in the copper bucket so that a cylender of soft iron or a bundle of magnets can be introduced through the opening (*a* Fig 5) without disturbing the apparatus after it has been charged with acid. If the action of the coil be very powerful both parts will revolve when the whole article is supported on the lower point.

Yours truly

J. Henry[11]

---

[11] A file note by Silliman dates the receipt of Henry's letter and also mentions "Dr Js. R. Chilton's Directions," which have not been found.

FROM JOHN TORREY
Henry Papers, Smithsonian Archives

New York, March 23rd, 1836

My dear friend,

As I expected it would happen, so has been the event. You did not come & lecture for me, neither did you send the apparatus & notes for me to attempt the subject myself[1]—but I will not scold you now, as I have another matter to talk about. You have heard, doubtless, of the great geological survey of the State which is to take place. Perhaps you have seen the full & able Report of Gen![l] Dix—which (by the way) was certainly prepared by T. R. Beck.[2] There are to be 6 or 8 geologists, 1 botanist, & 1 zoologist, who are to receive $1500. a year each. There will be also 6 draughtsmen, at $800. each. Four years will be occupied in this work.[3] I shall probably have something to do with this business, & I should not be unwilling to engage in it, provided my associates were the right sort of men. The botany would suit me best, but I am pretty sure that L. C. Beck is driving after this, & if so, he

---

[1] Henry had decided not to speak to Torrey's class (see note 2 of Henry to Bache, January 18, 1836, above). However, he did prepare a detailed outline from which Torrey could lecture on electromagnetism himself. These notes, now in Box 19 of the Henry Papers at the Smithsonian Archives, may never have been sent to Torrey. Henry drafted a lecture using relatively simple equipment, such as small batteries and magnets in conjunction with ribbon coils and various lengths of wire, to demonstrate the latest findings and concepts of electromagnetism. The treatment was much briefer than Henry's coverage of the same topics in his course at Princeton.

[2] At the request of the Assembly, Secretary of State John Adams Dix had presented a long report on the desirability of a state-financed natural history survey. Dix (1798–1879) had been educated partly at Phillips-Exeter and the College of Montreal and partly by private tutors. He served in the War of 1812 and remained in the Army until 1826, when he resigned to practice law and to manage his father-in-law's land holdings. Dix became active in Democratic party politics on the state level and eventually held federal positions, but his advocacy of abolition during the 1840s cost him political influence until the Civil War, when Republicans elevated him to national office despite his Democratic affiliation. *DAB.*

In a speech many years later (Albany Institute *Transactions*, 1872, 7:19), Orlando Meads reiterated the accusation that Theodric Romeyn Beck (*Henry Papers*, *1*:4–5) drafted Dix's report. Lewis Caleb Beck said in 1851 that "the materials for the report . . . were furnished . . . by my brother T.R.B." which could mean that he had lent books to Dix or that he had prepared a written text. However, the recollections of Morgan Dix, in his memoirs of his father (1889), support John Dix's authorship of the report. Michele L. Aldrich, "New York Natural History Survey, 1836–1845," (Ph.D. dissertation, University of Texas, 1974), pp. 379–380.

[3] The bill for the survey, which passed the Legislature on April 15, left appointive and administrative powers in the hands of Governor William L. Marcy (*Henry Papers*, 2:34). He chose four field geologists and allowed each one an assistant. The botanist and the zoologist each could hire a draftsman. Marcy added a mineralogist to the scientific corps in 1836 and a paleontologist in 1837. The survey scientists spent four years in research, obtained an additional year to complete their field work, and published thirteen volumes of final reports in 1842–1845. Aldrich, "New York Survey," pp. 87, 93, 157, 236, 448, 451, and 456. Copies of several of the annual and final reports of the survey survive in Henry's Library.

will probably get it, his brother being on the spot, & having great influence with the governor. It would suit me nearly as well if my friend D[r] Gray had the botany, & I took one of the geological districts, as we could play into each others hands, & thus produce a botanical report that would not injure the reputation of the State. Now you have some powerful friends at Albany, & you might assist us in our plans. This is what I wish. Let me have the charge of the botanical dept., & I will *also* aid in the geology of at least one of the districts—particularly in the investigation of metallic & useful minerals, & the chemical analysis of these. A vast deal of labour will be required to analyse the various materials that will be collected, & here, you know I am quite at home. D[r] Gray could also attend to botanical matters as well as myself. Indeed there is not a more sound & philosophical, as well practical botanist, in the United States. He is also an excellent mineralogist, & has paid great attention to the Geology of the State of New York. His services ought by all means to be secured. I have worked with him, side by side, for three years, & know him through & through. D[r] Gray has asked D[r] L. Beck whether he intended to apply for the botany, but he gave a *noncommittal* answer.[4] Now I wish to tell you *in confidence*, that a distinguished political gentleman of this city, who has just returned from Albany, called on me to-day, & informs me that he has seen the Governor on this business, & he wishes me to come up the river, as soon as the navigation opens, & converse with him about it. Cannot you give me a letter to one of the big wigs there? Are you acquainted with Gen. Dix? I presume that it will be proper for me to call on him, for he sent me a copy of his Report, with his compliments, & I have acknowledged the receipt of it. I hope the governor will take care who he appoints. A host of hungry chaps will doubtless urge their claims, & there may be some political favoritism.[5] If the right men are selected, the work will of course be well done, & our State, & those who have accomplished the measure, will receive lasting honor, but there is great danger of a failure from the appointment of incompetent persons.

I have not heard a word about Princeton since I saw you last. What are you all doing? Are you all frozen stiff? No doubt you are as busy as ever,

---

[4] Marcy appointed L. C. Beck as the mineralogist and eventually persuaded Torrey to accept the job of botanist. Asa Gray (*Henry Papers*, 2:281–282) became curator of the New York Lyceum of Natural History and informally helped Torrey on the survey by providing duplicate specimens of plants for the several herbaria that Torrey was required to create for the state's colleges. Aldrich, "New York Survey," pp. 134 and 139.

[5] At least one candidate hinted that Democratic connections entitled him to special consideration, but Marcy rejected his application. One of the survey geologists recalled some years later that seven of the eight scientists appointed by Marcy were in fact Whigs rather than Democrats. Aldrich, "New York Survey," p. 94.

but I should like to hear what are your particular occupations. Tell me whether anything has been done towards the completion of the laboratory & chemical lecture-room. I fear that every thing remains in *status quo* ...

You must let me know what success the Agent for collecting subscriptions has met with, for I think Mr. Newell was engaged a second time. If something is not done to secure the sum proposed to be raised by the Alumni, the subscriptions already obtained will be lost.[6] It is as good a time as we shall ever have to obtain money. The country was never more prosperous.

If you are particularly anxious to have your electromagnetic apparatus, I will see that every piece is returned forthwith. Perhaps, however, they had better be retained till Chilton[7] sends something on.

Silliman will be here again, about the 18th of April. By that time I hope to commence my botanical lectures in the new lecture room of the Lyceum. We shall have splendid quarters in this edifice. You must try & be with us at the opening of the Halls, on the 11th of May.[8] Give my kind regards to Mrs. Henry, & all the other members of your family, & believe me, ever yours

John Torrey

Send me a letter to Mr. Bloodgood[9]—the wealthy gentleman who patronizes Nat. Science.

[6] On Daniel Newell and the attempt to increase the College endowment by $100,000, see *Henry Papers*, 2:175–177. The fund-raising drive had failed by this time. The terms provided that subscriptions would be paid in five yearly installments. Unless the subscriptions totaled $50,000 by January 1, 1836, however, only the first installment, or twenty percent of each subscription, would be considered binding. With the failure to meet the deadline, and the fee paid to Newell, the drive yielded only a few thousand dollars. *Maclean*, 2:360–364.

[7] The instrument maker and dealer James R. Chilton (*Henry Papers*, 2:20).

[8] Having met in rented halls since its founding in 1817, the New York Lyceum of Natural History finally succeeded in constructing its own building in 1835. The organization convened for the first time in their new headquarters on May 9, 1836. Herman L. Fairchild, *A History of the New York Academy of Sciences Formerly the Lyceum of Natural History* (New York, 1887), p. 39.

[9] Possibly the lawyer and banker Francis Bloodgood (*Henry Papers*, 1:12), active in Democratic politics and therefore apt to have influence with the Governor, or the lawyer and merchant Simeon DeWitt Bloodgood (*Henry Papers*, 2:345), a founding member of the Albany Lyceum of Natural History (Lyceum Minutes, January 7 through January 18, 1823, Library, Albany Institute of History and Art).

TO JOHN TORREY

Torrey Papers, Library, New York Botanical Garden

Princeton Monday
March 28th 1836[1]

My Dear D[r]

Your letter of the 23[2] was received on saturday. I now answer it by the mail of monday. I am not intimately acquainted with Gen Dix but am on tolerably intimate terms with the Governor. The Surveyor General Dr Campbell is one of my oldest and warmest friends and will do much to oblige me; he is also on very intimate and friendly terms with Gen. Dix. I will write to him[3] and urge him to exert his influence to have none but good men appointed on the Survey and will mention what you request relative to Dr Gray and yourself. That I may act more efficiently in this matter I will leave Princeton for Albany immediately on the close of our term. I have business at Athens on the Hudson and also in Schoharie Co. and may as well attend to it now as at another time. The term closes on Monday after the next and I will probably start for N.Y. on tuesday. As the river may not be open before that time we will go together. I understand something of the art of managing in such matters and you may be assured I will do all I can to assist in forwarding your wishes.

The affairs of Princeton I must leave until we meet. I have never worked as hard as I have done this winter, have been in very bad health and worse spirits. The mail I fear will close before I can get this to the office if I scribble more.

Yours as ever
Jos Henry

P.S. I close my cours[e] of lectures this week and am therefore unusually [?hurrying].

---

[1] A file note indicates this letter was received on March 29.

[2] Printed immediately above.

[3] We have not found Henry's letter to William Campbell, for whom see *Henry Papers, 1*:100. He was Chief Engineer of the 1825 State Road Survey in which Henry participated and in 1835 became Surveyor General of New York. Although he was in a position to influence policies and staffing, he had no official connection with the New York Natural History Survey.

HENRY NOTEBOOK ENTRY

Notebook [23894], page [39],[1] Henry Papers, Smithsonian Archives

March 1836[2]

When a drop of water is put on the ball of the prime conductor and the machine turned a very curious appearance is exhibited thus. The lower point of the drop is repeled downwards so as to form a very sharp cone—thus *a* the drop unelectrified *b* do electrified. This was noticed by my assistant W.B.[3]

NB. Present a point under this elongated drop. Note the effect. Does not this elongation illustrate the attraction of a point for electricity. The fluid may be supposed thus to be elongated, towards the point, from the side of a charged conductor on account of the highly negative state of the point &c.[4]

---

[1] This entry is in a section on attraction and repulsion.

[2] In the original the date is after the initials "W.B."

[3] William Bullions. Following this, in a different ink, is a later note by Henry: "See Faraday 13th Series." Faraday's Thirteenth Series of Experimental Researches in Electricity (*Phil. Trans.*, 1838, pp. 125–168) is dated February 1838. In section 10, Faraday discusses convective discharge. Among several ways of illustrating the discharge, Faraday used water and other fluid terminations, instead of rigid points. When the conductor was charged, the surrounding air was thought to become similarly charged. Because of repulsion the charged air molecules moved off from the discharge point, carrying with them uncharged air molecules, and caused an air current termed the electric wind. When a fluid drop was used, the passage of the air caused the drop to become elongated.

Although the mechanism assumed by Faraday and others was attacked by later investigators who doubted that gaseous particles could be electrified and instead proposed explanations based on air resistance, recoil and dust, the 1896 discovery of the gaseous ion essentially confirmed it. See Myron Robinson, "A History of the Electric Wind," *American Journal of Physics*, 1962, 30:366–372, which includes a selective bibliography. The article was in response to a revival of interest in the electric wind, manifested by proposed applications to "fluid pumps, high-voltage generators, loudspeakers, thermoelectric converters, and other devices."

[4] This paragraph is also in a different ink from the first. When Faraday introduced a point beneath the drop, the point lost its elongation and became round again, and the current of air stopped and was replaced by a reverse current of air from the point (paragraph 1587). It is unclear whether Henry actually tried the experiment and somehow got further elongation or whether he is anticipating the result of a proposed experiment and speculating on the cause.

HENRY NOTEBOOK ENTRY

Notebook [23894],[1] page [97], Henry Papers, Smithsonian Archives

March 1836[2]

The lateral action very strong in a case of the heavy spark from the long conductor—when the long conductor is connected with the machine and a wire attached to the small conductor. When sparkes are drawn this wire

becomes so active as to give shocks to all surrounding bodies: if a wire *a* be placed along the table a pistol may be fired along it or if a bladder

of hydrogen & air be laid on it an explosion is produced.[3] J. H

[1] This entry is in a section devoted to lateral discharge.

[2] In the original, the date and Henry's initials are under his sketch.

[3] A similar experiment is given in the "Record of Experiments" entry of May 6, 1836, printed below, in which the phenomenon of lateral discharge is explained.

TO JAMES HENRY

Family Correspondence, Henry Papers, Smithsonian Archives

[April 2, 1836][1]

Dear James

Your letter[2] was received to day & I answer it by the next mail so that you may not have quite as much cause for complaint on the score of tardiness in writing as before. Harriet and the children are well. The new girl[3] thus far has been very good and for so small a lady gives comparitively little trouble.

We are grieved to hear that Caroline is in bad health and sincerely hope that she may soon be better. You should write to Nancy informing her of Carolines situation and she would undoubtedly hasten her return from Galway and at this time would be of much service in assisting and cheering Caroline.

I intend to visit albany as soon as the term closes which will be the be-

[1] The date is from the postmark.

[2] Not found.

[3] Henry's third child and second daughter,

Helen Louisa Henry (1836–1912). We have not located a record of her date of birth; she was probably born in February or March.

ginning of the week after next. I see by the papers that the state has made a most munificent appropriation for a geological survey of the state.[4] I am anxious to receive a copy of General Dix's report. Can you procure one from my friend B. Van Rens. and send it by mail. I forwarded a package some weeks since to Van Rens. which I suppose he has received before this time. If the Survey of the state is to include a series of observations on magnetism, the variation of the needle &c which it should do I will become a candidate for the charge of them as I can so manage my college duties as to be absent about 4 months next summer. I wish you would make some inquiries in a private way on this subject of B. Van Rens. and inform me of what he communicates. I do not know that magnetic observations are intended but it is very probable that they are.[5]

For the sake of science in this country I would be very sorry that they should fall into the hands of some incompetent person. I can say without egotism that I have paid more attention to that subject than any other person in the United States. I think it best at present to keep it secret that I wish to become an applicant.

I have just finished my course of lectures. My last one was given yesterday afternoon so to day I feel as if a heavy pressure were suddenly removed and make the first use of my liberty in writing a number of Letters.

I have given your thanks to Steven and shewn him the P.S. at the bottom of your letter. He did receive a letter to day which appears to have accompanied yours. The contents of this letter I was of course not permitted to read. I think it not improbable that the gentleman will eventually become one of us[6] but when or where time will determine.

I intend to visit Schoharie when I come to Albany and it was with this intention that I first though[t] of going up the river this spring. The survey will now however form another inducement.

Aunt is well and would give you many good wishes for your inquiries relative to her were she in Albany. She is much engaged with the children.

Your Brother

[4] Henry had already been in correspondence with Torrey about the Survey. See Torrey's letter of March 23, 1836, printed above.

[5] Terrestrial magnetism was not included. Henry arrived in Albany the day the bill passed the legislature and was thus too late to attempt to have it added. See his letter to Harriet Henry of April 18, printed below.

[6] i.e., a married man.

TO HARRIET HENRY

Family Correspondence, Henry Papers, Smithsonian Archives

Albany April 15th [1836]
Friday afternoon

My Dear Wife

I arrived here this morning about 6 oclock in the Steamboat Erie in company with Stephen whom I found on the warf waiting my arrival. Our journey to New York was quite plesant and our passage up the river was also not unpleasant although we were not accomodated with berths. After calling on the barber and the tailor I went to James' and there with Stephen took breakfast. Our trunks had before been forwarded to the same place. James' wife is much better. She has a very large boy[1] who look[s]much like Mrs Ludlows younges[t] boy[2] or as he did when he was a baby. Nancy has returned from Galway was much pleased to see us. She has been absent more than 4 months.

I took dinner at Mr Meads[3] not however until after the family had dined. I met Dr Torrey shortely after my arrival who is here on the business of the Geological survey. He is a candidate for the Botanical department and is a rival to Dr Lewis.[4] This has lead to some unplesant circumstances and will probably produce much ill will. Dr T. came to albany the same evening that Stephen arrived in New York. He returns this evening. Stephen stopped at Dr Torreys. Mrs T was very kind and pleased to see him.

The Meads family are all well. Louisa looks very thin. She appears to have had much trouble for some weeks past. S. Alexander has written her rather a short letter, returned all her communications and requested his. She has been quite unhapy on account of it but now appears cheerful.

Dr T starts in a few minutes. I must therefore reserve my other communications for my next.

Kiss all *three* of the little ones for me and be assured that amid all the

---

[1] John Platt Henry, who was born in Albany on March 12, 1836. John graduated from the Albany Academy in 1852, served a stint in the Union Army during the Civil War, and finally settled down as a bookseller in Albany. He died in 1905. Hun, "Albany Academy."

[2] Perhaps Mrs. John R. Ludlow's son Richard. See *Henry Papers*, 2:338n.

[3] John Meads, an Albany cabinetmaker (see *Henry Papers*, 2:15n).

[4] Lewis C. Beck. Torrey was in Albany at this time to lobby in his own behalf for a position as botanist for the newly formed New York Natural History Survey. (See Torrey to Henry, March 23, 1836, footnote 4.) On the day Henry penned this letter, the New York legislature formally appropriated $26,000 to establish the Survey. See *Report . . . on . . . the Natural History of the State of New-York* (Albany, 1850), pp. 4, 6.

bustle &c of the city I will not cease to think of those most dear to me who I have lef[t] at home.

Your own husband

J H

TO HARRIET HENRY

Family Correspondence, Henry Papers, Smithsonian Archives

Albany April 18th 1836

Monday

My Dear Wife

I write this from Louisa's desk. She has given me the use of her best paper on condition that I will send you her and Charlottes best and warmest love. Since my last letter[1] I have been engaged principally in calling on my friends and acquaintances. The visit thus far has been very plesant both to myself and Stephen. On Saturday night I stoped at Shanklands[2] and on Sunday night Stephen and myself slept at Mr Meads'. We have each slept one night but not together at James' house where our trunks are deposited. Stephen has left to day for Schenectady in order to get his cloathes in the hands of the maker. Dr Miller[3] preached yesterday morning in Dr Campbells church[4] and in the afternoon in Dr Spragues.[5] He stopes at Mrs James'.[6] I called on him on Saturday and escorted him to the capitol, the Institute and several other places [and] introduced him to Dr Beck,[7] Governor Marcey and several of the members of the Legislature with all of which the Dr appeared well pleased.

I have been treated with much respect and politeness by almost every person with whom I have met since my arrival. The Governor in particular

---

[1] Printed immediately above.

[2] Peter V. and Susannah Shankland, old friends of the Henrys. See *Henry Papers*, *1*: 284n.

[3] Samuel Miller, one of the founders of the Princeton Theological Seminary and a Princeton Trustee. See *Henry Papers*, 2:438n.

[4] John N. Campbell (1798–1864) had been the pastor of the First Presbyterian Church of Albany since June 1830. He remained at this church until his death. Alfred Nevin, ed., *Encyclopaedia of the Presbyterian Church in the United States of America* (Philadelphia, 1884),

p. 123; *Howell and Tenney*, p. 768.

[5] William Buell Sprague was pastor of Albany's Second Presbyterian Church. He is discussed in the *Henry Papers*, *1*:464n and 2:79–80.

[6] Catherine Barber James (1782–1859), the third wife of William James (1771–1832) and the mother of Henry James (1811–1882). She married William James in 1803 and bore him ten children. Katherine Hastings, *William James of Albany* (New York, 1924), pp. 5–6.

[7] T. R. Beck.

and General Dix have honored me by sending a request that I would communicate with them on the subject of the great Geological survey. The governor has requested me to look over the list of applicants and to give him
in confidence my opinion in reference to those best qualified. I have stated
to him that although the task is an unplesant one I will give what information I possess as the cause of science requires that the best men should be
selected. Nothing will be done this season in the way of a magnetic survey
as the law had passed without including that object before my arrival. I
had an interview with General Dix in which I gave him a sketch of the
practical and scientific importance of a survey of the kind; he became much
interested in the subject and stated that something of the kind should be
done either by the Legislature or the Regents of the University in the course
of another year.[8] I dined on Saturday with Mr and Mrs McIntyre.[9] They
appear much affected with the conduct of James and have concluded that
he cannot return to College unless I can take him into our family.[10] They
are very grateful for the care I have had over their son. Mr Mc very cheerfully agreed to pay the full ammount of J.N.'s[11] bill and said that so good a
boy should not want for support if his Father[12] was not able to educate him.
He Mr Mc would advance himself although James should not return to
college.

Mr McIntyre has the most plesant and best furnished house that I have

---

[8] Despite Dix's assurances to Henry that terrestrial magnetic observations would become
part of the New York Natural History Survey,
nothing of that sort occurred. Physics had no
place in the survey. Michele L. Aldrich, "New
York Natural History Survey, 1836–1845"
(Ph.D. dissertation, University of Texas, 1974),
p. 90.

[9] Archibald McIntyre (*Henry Papers*, 1:10
and 2:24) and his wife Eliza (1781–1859), who
was born in Scotland but had been brought to
this country at age twelve. The daughter of
the Rev. John McDonald, she was educated at
the Moravian School in Bethlehem, Pennsylvania. Eliza married McIntyre in 1804 and
bore him eight children. William B. Sprague,
*A Sermon Delivered in the Second Presby-
terian Church, Albany, Sunday Morning, November 6, 1859, on the Occasion of the Death
of Mrs. Eliza McIntyre, Wife of the Late Hon.
Archibald McIntyre* (Albany, 1859), pp. 23–24,
36.

[10] This decision was made in spite of the fact
that an earlier attempt to board young Mc-
Intyre with a faculty member had drawn the
following pessimistic response from a member
of the Amherst faculty:

> I would remark here however that it is a
> mistaken idea which prevails abroad that it
> is any great security to a young man's mo-
> rality to have him in the family of an officer
> of College. If disposed to mischief it will in-
> deed make him a little more shy in his
> tricks: but he will find opportunities for
> mischief in spite of the vigilance of any man.
> If a young man has not himself resolved to
> resist evil influences he had better keep
> away from College. If he is willing to take
> a steady pious judicious student for a room
> mate one whom he respects it is a better
> security than the oversight of a professor.

Edward Hitchcock to William B. Sprague, September 3, 1835, Box 6, Edward Hitchcock Papers, Archives and Special Collections, Robert
Frost Library, Amherst College. Although the
young man moved in with Henry, his conduct
did not improve. He was sent home at the end
of his Junior year.

[11] John Newland.

[12] Luke F. Newland (ca. 1793–1855). See
Henry Papers, 2:72n.

seen in albany. Young Mrs Meads[13] and her sister under the escort of Old Mr Meads started this morning for New York. The lady will remain in Elizabeth town about 4 or 5 weeks. The boy is called John *Hun*.[14] Mr. Meads is delighted with his grandson and is constantly nursing him when he is at Orlando's.

The affair of Stephen and Louisa appears to have given very general satisfaction to Mr M's family. The Old Gentleman himself was much pleased with the idea. I believe that it is settled that they are to be married in one year from this time. Louisa says that the Shaker hats[15] are very much worn by little girls. Would you like one of these for *Sis* the *elder*? Catherine Beck is to be married in June next. The family are all said to be well pleased with the affair but the public say that although the gentleman is well *born* and has a great fortune yet he is blessed with but a very small quantum of brain and does not make the very best use of that.[16]

I fear you will find this a very dull letter as I have written it immediately after a dinner at which I was too plentifully supplied with the evidences of Louisas good housewifery. Mrs Meads has the sick headache and has been confined to her bed all day. Orlando has taken up his abode at this house until the return of his wife. We think of starting for Schoharie on Wednesday and will return as soon as possible. I am beginning already to think of home. The days however pass with surprising rapidity and I have done nothing since my arrival but shake hands with old acquaintances.

I had almost forgotten to inform you that Charlotte is not very well. She suddenly became deaf on the day of our arrival. Louisa says that it is a very convenient deafness since she hears all that she should not.

Mrs. Bullions[17] is also unwell. I have not as yet seen her. She was confined to her room the day I called. I most sincerely hope she is not again in the

---

[13] Elizabeth Wilson Meads (1785–1850), the wife of Orlando Meads, a friend of Henry's. *Henry Papers*, 2:71n, 173n; *Albany Journal*, December 31, 1850.

[14] John Hun Meads (1836–1855), the son of Orlando and Elizabeth Meads. He had a distinguished record at the Albany Academy, graduating in 1853. He then went on to enter Princeton as a member of the Junior class. He died at sea in August 1855. Hun, "Albany Academy;" *Princeton Annual Catalogue*, 1855.

[15] Shaker communities produced distinctive housewares, furniture, and clothing for sale to the outside world. Straw bonnets and other goods were distributed throughout the United States by Shaker peddlers. In Henry's day one could purchase Shaker goods from merchants in the city of Albany. Edward D. Andrews,

The People Called Shakers: A Search for the Perfect Society (New York, 1953).

[16] Catherine Elizabeth Beck married Pierre Van Cortlandt (1815–1884) on June 14, 1836. Van Cortlandt was the heir to family lands in Westchester County, a manor house, and a name of some significance in the political and military history of the United States. He was, as Henry indicates, unfortunately one of the more undistinguished members of his family. Louis E. De Forest, *The Van Cortlandt Family* (New York, 1930), n.p.; *Henry Papers*, 2:172.

[17] Mrs. Elizabeth Blyth Bullions (1792–1853), the wife of the Reverend Peter Bullions (1791–1864). The latter was Professor of Latin and Greek at the Albany Academy. *New York Times*, July 9, 1853; *Henry Papers*, 1:129n.

family way. I called to day at Newland's in N Market street. Many inquiries were made for Mrs Hand and her son.[18] I have seen several times Mr L F Newland. Both his wife and daughter are as ladies wish to be who love their lords. I have not seen either of them yet.

You must not complain of the shortness of this letter since I have taken some pains to fill it with scraps of news which I thought would interest you. I have not given many expressions of extravagant regard because I know that you do not require assertions of the kind to convince you that you are to me the neares and deares person that has or will ever exist. I will not inform you that I long to press you to my bosom and assure myself that you are well. This you know. I must however say that I find myself looking with peculiar interest at every little boy and girl that I meet with and endeavor to trace some resemblance to our own little ones. I have scribbled so much that I have now no room to say that I remain *Yours*

---

[18] The Hands were then living in Princeton. See above, Henry to James Henry, January 22, 1836.

TO HARRIET HENRY
Family Correspondence, Henry Papers, Smithsonian Archives

Albany Wednesday
April 20th 1836

My Dear Harriet

I have written twice since my leaving home but have as yet heard nothing from you. I have been at the Post Office myself and sent several times but always with disappointement. The New York boat arrived this morning without the mail which was left by some accident. Steven and myself entended to start to day for Schoharrie but on account of the extreme badness of the roads we have been detered from making the journey in a one horse wagon as we intended and the stage I find does not go but twice a week and the next passage is on friday. I have some thoughts of going to Schenectady this afternoon and settling all my affairs so that when we return from Schoharrie I may immediatly start for home.

Stephen will probably remain a short time longer. We attended last night the Annual meeting of the Institute to hear the Address of Mr Barnard. Steven and Louisa were there as cosy as man and wife. The address was eloquent and interesting but quite visionary. It was on the subject of common school education and the founding of a great University *at* Albany.[1]

I have nothing new to communicate since I last wrote. Yesterday I spent in the Library of the Institute in posting up some articles from the Journals. I took dinner at Mr [Meads] also breakfast as Steven and myself slept there on Monday night—last night we slept at James'. Mrs Meads was confined to her room and Charlotte has her head bound up on account of deafness.

Mr Meads as [I] informed you in my last letter has gone to New York. Orlando has removed for the present to his fathers. I am becoming quite anxious to get home but the state of the roads will not permit us to visit Schoharie until the latter part of this week. We will not probably return until monday.

I commenced this letter in the Surveyor Generals[2] office and am now finishing it at James' store. I have just finished my dinner at Mr Meads' and am waiting for the starting of the Rail road cars for Schenectady. Mrs Meads is much better to day and has been out making calls. The streets are alive at this time with persons watching for the Procession which is to pass up state street with the body of *General North*[3] an old revolutionary soldier who has been residing for some time at New York but who lived in Duanesburgh and married a Miss Duane[4] of Schenectady. The body arrived this morning in the steam boat and has been received with military and civil honors.

Dr Miller[5] left Albany on Tuesday. He and Mr Breckinridge[6] have done

---

[1] The lawyer Daniel Dewey Barnard's (*Henry Papers*, 2:150) annual address of April 19 was printed in *Transactions of the Albany Institute*, 1833–1852, 2:113–151. Barnard called for an upgrading and rationalization of the public school system and for a vastly increased State endowment for education. He also believed that the State of New York should bring the academies and colleges into its orbit, removing the latter from ecclesiastical domination. Barnard proposed attaching a learned society to every public college and academy for the purpose of fostering a communion between society and educational institutions. Among the expected benefits was an increased popular diffusion of science and useful knowledge, and, at the same time, public support of scientific and learned associations. Specifically, he proposed converting the Albany Academy into a "proper college" and attaching it to the Albany Institute, which would offer popular lectures on science and the arts. The capstone of Barnard's proposals was the realization of a great State University at Albany, supported by no less than one million dollars in State appropriations and modeled after Göttingen. His principal justification for the proposed institution was the advancement of speculative science as a symbol of man's highest aspirations.

[2] William Campbell.

[3] William North (1755–1836). Strangely, the *DAB* has him dying on January 3. After Revolutionary War service North served New York State in various official capacities. North was one of the commissioners who recommended the building of the Erie Canal. *DAB.*

[4] In 1787 North married Mary Duane, daughter of New York City Mayor James Duane. *DAB,* s.v. "William North."

[5] Samuel Miller, identified in *Henry Papers,* 2:438n.

[6] John Breckinridge (1797–1841), Presbyterian clergyman, a zealous missionary and opponent of the New School theology. In 1832, he was elected to the Board of Directors of Princeton Theological Seminary and served, from 1836 to 1838, as Professor of Pastoral

very well in Albany having raised upwards of 3 thousand dollars between the 1st & 2nd Presby Churches. Dr Miller attended morning prayers at the Albany female Academy and made quite a galant speech. He commenced by saying that women had been sometimes called Angels and with proper qualification he thought the term quite appropriate.

His sermons were much admired and produced quite an effect. I [was] induced to visit the Female academy myself by the pressing invitation of (Dr) Gideon Hawley.[7] It is certainly a very interesting school. The Dr very formerly introduced me as Prof. Henry of Princeton to more than one hundred half grown Ladies.

I have given Louisa liberty to receive your letter and keep it until I return (*ie* the letter which I expect from you by the evening boat).

I am beginning to be anxious to return home and were it not for the Schoharie affair I would start this week. Kiss the children for me. I will endeavour to purchase some articles for Bub and *Sis* in *New York*. The little lady without a name is the subject of many inquiries. More than a doz. have asked her name.[8] All think that Josephine is a beautiful one. My only objection is that she will I fear be nicknamed Jo. The affair of Stephen & Louisa is already known to many persons. Susan Shankland said I told you so, I knew they would catch him. Shanklands family are all well. Miss Shankland from Cooperstown has been staying with them during the winter.

Dr Campbell has received a long communication from his adopted Daughter Judith. She stoped some months in Constantinople and visited with her husband in his character of a physician[9] many of the rich Turkish houses, was introduced to the females of the harem &c.

I took tea last evening first with Old Mrs Shephard and her two daughters. From them I received an account of much of the news of the city. I next called on Richard DeWitt and again took tea with the gentleman [&] his wife.[10] Richard says that his affairs will end well and that his property will not be much the worse for the difficulty which he has incurred. Miss

---

Theology there.

Breckinridge was married to Samuel Miller's daughter Margaret. *DAB*; *Roberts*, pp. x, xx, 16.

[7] Active in the expansion of public education in New York State, Hawley is identified in *Henry Papers*, *1*:50n. For the Female Academy see *Henry Papers*, *1*:450.

[8] Helen Henry.

[9] William Campbell's daughter Judith (1811–1839), married to the physician and missionary Asahel Grant (1807–1844). In 1835, Asahel and Judith went abroad to establish a mission for the Nestorian Christians in Persia. *DAB*. Also, information from the Cherry Valley Historical Association.

[10] Richard Varick DeWitt (*Henry Papers*, *1*: 62n) was married to the former Sarah Walsh (1805–1842) of Albany. Cuyler Reynolds, *Hudson-Mohawk Genealogy and Family Memoirs*, 4 vols. (New York, 1911), *1*:366.

Susan DeWitt is to be married in May to General Hubble.[11] Linn[12] is engaged on the Connecticut Railway, is doing very well. His Brother wishes to put him under my charge if I should go to Europe. Is not this a very long letter? Will you not owe me many kisses for it? You must not fail to write—recollect that I am some what anxious to hear from you and our little ones. The cars are about starting so that I must conclude with assuring you that I am as ever   your Hubby

[11] Susan DeWitt, sister of Richard Varick DeWitt, married Levi Hubbell (1808–1876). *Herringshaw*; *Ithaca Journal*, October 14, 1903, "Ithaca's Founder of Holland Stock."

[12] William Linn DeWitt (1817–1903), half-brother of Richard Varick DeWitt (*Henry Papers*, 2:310n).

"RECORD OF EXPERIMENTS"
Henry Papers, Smithsonian Archives

May 3rd 1836

Exp on the comparative action of common and electro magnetic magnets.

Exp 1 It has been aserted in the Phil. Mag for Dec 1835[1] that there is a difference in the action of electro magnetic magnets and common magnets[2] in the following particular—viz when a bar of iron is placed in contact with an electro magnet at the north pole then the bar becomes throughout a north pole.

This was tested by placing a bar in contact with the north pole of a magnet. At first sight it appeared as if the whole bar was of the same kind of magnetism as the pole in contact but when the same exp was tried with a steel magnet the same result was produced. In this respect there is no difference in the action of common an[d] electro-magnets.

Exp 2 When a piece of soft iron was placed in contact with the one pole of a galvanic magnet and then filings sprinkled over the iron magnetic curves were

[1] Henry undoubtedly was referring to E. M. Clarke, "Remarks on a Peculiar State of Polarity Induced in Soft Iron by Voltaic Magnetism," *Phil. Mag.*, November 1835, 3d ser. 7:422–423. The error in the reference to the month of publication was probably a reflection of Henry receiving English journals one month after their publication (see his letter to Forbes, dated June 7, 1836, printed below).

[2] Nowhere did Clarke explicitly state that he was discussing differences between the two types of magnets. All he did was indicate some phenomena relating to electromagnets without any reference to common magnets.

formed. When the same arrangement was made with the steel magnet the same arrangement of curves was produced in both. No difference of action is therefore observable between the action of common and electro-magnets.

"RECORD OF EXPERIMENTS"[1]
Henry Papers, Smithsonian Archives

May 5th [1836]

Ex 3   A horseshoe galvanic magnet was prepaired of precicely the same form and size as that of a steel magnet [co]mposed of two plate horseshoes. The lifting power was probably about 50 lbs as it readily took up the large lifter weighing 27 lbs. The lifting power of the steel magnet was about 6 lbs. Two steel bars were rubbed on these. According to the method of double touch each received 20 strokes on each side. The magnetism of the two bars appeared to be about equal

Magnetized the electro magnet to the same strength of the steel magnet, the lifting power of each being 6 lbs as determined by the spring weighing apparatus. The electro magnet was fastened in a vice and a bar of steel, an ole file with the point and stem broken off, was then rubbed across the poles 20 times on each flat side; after an intervel of a few minutes each side was again rubbed from end to end 20 times; the steel magnet was next substituted for the electro magnet and an other piece of steel of the same dimentions and temper was rubbed the same number of times. When the magnetism of these bars was tested the one rubbed on the steel magnet was found to be much stronger magnetized than the other: the relative intensities were determined by vibrating before each a magnetic needle. Before the bar magnetized by the steel magnet the needle made 10 vibs in 14½" seconds, before the other bar 10 vibrations in 18¾" seconds: by the magnetism of the earth alone the needle made 10 vibs in 22½ seconds

From this exp it is evident that the power to develope magnetism in steel is not as great with the same intensity or lifting power in the electro magnetic magnet as in the permanent

---

[1] This entry is a continuation of Henry's May 3 experiments on the comparative action of common magnets and electromagnets. Here he investigates the comparative intensity of magnetism induced in steel, an aspect not discussed in Clarke's article. Henry had addressed himself to this problem in 1835, particularly in his May 1 oral communication to the American Philosophical Society (see *Henry Papers,* 2:385–386). It is unclear why he revives the topic at this time; he may still have been contemplating a major publication on magnetism. As in 1835, however, he drops the subject and turns to an investigation of lateral discharge.

May 6, 1836

"RECORD OF EXPERIMENTS"
Henry Papers, Smithsonian Archives

May 6th 1836

Lateral discharge[1]

Exp on the lateral action of currents of common electricity—

Exp 1 A thick copper wire was attached to one end of an insulated conductor which was placed at a fixed distance from the prime conductor. When a

[1] During 1836 and 1837 Henry's laboratory investigations centered on the phenomenon known as lateral discharge, a long-known but incompletely understood aspect of static electricity. Henry undertook this interim study chiefly to clarify projected researches on mutual induction which occupied him in 1838 and were incorporated in his next major scientific publication, "Contributions III: Electro-Dynamic Induction." These later researches will be covered in the next volume of the *Henry Papers*. Although recognized as distinct effects, lateral discharge and mutual induction were subject to confusion in that both were vaguely conceived of as "lateral" effects. For example, when inducing a secondary current with parallel conductors, Henry considered the possibility that, rather than "inducing" a current, the primary wire had "discharged" its energy onto the neighboring wire. This distinction became especially important when Henry undertook the study of mutual induction from static electricity.

Contemporary theory described the lateral discharge as the "tendency in the [electric] fluid to diverge from the direct line of its course, and to fly off to different objects in the vicinity." P. M. Roget, *Treatises on Electricity, Galvanism, Magnetism, and Electro-Magnetism* (London, 1832), "Electricity," p. 40. The irregular course of lightning upon striking a building was given as a common illustration of the phenomenon. In the laboratory, lateral discharges could be drawn from the Leyden jar. Early investigators like Priestley and Biot suggested techniques for doing this. When a large jar was discharged with a non-insulated metal rod, the hand holding the rod experienced a mild shock. To make the effect visible, one end of a metal chain was connected with the outer coating of the jar. The rest of the chain lay loose, free of other electrical con-

nections. When the jar was discharged by the rod, sparks jumped visibly along the links of the chain, even though the chain did not form part of the discharging circuit.

While abroad in 1837, Henry drew on his laboratory results to prepare a paper on the lateral discharge for the British Association, which printed an abstract of his remarks in its 1837 *Report* (1838), part 2, pp. 22–24. While Henry noted in his paper that Roget's *Treatises* prompted his inquiries into the subject, his theoretical views were in accord with Biot's idea that "the lateral discharge is due only to the escape of the small quantity of redundant electricity which always exists on one or the other side of a jar, and not to the whole discharge" (p. 22). Redundant, or, as it was also called, free electricity, was defined as the excess of positive or negative electrical fluid in a non-neutral body. (In equivalent single-fluid terminology, it was the excess of the electrical fluid in a positively electrified body or the excess of matter in a negatively charged body.) In Leyden jars and other capacitors, the positive and negative charges on the opposing conductors were "bound" in a state of equilibrium. However, the quantities of opposing fluids were never precisely equal, the excess charge on either plate being designated as free or redundant. (Compare with the modern notion of free and bound electrons.) The amount of free electricity present was directly proportional to the thickness of the insulating layer between the metallic coatings or plates. In addition to Biot's notion, Henry attributed inertia or momentum without weight to the electric fluid to explain why, for example, "the same quantity of electricity could be made to remain on the wire if gradually communicated; but when thrown on in the form of a spark, it is dissipated as before described" (p. 23). None of this theory appears explicitly in

53

discharge was passed through a spark was perceived between the wire and a key at any point of the former between the negative and positive side of a jar connected with the prime conductor[2]

To determine the kind of electricity thus given off a small Leyden phial was held with its knob within about an 8th of an inch of the wire and when the discharge was made the sparke from the wire communicated a feeble charge to the phial which when tested by an electrometer and sealing wax proved to be + electricity[3]—

Exp 2nd To determine whether intensity or quantity of electricity was most powerful in producing the lateral discharge; the conductor was placed at a fixed distance from the knob of the prime conductor and first the discharge from a small jar which required only 17 turns of the machine to produce an explosion;[4] the <*quantity of*> electricity produced by the lateral action was received as before by the knob of a Leyden jar and its quantity tested by the divergency of a silver leaf electrometer

The discharge was next sent through the same wire and at the same striking distance from a jar which required 100 turns of the cylinder to produce a discharge. The electricity from the lateral discharge being measured as before was found to be the same in quantity as with the small jar. It would appear from this experiment that intensity and not quantity was necessary to produce the lateral action. The intensity in these two cases was the same

---

Henry's laboratory journal, yet he had confidence in its explanatory power. In his article, for instance, he explained the branching of lightning bolts by comparing the electrical relationship of the clouds and the ground to the two coatings of the Leyden jar, with the air corresponding to the glass. The great expanse of air between earth and clouds created vast potential for lateral discharge. Henry probably derived these and other theoretical notions on the lateral discharge from J. B. Biot's *Traité de Physique* (Paris, 1816), which he acquired for his Library, apparently in 1836. (See *Traité,* 2:451–453.)

[2] In view of the vagueness of Henry's description of his experimental set-up, we cannot be certain of the following analysis. Henry apparently created a static-electric circuit. The prime conductor, where the spark is emitted from the static electrical machine, passes a spark across a gap to an insulated conductor, a metal rod supported horizontally on an insulating stand, which is in turn connected to an extended copper wire. Completing the circuit is the Leyden jar, the knob, or positive pole, of which is connected to the

prime conductor while its outer coating is connected to a key, placed close to the copper wire. Henry found that the key drew sparks at any point along the wire rather than only at the end toward which the discharge is principally conducted. Bernard S. Finn, Curator of Electricity, National Museum of History and Technology, has aided us in our reconstruction of this experiment.

[3] A standard method for collecting and testing static charge. Next to experiment 1, in the left margin, is the notation: "Erman observed the effect of a spark on long wire. See Archives des descouvertes 1830, p. 167." The reference must be to the Berlin physicist Paul Erman, but Henry is mistaken in his citation. We are unable to locate the article.

[4] The plate of the electrical machine was cranked seventeen times. The grounded Leyden jar, introduced to store the charge generated by the machine, was connected to the prime conductor, accumulating electricity until it reached its capacity when it discharged spontaneously. As in the previous experiment, the discharge was passed onto the insulated conductor and wire.

since the jars spontaneously discharged themselves through the same thickness of air[5]

When a strong discharge is passed through a thin wire the electricity is given off abundantly at any angular points of the wire. *Illustration*. charge the large jar and charge through fine copper wire in which twists as at (a) are made at intervals. The electricity will be given off at the ends of these when the discharge is not sufficient to disipate the elect.[6]

Exp 3 Two wires of very different diameters were next used to determine if the action was due to the thinness of the wire which might cause it to act as a partial conductor.[7] No difference however could be observed in the effect when either the small or the large jar was used—

(This exp however should be repeated with two long wires of different diameters; the difference in action in this case if any would be more perceptable)

Exp 3[8] A large copper wire was attached at one end to the insulated conductor and the other passed into a deep well which always yields an abundant supply of water for the use of a large refrectory—thus indicating a communication with a large reservoir of water. The end of the insulated conductor was placed about 2 inches from a large globe covered with tin foil and in connection with the prime conductor. The use of this globe was to increase the intensity of the charge. When sparkes were passed between the globe and the insulated conductor the electricity was conveyed to the water in the well along the thick wire; (in order to make the contact more perfect with the water of the well abo[u]t the wire was immersed to the depth of about 12 feet.) Although the connection with the earth was as perfect as possible, yet the lateral action of the large wire was such as to fire a mixture of hydrogen and atmospheric air in a voltaic pistol at all points between the well and the machine[9]

In order to render the conduction off still more perfect a wire was con-

---

[5] i.e., the spark-gap between the prime and insulated conductors.

[6] This paragraph originally appeared in the margin next to the entry for the second experiment.

[7] Henry meant a less-than-perfect conductor. Roget adopted the rather mechanical explanation that the lateral discharge was caused by obstructions to the passage of the discharge through conductors which forced the electric fluid out laterally. Roget, *Treatises*, "Electricity," p. 40. Henry is evidently testing this

theory. However, in experiment 4 below he discounts it.

[8] So numbered by Henry.

[9] A popular demonstration item, the Pistol of Volta consisted of a chamber in which a mixture of hydrogen and oxygen was ignited by a spark, ejecting the stopper of the vessel. Beside this experiment in the margin Henry added: "the same exp may be shown by placing a bladder of hydrogen in contact with the rod; an explosion will take place."

nected with the wire leading to the well and also to the rubber of the machine[10]—The sparks were as vivid as before and a small Leyden jar was charged so as to give a disagreeable shock.[11] This exp if I be not deceived has an important bearing on the erection of thunder rods particularly as connected with pow[d]er houses—

Exp 4 A very fine copper wire was next used, the cork wire[12] of commerce in place of the thick copper wire of the last exp. The intensity & quantity of the spark from the machine, being the same, the spark from the lateral action of the wire was about the same as that from the other wire. This would seem to indicate that the cause of the phenominon was not the obstruction to the discharge through the wire, as in this supposition the smaller wire should give much the larger spark, since the obstruction from partial conduction would be greater— Another circumstance was noticed, namely that the spark appeared larger near the end of the wire, or at the distance of about 40 feet from the machine, than within 2 feet of the same.[13] The distance of the end of the wire was too great from the machine to suppose that the inductive action of the spark through the air, or the sudden change in the state of the large conductor could have any influence

---

[10] The component of the machine which rubbed against the revolving plate or cylinder and generated the charge.

[11] Above this sentence is written: "On the lateral action see Despretze p 436. Also Peclet p 58 vol 2nd," referring to C. M. Despretz, *Traité élémentaire de physique* (Paris, 1832) and J. C. E. Péclet, *Traité élémentaire de physique*, 2 vols. (London, 1830). Henry owned both.

[12] Henry's term for the wire used in corking bottles.

[13] In the margin: "I found that the phenomenon of the long wire luminous was observed by Mr Emmet Phil Mag & ann vol 5 p 170." The citation is J. B. Emmett, "On an Electrical Phenomenon," *Phil. Mag.*, 1829, 2d ser. 5:170–172. The wire became illuminated whenever a spark passed. Emmett experimented with different types of wires (copper and silver) and lengths up to 80 feet.

See "Record of Experiments," August 31, 1836, below, where Henry tests the luminosity effect for himself.

"RECORD OF EXPERIMENTS"

Henry Papers, Smithsonian Archives

May 7th [1836]

Exp 5 When a spark was passed through a spiral enclosing a glass tube through which was passed a thick iron wire a spark was given off at each end of the wire. The kind of elect was determined by the electrometer and found to be the same at each end, namely positive, so that the spark in this case is not as I was led to suppose a current induced by the current in the helix but merely the dead inert action similar to that which causes a spark to be given off from the outside of a jar when a spark is given to the inside.[1]

Magnetism by gal—exp in elect.
May 7th 1836 Bad day for common electricity, rainy—

Exp 1st Covered a large file with copper ribbon about 30 feet long; connected ends with small battery. The file became magnetic while the current was passing through the ribbon but almost interely disappeared when the current was interrupted. When the current was passed through the ribbon for some minutes it became perminently magnetic—

The current in the first place was not sufficiently powerful to overcome the coersive force of the steel. The steel took on as it were a forced magnetic state

[1] The positive sparks at each end of the wire indicated no current flow. Henry, therefore, concluded that he had a case of ordinary, static-electric induction occurring, for example, when a charged insulated conductor approaches a neutral insulated conductor. Henry later detected an induced current. A marginal annotation to this experiment reads: "There is besides this a current which I detected in May 1838," possibly a reference to experiment 4 of May 8, 1838, to be printed in *Henry Papers, 4.*

"RECORD OF EXPERIMENTS"

Henry Papers, Smithsonian Archives

May 9th [1836]

In the last no. of sillimans journal or the last but one an article appeared stating that if a hole be made in the bottom of a vessel containing water the spouting fluid will assume a spiral form and that the twist will always be in a direction contrary to the motion of the sun.[1] The explanation given of the phenominon is ridiculous and by no means sufficient to account for it if it were a true fact. As the article has been copied into many of the public

[1] Alan W. Carson, "On Currents in Water," *Silliman's Journal*, 1836, *29*:340–344. The actual author of the theory given in the article was George Kenderdine, described by Carson as "an ingenious and scientific master millwright." Kenderdine argued that whirlpools, whirlwinds, and fluids going down a drain would all rotate counter-clockwise in the Northern Hemisphere and clockwise in the Southern Hemisphere. The cause was the rotation of the earth; specifically, the difference in velocity of different points on the earth's surface as it rotates would cause water traveling in a north-south direction to be deflected from a true north-south path. His thinking was fuzzy and frequently incorrect, but Kenderdine did have a kernel of truth in his paper.

papers I was induced this morning to try it although on no principle of Physiques could I hope for success. The result was in accordance with the anticipation as the whirling of the stream was as often in one direction as in the other.[2] Articles of this kind do much injury to the scientific reputation of the country.[3]

This morning also made a number of experiments with J.M.[4] of the

---

[2] There was some disagreement over the empirical question of whether water discharging through a hole at the bottom of a basin whirled, and, if it did, in what direction. James Espy reported that the contents of a tub exited without any sign of circular motion. Henry's opinion, expressed in an annotation to the Carson paper (Henry's personal copy of this volume of *Silliman's Journal* is in the Henry Library), was that the nature of the hole determined the direction of any observed rotary motion. But Charles Tracy, in a paper ignored by his contemporaries, argued that should the basin be broad and the orifice in the center, then the discharging water would always form a vortex which whirled counterclockwise in the Northern Hemisphere. The water had to follow that course, according to Tracy, because of the deflection caused by the rotation of the earth. It remained for William Ferrel (1817–1891, *DSB*) to independently realize and then quantify the effect of the earth's rotation on wind and water.

Modern science has named the deflective force due to the earth's rotation after Gustave Gaspard Coriolis in honor of his 1835 paper in which he considers acceleration in relative coordinate systems. But Henry's contemporaries, particularly those in meteorology, were either unaware of Coriolis's work or failed to see the connection between his theoretical mechanics and their concrete problems. Recognition of Coriolis's contribution has been a post-1930 phenomenon.

James P. Espy, *The Philosophy of Storms* (Boston, 1841), p. xxx; Charles Tracy, "On the Rotary Action of Storms," *Silliman's Journal*, 1843, *45*:65–72; C. L. Jordan, "On Coriolis and the Deflective Force," *Bulletin of the American Meteorological Society*, 1966, *47*:401–402; H. E. Landsberg, "Why Indeed Coriolis?" *Bulletin of the American Meteorological Society*, 1966, *47*:887–889; Harold L. Burstyn, "The Deflecting Force and Coriolis," *Bulletin of the American Meteorological Society*, 1966, *47*:890–891.

[3] Henry's harsh response to Kenderdine's theory was a result of his feelings that American science in general—and *Silliman's Journal* in particular—was not paying sufficient attention to the refereeing process. Silliman had admitted in a footnote to the Carson paper (p. 340) that the paper had been published without any attempt to verify the statements made in it. The only judgment made was on the style. The paper was "well written," and that was adequate reason for Silliman to publish it. That the prestige of American science might be harmed by the publication of what Henry often termed "trash" never seemed to cross Silliman's mind. Not until the 1840s did Silliman institute a peer review process for papers submitted to his journal.

Because Henry viewed a scientific paper not merely as the personal statement of the author, but a reflection upon the entire community, he felt that the role of the review process was to improve the quality of the scientific endeavor in the United States. His stand, which could be called elitist or professional, was that the editor's job was to screen out the work of charlatans and the incompetent. In this he differed sharply from Silliman, who preferred to allow an ill-founded theory to "take its chance with the scientific world" (p. 340).

Henry frequently tried, with some success, to put his vision into practice. In an attempt to stem the flow of trivial or inaccurate articles into *Silliman's Journal* he suggested that a physicist be added to the editorial board, a suggestion that was initially refused. When the Smithsonian, under his leadership, began publishing its *Contributions to Knowledge* in 1848, Henry provided for a review process. When he was personally called upon to referee a paper, he was careful to distinguish the valuable from the trash; he always had his eye out for both the reputation of the author and of American science as a whole.

Sally G. Kohlstedt, *The Formation of the American Scientific Community: The American Association for the Advancement of Science, 1848–1860* (Urbana, Illinois, 1976), p. 139; Henry to Alexander Dallas Bache, August 9, 1838, Bache Papers, Smithsonian Archives.

[4] John Miller, identified in *Henry Papers, 2*: 478.

senior class, in order to determine the cause of a peculiar action observed by him in the motion of the dancing images.[5] When the two plates used in this exp. are connected one with the inside & the other with the outside of an insulated Leyden jar the dancing of course will continue for some time without the use of the machine. If while the dancing is going on the upper plate be touched so as to draw off the extra particle, the image will move from the centre of the plates towards their circumference and if the touch be renewed, it will fly from the plate. If however when the plate[6] is near the edge the under plate be touched the image returns to the centre of the plate and shows no indications of jumping off. By touching one and then the other the image may be made to dance from the centre to the circumference and back again many times in succession.

To explain this phenominon it first determined that it depended alone on the circumstance of the *upper* plate being touched and not on its being + or — electrified. The explanation suggested by myself is as follows. The two plates being in contact with the two sides of the jar become alternately neutral and positive that is the upper one; and the lower negative and neutral and in these states the dancing is produced in a very regular manner; but when the upper plate is touched if it be connected with the + side of the jar it becomes neutral, and the image is thrown up from the lower plate by repulsion which acts in every direction from the centre of the plate or would thus act if the plate was a part of the surface of a great sphere; as it is however a plate the action is from near the middle outwards. When the under plate is touched, the image is drawn up by attraction and the action will be towards the centre of the plate or in the opposite direction to that of the repulsion from the lower plate. The action in this arangement of the experiment is different from that where the lower plate is put in contact with the ground for then the lower plate is always neutral but never negative but in the arrangement above described the lower plate is absolutely negative as much as the upper is positive so that it will give a spark when touched which is not the case with the common arrangement. This on the whole is a very pretty modification of an old exp.

---

[5] Dancing images were a common method of illustrating the alternating attraction and repulsion of an object due to an electrical charge. The usual arrangement was to connect the upper plate to the prime conductor and to ground the lower plate. P. M. Roget, *Treatises on Electricity, Galvanism, Magnetism, and Electro-Magnetism* (London, 1832), "Electricity," pp. 17–18.

Henry also mentions the phenomenon of the dancing images in his lecture notebook devoted to electricity—Notebook [23894], p. [43], Henry Papers, Smithsonian Archives.

[6] This sentence only makes sense if Henry meant to write "image" instead.

TO ALEXANDER DALLAS BACHE

Bache Papers,[1] *Smithsonian Archives*

Princeton May 10th 1836

My Dear Bache

I returned from Albany about a week since without effecting much in the way of the magnetic survey of the state. I however explained to the Governor and General Dix the importance of a survey of the kind and convinced them that it should not be intrusted to an ordinary surveyor or be made an apendix to the duty of the *botanist* or geologist. General Dix informed me that it would be impossible to do any thing in reference to it this summer but that he would use his influence to have a survey of the kind made either by the Board of Regents of the University or as a part of the Geological survey if there should be any funds to spare from the latter.[2] I fear the Geological survey will not amount to much in the way of science. The appropriation although large (26 thousand dollars a year) is to be divided among so many persons that men of reputation and acquirement will not engage in the work.[3]

The Governor appointed Dr Torrey to the department of botany but stated that as he would (Dr Torrey) would not be engaged in the field but a part of the year it was thought proper that his salary should be curtailed from 1,500 to 1,200 dollars. The Dr declined the office on these conditions.[4] The persons to whom the charge of the Geological department is to be offered are Jackson[5] of Boston, Conrad[6] of Philad[a], Emmons[7] of Williams College & Hichcock[8] of Amherst.

[1] This letter shows the marks of Mary Henry's handiwork (see "Notes on Style" at the front of this volume). At the top of the first page of the original she noted in 1893 that this document was to be preserved, suggesting, incidentally, that other correspondence between Henry and Bache might have been destroyed. Two transcribed copies survive in the Henry Papers in the Smithsonian Archives.

[2] The Board of Regents already collected minimal data on terrestrial magnetism. Since 1832 the institutions that reported meteorological observations were requested to include measurements of the magnetic meridian at their locations. See *Henry Papers*, 2:205n.

[3] Despite Henry's pessimistic appraisal of the Survey's prospects, the project succeeded in enlisting a number of prominent American scientists, and later, in 1840, the New York legislature increased the appropriation for the Survey to $104,000. *Report of the Select Committee of the Legislature of 1849, on the Publication of the Natural History of the State of New York* (Albany, 1850), p. 10.

[4] Although Torrey may have initially declined, he eventually accepted the position as botanist on the Survey at the reduced salary. Because of their institutional connections, Torrey and Lewis C. Beck received a yearly stipend of $1,200 while those scientists who could devote their entire efforts to the project were taken on at $1,500 per year. *Report of the Select Committee* . . . (Albany, 1850), p. 7. Torrey remained with the Survey until 1843, when he published his *Flora of the State of New York* (2 vols.; Albany). *DSB*.

[5] Charles Thomas Jackson (1805–1880) was one of Governor Marcy's first choices for a position as a geologist with the Survey. Because of his commitment at the time as the state

I have been busily engaged since my return from Albany on a series of experiments on the inductive action of common electricity in motion and propose submitting a paper as soon as possible to the society on the subject.[9] I have written to our friend Mr Vaughan this evening stating that I intend visiting your city the beginning of next week for the purpose of a few days study in the Library.[10]

The special object of my troubling you this evening with this scrawl is to inform you that Mr Alexander and myself (as an assistant) will observe the eclipse on Sunday next. If you wish to have any cotemporaneous observations of any kind made during the eclipse write me an account of them as soon as possible that I may make the necessary preparations.[11]

My respects to Mrs Bache,[12] Courtenay[13] & Espy. As I will stop in your

---

geologist of Maine and Massachusetts and the unattractively low salary, however, Jackson declined Marcy's offer. Michele L. Aldrich, "New York Natural History Survey, 1836–1845" (Ph.D. dissertation, University of Texas, 1974), p. 95.

[6] Though a specialist in conchology, Timothy Abbott Conrad (1803–1877) was nevertheless appointed paleontologist for the Survey on the strength of a recommendation from Samuel George Morton, the distinguished Philadelphia naturalist (for whom see *Henry Papers, 1*:461n). Aldrich, "New York Natural History Survey," pp. 116–118. Largely self-educated, Conrad was born in New Jersey of Quaker antecedents. His father, a printer, had been Professor of Botany at the University of Pennsylvania, and the family often entertained such scientific notables as Thomas Say, Thomas Nuttall, and Constantine Rafinesque. Before joining the Survey, he had published a number of scientific papers on fossils and later, in 1840, helped organize the Association of American Geologists, the predecessor of the American Association for the Advancement of Science. *DSB.*

[7] At this time Ebenezer Emmons (see *Henry Papers, 1*:347n) held a joint appointment as a lecturer in chemistry at Williams College and as a junior professor at Rensselaer Polytechnic Institute. As field geologist for the second district of New York in the Adirondacks until 1842, Emmons worked out the Taconic system of geological classification that became a focus of great controversy in American geological circles. Aldrich, "New York Natural History Survey," pp. 119–121; *DAB*; *DSB*.

[8] Edward Hitchcock (1793–1864) quit the Survey only one month after his appointment.

At this time he was professor of chemistry and natural history at Amherst and in 1837 resumed his work as the state geologist for Massachusetts. Aldrich, "New York Natural History Survey," pp. 121–124; *DSB*. See also *Henry Papers, 1*:142n.

[9] Henry did not present his paper on electrodynamic induction to the American Philosophical Society until November 2, 1838. In his introduction he stated that he began a series of experiments on inductive action in common electricity in the spring of 1836 but became diverted by a new investigation into the phenomenon of lateral discharge (the results of which appeared in "Notices of Electrical Researches" in *BAAS Report, 1837* [1838], part 2, pp. 22–24). He finally resumed his original research in April 1838. "Contributions III: Electro-Dynamic Induction," p. 304.

[10] Henry's letter to John Vaughan cannot be found. In a letter of May 15, 1836, Charles Hodge mentioned to his brother Hugh that Henry intended to travel to Philadelphia the next morning. Charles Hodge to Hugh L. Hodge, May 15, 1836, Charles Hodge Collection, Princeton University Library.

[11] In the *Journal of the Franklin Institute*, Bache did publish a table of observations made at various locations in the path of the eclipse, but Alexander's readings were not included. "Observations of the Solar Eclipse of May 15th, 1836," *Journal of the Franklin Institute*, August 1836, n.s. *18*:100.

[12] Nancy Clarke Fowler Bache (1803–1870) is identified in *Henry Papers, 2*:112n.

[13] For Edward Courtenay (1803–1853), see *Henry Papers, 2*:32n. At this time he was teaching mathematics at the University of Pennsylvania.

City a few days we must have several meetings of the club[14] in that time.

Yours in much haste

Jos Henry

[14] We have not found any later references toume. For comments on its decline, see above, "the club" in the period covered by this vol-Bache to Henry, January 22–28, 1836.

"RECORD OF EXPERIMENTS"

Henry Papers, Smithsonian Archives

May 10th 1836

Exp 1 Made this day a double helix of tin foil by pasting on the outside and directly opposite on the outside,[1] a slip of tin foil about 20 feet long and $1/4$ of an inch wide. When a discharge was sent through the inside helix from the prime conductor, a slight shock was felt by touching either end of the outside coil. When the discharge was passed from a Leyden jar the effect was the same. The kind of electricity given off as tested by the small jar and the electrometer depended on the side of the jar the communication was last made with. When one end of the helix was put in communication with the outside of the jar and the other end made to touch the knob communicating with the inside the other helix gave off + electricity. When the negative side was last touched the same helix gave off negative electricity.[2]

Exp 2[3] took the electrical machine to the new College into the second story, attached the insulated conductor to the lightning rod. Worked the machine so that a spark of about one $1/2$ inch passed between the prime conductor furnished with a large ball and the insulated conductor. The electricity instead of being silently discharged into the earth by the lightning rod, gave sparks to a near object sufficiently large to fire the voltaic pistol. (Describe the lightning rod)[4] The lightning rod descends perpendicularly into the earth about 4 feet; then passes off horizontally and at right angles to the building to the distance of 12 feet, then descends perpendicularly into the

[1] Henry meant inside. We assume that the helices were coiled on the inside and outside of a cylinder consisting of an insulating material like glass.

[2] Henry switched the connections at the Leyden jar. Henry later added this editorial comment: "Afterwards made use of this apparatus in 1838 and determined by it the induced currents from common electricity"—experiments to appear in *Henry Papers, 4.*

[3] In the left margin Henry singled this out as an "Important" experiment. For part of his experimental set-up, see above experiments 1–3 of "Record of Experiments," May 6, 1836.

[4] From the cramped handwriting it appears that the lightning rod description was inserted at some later time.

earth 3½ feet; all the part of the rod under ground is surrounded with charcoal. The machine was placed about 15 feet from the surface of the ground. The connection of the several parts of the rod was as intimate as possible, being screwed together. The sparkes were not always of the same intensity but appeared to vary on some account very much in intensity.

The same rod gave sparkes from the upper part as far as the eaves of the building which was reached from the 4th story by means of a rod.[5] NB This exp would be more striking if oxygen and hydrogen could be fired, also if the sparkes were produced by the prime conductor alone and a ball attached to the lightning rod.

The action was more intense in the wire which connected the insulated conductor with the rod than in the rod itself; this may have been produced by the rod's giving off above and below and the wire being a better conductor.

I am informed by Dr Carnahan[6] that when he was a student in college the lightning passed down the rod and that the persons in the room nearest observed the whole rod apparently luminous. A Friend informes me that the lightening has been several times seen by him passing for a mile or more along the rail way like a running fire (Mr Nice[7] now of New Haven). The rail way by its great length would become powerfully negative by a cloud positively charged which, over the mile of the length of the road, each end would become highly positive.[8,9]

---

[5] A further test of the lateral discharge. Above this experiment Henry wrote *"Lateral action."*

[6] James Carnahan, President of Princeton.

[7] Benjamin Markley Nyce, a former student at Princeton (*Henry Papers*, 2:465n).

[8] Henry later encountered similar phenomena with the telegraph and presented his results to the American Philosophical Society. See his "On the Relation of Telegraph Lines to Lightning," APS *Proceedings*, June 19, 1846, 4:260–268.

[9] Henry later appended an observation: "Accident in NY 1838. House struck, persons stunned and candle melted in house 200 yards distant."

"RECORD OF EXPERIMENTS"

Henry Papers, Smithsonian Archives

May 14th 1836

Lateral action[1]

Exp 1 Charged the large jar. Discharged it through bell wire. An electrometer was placed near a bend in the wire. When the ball of the electrometer

---

[1] These experiments are a continuation of those of May 6.

was within about a 1/20 of an inch from the wire the leaves were made to diverge with + electricity as tested by sealing wax

Ex 2ⁿᵈ The electrometer was now removed to a little greater distance, the same intensity of charge sent through again but no disturbance of the electrometer was noticed. A smaller jar the ½ gallon was substituted. When this was discharged alone no effect was observed on the electrometer the distance remaining the same as in the last exp. The prime conductor of the machine was then connected with the large conductors suspended from the ceiling.[2] When the discharge was passed the electrometer was powerfully affected

Exp 3 The large jar was charged with 80 turns of the machine. The discharge produced no effect on the electrometer. The smal jar was then charged with 40 turns and connected with the long conductor the electricity[3] was powerfully affected

Ex 4 The small jar was charged fully. The discharge in connection with the long conductor powerfully affected the electrometer. The same charge was then given the same jar and afterwards the charge distributed between the large jar and the small one. In this case the discharge was weak and did not affect the electrometer

Exp 5 With a very fine platina wire and the large jar, the effect was greater than with a larger wire, copper bell wire. In this exp the long conductor was not used

Exp 6 The lateral action is most intense where there are points along the wire. When a discharge was sent through a fine platina wire sparks were seen at places w[h]ere there were the knots in the wire or kinks. The sparks were seen with and without the long conductor.

Exp 7 Fine platina wire dipped at a flex[ure] into a jar of water & finger put in jar. When the discharge from small jar passed through no commotion felt. When the globe was added to the prime conductor so as to increase the quantity of free electricity the discharge produced a shock on the finger through the water. When the long conductor was used the shock was much greater.

Exp 8 A large copper (bell) wire was substituted for the thin platina wire in the last exp. The commotion was about the same. When the globe or the

---

[2] The insulated conductor was interposed between the electrical machine and the wire passing the discharge. As in previous experiments, the insulated conductor served to collect a larger charge.

[3] Henry meant "electrometer."

large conductor was used so that with this arrangement and a small jar the lateral action is about the same with a large or small wire

Exp 9 Large jar used with thick wire in water. Without long conductor no commotion. With long conductor commotion. With smal wire, finger in water. Large jar effect less than with large wire, the long conductor connected. Without the long conductor no effect.

Exp 10 With a battery of 8 jars the small wire gave a slight commotion to the water without the long conductor. With a large copper wire no commotion whatever.

The charge from the battery 8 jars was again passed through the copper wire in the water with the long conductor added. (The charge in these experiments does not pass through the long conductor but the latter only serves to extend the coating of the inner surface of the jar).[4] With this the commotion very intense was given to the jar. The small wire was substituted for the large one, the arrangement of the long conductor as before. The lateral action about the same, the wire became red hot

Exp 11 When the discharge from a battery or the smaller jar is sent through the spiral conductor around the jar the whole becomes luminous. Try this exp in the dark.[5]

Exp 12 Attached iron wire to the insulated conductor in the back room of Phil Hall, carried the same out of the front window and then across the campus to the library. The wire unfortunately touched one of the trees. Still the effect of a spark near the farther end was very intense, was taken with the knuckle, it was felt in the heel. Ether was readily fired; is not the intensity of the spark in this case due in some degree to the principle of the spiral conductor?[6] The effect is not due intirely to distribution in a long wire for when the electricity was communicated directly from the prime conductor of the machine to the long wire the spark was very feeble on account of the imperfect conduction of so long a wire

Send charge through small copper wire in water. Add one conductor, 2 conductors 3 con &c. Send charge thr[7]

---

[4] This set-up is unclear to us. The long conductor, we suspect, was attached to one of the knobs of the serially-connected Leyden jars.

[5] See "Record of Experiments," August 31, 1836, footnote 1.

[6] An example of a case where the effects of lateral discharge and (self-) induction may be acting simultaneously.

[7] This fragmentary entry appears at the bottom of the original, somewhat detached from the other experiments, but is probably related to preceding experiments 7–10.

HENRY NOTEBOOK ENTRY

Notebook [23894],[1] page [35], Henry Papers, Smithsonian Archives

May 1836[2]

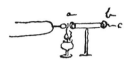 To show that flame is a conductor or that heat renders air a conductor arrange the apparatus as in the margin put a lamp at (a) of alcohol. Sparkes can then be drawn from (b) although none will pass between the two knobs[3]—J.H

[1] This entry is in a section on insulation and conduction.

[2] In the original the date follows Henry's initials.

[3] In 1834 William Snow Harris refuted the assertion that heated air, as such, was a conductor of electricity. Harris claimed that earlier experimenters had neglected to consider variations in the density of the air caused by heating it. By using a receiver, he was able to isolate the effects of variation of temperature and of density on electrical discharge. At a constant pressure, variations in temperature had no effect. But at a constant temperature, the quantity of electricity necessary for discharge was directly proportional to the density of the air. He concluded "that heated air is not, as frequently stated, a conductor of electricity, and that heat does not facilitate electrical transmission through air in any other way than by diminishing its density." "On Some Elementary Laws of Electricity," *Phil. Trans.*, 1834, pp. 213–245 (paragraphs 40–50). Faraday cited Harris's conclusions in his Twelfth Series of Experimental Researches in Electricity, "18. On Induction (continued)," *Phil. Trans.*, 1838, pp. 83–123 (paragraphs 1363–1367, 1380).

TO ALEXANDER DALLAS BACHE

Bache Papers, Smithsonian Archives

Princeton June 4th [1836] Saturday

My Dear Bache

A Mr Boyd of the Theological Seminary has just informed me that during the vacation his friends have concluded to send him to Edinburgh inorder to attend a course of Theological and other lectures in the university of that city. He leaves here this morning and I have promised to forward a package to him at New York on Tuesday for Forbes as Mr B is anxious to take charge of something of the kind which may serve as an introduction to the Professor whose lectures he will probably attend.[1]

[1] Andrew Hunter Holmes Boyd (1814–1865), a native of Virginia, graduated from Jefferson College in 1830 or 1831. After two years of study at New Haven, he attended the Princeton Theological Seminary from 1833 to 1836. Nevin records that while at Edinburgh during the trip Henry mentions here, Boyd attended the lectures of Thomas Chalmers (1780–1847), Professor of Divinity, and Sir William Hamilton (1788–1856), Professor of Logic and Meta-

Send me copies of your papers on magnetism particularly the last if possible,[2] also of the papers on the Bursting of boilers from the Franklin journal and I will mention in my letter if it be agreeable to you that the experiments detailed were made under your direction.[3]

---

physics. Forbes was Professor of Natural Philosophy at Edinburgh. Upon his return to the United States, Boyd was ordained and spent the rest of his life as a minister in Virginia. Alfred Nevin, ed., *Encyclopaedia of the Presbyterian Church in the United States of America* (Philadelphia, 1884), p. 90; *Roberts*, p. 82.

[2] In the last few years, Bache had published a number of papers on terrestrial magnetism. His most recent article, in conjunction with Edward H. Courtenay, was "On the Relative Horizontal Intensities of Terrestrial Magnetism at Several Places in the United States, with the Investigation of Corrections for Temperature, and Comparisons of the Methods of Oscillation in Full and in Rarefied Air," *Transactions of the American Philosophical Society*, 1837, n.s. 5:427–457. This paper was read on May 6, 1836, and was not yet in print.

[3] In 1831, at the request of the Treasury Department, the Franklin Institute began an investigation of the causes of steam boiler explosions. In 1832 Bache became chairman of the investigating committee which included two subcommittees, one on the causes of explosions and the other on the strength of materials employed in boiler construction. The first subcommittee, headed by Bache, completed its work in May 1835. Its report was printed in January 1836: *Report of the Committee of the Franklin Institute . . . on the Explosions of Steam-Boilers. Part I. Containing the First Report of Experiments Made by the Committee, For the Treasury Department of the U. States* (Philadelphia, 1836).

The second subcommittee, headed by Walter R. Johnson, took longer to finish its work, a cause of friction between Bache and Johnson. In September 1836, Bache, not waiting for the submission of Johnson's report, submitted the general report of the committee: *General Report on the Explosions of Steam-Boilers, By a Committee of the Franklin Institute . . .* (Philadelphia, 1836). Three months later, after Bache had left for Europe, Johnson presented the work of his subcommittee: *Report of the Committee of the Franklin Institute . . . on the Explosions of Steam Boilers . . . Part II. Containing the Report of the Sub-Committee, to whom was Referred the Examination of the Strength of Materials Employed in the Construction of Steam Boilers* (Philadelphia, 1837).

With the approval of the Secretary of the Treasury, each of the reports also appeared serially in the *Journal of the Franklin Institute*: the first from January through May 1836, the general report in October, November, and December 1836, and the second subcommittee report from February through August 1837. Henry is referring here to the *Journal* version of the first report. In addition to the *Journal*, Henry's Library contains the three reports, bound as one volume, with Henry's annotations.

Bruce Sinclair gives a full treatment of the Franklin Institute's investigation in *Philadelphia's Philosopher Mechanics: A History of the Franklin Institute, 1824–1865* (Baltimore, 1974), pp. 170–191, and in an earlier monograph, *Early Research at the Franklin Institute: The Investigation into the Causes of Steam Boiler Explosions, 1830–1837* (Philadelphia, 1966), which includes a reprint of the general report.

In this document and elsewhere, Henry expresses concern that Bache get proper credit for his active role in the investigation. In his letter to Forbes of September 19, 1836, printed below, Henry states that the experiments covered by the first report were made entirely by Bache. Years later, in an article on steam boiler explosions in the supplementary volume of the *Encyclopaedia Americana* (Philadelphia, 1847), *14*:651–652, Henry wrote that Bache "devoted the greater part of all his leisure hours during four years to the investigation."

While in Europe in 1837, Henry was asked to review the general report for *The Magazine of Popular Science*, which had already printed a review critical of the first report. The gross distortion of Henry's review by the editor led to a second review, printed as Henry had written it, in *The Analyst*. See Henry's letter to Harriet Henry of May 9, 1837, and Bache's letter to Henry of June 7, 1837, printed below.

Also send if possible copies of Espy's papers on Meteorology[4] and of Rogers' Report of the Geology of this state.[5]

I will inform Forbes that we intend sending him a vacuum apparatus of your contriving[6] and that it will probably be forwarded by a gentleman (A Mr Brown)[7] who sails in the packet of the 8th of July. Cannot the article be furnished before this time.

Mr Brown is a young Scotchman who has resided for two years past at St Petersburgh in Russia; he returns to his station after visiting Scotland in the Autumn and will pass through Christiana in Norway and will take charge of any article for Hansteen should you wish to open a correspondence with that Gentleman.[8]

I am much indebted to you for the trouble you were put to in looking over the journal on the subject of Lateral discharge.[9] The long long continuance of the easterly storm has rendered all experiments on electricity with my apparatus interely out of the question. When the sun will again appear I know not (perhaps our Friend Mr E[10] can give some information on this head) but as soon as the dew-point is in a proper state for electrical excitement I will go on with my paper, and must trouble you to procure for

---

[4] Since 1831 Espy had published numerous articles on meteorology. See the listing in the *Royal Society Catalogue.*

[5] Henry Darwin Rogers, *Report on the Geological Survey of the State of New Jersey* (Philadelphia, 1836). Henry's Library contains a presentation copy of the report.

[6] Bache had modified Hansteen's intensity apparatus so that the needles vibrated in a vacuum. He and Courtenay had noticed anomalies in their observations which they attributed to effects of currents of air on the needles. The apparatus is described on page 432 of the article cited in footnote 2. In this article Bache states that although Snow Harris had remarked in an 1831 article (*Phil. Trans.*, pp. 67–90) on the effects of air currents and had used a vacuum to overcome them, he believes he and Courtenay are publishing the first intensity observations using vibration in a vacuum.

The vacuum apparatus was not yet ready to be sent to Forbes. Lacking proper materials, Bache had to use a jar of the wrong size for the original version. It was apparently a second version that Bache exhibited to the American Philosophical Society on September 19, 1836, just before leaving for Europe. (*Early Proceedings of the American Philosophical Society ... From 1744 to 1838* [Philadelphia, 1884], p. 692.) According to Henry's letter introducing Bache to Forbes (September 19, 1836, below), Bache was to present Forbes with the apparatus in person.

Although Bache and Courtenay claimed greatly superior accuracy with the vacuum apparatus, it does not seem to have been widely adopted. Gauss's use of larger needles also minimized the effect of air currents. The Hansteen apparatus and the vibration method itself were being supplemented and superseded by new apparatus and methods for the determination of intensity. Henry, however, in his 1847 article on magnetism in the *Encyclopaedia Americana* (*14*:419), called Bache's apparatus "a very important improvement in the method of obtaining the intensity."

[7] We have been unable to identify Mr. Brown.

[8] Bache apparently did not take Henry's suggestion at this time. In the Hansteen Papers, Institute of Theoretical Astrophysics, University of Oslo, there are four letters from Bache to Hansteen. The earliest of these, dated December 21, 1855, is probably the first direct correspondence between Bache and Hansteen.

[9] Henry had evidently asked Bache to review some of the literature for reports on lateral discharge. He may be referring to the Franklin Institute *Journal* or *Silliman's Journal.*

[10] James P. Espy.

me from one of the Libraries if it be in your city a copy of *Wilson Experiments Made at the Pantheon on the Nature and Use of Conductors London* 1778.[11] I know not in what form these exp. were published but should judge that they appeared in a pamphlet.

Col. Abert[12] of the War Dep has forwarded for me to the care of Dr Harlan[13] of your city a piece of pure Zinc manufactured by Prof Hasler.[14] If you will send for the article to the Dr's you may bisect the article and retain one half for your own use. I will send for the other half and the book by the first opportunity.

Send the pamphlets by mail if possible on monday morning or on monday evening. See that they are mailed on monday before 5 o'clock as in that case I will receive them early on tuesday morning.

Send them as early as possible—perhaps they may be mailed this evening. I will then get them from the office early on monday morning. I will send you the account of the shooting stars[15] on some day next week.

The mail is about
closing so in[16]

There is an appearance of sun shine at this moment. I hail it with pleasure. PS I find that this letter cannot leave here until 9 o'clock this evening.

J.H.

[11] Benjamin Wilson, "New Experiments and Observations on the Nature and Use of Conductors," *Phil. Trans.*, 1778, pp. 245–313. Henry cited Wilson in "Contributions III: Electro-Dynamic Induction," p. 334, in his attempt to show self-induction in ordinary electricity.

[12] John James Abert (1788–1863) was at this time Chief of the Topographical Bureau of the War Department. After attending West Point, Abert served as assistant to the chief clerk of the War Office while studying law in Washington. Abert practiced law for a short time until he volunteered during the War of 1812. Following the war, Abert became a major in the Topographical Engineers. From 1814 to 1829 he served as an assistant to F. R. Hassler, Superintendent of the Coast Survey. Abert was Chief of the Topographical Bureau from 1834 until his retirement in 1861. *DAB.*

[13] Richard Harlan (*Henry Papers*, 2:265).

[14] In addition to being Superintendent of the Coast Survey, Hassler was in charge of the construction of standard weights and measures for the customhouses and the states and territories of the United States. To make the brass standards, Hassler needed pure zinc. He could either purify commercially available zinc spelter or produce zinc spelter directly by refining zinc ore. Claiming that imported commercial zinc was impure, not malleable, frequently unavailable, and often expensive, Hassler equipped the government arsenal at Washington for the manufacture of zinc spelter from New Jersey and Pennsylvania zinc ore. The result, according to Hassler, was "the *first pure zinc* ever produced in this country, as far as I know and I am informed." Although the zinc was of superior quality, the expense of the process made it unfeasible commercially. F. R. Hassler, *Documents Relating to the Construction of Standards of Weights and Measures for the Customs Houses from March to November 1835* (New York, 1835); quote from p. 23. Further information on the construction of the standards is in *Principal Documents Relating to the Survey of the Coast and the Construction of Uniform Standards of Weights and Measures*, 3 vols. (New York, 1834–1836). See also Walter Renton Ingalls, *Lead and Zinc in the United States* (New York, 1908), pp. 259. 279.

[15] Not found.

[16] Henry's signature and the last word or words of the closing have been cut out of the original.

TO JAMES HENRY

Family Correspondence, Henry Papers, Smithsonian Archives

Princeton June 6th 1836

Dear James

We have heard nothing direct from your family since Stephen le[f]t Albany although through a certain channel we have not been ignorant on the subject of Albany affairs and have had repeted information concerning you and yours.

I have only to plead for my long silence the old excuse of many engagements since my return and since the beginning of the College term. The Institution continues to flourish and the number of students to increase gradually and steadily. We have now on the ground a larger number than was ever before connected with College.[1] Dr Torrey did not accept the appointment of botanist to the great survey[2] and is now at Princeton in his usual capasity of Professor of Chemestry. He remains with us during the summer session.

William Bullions arrived here on Saturday last with the intention of remaining during the summer and assisting me in the Philosophical Hall as he had done during the winter but Capt. Beach the Engineer of the Morris canal, the Canajoharrie rail road &c[3] to whom I wrote while in Albany about William,[4] came on to Princeton last week for the purpose of informing me that he would take William and could immediatly place him in a good situation on the survey of a Railway about being made in the northern part of N.J.[5] William therefore left us on Saturday to join the *corpse* at Newark.

[1] At this time, after a number of years of declining enrollments, Princeton was finally entering a period of prosperity that would last until the Civil War. The initiator of this recovery was John Maclean, the driving force in President Carnahan's administration. By actively soliciting alumni support and recruiting well-known scholars like Joseph Henry in natural philosophy, Albert Baldwin Dod in mathematics, and John Torrey in chemistry, the school was able to augment its enrollment until by the year 1835–1836 it stood at 227 students. This trend, as Wertenbaker notes, continued until 1861 when it peaked at 314. *Wertenbaker*, pp. 178–180, 250, 270.

[2] Later in June, Torrey accepted the position and was appointed on July 1. Michele L. Aldrich, "New York Natural History Survey, 1836–1845" (Ph.D. dissertation, University of Texas, 1974), p. 133.

[3] Captain Ephraim Beach was a highly regarded canal and railroad engineer who had worked on a number of canal and railroad projects in New Jersey, Pennsylvania, and New York. Little biographical information on him seems to exist, although he was known to have been involved not only in the construction of the Morris Canal and the Canajoharie-Catskill Railroad but in surveying the route for the Susquehanna and Delaware Railroad in 1832. See, for example, Beach, *Report on the Survey of a Route for the Proposed Susquehanna and Delaware Railroad* (New York, 1832), pp. 7–13. Horace Jerome Cranmer, "The New Jersey Canal: State Policy and Private Enterprise, 1820–1832" (Ph.D. dissertation, Columbia University, 1955), p. 91. James Lee, *The Morris Canal: A Photographic History* (York, Pennsylvania, 1973), p. 3.

[4] We have not found Henry's letter to Beach.

[5] Perhaps the Camden and Amboy Railroad, although its public reports do not indicate that

The situation is a very good one and I most sincerely hope for the sake of his Father and himself that he will succeed in giving full satisfaction to his employer.

I have just learned that an Albany Lady has arrived in Princeton with Mrs Hand. I allude to Miss Margaret Newland.[6] We have not yet seen her as we did not know of her arrival until this morning and the weather is so rainy and the [walking] so bad that Harriet will scarcely be able to reach her to day.

We have had one of the most disagreeable seasons of rain and cold here that I ever remember having experienced. This day is the 14th since the storm commenced, the wind all the while has been steadily from the NE. I suppose that you have had your part of the drenching at Albany.

Stephen goes on to New York tomorrow. He has some urgent business in that city which he has lately discovered needs immediate attendance.

James McIntyre is an inmate of our house; he sleeps in the small room over the hall and has a study room in the Philosophical Hall.

I have nothing new to communicate. The death of Mr Levingston much disappointed one of the College Societies; he was a graduate of the College and had been elected to deliver an address at the next commencement.[7]

I see by the N. York Observer that Mr James and Deacon Plat have been sent to represent the Albany presbytery in the great meeting of the General Assembly of the Presbyterian Church at Pittsburgh. The meeting is expected to be one of great interest involving the unity of the church as it is expected that there may be danger of a split between the old and new school men. There are parties in church as well as State.[8]

---

either Beach or Bullions were employed on this project. In any event, Bullions was back at Princeton as Henry's assistant by the end of 1836.

[6] John Newland's sister.

[7] Edward Livingston died on May 23, 1836. The American Whig Society chose John Morin Scott to replace him. *Henry Papers*, 2:490.

[8] The *New York Observer* of May 28, 1836, listed the Albany delegation, which included William James and Ananias Platt.

At this time the Presbyterian Church in the United States was undergoing a schism between the Old School and New School parties that would last until after the Civil War. A number of factors converged to bring about the rift, but the most important were ortho-dox fears over the infiltration of heretical ideas on individual salvation, a dispute over the church's role in promoting religious revivals and social and moral reform, and growing sectional antagonisms over slavery. The controversy had been brewing for a number of years. Following the 1836 General Assembly, the Old School formed a coalition with the southerners and in 1837 expelled the New School party. Timothy L. Smith, *Revivalism and Social Reform: American Protestantism on the Eve of the Civil War* (New York, 1965), pp. 26–27, 185–186. C. Bruce Staiger, "Abolitionism and the Presbyterian Schism of 1837–1838," *Mississippi Valley Historical Review*, December 1949, *36*:391–414.

TO JAMES DAVID FORBES

Forbes Papers, Library, St. Andrews University, Scotland

Princeton New Jersey June 7th 1836[1]

My Dear Sir

My Friend Mr Boyd of Virginia who has been for some time a student in the Theological Seminary of this place has unexpectedly to me determined to start for Edinburgh in the Packet of tomorrow. His purpose is to attend a course of Theological and other lectures in your University and he has expressed a desire to be the bearer of a package which may give him an opportunity of meeting one of the Professors. I gladly avail myself of his offer and send a parcel of such articles as I happen to have on hand. I regret however that I have nothing more important than these to offer in return for the highly interesting papers you were so kind as to send me.

I am much indebted to you for the prompt and polite attention you paid my request in reference to the magnetic needles. I regret however to inform you that the package containing them did not reach me until more than six months after its arrival in this country.[2] The person to whom it was directed neglected to forward it to me and it remained in New York until after the return of Mr Turnbull.[3] I know not to what influence the needles were subjected in the interval although they were received safely packed in their boxes; yet the one I sent to you was found so entirely changed in its rate as to leave no doubt on my mind of its having been affected by some extraneous cause. The needles had remained so long in near approximation that I fear they eventually reacted on each other and that both have thus been permanently affected. I most sincerely hope you will pardon me for not before acknowledging the receipt of the package of papers and the needles and also of the last paper[4] you sent me from London in a box of Books directed to the College Library. The fact is I have been so much mortified by the circumstanc of the derangements of the needles that I could not summon resolution enough to write to you until I had made some observations which might in some respects repair the injury.

---

[1] There is also a Mary Henry Copy of this letter, dated June 6 (Henry Papers, Smithsonian Archives). Both versions cover essentially the same points, although they differ in the order of the paragraphs. One major difference is that the Mary Henry Copy, probably of Henry's draft, includes a sentence in which Henry complained of the problem of doing research in a country which suffers from "the difficulty and delay of publication."

[2] For Henry's problems in obtaining this package, see *Henry Papers*, 2:358n.

[3] John Turnbull, for whom see *Henry Papers*, 1:355n.

[4] Probably "On the Refraction and Polarization of Heat," *Transactions of the Royal Society of Edinburgh*, 1835, 13:131–168. A presentation copy of this article is in the Henry Library.

I vibrated your needle last Autumn vacation at Princeton, New Haven, West Point, and at Albany;[5] It has been for the last five months in the possession of my friend Professor D. Bache of Philadelphia who has made a series of observations on the influence of the change of temperature on the rate of the needle, and also a series of comparisons of the vibrations of the same needle, in a vacuum and in the air. The vibrations, in a vacuum, according to his results are so much more satisfactory that I have ordered an article to be constructed similar to the vacuum apparatus, used and devised by him, for your needle. This article was ordered to be made some months since in Philadelphia by Professor Bache, but it has not yet been finished; as soon as I receive it and the needle I will determine the present rate, of the latter in the vacuum at this place. (Prof Bache will do the same at Philadelphia) and then send it, with the vacuum apparatus[6] to you, through my Friend Dr John Torrey of New York who will forward it to Glasgow to the care of his correspondent Dr Hooker[7] the celebrated Botanist.

You will find in the package a copy of a report to the Legislature of the state of New York on the subject of a geological survey of the state. A Law has been passed authorizing this survey and a liberal appropriation made to defray the expense. Had I been in Albany (the seat of government of the state) before the passage of the law I think it probable a set of magnetic instruments would have been ordered, from Europe for the purpose of tracing the lines of intensity, dip and, variation through the state in connection with the geological survey. In a conversation which I had with the secretary of state on this subject he promised me that in the course of two years a survey of the kind should be made at the expense either of the Legislature or of the Board of Regents of the University. Should this survey be ordered Professor Bache and myself would probably have the direction of it.

The subject of terrestrial magnetism is of considerable practical importance in this country since the boundaries of all estates were originally fixed and described by the direction of the magnetic needle, the compass being

[5] For Henry's observations with Forbes's needle and Bache's experiments with vacuum apparatus described in the rest of this paragraph, see *Henry Papers,* 2:469–471, 251–252, 406.

[6] Bache himself delivered the completed apparatus. See Henry to Forbes, September 19, 1836, printed below.

[7] Sir William Jackson Hooker (1785–1865) had become Professor of Botany at the University of Glasgow in 1820. He had made Glasgow the center of an extensive and important network of correspondents embracing over

three hundred botanists and horticulturalists. Hooker was knighted in 1836 for service to botany. In 1841 he was appointed the first director of the Royal Botanic Gardens at Kew, a post he held until his death. Mea Allen, *The Hookers of Kew: 1785–1911* (London, 1967).

John Torrey had become a correspondent of Hooker prior to 1823. He spent some time with Hooker during his European trip of 1833. Andrew Denny Rodgers, *John Torrey: A Story of North American Botany* (Princeton, 1942), pp. 57–58, 105–109.

the only instrument of convenient use for the purpose of surveying in a country covered with thick woods. As the land becomes valuable the division lines are required to be settled with more accuracy. The original land markes, consisting generally, at first of marked trees, are soon lost and the boundary lines have often to be retraced by the compass; A knowledge therefore of the laws of the variation would obviate much perplexity on the part of the surveyor and much unfortunate dispute and Litegation on the part of the neighboring owners of the property.[8]

Dr Beck[9] has probably sent you copies of the Meteorological reports of the academies of the state of N. Y. I however have enclosed a copy for 1834 & 1835.[10] You will find many purilities in these reports but I hope in time they will be able to add something of value to the science of Meterology. The appearance of the aurora as noted in this country will probably interest you. The action of this meteor on a delicately suspended horizontal needle, in this country is most marked and energetic. We have had during the past months several unusually vivid displays of the aurora.

You will also find in the package two numbers of documents relative to the Trigonometrical survey of the coast of the United States a work now going on under the superintendance of Mr Hasler.[11] An account of the plan an[d] preliminary operations of this survey were published some years since in the 2nd vol of the Transactions of the American Philosophical Society (second series). This article will shortly be published in a separate work with notes and corrections by Mr Hasler.[12] I will send you a copy as soon as it appears.

The survey of the coast was a project commenced under the administration of Mr Jefferson in 1807 although actual field operations did not com-

---

[8] Confirmation of the correctness of Henry's remarks can be found in John Gummere, *A Treatise on Surveying, Containing the Theory and Practice*, 8th ed. (Philadelphia, 1837), pp. 83, 202–211; also see Silvio Bedini's discussion of colonial surveyors and surveying in *Thinkers and Tinkers: Early American Men of Science* (New York, 1975), pp. 51–70. Henry himself had had experience both surveying and teaching surveying techniques. *Henry Papers*, 1:97–105, 107–115, 190.

[9] T. R. Beck.

[10] On March 1, 1825, the Regents of the University of the State of New York directed each of the state's academies to conduct meteorological observations. Eight years later the Regents requested the academies to observe the Aurora Borealis according to the directions

set down in the circular of the British Association. Franklin B. Hough, comp., *Results of a Series of Meteorological Observations, Made in Obedience to Instructions from the Regents of the University, at Sundry Academies in the State of New-York, from 1826 to 1850 Inclusive* (Albany, 1855), pp. iii–ix. While Henry was at the Albany Academy, he and T. R. Beck made the required observations. *Henry Papers*, 1:106–107, 400n, 435–436.

[11] Ferdinand R. Hassler. We are uncertain as to the identity of the documents sent by Henry.

[12] There is a discussion of Hassler's article and the proposed separate publication of it in Vaughan to Henry, January 21, 1836, footnote 3, above.

mence until 1816 and were then only continued for one year. After 1817 nothing further was done until 1832 when the more enlightened policy of the present administration ordered the work to be renewed, and congress since then has made regular appropriations for its continuance.[13] A series of magnetic observations could be connected with this survey which would be valuable in determining the direction of the line of no variation and the lines of isodynamic intensity.

I enclose also a paper of Professor Bache on the variation of the needle.[14] He will send you a copy of his paper on the vibrations in a vacuum &c as soon as it is published.

I have promised a series of papers to the American Philosophical society on the subjects of electricity & magnetism; two of these under one cover you will find in the package, one a description of a galvanic battery used in my experiments and the other on the influence of a spiral conductor on a current of galvanism.[15] By a reference to the transactions of the Royal Society you will find that a paper was read on the same subject by Mr Faraday on the 5th of Feby.[16] My paper was read in Philadelphia on the 6th of the same month although the facts were communicated some weeks before. The first fact in my paper was discovered by me in 1832 and published in Sillimans Journal.[17] Mr Faraday has politely sent me a copy of his paper and stated to a friend that he had not seen my publication on the subject or he would have given me credit.[18]

My third paper on these subjects will appear in a few weeks.[19] I receive regularly one month after its publication the London and Edinburgh Magazine and allways look with eagerness for your papers particularly for your contributions to the subject of heat.

I am warned that the stage starts in a few minutes for New York. I will

---

[13] A. Hunter Dupree, *Science in the Federal Government: A History of Policies and Activities to 1940* (New York and Evanston, 1964), pp. 29–33 and 52–54, discusses the political trials of Hassler and the Coast Survey.

[14] Probably "On the Diurnal Variation of the Horizontal Needle," *Transactions of the American Philosophical Society*, 1837, n.s. 5: 1–22. The first part of this volume was already published and available at this time.

[15] "Contributions I: Battery" and "Contributions II: Spiral Conductor." We have discussed these papers in detail in *Henry Papers*, 2:101n, 220n–221n, and 329n–331n.

[16] The priority issue on this point is discussed in *Henry Papers*, 2:401.

[17] "On the Production of Currents and Sparks of Electricity from Magnetism," *Silliman's Journal*, 1832, 22:408.

[18] The friend was Petty Vaughan, who often acted as an intermediary between Philadelphia and London scientific societies. For more on Vaughan and Faraday's remark, see *Henry Papers*, 2:429–430.

[19] In fact "Contributions III" did not appear until 1838. Henry was, however, at this point contemplating writing papers on the magnetization of steel and the comparison of galvanic and steel magnets. For some reason, he failed to do so. For more detail, see *Henry Papers*, 2:385n–386n.

therefore no longer trespass on your valuable time and conclude by assuring you that

> With the highest respect I remain
> Your obliged and humble servt
> Joseph Henry

Any article sent to me directed the Care of Dr John Torrey New York or to the care of John Vaughn Esq librarian of the American Philosoph Society will be received without fail.

"RECORD OF EXPERIMENTS"
Henry Papers, Smithsonian Archives

June 8th 1836[1]

The experiment of the pierced card the hole being nearer the negative end will probably have some connection with the same phenominon as the divergence from a long wire.[2] 1 Try the effect of the divergence in a vaccuum with the large jars. 2 Send a charge over the gilt paper in air also in vacuum. Also with bottle charged and with conductor. 3 Also with small ball on + side & large ball on other and the reverse. 4 Send charge along fine wire through a vacuum. 5 Try Nobili's exp[3] Ency Brit. p. 583. Cover a metallic

[1] The date originally appeared at the bottom of the entry.

[2] Comparing the "divergent" effects of lateral discharges with the forces exerted by sparks, Henry discharges a battery of Leyden jars through a card and examines the form of the perforation. It was an old experiment familiar to static electricians. Electric explosions and perforations, as well as lateral explosions, are discussed, for example, in George Adams, *Essay on Electricity*, ed. William Jones, 5th ed. (London, 1799), pp. 272–274, 278–a work in Henry's Library. While in Europe Henry bought an apparatus for performing this experiment.

Henry later incorporated these results in "Contributions III: Electro-Dynamic Induction," using a variation of the current experiment:

It is well known that the discharge from an electrical battery possesses great divellent powers; that it entirely separates, in many instances, the particles of the body through which it passes. This force acts, in part, at least, in the direction of the line of the discharge, and appears to be analogous to the repulsive action discovered by Ampere, in the consecutive parts of the same galvanic circuit. To illustrate this, paste on a piece of glass a narrow slip of tinfoil, cut it through at several points, and loosen the ends from the glass at the places so cut. Pass a discharge through the tinfoil from about nine half gallon jars; the ends, at each separation, will be thrown up, and sometimes bent entirely back, as if by the action of a strong repulsive force between them. . . . In the popular experiment of the pierced card, the bur on each side appears to be due to an action of the same kind. [paragraph 126]

[3] This same experiment was singled out for repeating by Henry in August 1834. See *Henry Papers*, 2:237n. Henry later annotated this paragraph with the notation: "This has been found to be owing to the electricity passing from one spire to an other."

wire with silk. Form it into a close flat spiral of not more than twenty four revolutions *with the different* coils in contact. When a considerable charge is passed through 2 feet surface a vivid light originating in the centre will be seen even in daylight. 5th When a shock is felt by a galvanic instrument the effect is increased by alternating the current. Would not the effect also be increased by terminating the poles with cylinders of zinc and then breaking the circuit by rubbing them together. Try the exp[4]

[4] Henry later wrote "did this" below this experimental suggestion.

FROM JAMES P. ESPY

Minor Authors Collection, Barrett Library, University of Virginia Library

Phila[a] July 19th 1836

My Dear Friend,

I wish you would come down and spend Thursday Friday and saturday with us, and assist us in our *Kite experiments*. We have now about 3 miles of wire on our reel and 30 kites ready to take it up whenever the wind favours.

We have already sent up 1500 yards and drawn electricity from a clear sky too powerful to be taken without much pain, it decomposed hyriodade of potash,[1] the Iodine going to the pole connected with the reel. The sparks were about an inch long, and seemed to be much more *shocking* than sparks of similar size from the machine in common use.[2]

[1] Espy's terminology is garbled. He probably meant either potassium hydriodate or potassium hydriodide.

[2] Henry did join Espy and others for the kite experiments (see the two related letters printed immediately below). In "Contributions III:Electro-Dynamic Induction," paragraph 124, he gives the following account:

I was so fortunate as to witness a very interesting exhibition of this action during some experiments on atmospheric electricity made by a committee of the Franklin Institute, in 1836. Two kites were attached, one above the other, and raised with a small iron wire in place of a string. On the occasion at which I was present, the wire was extended by the kites to the length of about one mile. The day was perfectly clear, yet the sparks from the wire had so much projectile force (to use a convenient expression of Dr. Hare) that fifteen persons joining hands and standing on the ground, received the shock at once, when the first person of the series touched the wire.

Henry concluded that the remarkable pungency of the spark from the kite wire was due to induction in a long wire. He had previously reported this observation, with less detail, in his communication on lateral discharge to the British Association in 1837 (*BAAS Report, 1837* [1838], part 2, pp. 22–24).

As far as the records indicate, the Franklin Institute did not have any committee working on atmospheric electricity at this time. Henry probably meant to say that the experiments were made by the Franklin Kite Club. Very little is known of this Philadelphia group which used kites for observations on atmospheric electricity and meteorology, both subjects of great interest to Henry. Information on the Club is scattered in contemporary and retrospective accounts.

William B. Taylor (1821–1895), later a Patent Officer examiner, an assistant at the Smithsonian, and a close friend of Henry's, knew the Club as a young man. In a eulogy, William Jones Rhees attributes Taylor's first interest in science and particularly electrical phenomena to this exposure. Rhees gives the following description of the Club:

> In 1835–36 several gentlemen formed a society with the name of The Franklin Kite Club, for the purpose of making electrical experiments. For a considerable time they met once a week at the Philadelphia City Hospital grounds and flew their kites. These were generally square in shape, made of muslin or silk, stretched over a framework of cane reeds, varying in size from 6 feet upward, some being as large as 20 feet square. For flying the kites annealed copper wire was used, wound upon a heavy reel 2 or 3 feet in diameter, insulated by being placed on glass supports. When one kite was up, sometimes a number of others would be sent up on the same string.

Smithsonian Institution Annual Report for 1896 (Washington, 1898), p. 646.

A contemporary reference by James Swaim in an article on his own kite experiments gives further details of the Club's equipment:

> Wire No. 30 was used, which was wound on a reel four feet in circumference, having a glass axle running on a frame about three feet high, which was made in the same manner as the one used by the Franklin Kite Club of Philadelphia.

A plate picturing the apparatus accompanies the article. "Electro-Meteorological Observations," *Silliman's Journal*, 1837, *32*:304–307. Swaim's use of wire instead of cord to fly his kites is the earliest such use in the United States mentioned by Middleton (see below).

The Club's major interest was probably atmospheric electricity. In 1836 they published "History of Experiments on Atmospheric Electricity, Being a Report Presented by a Committee of the 'Franklin Kite Club,' at the Request of the Club," *Journal of the Franklin Institute*, 1836, n.s. *18*:166–172. Under the chairmanship of John C. Cresson, the committee reviewed eighteenth-century experiments

in atmospheric electricity, expressed regret at the subsequent lack of work in the field and recommended that experiments be made with good conductors and at far greater heights than previously attempted, i.e., at 10,000 or 15,000 feet.

With Espy a member, it is not surprising that the Club also made meteorological observations. Espy calculated the height of clouds with a dew-point formula and then verified his calculations with kites. J. N. Nicollet reports an observation by the Club on columnar clouds:

> The Franklin Kite Club, at Philadelphia, have lately discovered that in those days when columnar clouds form rapidly and numerously, their kite was frequently carried upwards nearly perpendicularly by clouds of ascending air; and they say, in their report, that this circumstance became so familiar during the course of their experiments, that, on the approach of a columnar cloud just forming, they could predict whether it would come near enough to affect their kite; for, if the cloud did not pass directly over the kite, the kite would only move sideways towards the cloud.

This paragraph originally appeared as part of an October 1836 report of an American Philosophical Society committee on the Wilkes Expedition (*House Executive Documents*, 25th Congress, 2d Session, 1837–1838, No. 147, p. 520). It subsequently appeared in Nicollet's *Essay on Meteorological Observations* ([Washington], 1839) p. 40, and was quoted by Espy in his *Philosophy of Storms* (Boston, 1841), p. 167. The report which Nicollet refers to, evidently a report by the Club on its own work, has not been located.

In the 1890s, during a resurgence of interest in the use of kites for meteorological observations, Cleveland Abbe compiled information on early work in the United States. He found the references to the Franklin Kite Club in Espy's book, Nicollet's essay, and Swaim's article but did not locate the Club's report on its own work or any further descriptive information despite an appeal to the Franklin Institute which advertised for information in a Philadelphia newspaper. See the various editor's remarks by Abbe in the *Monthly Weather Review*, 1896, *24*:206, 334, and 1897, *25*:162–166.

For further information and sources on the use of kites in meteorology, see W. E. K. Middleton, *Invention of the Meteorological Instruments* (Baltimore, 1969), pp. 291–298.

We wish to have your skill in the further prosecution of our experiments. Mrs Espy joins me in love to Mrs Henry and to yourself.

Yours truly
James P. Espy

While at Princeton, Henry worked at least one other time with kites. In a long letter to Samuel Bayard Dod of December 4, 1876, in which Henry describes his scientific researches at Princeton, is the following:

The next series of investigations related to atmospheric induction. The first of these consisted of experiments with two large kites, the lower end of the string of one being attached to the upper surface of a second kite, the string of each consisting of fine wire, the terminal end of the whole being coiled around an insulated drum. I was assisted in these experiments by MR. BROWN, of Philadelphia, who furnished the kites. When they were elevated, at a time when the sky was perfectly clear, sparks were drawn of surprising intensity and pungency, the electricity being supplied from the air, and the intensity being attributed to the induction of the long wire on itself.

The date of these experiments is not given, nor is any reference made to the Club. The description follows that of his work for "Contributions V" which was presented to the American Philosophical Society in 1842. The letter to Dod is published in *A Memorial of Joseph Henry* (Washington, 1880); the passage quoted is on page 152.

FROM ALEXANDER DALLAS BACHE

Gratz Collection, Historical Society of Pennsylvania

Philad. July 20th. 1836.

My dear friend,

I have only time to say that the Trustees of the Girard College have elected me Pres^t of the institution, to proceed to Europe in the autumn.[1] I want much to see you. Besides our kite experiments will interest you, effects of a long conductor. Do come down if it is only for a day.

Yours ever truly
A D Bache

---

[1] To report on various European educational institutions. See *Henry Papers*, 2:192. Like Henry, Bache kept an extensive diary of his travels which we will use on occasion to fill in gaps in Henry's account.

TO HARRIET HENRY

Mary Henry Copy, Family Correspondence, Henry Papers,
Smithsonian Archives

Philadelphia July 23, 1836.

My dear wife

I could not find time to write yesterday as I was engaged the whole day in the experiments on Electricity about a mile out of town and returned in the evening very much fatigued; then attended an informal meeting of the Philosophical Society and, after that, returned to Bache's. This morning, we again went to the field and remained several hours; came back because there was no wind to raise the kite. I am to return to the field in a few moments as soon as I am called for by a gentleman who takes me to the field in his carriage. . . .

It is not impossible that the changes in the University may cause me some perplexity, similar to that which I experienced last year in reference to Virginia. A residence in Philadelphia would doubtless be very desirable to us all. If I desire the situation of Natural Philosophy in the University, I have been told that I can get it; but would the change be for the better? I have not, as yet, had any very serious thoughts on the subject and do not, just at this time, wish to be troubled with it. . . . My feelings, at present, are not favorable to the change although I intend to think more on the subject.[1]

[1] Shortly after arriving in Philadelphia on July 21, Henry had learned from Mrs. Bache that Edward H. Courtenay, Professor of Mathematics, had left the University of Pennsylvania and that Bache, Professor of Natural Philosophy and Chemistry, was going to Europe for two years on behalf of Girard College (Henry to Harriet Henry, July [21], 1836, Family Correspondence, Henry Papers, Smithsonian Archives). Henry deliberated for almost a month over whether to accept the Chair of Natural Philosophy and Chemistry if offered to him. Torrey, who was still in Princeton when Henry returned, was against the change: "I don't like the idea of his removing to Philadelphia, for I think that the men of science there will have an unfavorable influence upon his spiritual welfare." (Torrey to Gray, July 28, 1836, Historic Letter File, Gray Herbarium Library, Harvard University.) Henry eventually withdrew from consideration, stating his reasons in a letter to R. M. Patterson of August 20, printed below.

FROM JOHN MACLEAN

Henry Papers, Smithsonian Archives

Boston, July 25, 1836

My dear Sir

Since I left home, I have visited Yale, Washington College at Hartford,[1]

[1] Trinity College at Hartford, Connecticut.

Amherst College, & Cambridge University;[2] and I am prepared to come into your views for the improvement of our own College. These different institutions have suggested to me various hints for the improvement of our own course of study & instruction. Although absent from my friends and colleagues, I have not been unmindful of their labours, or of the institution in which we have a common interest. I wish you could have been with me; as I know you would have been much gratified. As it regards their Philosophical apparatus, in the Colleges mentioned, we can, at a small expense, surpass the best of them and we must do so; and if you are willing, arrangements must be made for you to proceed next spring to Europe, to spend there as much time as you desire, & procure whatever apparatus we need.[3] As regards your house, Mr Lenox[4] semed to be considerably out of humour, that nothing was yet done with respect to it. By the time of your return from Europe, a new house must be completed for your accommodation. I know that the Trustees will take effectual order on this subject at their next meeting; and I believe that they will come into our views in relation to the position of the buildings.[5] Mr Lenox has a plan of his own in regard to this point, but I believe his object will be better attained upon the one agreed upon by us as the best. I hope the plan of lecturing suggested by yourself will be adopted by all the Professors & the President too and that the plan may be carried into effect as soon as possible.[6]

Would it not be best to authorize the Professors to issue tickets for admission to their lectures to persons not connected with the College, and to receive the avails of the tickets in addition to their salaries.[7] My own belief

---

[2] Harvard. Although Maclean is evidently making a comparative educational survey on his trip, the Princeton Trustees' minutes for April 12, 1836 (Princeton University Archives), only note that Maclean had been granted leave for travel for the benefit of his health.

[3] Henry may have been anticipating a European trip for this purpose as far back as January (see above, Henry to James Henry, January 22, 1836). His efforts on behalf of Princeton science were part of a general attempt in American colleges, starting in the late 1820s, to upgrade their science programs. Expenditures on apparatus were drastically increased. Henry was only one of a number of science professors, college presidents, or their agents sent abroad in this period to procure philosophical apparatus. Stanley M. Guralnick, *Science and the Ante-Bellum American College* (Philadelphia, 1975), pp. 71–73.

[4] Trustee James Lenox. *Henry Papers*, 2: 423n.

[5] At the meeting of September 29, 1836 (see the Minutes, below), the Trustees authorized a new house for Henry and also adopted his plan for the campus.

[6] Henry was the most active promoter of the lecture method at Princeton. His Natural Philosophy course emphasized lecturing rather than traditional recitation. Henry advocated extending the technique to some of the non-science courses. According to *Maclean* (2:314), Henry was "desirous that the method of instruction by lectures be generally adopted by his colleagues," and suggested to Professor Dod that he take architecture as a subject for lectures, which Dod went on to do.

[7] On September 29, 1836, the Princeton Trustees "*Resolved* that the Professors of the College be authorized to admit to their lectures such persons as they please, not connected with the College, but being graduates of this or other Colleges, and to exact of them a fee for admission provided that nothing shall

is, that if this were done regularly, & that if gentlemen residing in the town, and some of the Theological Students should be led to regard their admission as a matter of course, upon the payment of the usual fee, and not as a favour many of them would attend, and a few[. . .][8] might be added to the salaries of Dr Torrey & yourself.

I have frequently been much troubled at the circumstance, that owing to the negligence or inefficiency of those, who should have attended to it, that the New Chemical Laboratory has not yet been fitted up: but after frequent consideration, I am inclined to view it as kindly ordered in Providence, to prevent your applying your mind with that intenseness, you are wont to do when engaged in such researches. For I am satisfied, that it would be a sacrifice of not only health but of life of itself, for you to apply yourself so closely for months in succession. For your health, I feel deeply interested, not merely from feelings of friendship, but in a very great degree from a regard to the College, whose reputation is becoming more & more identified with your own.

I hope you can read what I have written. My best respects to your family. I hope they consider our garden as their own, during our absence. Tell my brother, that my sisters[9] will write to him soon. My respects to all friends, especially Dr Torrey, Mr Dod, and the other members of the Faculty. On Tuesday I expect to go to Providence.

> With the most sincere esteem
> Your friend
> J. Maclean

---

be done, that shall interfere with the convenience, and full instruction of the undergraduates."

[8] One word obliterated by the seal.

[9] Mary Bainbridge Maclean (1801–1849) and Agnes Maclean (1808–1843). Francis Bazley Lee, ed., *Genealogical and Memorial History of the State of New Jersey*, 4 vols. (New York, 1910), *1*:50.

FROM ROBERT M. PATTERSON[1]
Henry Papers, Smithsonian Archives

Philadelphia, Aug. 14, 1836.

Dear Sir,

The election of Professor of Natural Philosophy & Chemistry in the Uni-

---

[1] Robert Maskell Patterson (1787–1854) was Director of the United States Mint in Philadelphia and a trustee of the University of Pennsylvania. For further biographical information see *Henry Papers*, 2:413n.

versity of Pennsylvania will take place on the 23d; and I have taken the liberty of putting you on nomination. By this time, you have, I hope, thought well upon the subject, and are ready to say whether you would be willing to accept the chair, if chosen to it. I believe you are in possession of the grounds on which your decision should be founded.

Let me ask you, then, in the course of the week, to let me know your mind, in order that, if you cannot accept the chair another may be chosen.[2] The approaching session is at hand, and it is important that our election should really *supply* the vacancy.

> Very truly your friend &c.
> R. M. Patterson.

[2] For Henry's reply, see below, Henry to Patterson, August 20, 1836.

TO JOHN TORREY

Torrey Papers, Library, New York Botanical Garden

Princeton Aug 17th 1836[1]

My Dear Dr.

Your kind letter and liberal present were received a few days since. I accept with much pleasure the articles and hope long to preserve them as an interesting memento of your friendship.[2]

The senior class was dismissed yesterday after a very tedious examination of eight days. Baird[3] stood first, J Miller (the younger of the two Brothers)[4] second, Maitland[5] third and McCulloh[6] fourth.

[1] Torrey's file note indicates that he received this letter on August 29 and answered it on September 26 (printed below).

[2] We have not found this Torrey letter. The articles may have included the miniature of Torrey printed in the second volume of the *Henry Papers*, facing p. 249. A note by Henry on the miniature (in the Smithsonian Archives) reads: "Dr John Torrey aged about forty years. J.H"

[3] Benjamin Rice Baird. *Princeton Catalogue*, p. 149.

[4] John Miller (*Henry Papers*, 2:478) and his brother Elihu Spencer Miller were in the same class at Princeton.

[5] Robert Lenox Maitland (1818–1870), who became a merchant, was a grandson of Robert Lenox (1759–1839) and nephew of James Lenox (1800–1880). Harry Miller Lydenberg, *History of the New York Public Library . . .* (New York, 1972), p. 100. George Harrison, *A Genealogical and Historical Account of the Maitland Family* (London, 1869), p. 10.

[6] Richard Sears McCulloh (1818–1894), one of Henry's most interesting students, remained an obscure figure until his life was chronicled by Milton Halsey Thomas in "Professor McCulloh of Princeton, Columbia, and Points South," *The Princeton University Library Chronicle*, November 1947, 9:17–29.

McCulloh entered Princeton as a sophomore. According to a Henry recommendation,

I have done double duty since you left in the way of examination and Lectures on Architecture to the Junior class. After I finish my course with the Juniors I do not intend to do anything more in the way of instruction this session.[7]

I received a letter a few days since from Bache.[8] He requested me to procure some letters for him to men of science in Europe. You of course will furnish him with some to London, Edinburgh or Paris which will be serviceable to him. Cannot you send them to him by mail or put them in a package and direct them to me. I do not know when he sails but am under the impression that he informed me when in Philadelphia that he intended to start in September. He will be pleased to carry any package for you which may serve as a letter of introduction and if you have anything of the kind which you wish to put under his charge you may send the article to me and I will deliver it to him. I write to you thus on the supposition that you will be in the Western part of the State and not meet with Bache before he sails.[9]

McCulloh occasionally assisted him in experiments. This recommendation and another by Henry are in *Testimonials of the Qualifications of Richard S. McCulloh*, an undated (ca. 1843) fifteen-page pamphlet printed for private use. Following his graduation McCulloh studied chemistry with James C. Booth in Philadelphia (at Henry's suggestion), did a hydrodynamic survey on the Chesapeake and Ohio Canal, and observed at the magnetic observatory of Girard College.

From 1841 to 1843 McCulloh was Professor of Natural Philosophy, Mathematics and Chemistry at Jefferson College. From 1846 to 1849 he was Melter and Refiner at the Mint in Philadelphia, then succeeded Elias Loomis at Princeton as Professor of Natural Philosophy. In 1854 he won a controversial election from Oliver Wolcott Gibbs to become Professor of Natural and Experimental Philosophy and Chemistry at Columbia College.

In 1863, in a letter from Richmond, McCulloh suddenly resigned from Columbia and announced his allegiance to the South. The trustees ignored his resignation and indignantly expelled him, resolving that a note describing the grounds of his expulsion accompany his name in all future Columbia catalogs. McCulloh served the Confederacy as a consulting chemist until his arrest in mid-1865.

In response to a request from McCulloh's brother who was trying to get him released, Henry provided another testimonial. He endorsed McCulloh's ability and moral character and attributed his defection to the South to "an attack of monomania" (Henry to J. W. McCulloh, November 13, 1865, private letterpress, Henry Papers, Smithsonian Archives). Following the War, Henry remained in contact with McCulloh, who taught first at Washington College and later at Louisiana State University. McCulloh's only textbook, *Treatise on the Mechanical Theory of Heat and its Applications to the Steam Engine* (New York, 1876), is dedicated to Henry.

The *Royal Society Catalogue* lists only one article by McCulloh. Most of his publications were in the form of government reports, such as his work under A. D. Bache on hydrometers and spirits and his extensive chemical analyses of sugars. The *National Union Catalog* lists twenty-four of his publications.

[7] Following the senior examinations in August, there were still several weeks of classes for freshmen, sophomores, and juniors before their examinations near the end of September.

[8] Not found.

[9] Torrey didn't provide Bache with letters of introduction and Bache was irritated. See below, Henry to Torrey, February 13, 1837.

I have done nothing as yet in reference to the Philadelphia affair but have received a letter from Dr Patterson requesting my answer this week. I would that the election could be postponed until after the meeting of the Trustees of Princeton. I could then give an unhesitating answer.[10]

I hope you are enjoying yourself with your amiable family in your western excursion[11] and that all the anticipations they and you have formed of its pleasures may be more than realized.

> With the highest respect
> Your Friend
> Jos. Henry

P.S.

Mr Maclean has returned from Saratoga where he has been for about a week past. I know not if he intends to stop at home the remainder of the session. The faculty have a meeting tomorrow which has been called at my request to take into consideration the moral state of the College. I wish something done in this matter before I refuse to be a candidate for the Chair in the University of Pennsylvania.[12]

Holles[13] has failed and left Princeton with a character as dark as his deeds.   J.H.

Mr Whiggens[14] is still an inmate of the Hall. He is as great a recluse as ever but has somewhat changed his views in reference to knowledge and has actually become interested in Architecture. He has besides bought a new hat and is considerably improved in appearance. He is very obliging and does every thing I ask with apparent cheerfulness.   J.H.

---

[10] Patterson's letter is printed immediately above. The Trustees were not scheduled to meet until the end of September.

[11] After leaving Princeton early in August, Torrey spent the rest of the summer doing field work for the New York Natural History Survey. See Michele L. Aldrich, "New York Natural History Survey, 1836–1845" (Ph.D. dissertation, University of Texas, 1974), pp. 133–136.

[12] A faculty meeting was held on August 19 but there is no record of any discussion of the "moral state of the College." A freshman was suspended for card playing and steps were taken to have two other students removed. Faculty Minutes, August 19, 1836, Princeton University Archives. At the Trustees' meeting at April 11, 1837, a committee to examine the faculty minutes were "constrained to express their regret that so many cases calling for the discipline of the College, have occurred." Trustees' Minutes, April 11, 1837, Princeton University Archives.

[13] Not identified.

[14] Mr. Whiggens or Wiggins seems to have been a helper whom Torrey brought from New York. He stayed with Henry in Princeton until late September or early October.

TO ROBERT M. PATTERSON[1]

Draft,[2] Henry Papers, Smithsonian Archives

Princeton Aug. 20th 1836

Dear Sir

After much deliberation I have come to the conclusion that I cannot accept the appointement in the University were the situation now offered to me. I have not arrived at this conclusion without some hesitation <*and much regret*> even [regret] since I am strongly attached to the scientific institu[tions] of your city and beleive that they would afford me a <*much*> better oppertunity than <*the one I now have for the prosecution of science*> any I have ever had for prosecuting of the objects nearest my heart, the extension of science. But there are other circumstances connected with the situation which do not strike me so favourable. These with my dislike to change and the additional inducements which my friends in Princeton now hold out for my remaining <*throw the preponderance*> in favour of <*Princeton*> have induced the determination stated above. I have delayed answer[ing] your letter with the intention of visiting you <*this week*> on <*saturday*> today (saturday) relative to the business to which it refered but I am disappointed on account of the absence of one of the members of our faculty whoes class I must attend to on monday morning. Perhaps however it is as well for me that I cannot have an other interview with you on this subject until after the election since I fear my judgment would scarcely sustain the unequal contest with your arguments and my own <*desires*> predelections.

I will probably be in Philadelphia in the course of two weeks and will then give you my views[. . .][3] at large.

I am with the highest respe[ct] & esteem,

Yours &c

Joseph Henry

[1] This is a reply to Patterson's letter of August 14, 1836, above.

[2] The only version of this letter which we have been able to locate is Henry's rough draft. Interlineations, canceled material, and incomplete phrases abound. While the editors have made some attempt at cleaning up this draft for clarity, we would not venture a guess as to how the final version of this document read.

[3] There are two illegible words at this point.

FROM ROBERT M. PATTERSON
Henry Papers, Smithsonian Archives

Philadelphia, Aug. 23d, '36.

Dear Sir,

Your letter, *mailed yesterday*, was not received by me till this afternoon, and the meeting of Trustees was held this morning. I was not a little embarrassed by being unable to give a positive answer as to your intentions; but, as it is extremely difficult to get an election-quorum together at this season of the year, and as it was essential that the vacant chair should be *filled*, it was concluded not to consider you as a candidate. I am relieved by finding that our determination was right. If your decision had been different from what it is, I should [have] been exceedingly mortified at the result. In fear of it, it was almost with trepidation that I opened your letter.

We this morning elected Mr. Henry Vethake[1] professor of Mathematics, and Mr. Roswell Park[2] professor of Natural Philosophy and Chemistry.

I need not say how much I regret that you have declined becoming a Philadelphian; let me hope, however, that you will at least visit us more frequently.

With high regard,
Very faithfully yours,
R. M. Patterson

[1] Identified in *Henry Papers, 1:17.*

[2] A graduate of West Point, Roswell Park (1807–1869) took the position at the University of Pennsylvania after several years in the Army Corps of Engineers. He resigned the Pennsylvania professorship in 1842 to join the Protestant Episcopal ministry. Thereafter he directed various preparatory schools and colleges in the Midwest, where he was known for introducing scientific studies into the curriculum. Author of books of poetry, a history of West Point, and an attempted one-volume synthesis of human knowledge, Park also published *An Outline of Magnetism* [1840] for the use of his students at Pennsylvania. Park was the father of the famous surgeon by the same name. Stanley M. Guralnick, *Science and the Ante-Bellum American College* (Philadelphia, 1975), p. 202.

AMERICAN WHIG SOCIETY CIRCULAR[1]

Henry Papers, Smithsonian Archives

Princeton August 30ᵗʰ 1836.

Brethren of the American Whig Society[2]

We have the honor to address you in the name and by order of our venerable and beloved Society, on a subject intimately connected with the well being, the honor and perhaps the existence of the Institution. It has been unanimously resolved by its present regular members, with the full concurrence of all the graduate and honorary members within our reach to erect

---

[1] This lithographed circular, partially drafted by Henry, is an appeal for funds to build a hall for the society. Whig's rival, the Cliosophic Society, had reacted to their overcrowded quarters in the Library by appointing a committee to consider a new hall in June 1835; Whig followed suit in September 1835.

The Whig Society minutes in the Princeton University Archives chronicle a succession of resolutions and committees appointed to deal with various aspects of the undertaking; Henry shows up as a major participant. On March 21, 1836, Henry proposed "that each member of this Society be individually authorized to solicit subscriptions during the next vacation for the purpose of erecting a new Hall for the better accomodation of this Association." A week later, Henry was appointed to a six-member committee "to draft an address to the Honorary, graduate, & sub-graduate members explaining the reasons why subscriptions are asked from them for the purpose of building a new hall for this society." On April 4, 1836, this committee presented a short address containing the appeal for funds, concluding with the warning that "the rival society is proceeding with great spirit towards the execution of a plan exactly similar." On June 20, 1836, the committee requested and received authority to confer with the Cliosophic Society "in case it shall be absolutely necessary. . . ." The final report of the committee was not made until the meeting of September 19, 1836, almost three weeks after the date of this circular. The committee explained that getting the signatures of prominent members had caused considerable delay. As the lithographed circular was to be sent to all members, they proposed the compilation of a list of addresses, stressing

the danger of "indiscriminate distribution." This undoubtedly caused further delay. A copy of the circular sent to Mahlon Dickerson (Dickerson Papers, Rutgers University Library) is postmarked February 7, [1837].

John Haviland of Philadelphia (*DAB*) was chosen to be the architect of the buildings. The design for both was "of the Ionic order, sixty-two feet long, fifty-one feet wide, and two stories high; the columns of the Porticos are copied from those of the Temple on the Illisus. A Temple in the Island of Teos is a model of the buildings in other respects." *Princeton Annual Catalogue*, 1837, p. 19. *Wertenbaker* (p. 252) claims that Princeton thus "lost its opportunity for uniformity in its architecture."

The cornerstone of Whig Hall was laid in the summer of 1837, and in September 1838 the new hall was occupied. Clio Hall had been finished the previous March. These halls remained in use until their demolition in 1889, followed by the construction of similar halls covered in marble.

For accounts of the halls, see Jacob N. Beam, *The American Whig Society of Princeton University* (Princeton, 1933), pp. 79–101; portions of the circular are printed on pp. 86–87. Charles Richard Williams, *The Cliosophic Society, Princeton University* (Princeton, 1916), pp. 60–72. *Wertenbaker*, pp. 252, 355–356. *Maclean*, 2:304–305. For a short sketch of the societies, see *Henry Papers*, 2:47–48.

[2] According to an annotation by Henry, quoted in footnote 7, the opening part of the circular was written by John Breckinridge while the last part, following the signatures, was written by Henry. Excluding the signatures, the whole document is in a neat, scribe's hand.

a new and capacious Hall, adapted in its structure and dimensions to the dignity and increasing numbers of the Society.

The very confined and uncomfortable upper chamber in which the Society has heretofore convened (since the burning of the College edifice[3]) was wholly unfit for the accomodation of its members and for the due performance of its important exercises even during the most depressed condition of the College of New Jersey. But in the present unexampled prosperity of our venerable Alma Mater, such is the increase of the members of the Society that the Hall is crowded to excess and it has ceased to be edifying, pleasant or even safe to participate in its once invaluable services.

In consideration of the acknowledged importance of the Literary Societies to the best cultivation and government of the students, it might perhaps be thought that the College ought to make provision for such an exigency. But the varied and extensive improvements, in which the College is now engaged must unquestionably swallow up all her funds and other means. All that we can in reason therefore look for from this source is the continued occupation of the Hall now appropriated to our use.

In such circumstances we see no alternative but the speedy erection, by voluntary contributions, of a new Hall or the inevitable decay and perhaps dissolution of the American Whig Society. No man worthy of the honored name we bear can for a moment endure the thought of abandoning an institution so beloved and so noble. Yet it is fully known to all her members that she has no dowry but her illustrious name. Her sons compose her only treasure. They are her last but unfailing resource; and therefore in this hour of her extreme necessity, she appeals with a confidence which admits of no distrust to the gratitude, the honor, the public spirit and the unabated love of all her sons. She has heard of their honorable success and advancement in every walk of life. She has traced with elevated joy their upward steps from youth to age, along every eminence of public service and of national honor; and with a parent's heart shared the renown which they have reflected on her, from every part of our common country. And now in the peculiar crisis of her own existence she casts her life upon their care, and without reserve commits her sacred honor to their hands. There can be no doubt as to the result. We have already been cheered by several most interesting communications, from our fellow members. Some far advanced

[3] The Whig Society had shared the top floor of the Library (later Stanhope Hall) with the Cliosophic Society since its construction in 1804. Previously they had met in Nassau Hall which burned in 1802 and was later reconstructed. *Wertenbaker*, pp. 131, 252. Constance M. Greiff, Mary W. Gibbons, and Elizabeth G. C. Menzies, *Princeton Architecture* (Princeton, 1967), pp. 80–81.

in life, revert with a force unabated by time, affliction and public labours to the venerable Society for which we plead. It may not be unacceptable to insert one of these communications at once to incite and gratify our fellow members.

"A note subscribed by certain members of the Whig Society of Nassau Hall N J has been addressed to me under date of the 22^d inst, which reached me this day, requesting that I would permit my name to be placed on a Committee, to solicit contributions for the erection of a new Hall, for the accomodation of the increased and increasing number of members."

"It is some years more than half a century, since with much youthful ardour, I took a leading part in the reorganization of the American Whig Society in the College of New Jersey, after the revolutionary war of our country, during which all the operations of the Society had been suspended. The frost of age has not extinguished the glow of my attachment to that institution, and if it will be of any use to put my name on the contemplated Committee you may place it there with the understanding that I shall think it honored by such a location."

It has been estimated that not less than Ten thousand Dollars will be required to build and furnish a Hall,[4] which shall be suited to the wants and reputation of our own Society and correspond with the plan proposed by our Cliosophic rival, as well as with the general scale of improvements projected by the patrons and trustees of this College. Please to address all communications to Louis P Smith Esq,[5] Princeton N.J.

> With fraternal regards and high considerations
> We remain Your brethren & fellow servants[6]

Mahlon Dickerson.	Rich^d H Bayard of Delaware
Saml Sprigg of Maryland.	E. E. Boudinot of New Jersey
J R Ingersoll of Pennsylvania	J. J. Milligan of Delaware
Thomson F Mason	J. A. Bayard of Delaware
of District of Columbia	Kensey Johns Jr of Delaware
Manuel Eyre of Pennsylvania	Hugh L. Hodge of Penns^a
J M Scott of Pennsylvania	Rich' Yates of New York
Ashbel Green of Pennsylvania	Ja^s Bayard of Penn^a
Frederick Beasley of New Jersey	Richd B^n Carmichael of Maryland
J. Johns of Maryland	Clement Cox of District of Columbia

[4] Apparently only $3,425 was ever collected. Another $4,000 was borrowed to pay the builder. In 1841 Robert F. Stockton liquidated the debt by a gift of this amount. Beam, *Whig Society*, p. 89.

[5] Louis P. Smith was cashier of the Princeton Bank from about 1834 until his resignation in 1851. *Hageman*, 2:25.

[6] The lithograph reproduced the signatures of the subscribers, all graduates of Princeton or current students.

Rob:^t G. Johnson of New Jersey
Phil: C: Pendleton of Virginia
Thos. C. Ryerson of New Jersey
Edwd Colston of Virginia
W C Alexander
Charles S. Hammond Md
Jno. Thomson Mason Md

F. Anderson of Maryland
John R. Livingston Jun:^r of
  New York
William James of New York
James Latimer jun of Delaware
John S. Maxwell
Saml Humes Porter

The[7] Subscribers, members of the American Whig Society residing in Princeton, respectfully join in soliciting your aid to effect the object set forth in the above appeal. The project of erecting a new Hall is not only of vital importance to the Society itself, but also forms an essential part of a system of improvements commenced by the Alumni, and intended to render our College not inferior to any institution of the kind in this country.[8]

These improvements relate to the College grounds, the Edifices, the Philosophical and Chemical apparatus; the Mineralogical and Geological collections; the formation of a Cabinet of Drawings, Casts and models for the illustration of Classical literature and the fine arts; in short to the furnishing of the Institution with all the implements and facilities for a liberal and extended course of instruction.

---

[7] Henry's copy of the circular contains an annotation in his handwriting immediately preceding this concluding section:

> The following letter was written by myself and the appeal <*was*> by Dr Brackenridge. The plan of the improvement of the grounds is also due to me. The bu[i]ldings were erected during my visit to Europe and I regret that the committee did not strictly adhere to the plan. The buildings should have been put as in the plan on the back line of the college grounds and then space would have been left for building lots between the colleges and the halls.

Henry's claim to authorship of this part of the circular is supported by his "Points Which May Be Noticed in the Circular of the Whig Society," August 1836, printed below.

Henry's plan for the arrangement of the campus was formally adopted by the Trustees on September 29, 1836. See the Trustees' Minutes of that date, printed below.

The Whigs were later upset when one aspect of the plan was not enacted. Until moved as Henry's plan indicated, the Professor's House (Henry's) and the Steward's House blocked the view from Nassau Street of Clio Hall and Whig Hall, respectively. Henry's house was dismantled when his new house was erected, but the Steward's House remained for a number of years. See Beam, *Whig Society*, p. 94.

[8] While Breckinridge had written a passionate appeal to Whig loyalty, Henry is here stressing loyalty to Princeton and its ambition to become one of the best colleges in the country. Since the early 1830s Princeton had been searching for funds to upgrade its faculty and facilities. In 1834 and 1835 Henry had been active in the Alumni Association's $100,000 fund-raising drive and had lobbied hard for the extension and renovation of Philosophical Hall. In 1836 he directed his attention to equipping the new science facilities, particularly his own with a contemplated trip to Europe to purchase apparatus. Henry places the campaign for a new Whig Hall in the context of general Princeton improvement.

For the Alumni's fund-raising drive and the improvement of Philosophical Hall, see the second volume of the *Henry Papers*, especially pp. 175–177, 371–372, 375–384.

The erection of the new Halls is intimately connected with the improvement of the College grounds, as these edifices can be so placed in reference to the buildings now erected as to form with the latter a convenient and beautiful architectural arrangement. The plan of the disposition of the whole will readily be understood by a reference to the annexed Map. It will be seen that the buildings occupy the three sides of a parallelogram with the old College (Nassau Hall) in the middle.

We take great pleasure in directing attention to the very weighty names attached to the preceding circular, as an evidence that we are sustained by the judgment of so many distinguished men in high stations and from every part of the country.[9]

	A. Alexander
James Carnahan	Sam.¹ Miller.
Joseph Henry	C. Hodge
Richard S Field	James W. Alexander.
Ja.ˢ S. Green	Jno Breckinridge

A *Old Nassau*
BB *New Colleges*
CC *Library Philosophical Hall & er*
DD *Present sites of Professor's*
    & Steward's Houses
    These to be removed to G & G
E *Site reserved for Chapel or*
GG *Intended sites of Professor's*
    & Steward's Houses
I *President's House*
F *Vice President's House*
HH *Sites of the new Society Halls*

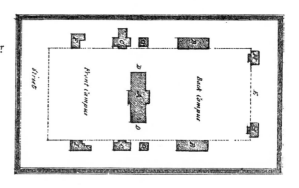

[9] Again the signatures of the subscribers are reproduced on the lithograph.

"RECORD OF EXPERIMENTS"
Henry Papers, Smithsonian Archives

Aug 31ˢᵗ 1836

1 Stretched a copper wire No 22 from the window of the back room of the Phil. Hall to Prof Dod's fence opposite his house. Then threw sparkes from the long conductors on one end by means of the short conductor. The sparks were very pungent at the other end of the wire and [?much] more so in proportion to the quantity of electricity than from the conductor in the room with the machine

2 The wire throughout its whole length became luminous, giving off rays on all sides.[1]

3 The farther end of the wire placed in contack with the lightning rod. A loud snap was given at each discharge of the machine although the wire was in contact with the rod no shocks were felt by the [...][2] from the wire, or sparks could be drawn from the rod similar to those which were produced by the lateral discharge in some of the preceding experiments

4 When several persons took hold of the wire at different distances from the end of the wire, the person at the end alone felt the shock or felt it very slightly.

See some remarkes on the firing powder by long wire. Phil Mag p 344, 345[3]

---

[1] Static electricians had long known of this luminous effect. In his lecture notes (Henry notebook [23894], p. 119) Henry wrote:

> A fine copper wire attached to a large globe receiving sparkes from the machine of about 2 inches long. When the wire is supported on glass it discharges the electricity in the air and appears luminous throughout its whole length; a beautiful exp and is probably similar to the one described by De la Rive. This fact was first observed by me on the 24th of Feby 1836.

Henry described how he exhibited it to his classes, noting that Van Marum's great machine was used to illuminate 207 feet of wire. See also Becquerel's *Traité de l'Électricité* (Paris, 1834), 2:208, a section on electrical illumination cited by Henry.

In the current experiment Henry connects the luminosity to the effect of lateral discharge.

[2] At least one word is missing.

[3] We are unable to verify the citation as given.

"POINTS WHICH MAY BE NOTICED IN THE CIRCULAR OF THE WHIG SOCIETY"[1]
Henry Papers,[2] Smithsonian Archives

[August 1836]

1   Crowded state of the Hall—unhealth—prevents the proper transactions of the regular business of the society.

2   Want of room for the library in its present state.

---

[1] This is Henry's title for a rough listing of things he wanted covered in the American Whig Society Circular of August 30, 1836, printed above. It must have been written prior to the circular, probably sometime in August. Some of Henry's points, such as the crowded, unhealthy condition of the Hall, the College's commitment of funds elsewhere, and the rivalry with the Cliosophic Society, were covered in the part of the circular written by John Breckinridge.

[2] The original is in Box 28, in a folder entitled "Unsorted Material."

3   These difficulties will increase with the rapidly increasing prosperity of the college.

4   The Cliosophic Society have made vigerous and successful efforts for the erection of a Hall. Unless the Whichs can do something of the kind the association can no longer compete with its more successful rival.

5   It is the design of the Trustees to make the college of New Jersey if possible the first in the country. Nothing will prevent this but the want of funds and of these but a comparitively small ammount.

6   The great improvements made within a few years past in the course of instruction and the rapid increase of students consequent on this leaves but little doubt of the result when a determination is manifest to persue the same liberal pol[i]cy.

7   Within two years a large college edifice has been erected and an other of the same dimensions is now in the progress of building. Also a new refectory, a important addition to the philosophical Hall and the basement story of the same building filled up as more commodious appartmens for the use of the old refectory.[3]

8   These improvements have been made by the trustees with the funds of the Institu[tion] and therefor no aid can be expected by the Which Soci[e]ty from this quarter particularly since further additions of the same kind will soon be required as the present accomodations are when complete only sufficient for the number of students now in the college.

9   The Alumni of the college as you know are making a generous effort to raise a large sum for the extension of the Institu[tion] and they have been in a measure successful[4] but the funds collected by them will all be required to complete the plans already commenced namely purchase of a comp[l]ete apparatus for experimental philosop[h]y and chemestry, for a more extensive cabinet of mineralogy and geology, for the increase of the Library, for the purchase of maps, drawings, casts, models for the illustration of clasical literature and for the general improvement of the college grounds and edif[i]ces.

---

[3] East College had been completed in 1834 and West College was almost finished. The new refectory, which included housing for the second steward, was ready for occupancy in December 1834 (Trustees' Minutes, April 14, 1835, Princeton University Archives). Henry had been very involved with the addition to Philosophical Hall (see *Henry Papers*, 2:371–372, 375–384).

[4] See the second volume of the *Henry Papers*, especially pp. 175–177, and above, Torrey to Henry, March 23, 1836, footnote 6.

11[5] By aiding the Whig soci[e]ty in the erection of a hall an indirect benefit will be bestowed on the college since the two societies now occupy
the whole upper story of the Library building which on the removal
of the societies could be converted into one appartment and devoted to
the *museum*. The college would thus be saved the expense of an additional bui[ldin]g now much wanted.

12 It is proposed to erect a building which will accomodate the soci[e]ty
and be an ornament to the same.

---

[5] Henry skipped 10 in his numbering.

TO HARRIET HENRY

Family Correspondence, Henry Papers, Smithsonian Archives

New York Saturday
Evening [September 10, 1836][1]

My Dear Wife

I arrived safely at Jersey City after a very plesant pasage about 6 o'clock.
I had considerable conversation with James[2] who appeared much affected
with what I said to him and agreed with me that it was by far the best that
he should return home. I promised if he did well after this that I would
use my influence in getting a degree for him. I staid last evening at Mr
Henderson's[3] in Jersey City and have promised to return this evening.
Mr Henderson took charge of James and promised to see him off in the
evening boat. I gave him the letter to his father after reading to him the
contents. He promised to deliver it and I have no doubt but that he will do
so. I felt quite unwell wen I arrived but not eating anything at tea and also
almost fasting interely to day I now feel quite better.

Old Mr Chilton is quite unwell and scarcely leaves his room; his son does
not think he will recover his hea[l]th.[4]

I wish that you would ask Stephen to inform Professor Dod that I cannot
be home on monday in time for hearing the class in architecture and wish
that he would take them in Mechanics. I will probably be home on monday.
I say probably because it is possible that I may not get away from here in

---

[1] The date was ascertained from the postmark.
[2] James McIntyre.

[3] Not identified.
[4] The chemist and instrument maker George
Chilton died in 1836.

time to go farther than Newark. I will either remain in N.Y. or Jersey city tomorrow.

I attended to day the fair of the Mechanics Institute and was confused and surprised with the great variety and beauty of the articles.[5]

> I am My Dear Wife
> As Ever Your
> Husband

Kiss the children for me.

[5] In a letter of August 25, 1836 (Henry Papers, Smithsonian Archives), the Mechanics Institute requested Henry to judge models of machinery and philosophical apparatus at their fair, beginning September 5th. Henry's reply, if any, has not been found and, while he may have taken this trip to see the fair, it does not appear he took an official role in the events. The Mechanics Institute, which had solicited Henry's assistance also in 1835, is discussed in *Henry Papers*, 2:454–455.

TO JAMES DAVID FORBES[1]

Forbes Papers, Library, St. Andrews University, Scotland

Princeton Sept 19th 1836

My Dear Sir

My Friend Professor Bache and his amiable Lady sail for Liverpool in the packet of Tomorrow. They first visit Dublin and then go to Edinburgh. He carries letters to several persons in your city but will I presume be most pleased with the opportunity of forming a personal acquaintance with you.[2] Although from the limited nature of our correspondence I am not entirely free to address you a formal letter of introduction yet as you are only acquainted with the scientific character of my Friend you will permit me to assure you that he is a gentleman of the highest moral worth whoes private character eminently entitles him to any attentions which he may receive in your city, celebrated as it is for refined hospitality as well as for Literature and Science.

No person of his years is more highly esteemed in this country than Professor Bache. He is a Grandson[3] of Dr Franklin, a graduate of the military

[1] A rough draft of this letter in Henry's hand is in the Henry Papers, Smithsonian Archives. Except for a few minor stylistic changes, it is identical with the text sent to Forbes.

[2] We have not found any significant body of correspondence between Bache and Forbes. In the Forbes Papers at St. Andrews University are two letters from Bache—one dated February 8, 1837, and the other February 21, 1837—containing the results of some magnetic readings made while in Europe.

[3] In fact, Bache was Franklin's great-grandson.

school at West Point; for several years has been Professor of Chemestry and Natural Philosophy in the University of Pennsylvania and in this situation has exerted an important influence on the scientific character not only of Philadelphia but also of this country. In the high estimation of his fellow citizens he has lately been unanimously elected President of the Girard College; a new Institution richly endowed by the will of the late Stephen Girard and designed for the support and liberal education of orphans; particularly those of Pennsylvania.

Professor Bache under the direction of the trustees of the College now goes to Europe for the purpose of inspecting similar Institutions and also to collect such knowledge relative to Education and Science as may tend to advance these objects in the United States.

Professor Bache will return your magnetic needle and will also present you with his apparatus for the vibration of the needle in a vacuum. This article you may reccollect I mentioned in my last letter. I was accidentally prevented from sending, as I intended in my package to you by Mr Boyd, a copy of Professor Baches paper on the variation of the magnetic needle and also the report of the Franklin Institute on the explosion of steam boilers.[4] This last article you will find contains a series of valuable experiments on a highly important practical subject. I mention this paper inorder to do justice to my friend Professor Bache. The experiments which cost months of labor were made entirely by him. His name however only appears as chairman of the committee.

I send you a small package of articles in the scientific line. Among these you will find a report on the survey of a route for a ship canal around the Falls of Niagara and since you are a contributor to the science of Geology as well Natural Philosophy, Meteorology, Architecture &c this may possibly interest you as affording some topographical information relative to this celebrated region. One of the maps contains a small but admirable bird's-eye vew of the country between the two lakes which gives the best possible idea of the nature of the surface around the falls.[5]

---

[4] A reference to the essay and the Franklin Institute report which Henry requested from Bache in his letter of June 4, 1836, printed above.

[5] Henry may be alluding to an 1836 report by Captain William G. Williams of the United States Topographical Engineers outlining four possible routes for a ship canal to connect Lakes Erie and Ontario. The idea for such a project had been bandied about western New York for a number of years. In 1826, for example, Nathan S. Roberts, an engineer with the Erie Canal, was engaged by a group of private individuals to make a survey for a proposed canal around Niagara Falls. Nothing came of this idea, however, in large part because influential American businessmen and politicians felt that American commerce from the Great Lakes would be diverted from the Erie Canal to the St. Lawrence waterway. Williams's report and the maps for the proposed routes are contained in *House Documents*, 24th Congress, 1st Session, 1836, No. 214. See also Henry W. Hill, "Historical Sketch of

Accept my thanks for the copy of the address of the President of the Royal Society of Edinburgh and permit me to tender you my sincere congratulations on the occasion which called it fourth.[6]

> With the highest Respect
> I am Sir Yours—
> Joseph Henry

Niagara Ship Canal Projects," *Buffalo Historical Society Publications*, 1918, 22:203–215, and William P. Judson, *History of Various Projects, Reports, Discussions and Estimates for Reaching the Great Lakes from Tidewater, 1768–1901* ([Oswego, New York, 1901]).

[6] On February 15, 1836, Forbes received the Keith Prize from the Royal Society of Edinburgh for his essay "On the Refraction and Polarization of Heat," read on January 5, 1835,

and published in volume 13 of the Society's *Transactions*. At the presentation of the award, Thomas Charles Hope, a chemist and Vice-President of the Royal Society, delivered an address, a summary of which appeared in the *Proceedings of the Royal Society of Edinburgh*, 1836, *1*:114–121. Both a copy of the *Proceedings* and a presentation copy of the Forbes article are in the Henry Library.

FROM JAMES DAVID FORBES

Retained Copy,[1] Forbes Papers, Library, St. Andrews University, Scotland

Edinburgh 22ᵈ Sept. 1836

My Dear Sir

I thank you very much for your letter of the 7ᵗʰ June[2] and for your interesting enclosures. I regret extremely to find that the needles have undergone such changes. Indeed *my* needle A has certainly been very unsteady for some years. My experience leads me to think that the near approach of two needles in packing, is not at all disadvantageous, perhaps the reverse, when the poles are opposed to one another. I have lately been reducing an extensive series of intensity & dip observations made in the Alps and Pyrenees at great heights, 4 years ago, from which I expect to deduce pretty confidently whether there is any diminution of intensity with elevation appreciable by ordinary instruments. I have made 44 series at heights between 6000 & 9000 feet above the sea, with connecting ones in the vallies. I am eliminating the coefficients of variation in Lat. Long. and Height by the method of least squares & shall soon be able to send you the results.[3]

---

[1] We have not found the outgoing letter.

[2] Printed above.

[3] Forbes had mentioned these observations to Henry two years earlier (*Henry Papers*, 2:255). He gave a brief description of his work

to the British Association in 1836 (*Report*, part 2, pp. 30–31). After completing the reductions, he presented the paper to the Royal Society of Edinburgh in December 1836: "Account of Some Experiments Made in Different

I send you a second paper on polarized heat.[4]

The annular eclipse of May 15th was admirably seen here. I took occasion to examine optically the light proceeding from the sun's edges during the continuance of the ring, which of course passes with extreme obliquity through his atmosphere, in order to test the current opinion that the deficient rays of the solar light are lost in the sun's atmosphere; but I found the strongest negative evidence against such an opinion.[5]

We have had a great scientific meeting at Bristol, where some of your countrymen were present. One of these, Dr Fiske is good enough to take charge of this.[6] May I request you to give my best thanks to Prof^{r} Bache for his valuable papers. I congratulate you on the activity in matters of science which evidently prevails in America: and I am certain you will find every disposition on this side of the Atlantic to acknowledge & appreciate your discoveries.

Pray do you think that I might address papers to other persons than your-

---

Parts of Europe, on Terrestrial Magnetic Intensity, Particularly with Reference to the Effect of Height," *Transactions of the Royal Society of Edinburgh*, 1840, *14*:1–29. Forbes found that contrary to the assertion of A. T. Kupffer, the diminution of intensity with an increase in height was minimal, only .001 for every 3000 feet.

[4] A presentation copy of Forbes, "Researches on Heat. Second Series," *Transactions of the Royal Society of Edinburgh*, 1836, *13*:446–471, is in the Henry Library.

[5] Forbes described his experiment in "Note Relative to the Supposed Origin of the Deficient Rays in the Solar Spectrum; being an Account of an Experiment Made at Edinburgh During the Annular Eclipse of 15th May 1836," *Phil. Trans.*, 1836, pp. 453–455. Forbes speculated that if, as others supposed, the sun's atmosphere absorbed certain rays, absorption would be greatest on rays from the sun's edges. He observed the spectrum before and during the eclipse but found no difference in the number, position, or thickness of the dark lines. He concluded that solar light might be "primitively incomplete." Forbes's conclusion that the dark lines in the solar spectrum were not due to absorption by a solar atmosphere was widely accepted for the next twenty-five years; although the subject received attention, the precise cause of the dark lines remained a mystery. See William McGucken, *Nineteenth-Century Spectroscopy* (Baltimore, 1969), pp. 19–34.

Forbes's article correctly traced the observation of dark lines in the solar spectrum to William Hyde Wollaston in 1802 and to the later work of Joseph Fraunhofer, who made extensive mappings of these lines (designating many distinct ones with capital letters). Fraunhofer also noted but did not explain a correspondence between some of the dark lines and many of the bright spectral lines emitted by colored flames of heated materials. This correspondence and other spectral observations of celestial bodies were fully developed in the classic spectroscopic work of Kirchhoff and Bunsen. In 1859 Kirchhoff discovered that materials emitting certain spectral lines were unusually capable of absorbing light of the same wavelength. From this he deduced, for example, that the dark D lines in the solar spectrum were due to the absorption by sodium in the solar atmosphere. In the 1860s Kirchhoff and Bunsen developed spectroscopic methods of analyzing the composition of terrestrial and celestial materials. See *DSB*, s.v. "Fraunhofer," "Bunsen," "Kirchhoff."

[6] Wilbur Fisk (1792–1839, *DAB*), a Methodist clergyman and President of Wesleyan University in Middletown, Connecticut. Fisk had been sent to Europe for his health and to study educational institutions. On his return, he published *Travels in Europe* (New York, 1838), which includes a description of the Bristol meeting of the British Association for the Advancement of Science. Robert Hare was one of the Americans at the meeting.

self to the care of D.<u>r</u> John Torrey,[7]—for instance to the American Phil. Society, Albany Institute, Prof. Silliman, D.<u>r</u> Beck[8] &c. It is annoying to think that they may be as in the case of the needles, detained an indefinite time.

May I hope to have the pleasure of hearing again from you soon, & occasionally. And believe me with much respect & regard

Yours sincerely
James D. Forbes

[7] Torrey facilitated exchanges of books, instruments, specimens, and papers between Americans and between Europeans and Amer-

icans. See *Henry Papers*, 2:224n.

[8] T. R. Beck.

TO HARRIET HENRY

Family Correspondence, Henry Papers, Smithsonian Archives

Princeton Fryday 23.<u>rd</u> Sep 1836
12 o'clock noon

My Dear H

I arrived safely at home yesterday afternoon at about ½ past one o'clock after a very plesant ride. I left N Y at ½ past 8 o'clock. The cars stoped for a moment at Newark to put on the locomotive; in looking out I accidentally saw a gentleman's back that very much resembled the one formerly worn by Mr. Bullions. I called—the gentleman turned when lo! it was Mr B. himself. He had come from New York in the same train with me but in a different car with the intention of giving William a hasty call. In the car from Newark I met with Prof. Maclean who was going on to Elizabethtown. It commenced raining when we arrived at New Brunswick and continued to rain until towards evening. Wen I arrived at home the house appeared very lonely and much in confusion as the carpet had been loosened preparatory to the process of cleaning which has taken place to day with much vigour. I found Mayme in the Kitchen at the table on her high chair with both hands in a bowl of sugar and her face & cloathes plentifully supplied with the sacrine matter. She appeared somewhat pleased to see me asked for Mamma and Bubbe but did not say much until Mother had washed her face and hands and I had taken off my coat. She then came to me and when I took her on my lap she gave me a very inquiring look and then asked *"Why didint mother take me with her. Was her fraid I would be frighten.* She has been very good since you have been gone and has scarcely cried any.

She said very little about you after you left but has asked several times *when Mama come back."* She has been nearly the whole forenoon with me in the hall and has amused herself with looking at the architectural drawings which I have had pasted on pasteboard and has been very busy in piling them first on one chair then on the other. I took her with me to the hall because the house is in the process of being cleaned. Daffey and James Racket[1] are both engaged or have been so this fore noon. Daffey however went home just before 12 o'clock to see her sick son Arch, who was taken sick at Mrs. Howells[2] yesterday or the day before.

Dr Woodhull[3] is in about the same state, Thomas Howell[4] is worse and scarcely a hope left of his recovery. Little Fanney[5] is also no better. The youngest son[6] was also seazed with symptoms of the same feever[7] yesterday.

I will finish this letter just before the closing of the mail this evening and give the latest intelligence.

Stephen bids me say that he has ingaged Mr Miller[8] to accompany him to albany on the important occasion of Monday week.[9] *Mr* Dr Campbell[10] and his Lady arrived in Town this afternoon. Many strangers have already come on and there is a prospect of a great crowd on commencement day. Mr Brown[11] informed me that he intended to close the house in which Dr Woodhull is confined and if possible to get the ball despenced with. I suggested the propriety of using the Philosophic Hall as a room for a Partey.

---

[1] Probably Henry's Black servants. During his tenure at Princeton Henry's household always had at least one live-in servant. The 1840 Census lists one colored male and two colored females, undoubtedly live-in servants, as residing in the Henry household. It is clear that Henry's salary of $1500 a year plus a rent-free house was sufficient to allow him to live in Princeton in comfort. Sixth Census of the United States, 1840: Mercer County, New Jersey, Record Group 29, National Archives; *Henry Papers*, 2:xiii.

[2] Mary Harrison Clayton Howell (d. 1852), the widow of Dr. Samuel L. Howell (*Henry Papers*, 2:92n–93n). She married Howell in 1809 and bore him ten children. Frances Howell, *The Book of John Howell & His Descendants*, 2 vols. (New York, 1897), 2:586–587.

[3] Alfred Alexander Woodhull (1809–1836) died on October 5. The son of Rev. George S. Woodhull, the pastor of the Presbyterian Church of Princeton, Alfred Woodhull graduated Princeton in 1828 and received his medical degree from the University of Pennsylvania in 1831. At the time of his death he was practicing medicine in Princeton, and was probably the Henry family physician. *Princeton Whig*, October 7, 1836 and October 14, 1836.

[4] Thomas C. Howell, a member of the class of 1834 at Princeton and the eldest son of Samuel L. Howell, died on September 25, 1836. *Princeton Whig*, September 30, 1836; *Princeton Catalogue*, p. 146.

[5] Fanny Howell, the youngest child of Samuel L. Howell, died October 3, 1836, age 8. *Princeton Whig*, October 7, 1836.

[6] Samuel Harrison Howell (1821–1877) was the only Howell son to live long enough to marry and raise a family. Other than his serving as the superintendent of a mission Sabbath school for twenty-three years, we know little of his life. *The Presbyterian*, December 8, 1877; Howell, *The Book of John Howell*, 2:587.

[7] Typhus. For more on the trials of this family, see *Henry Papers*, 2:472n.

[8] Samuel Miller.

[9] Stephen Alexander married Louisa Meads on Monday evening, October 3, 1836, in Albany. *Princeton Whig*, October 7, 1836.

[10] William Campbell.

[11] Isaac V. Brown, a Trustee of Princeton. *Henry Papers*, 2:376n.

Mr Maclean has agreed to this as a good substitute for the ball but it is doubtfull if the students which are graduating will consent to have no Ball.[12] Professor Maclean and myself are on a committee to make arrangements for the commencement. The exercises are to be held in the church which is temporarily flowered for the occasion. Mother appears very well. She complained somewhat of being fatigued last evening. Stephen and myself slept together in the spare bed room. Mr Newland[13] occupied the little bed room. *Mame* came to me at noon and said Mitty Newland in McIntyre[14] room—where McIntyre. I have received a letter from Mr McIntyre[15] requesting that I would bring on with me James' books. I wish you would call there and state what you know in reference to the good qualities of James and also some of the weak points of his character. We have heard some very disagreable news concerning *Deacon Rider*[16] of Dr Campbell's[17] church. I suppose you have heard the whole story bad as it is in albany.

[. . .][18] a little this morning before I was out of bead for her Grand Mother to come up stairs. She wanted something to eat. I arose, went down to the kitchen and got for her a pice of apple pie. Then took her into the room with me, placed her on the litle chair while I red the newspaper. She sat there nearly an hour perfectly quiet. We then came down to breakfast. At dinner she was not at the table at first but was very busily ingaged in reading to herself upstairs. She read so loud that her voice might have been

[12] The custom of having a ball as part of the commencement activities at Princeton goes back to the eighteenth century. But on April 12, 1836, at the suggestion of President Carnahan, the Trustees of Princeton voted "that the faculty address a circular letter to the parents and guardians of the students, pointing out the evils of the practice which had prevailed; and earnestly requesting them to prevent their sons and wards from contributing funds to pay for a Ball and a supper, and from attending them." As Henry indicated, this was not a popular decision with the students. On September 27, 1836, the Trustees voted to reconsider their decision. After much debate and a number of delays, the Trustees finally reconfirmed, on April 10, 1838, their opposition to the ball and supper; they asked the faculty "to take all practical measures to prevent the same." It did them no good. The students were not about to listen to the objections of the Trustees. Both the ball and supper were funded by the students, not the College. Moreover, they were held in the town, not on College grounds. If the students resolved to hold

a ball, there was little Princeton could actually do about it. Indeed, by 1846 there were two commencement dances, one formal and the other informal. Minutes of the Trustees, College of New Jersey, *3*:317–343, Princeton University Archives; *Wertenbaker*, pp. 196–197; Henry Lyttleton Savage, ed., *Nassau Hall: 1756–1956* (Princeton, 1956), p. 144.

[13] John Newland.

[14] James McIntyre.

[15] Archibald McIntyre.

[16] Perhaps Henry is speaking of Col. Walter De Ridder, who drowned in the Hudson River on August 24, 1836. *Daily Albany Argus*, September 2, 1836.

[17] John N. Campbell.

[18] The second sheet of this letter, with the signature and an undetermined amount of material, is missing. From this point on, the order of the paragraphs is somewhat arbitrary. Henry attempted to fill every possible space on the paper, writing afterthoughts in the margin, the space between the salutation and the date, and between the date and the body of the letter.

heard in the campus. I brought her down to the table and after giving her dinner took her up stairs and plaid with her for more than an hour on the [floor].

Stephen and myself and also Mr Miller will probably leave Princeton next friday so as to go up the river in the day boat.

You must have had a very plesant passage up the river and have got to Albany in good season since Mr Newland met the *Swallow* your boat near alb^y at about 6 o'clock.

TO HARRIET HENRY

Family Correspondence, Henry Papers, Smithsonian Archives

> Princeton Sept 26th 1836
> Monday evening Dr
> Carnahans study
> Faculty meeting

My Dear H

We are all well but much ingaged in preparation for the business of tuesday & wednesday.[1] This day has been a busy one and would have been a very gloomy time but for the number of strangers and the bustle of receiving them &c. Thomas Howell was buried this afternoon from the college chappell. He died yesterday morning at about 3 o'clock. Dr Woodhull remains in about the same state. I would not be surprised to hear of his death tomorrow morning. Little Fany was not expected to live the early part of the afternoon. Since then I have not heard from her. Dr Sprague arrived this morning and was with me for several hours. Immediatly after he left me Dr Cuyler[2] made his appearance and shortely after Dr Hilliar[3] came.

We have a fire in the Parlour this evening and it appears and feels very comfortable. The Philosophical Hall is under a process of great change. The old dining room is to be used as a ball room. Dr Torrey's room is to be

---

[1] Henry is referring to preparations for the 1836 commencement, which took place that Wednesday, September 28. *Maclean*, 2:302.

[2] Cornelius C. Cuyler (1783–1850), pastor of the Second Presbyterian Church in Philadelphia, is identified in *Henry Papers*, 2:267n.

[3] Asa Hillyer (1763–1840), a retired Presbyterian clergyman from Orange, New Jersey, and a director of Princeton Theological Seminary, was at this time a trustee of the College.

Born in Granby, Connecticut, Hillyer graduated from Yale in 1786 and after studying for the ministry in New York City served as a pastor to a Long Island parish. In 1798 the General Assembly appointed him an itinerant preacher for northern Pennsylvania and western New York. In 1801 he settled in Orange and retired from his clerical post in 1833. Sprague, *Annals*, 3:533–535.

used as the supper room for the Ladies and my room upstairs to be converted into a Ladies dressing room.

Little Mamy has not yet gone to bed and is at [...][4] She has been a very good girl to day. Took a nap in the middle of the day which is the cause of her wakefullness. She took her seat at the tea table alone and then sat for half an hour calling out at the top of her voice *"come to dinner—"come to dinner"*. She behaved very prettily at the table, put her hands to her face and was very soseable to the gentlemen talking all the time. *Jane* has been at the house assisting to day. Mrs Kline[5] has been making a vest for Stephen and has agreed to come the day after the commencement to make me a pair of pantaloons.

I forgot to mention that Mrs Howell's younger son[6] was taken to day in a carriage to the railway for Philadelphia. He was accompanied by Anna and some other relatives.

I am scribbling this letter in the Dr study while the Faculty are wating for the arrival of Mr McClean and James Alexander. Mother appears very well but is as you may suppose quite busy. Mr Newland and John start the day after commencement. Stephen, Mr Miller and myself will start most probably on Friday. Stephen received a letter to day informing him of your safe arrival but that you had been again afflicted with tooth ache. I had hoped that the jaunt to Albany would have so improved your health that a recurrence of the agu[e] would not have troubled you again.

[...][7] by the Albany papers that Mr Ferdinand Ward[8] formerly of the Theological seminary was married a short time since to Miss Jane Shaw—is this not the sister of Mrs Torrey.[9] I have nothing more to communicate except that which I need not add namely that I am yours as ever

JH.

---

[4] The original document is torn at this point (the bottom of the first page); almost two lines are missing.

[5] "Jane" and Mrs. Kline are not identified.

[6] Samuel Harrison Howell.

[7] The first words of this sentence were obliterated by the tear in the paper.

[8] Ferdinand DeWilton Ward (1812–1891) married Jane Shaw on September 21, 1836. Born in Bergen, New York, Ward graduated from Union College in 1831 and spent two and a half years at the Princeton Theological Seminary before leaving to preach to several parishes in upstate New York and in Philadelphia. After their marriage, he and his wife spent eleven years as missionaries for the American Board in Madura and Madras in southern India. Upon returning to the United States in 1847, Ward served as a pastor to the Central Presbyterian Church in Geneseo, New York. Jane Shaw Ward died in Rochester in 1888, and Ferdinand Ward died at the home of his son, William S. Ward, at Clarens, Switzerland. *Necrological Report Presented to the Alumni Association of Princeton Theological Seminary at its Annual Meeting, May 3rd, 1892* (Princeton, 1892), pp. 123–125.

[9] We have not been able to discover any kinship between Jane Shaw Ward and Eliza Shaw Torrey. According to one genealogist, Jane Shaw (1812–1888) was the daughter of William and Jane Robertson Shaw of New York City (George K. Ward, comp., *Andrew Ward and His Descendants, 1597–1910* [New York, 1910], p. 226), while the parents of Eliza Torrey have been identified as William and Eliza Robertson Shaw, also of New York City (see *Henry Papers*, 2:171n).

FROM JOHN TORREY
Henry Papers, Smithsonian Archives[1]

New York, Sept. 26th 1836.

My dear friend

I have been chasing about the country so much since I rec^d your letter of Augt last,[2] that I have hardly had time to reply to it. If possible I will endeavour to write several letters for Bache if he has not sailed. Pray let me know.

Have you heard of the great national voyage of discovery for which preparation is now making?[3] There are several vessels to be sent out by our government in about 2 months—a frigate & 3 or 4 sloops of war, under the command of Capt. Jones.[4] There will be a scientific Corps, the members

[1] This letter appears also in Nathan Reingold, ed., *Science in Nineteenth-Century America* (New York, 1964), pp. 111–112.

[2] August 17, 1836, printed above.

[3] The United States Exploring Expedition, or Wilkes Expedition. Although the Expedition itself took only four years, it was a concern of the scientific community for much longer. In the two years between passage of the bill in Congress and the sailing of the squadron, the role of science in the Expedition had to be protected and defined, and the civilian scientific corps had to be chosen and shielded from encroachment by navy officers. The enormous amount of maneuvering which occurred in the planning stages is documented in the first seven rolls of NARS microcopy 75, Records Relating to the United States Exploring Expedition Under the Command of Lt. Charles Wilkes, 1836–1842 (from RG 45) and in *House Executive Documents*, 25th Congress, 2d Session, 1837–1838, No. 147, which prints correspondence and reports relating to the Expedition preparations.

Henry was only minimally involved in the planning of the Expedition. He wrote a recommendation for James Eights (November 17, 1836, printed below) and had a long conversation with Mahlon Dickerson in Washington in December 1836. Preparations for his trip abroad occupied his time and the trip itself removed him for most of 1837. In general, the naturalists were much more involved than the physical scientists; physical science, never heavily represented in the civilian scientific corps, was eventually totally removed to the control of navy officers.

Henry was more involved in the many years of aftermath. The Expedition's publications were not completed until 1874, and Henry was drawn in repeatedly through Agassiz, Torrey, and Gray who authored some of the reports. After great resistance on Henry's part, and only after he had secured government appropriations for their transfer and maintenance, the Smithsonian ended up with the Expedition's collections.

See William Stanton, *The Great United States Exploring Expedition of 1838–1842* (Berkeley, 1975). For an extensive bibliography, see Daniel C. Haskell, *The United States Exploring Expedition, 1838–1842, and Its Publications, 1844–1874* (New York, 1942). See also A. Hunter Dupree, *Science in the Federal Government* (Cambridge, Massachusetts, 1957), pp. 56–61; John Kazar, "The United States Navy and Scientific Exploration, 1837–1860" (Ph.D. dissertation, University of Massachusetts, 1973), especially pp. 35–77; Nathan Reingold's essay and selected documents in *Science in Nineteenth-Century America* (New York, 1964), pp. 108–126.

[4] Thomas ap Catesby Jones (1790–1858) was appointed Commander of the Expedition in June 1836. He was repeatedly frustrated in his attempts to organize and outfit the Expedition by Mahlon Dickerson's indecisiveness and antipathy to the entire operation and Charles Wilkes's behind-the-scenes manipulations. In November 1837, "ill from worry and exasperation" (*DAB*), he resigned the command which was ultimately given to Charles Wilkes. Stanton, *Exploring Expedition*, pp. 35–56.

of which will be well paid. Pickering[5] & probably D.ʳ Gray[6] will go. It is supposed the salery will be 3000 doll.ˢ a year.[7] My object in writing now is to ascertain whether there is any probability that Alexander could be engaged for the expedition? The situation & salery would be made very desirable, but I fear his matrimonial engagement will be a barrier. He will have (if appointed) the best instruments that can be obtained for astronomical, magnetical, & meteoric observations. This is all *between ourselves* at present, but if he says *yes* we can put things in a train to consummate his wishes. The vessels will be absent 3 years. Perhaps, however, you know all about the affair, but I wish an answer as speedily as possible, for if Alexander

---

[5] Charles Pickering (1805–1878, *DAB*) eventually sailed with the Expedition as chief zoologist. Pickering had a medical degree from Harvard. In 1827 he located in Philadelphia where he practiced medicine and began a ten-year association with the Academy of Natural Sciences, serving as librarian and then curator.

Pickering was elected a member of the American Philosophical Society in 1828. In September 1837 he resigned his membership:

Having long seen with regret that the objects of your Institution were not appreciated among yourselves as a body, I have always looked upon your position in the Public eye as unfortunate, and a regard for the Infant cause of Science in our Country, as well as in some measure a feeling of self-respect, induces me to decline the association hereafter.

The letter of resignation, dated September 12, 1837, is in the Archives of the American Philosophical Society. Pickering's resignation is in contrast to the choice made by Henry, Torrey, and other young members to try to upgrade the work of the Society from within (*Henry Papers*, 2:278, 305).

Stanton (*Exploring Expedition*, pp. 58–59) puts Pickering's resignation in the context of professional-amateur conflict, naming as Pickering's chief antagonists at APS the amateur naturalists George Ord, J. K. Kane, and Clement C. Biddle. All three were on the Society's advisory commission for the Expedition. The commission's correspondence with Dickerson contains numerous criticisms of Pickering's abilities.

Following the Expedition's return, Pickering spent a year superintending the collections in Washington (Stanton, *Exploring Expedi-*

tion, pp. 297–303). After a trip to Egypt in 1843 he settled not in Philadelphia but in Boston, where he authored two volumes on anthropology and the geographical distribution of plants and animals for the Expedition's reports. His last years were devoted to his massive study, *The Chronological History of Plants: Man's Record of His Own Existence Illustrated Through Their Names, Uses and Companionship*, which was published posthumously by his widow in 1879.

[6] With backing from Jeremiah N. Reynolds and Torrey, Gray sought and received an appointment as botanist on the Expedition. Through the many months of delay, he grew increasingly uneasy at interference with the scientific corps in terms of personnel, equipment, and autonomy. Although Gray's own appointment was not in danger when the slashing of the scientific corps began in 1838, he resigned in July 1838 and took an appointment as Professor of Botany and Zoology at the University of Michigan. For Gray's involvement with the Expedition, the consequences of the resignation on his career, and his later authorship of the botanical reports, see A. Hunter Dupree, *Asa Gray, 1810–1888* (New York, 1968), especially pp. 57–69, and Stanton, *Exploring Expedition*.

[7] James E. DeKay and J. N. Reynolds argued that the principal members of the scientific corps should receive $3,500 per year. Dickerson thought $2,000 would be sufficient and that any larger sum would anger the naval officers. A two-tiered pay structure was eventually adopted, with principals receiving $2,500 per year and assistants $2,000. *House Executive Documents*, 25th Congress, 2d Session, 1837–1838, No. 147, pp. 17, 110, 113–114, 189.

won't go, they will look out for some other person.[8] They are determined to have a *big team*!

I have been working on the State Survey & am quite tired of travelling, but I explore about here & work at home.[9] It will not be in my power to visit Princeton this Commencement. I must preside at a pretty important meeting to be held tomorrow evening,[10] & on Wednesday ev[g]. also (D.V.) I shall be occupied. I regret that I cannot be with you—but so it is. Pray come here this vacation & let us have a long talk. I wish to know all your plans & feelings, & to tell you mine. How are college matters prospering?

My very kind regards to Mrs. Henry & all your amiable family, & in these Mrs. T. joins.

Ask Mr. Wiggins if he will be so good as to bring on the apparatus for condensing Carbonic acid gas[11] wh[ich] I left in one of the closets, near the door. I suppose he will remain a little while at Princeton yet. Remember me to him.

Yours truly
John Torrey

[8] There is no evidence that Stephen Alexander tried to get the position of astronomer. He was due to be married October 3. He could probably have had the position for the asking as this slot proved the hardest to fill in the scientific corps. In a strange sequence of events, Dickerson first offered the position in March of 1837 to Charles Wilkes as a civilian. Wilkes had previously been chosen by Dickerson to command one of the ships but was withdrawn when Jones strenuously objected to the appointment of a junior officer. Wilkes declined to accept the position of astronomer, citing unwillingness to suspend his navy status and irreconcilable differences with Jones. In April, Dickerson solicited Robert Treat Paine, who not only would not accept the position, but, after consulting Nathaniel Bowditch, did not know of any astronomer in New England who was both qualified and willing to go. He indicated that J. Ingersoll Bowditch and Sears C. Walker were able but would not accept. Robert M. Patterson reported that S. C. Walker was uninterested and suggested Robert Treat Paine and J. N. Nicollet, the French astronomer and geologist then in America. At Dickerson's request Matthew C. Perry approached Henry's friend James Dean in July and although Dean was interested, he feared he was too old and infirm. In September 1837 Dickerson finally signed Matthew F. Maury who, however, resigned several months later with Jones in protest over the conduct of the preparations. Charles Wilkes eventually gained not only command of the Expedition but also responsibility for the astronomical and physical observations. *House Executive Documents*, 25th Congress, 2d Session, 1837–1838, No. 147, pp. 271, 272–274, 281–282, 365–366, 491–492. Stanton, *Exploring Expedition*, pp. 48–49.

[9] Torrey's work during the first year of the survey is described in Michele L. Aldrich, "New York Natural History Survey, 1836–1845" (Ph.D. dissertation, University of Texas, 1974), pp. 133–136.

[10] We do not know what "important meeting" Torrey attended on the 27th. At the September 26 meeting of the New York Lyceum of Natural History, a report on the Exploring Expedition was presented. Final adoption was deferred until a list of interrogatories could be compiled (Minutes, New York Academy of Sciences).

Douglass Houghton of Detroit (*DAB*), a friend of Torrey's, attended this meeting as a visitor. It is possible Torrey planned to meet with him to discuss preliminary plans for the Michigan State Geological Survey and the University of Michigan.

[11] Torrey's work on condensing carbonic acid gas is briefly described in "Experiments on the Condensation of Carbonic, Sulphurous, and Chlorochromic Acid Gases," *Silliman's Journal*, 1839, *35*: 374–375.

FROM THE UNITED STATES NAVAL LYCEUM[1]

Henry Papers, Smithsonian Archives

US Naval Lyceum
Navy Yard   New York
Septr 27, 1836.

Sir,

The undersigned appointed a committee[2] of the US Naval Lyceum upon

---

[1] The United States Naval Lyceum, often referred to as the Brooklyn Naval Lyceum, was founded in 1833 by officers at the Brooklyn Navy Yard. The founding was engineered by Matthew C. Perry who had just arrived for an extended period of shore duty. He persuaded the Navy to provide space for the organization and soon it had a library, reading room, and museum in active operation, with plans for sponsoring lectures in the future. The Lyceum was incorporated by New York State in 1835. Besides the resident and "absent" members (whose dues provided the financing), corresponding and honorary members were elected. The former included college professors, naturalists, United States Army officers, United States consuls abroad, and the British explorers W. E. Parry, John Franklin, James Clark Ross, and George Back. The honorary members included President Jackson and cabinet members, ex-Presidents J. Q. Adams and James Madison, Lafayette, and the authors James Fenimore Cooper and Washington Irving.

A description of the Lyceum by Benjamin Silliman, an honorary member, appeared in *Silliman's Journal*, 1835, 27:390–393. The purposes of the Lyceum were spelled out in greater detail in the first issue of the *Naval Magazine*, a Lyceum publication (January 1836, *1*:2–18). The Lyceum was founded to encourage naval officers to broaden their professional and general knowledge, thus elevating the character of the Navy and fostering harmony within the service. In addition, the founders of the Lyceum wanted to take scientific advantage of the voyages of naval officers by advising them on the collection of natural history specimens, weather observations, data on terrestrial magnetism, astronomical observations, etc.

The continuing publication of the Lyceum's *Naval Magazine* was seen as critical for the full realization of its goals. The journal, issued bimonthly under the editorship of

Charles S. Stewart (1795–1870, *Herringshaw*), a Presbyterian clergyman, author, and navy chaplain, was eclectic. There were travel sketches and fictional fantasies, articles on the Navy, naval education, and navigation, as well as contributions by Redfield and Espy on meteorology. An appendix to the first volume contained messages by the President and the Secretary of the Navy, lists of U. S. Navy ships and officers, and the Lyceum's membership list with its constitution and bylaws. Unfortunately for the Lyceum, and our knowledge of it, a lack of funds caused the demise of the *Naval Magazine* with the November 1837 issue of the second volume.

The subsequent history of the Lyceum is not well documented. According to various sources, the decline began just before, during, or a long time after the Civil War. Although meetings were no longer held, the 1887 Griffis biography of Perry (see below) claimed that the Lyceum "is still flourishing and is visited by tens of thousands of persons from all parts of our country" (p. 103). Even the museum function died by 1892 when the records and collections were transferred to the United States Naval Academy in Annapolis. Study of the surviving records at the Naval Academy's Museum would be necessary to reconstruct the activities of the Lyceum after 1837.

Besides the *Silliman's Journal* and *Naval Magazine* articles on the Lyceum, there is information in two Perry biographies: William Elliot Griffis, *Matthew Calbraith Perry* (Boston, 1887), pp. 99–109, and Samuel Eliot Morison, *"Old Bruin" Commodore Matthew C. Perry, 1794–1858* (Boston, 1967), pp. 133–135. See also S. de Christofaro, "The Naval Lyceum," *United States Naval Institute Proceedings*, August 1951, 77:869–873.

[2] Besides the undersigned, the committee appointed at the meeting of September 6, 1836, originally included Charles S. Stewart and Alexander Slidell (1803–1848, *DAB*, known as

the "Exploring Expedition" now under equipment for the Antartic Seas, beg leave to invite your attention to the following extract of a letter from the Secretary of the Navy recently addressed to the Society upon this important and interesting topic. They do this with the confident hope and expectation that the magnitude and engrossing interest to the progress of Science and Natural philosophy which the plan of the expedition contemplates, will afford a sufficient pretext and apology for their earnestly soliciting your especial cooperation in enabling them to discharge the high and honorable duty which has been cast upon them by the principal of the Navy Department.

With the aid of individuals distinguished like yourself for preeminent knowledge in the several departments of natural history and philosophy, which this enterprize is intended to advance and illustrate, the committee will feel themselves competent to comply with the requirements of the Secretary: and in respectfully but urgently asking your assistance at as early a period as practicable to enable them to make a full and prompt report, they feel it due to you to add that, that report will acknowledge with gratitude and pride any aid they may receive in furnishing the comprehensive scheme of inquiry and instruction which is desired.

The committee would particularly request your assistance in propounding for solution by the results of the expedition such inquiries as are deemed paramount to subserve the progress of Geology with all its interesting accompaniments, and Mineralogy, and especially in the departments of Meteorology in reference to a general and accurate course of observation; magnetism in relation to the phenomena of the variation and inclination of the magnetic needle, and the intensity of the magnetic force; also how far the needle may be affected by local attraction and by the atmospherical electricity, and what effect may be produced on the needle on the appearance of the Aurora Australis. The length of a degree on the Meridian and the length of the seconds pendulum in different latitudes, especially as far south as may be practicable, and generally as respects subjects which may be deemed of importance in connection with this great national undertaking.[3]

Alexander Slidell Mackenzie from 1838), a brother-in-law of M. C. Perry. Minutes of the U.S. Naval Lyceum, U.S. Naval Academy Museum.

[3] The original of the committee's report of November 29, 1836, is in the Charles Wilkes Family Papers at the Library of Congress (Box 21, Exploring Expedition File, 1838–1842, "Reports: American Philosophical Society and the U.S. Naval Lyceum"). The report was printed in the *Naval Magazine*, January 1837, 2:64–86. According to Griffis, *Perry*, p. 108, M. C. Perry was primarily responsible for the content.

The report begins with a description of the effort to obtain advice from "eminent individuals," regretting that lack of time prevented solicitation of European experts. The committee also found it necessary "to express

We have the honor to be
Most respectfully
Your Obedt Servants[4]
Ch. G. Ridgely, President of N Lyceum
M. C. Perry 1st Vice President
Chas O. Handy Correspding Secty

Extract of a letter from the Secretary of the Navy[5] referred to in the preceding letter.

---

their deep regret that the professional engagements of some of these gentlemen, have been deemed too urgent to admit of their bestowing the necessary consideration, to enable them to furnish the information acquired [sic] . . . ." Henry was one of this group. Although we have not located any reply by him, he might very well have pleaded urgent professional engagements. The report expressed gratitude particularly to James Renwick whose response, with those of C. U. Shepard, Benjamin Silliman, and Edward Hitchcock, was printed in an appendix.

The committee decided to forego the opportunity to recommend specific individuals for appointment, and instead forwarded all recommendations received to Washington without further mentioning them in the report. They did however urge the government to offer generous salaries to attract superior talent.

The report focused on making general recommendations for the scientific departments. The authors singled out study of winds, currents, and tides, the determination of latitude and longitude of the places visited, observations on waves, determination of magnetic intensity at different heights, the need for data on the geographical distribution of animals, and philological studies. For their views on other subjects they referred to Renwick's communication.

The report then considered the equipment for the expedition, stressing the value of thoughtful planning and the importance of the health and comfort of the corps. Confident that their experience qualified them, the committee made detailed recommendations here, especially concerning food: "Tomato's catsup should be taken in large quantities;—there should also be carried, lemon, cranberry, quince, and apple marmalades . . . ."

The report concludes with an expression of hope for the success of the expedition, and, quoting Silliman, a plea for liberal monetary support from the government.

[4] Commodore Charles Goodwin Ridgely (1784–1848, *DAB*) was Commandant of the Navy Yard. Matthew C. Perry (1794–1858, *DAB*) was the second officer and, although more active in the Lyceum, probably held the vice presidency instead of the presidency in deference to Ridgely's higher rank. Charles O. Handy was a purser.

[5] Dickerson's letter was addressed to the President of the Lyceum and dated August 31, 1836. It is printed in full immediately before the Lyceum's report in the *Naval Magazine*.

As Secretary of the Navy from June 1834 to June 1838, Mahlon Dickerson (1770–1853, *DAB*) had the primary responsibility for the organization of the Exploring Expedition. Dickerson seemed well suited for the job. A graduate of Princeton (1789), Dickerson had practiced law in Philadelphia before assuming management of his late father's iron works in Succasunna, New Jersey, in 1810. Dickerson rose quickly in New Jersey politics, serving as Governor from 1815 to 1817 and United States Senator from 1817 to 1833. He was an amateur botanist and had belonged to the American Philosophical Society since 1807.

According to Stanton, however, Dickerson found his cabinet post, and the Exploring Expedition in particular, "a great bother" (p. 33). Dickerson's management of the organization of the Expedition was marked by antagonisms with Jeremiah N. Reynolds and Thomas ap Catesby Jones, by attempts to reduce the Expedition in size and make it exclusively naval, and by delay and confusion. In response to complaints about Dickerson's lack of progress, Van Buren asked Joel R. Poinsett, Secretary of War, to assist the Secretary of the Navy. Citing ill health, Dickerson resigned in June 1838, two months before the squadron sailed.

See William Stanton, *The Great United States Exploring Expedition of 1838–1842* (Berkeley, 1975), especially pp. 33–65.

"I take the liberty through you, of asking the advice of the Society, as to the formation of a Scientific Corps for this expedition; and their recommendations of scientific gentlemen of suitable age to be employed as members of this Corps, who may be well acquainted with Geology and Mineralogy, with botany, with zoology—in all its numerous branches—with meterology, magnetism, electricity and other subjects connected with Natural history. Also their recommendation of a philologist to collect Catalogues of words of the different languages, and an Artist to take the portraits of the Natives of the different Countries and Islands which may be visited.

I would also respectfully ask of your Society a series of inquiries as to subjects of Natural history, Meterorology, Magnetism and to which in their opinion the researches of this Corps should be particularly directed, together with such suggestions as they may believe calculated to promote the objects of the Expedition."[6]

[6] As mentioned above, we have not found any response by Henry to the Lyceum's solicitation. Nor have we found any response to Dickerson's direct solicitation of Henry in a letter of December 15, 1836, printed below. Henry did, however, meet with Dickerson in late December and presumably made suggestions then. (See below, Henry to Harriet Henry, December 28, 1836.)

TO HARRIET HENRY

Family Correspondence, Henry Papers, Smithsonian Archives

Princeton Commencement
night [September 28,] 1836

My Dear W.

This has been a very busy day and much yet remains to be done in the way of meetings, committes &c. We are all well and the day has thus far gone off very pleasantly. The exercises were very respectable and attended by a great number of strangers. Amoung the number was General Harrison the Whig candidate for the Presidency. He appears quite a plain old gentleman and made a speech on the Library stairs to the assembled mob in the campus.[1]

Mary has behaved remarkably well and is very obedient to me. I have not

[1] The *Princeton Whig* of September 30, 1836, reported on the commencement and William Henry Harrison's visit. Harrison, who was on a campaign tour in his unsuccessful bid for the Presidency, had been in Philadelphia and Trenton, where the New Jersey Whig convention was about to be held. Delegations from those cities and others accompanied him to Princeton. Henry was on a committee appointed by the Whig Society to greet Harrison (Whig Society Minutes, September 28, 1836, Princeton University Archives).

whiped her and have only on one occasion given her a scoalding. Mother is very well, has been assisted to day by Jane. There were no Gentlemen at dinner at our hous today but little Mr Whiggens. There were however the two Miss Comfors[2] and an acquaintance of theirs. Dr Woodhull has remained in bout the same state since when I last wrote. There is some slight hopes of his recovery. Little Fanny is also about in the same state. Mrs Howell's family have all removed to Judge Bayards.[3]

I have just received a letter from Dr Torrey[4] in which he informs that if Stephen will accept the office of *Astronomer* to the Southern expedition to sail in about two months for the Southern ocean he can have the appointement. The salary will be 3000 dollars a year and he will be furnished with all implements of the very best kind. The voyage however will occupy about 3 years. What would Louisa say to such an arrangement—were he not about to be married I would urge that he accept the appointment. I heard in Philadelphia that somebody at Princeton would be offered the situation but did not think much about it. I intend to make this till on the trustees immediatly.[5]

In great haste
Your H

This about Stephen must not be generally known as yet. We will start probably on Friday afternoon.

[2] Probably sisters of David Comfort, a Trustee of Princeton (*Henry Papers*, 2:376).

[3] Samuel Bayard (1767–1840, *DAB*) was a prominent Princeton citizen. After graduating from Princeton he practiced law in Philadelphia. Bayard spent several years in London prosecuting American claims in the British Admiralty Courts following the ratification of Jay's Treaty. After settling in Princeton in 1806 he became Presiding Judge of the Court of Common Pleas of Somerset County. Bayard had an imposing house with spacious grounds and was known for his hospitality. *Hageman,* 1:226–228.

[4] Torrey's letter of September 26 is printed above.

[5] Stephen Alexander had been Adjunct Professor of Mathematics at Princeton since 1834. At their meeting on the morning of September 28, the Trustees expanded Alexander's position by also naming him Lecturer on Astronomy and raised his salary to $700 a year. At the April 12, 1837, meeting, his salary was raised to $1000. Trustees' Minutes, Princeton University Archives.

EXCERPT,[1] MINUTES, TRUSTEES, COLLEGE OF NEW JERSEY
Trustees' Minutes, 3:327, 328, Princeton University Archives

Thursday September 29th: 1836, 8 Oclock A.M.

... The Board of Trustees, having learned, that Professor Henry, pro-

[1] We have omitted portions dealing with the construction of West College and other routine matters not directly related to Henry's activities at Princeton.

poses to visit Europe, during the ensuing year, hereby express their cordial approbation of the plan[2] ...

Resolved, that this Board adopt the *plan*, submitted by Professor Henry for the location of buildings on the College ground.

Resolved, that the plan laid before the board, by the Committee appointed to confer with the Whig and Cliosophic societies, on the location and erection of *New-Halls*, by and for, said societies, be, and hereby is, adopted.[3]

Resolved, that a house for Professor Henry be forthwith erected, that it be of stone, on the site shown by the plan of the grounds adopted by the board; and that a sum not exceeding four thousand dollars (with the materials now in the house occupied by Professor Henry) be appropriated for that object.[4]

Resolved, that Dᴿ Carnahan, Mᴿ Cooley[5] and Mᴿ Green[6] be a committee to carry the immediately preceeding resolution into effect ...

[2] For the gestation of Henry's European trip, see above, Henry to James Henry, January 22, 1836, and Maclean to Henry, July 25, 1836.

[3] For both Henry's plan and the new Whig and Cliosophic Society halls, see above, American Whig Society Circular, August 30, 1836.

[4] Henry had been informally promised a new house by the Princeton Trustees more than a year earlier, only to have the commitment withdrawn in favor of an offer to build an addition to the existing house. See *Henry Papers*, 2:428, 461–462, 464. On April 12, 1836, however, the Trustees made good on their original promise and authorized a committee to "make such arrangements for the accomodation of Professor Henry, with a house, as they shall think expedient." Trustees' Minutes, 3:314, Princeton University Archives. The formal go-ahead was given at this meeting of September 29, 1836.

Originally, the new house was to be ready

upon Henry's return from Europe in the fall of 1837. Repeated delays prevented even the start of construction by that time, however, and it was not until late 1838 that the house was finally ready for occupancy. See below, Torrey to Henry, November 1, 1837. In the meantime, the preference expressed at this meeting in favor of a stone structure had given way to a decision to build the facade of brick. Trustees' Minutes, April 10, 1838, Princeton University Archives.

Henry submitted at least one plan for the design of the house himself in January 1837 (Box 50, Henry Papers, Smithsonian Archives). While we do not know how much input Henry ultimately had in the design of the house, this particular drawing clearly differs from the structure that was actually built.

[5] Eli Field Cooley. *Henry Papers*, 2:438.

[6] James Sproat Green. *Henry Papers*, 1:440.

TO HARRIET HENRY
Family Correspondence, Henry Papers, Smithsonian Archives

Fulton Schoharie Coty Wednesday
Oct 12ᵗʰ 1836

My Dear H.

I am now confined to a house in this region of perpetual congelation by a snow storm which commenced last night and which by sunrise this morning had covered the ground to the depth of about 8 inches. It is at this time (4 oclok PM) snowing very fast and shows no signes of abatement; the farmers are preparing their sleghs and indeed this has been the only vehichel of travel during the day. I had a ride in one this morning from my residence at the Tavern near Capt. Fakes[1] to the house of a second cousin of my own, a Mr Mattice,[2] a distance of about one mile.

I would have written you before but have missed the mail and have been engaged in endeavoring to get some light on the dark subject of your Schoharrie Lands.[3] I left Albany for Schenectady the next morning after you left. Saw Mr Linn,[4] gave him the papers relative to the Hill property and wished him immediatly to commence the study of the subject with me. This however is said was impossible as his mind was not in a proper state for want of rest on account of the sickness of his child &c.

I then went on the hill to the house of the celebrated Mr *Trash*,[5] found the Family at dinner, was invited to partake, not however until the repast was nearly finished; I declined not almost without a slight inclination to accept, as the intense action of the gastric juice almost over came the repugnance caused by the appearance of no great degree of cleaness about the table. Mr Trash the *good man* has not returned from England—will probably remain some time—has discharged one Lawyer and employed another because the first was leagued with his opponent, the proof of this is strong as that from _____. The lawyer advised Mr Trash *to "settle for a thousand pounds"*!! Think of that. Oh! the monster! Jimme was too much of a Lawyer for that. Mrs. *Jimme* Trash says that she does not want to purchase as she cannot pay the price asked. They the family intend moving into the country. Wont pay for the *shed* which like *Monsieur Tonson*[6] has come up again, but will endeavour to make up a payment by the time

[1] Unidentified.

[2] Unidentified.

[3] Harriet's father, Alexander Alexander (1764 or 1765–1809), was a Schenectady merchant and grist mill operator. His estate was relatively large, and included land in Tioga County and the city of Schenectady, as well as land in Schoharie County. From what we can glean from correspondence, the income from the Alexander estate was of some significance to the financial situation of the Henry family. A number of Henry's letters to his brother, wife, and brother-in-law deal with these lands—selling, leasing, or settling with agents. *Henry Papers*, 1:109, 449; 2:98, 151, 174.

[4] Henry J. Linn, an Albany attorney. See

Henry Papers, 1:62.

[5] We have been unable to discover who the celebrated Mr. "Trash" was.

[6] The title character in a dramatic poem by John Taylor (1757–1832, *DNB*). Henry no doubt had in mind the final stanza of the poem:

As if some hideous spectre struck his sight
His senses seem'd bewildered with affright;
His face, indeed, bespoke a heart full sore—
Then, starting, he exclaim'd, in rueful strain,
"Begar! here's Monsieur Tonson, come again!"
Away he ran—and ne'er was heard of more.

John Taylor, *Monsieur Tonson* (Glasgow, ca. 1821), p. 8.

I return from Schoharrie. Very sory the "widdow has moved from Schenectady used to pay the rent and never feel it. After all the widdow is a wright clever woman. *"Aint She"*?

After returning from the Hill I made inquiries about a passage to this place. Took dinner at Davises was waited on at table by a Black boy who with a *grin* asked if I was not Mr Henry, at the same time informing me that he was John our quondam Servant. I told him to tell his Mother that it would not be convenient for us to send up his sister this Fall but that she should come home next spring. To smoothe this intelligence I gave the Black rogue 2/— which sent him off with a very sunny face. After dinner I started on my schoharrie pilgrimage mounted on a nagg which the owner assured would carry me easier than a coach. My carpet *bag* (a good article purchased in Albany for $5) was strapped on behind; a large white blanket was placed under the saddle to prevent its chafing the horse and to serve as a covering for the animal at night which concealed nearly the whole body from neck to tail. A large rope halter and short stirrups completed an equipment which rivaled that of Icabod Crane.[7]

I started about ½ past 2 got tolerably well out of the city. Soon found however that I had a penance to perform for my credulity in suffering myself to be persuaded to hire a horse to ride so great a distance. Resolved not to turn back. The carpet bag gave way. In picking this up the saddle turned over and I with it. Almost repented my having resolved to go on. Adjusted affairs took *bag* on before started again; trott of the horse hard; could only walk or gallop the beast. Mistook the road got a mile out of the way. Much annoyed by the carpet bag. [Some][8] reflections on comparitive merits of the carpet bag and [the] *valese* gave the preference to the latter. Stopped for [night at] a small tavern 14 miles from Schenectady. [Supper] apple pye and milk very good but had to wait until [nearly] 9 oclock for the cooking of the pye. Found a co[py of] the favorite first novel of Charlet Temple.[9] Read

---

[7] The passage Henry probably had in mind from "The Legend of Sleepy Hollow" described Crane's appearance upon departing for a party:

Ichabod was a suitable figure for such a steed. He rode with short stirrups, which brought his knees nearly up to the pommel of the saddle: his sharp elbows stuck out like grasshoppers'; he carried his whip perpendicularly in his hand, like a sceptre, and as the horse jogged on, the motion of his arms was not unlike the flapping of a pair of wings. A small wool hat rested on the top of his nose, for so his scanty strip of forehead might be called; and the skirts of his black coat fluttered out almost to the horse's tail. Such was the appearance of Ichabod and his steed, as they shambled out of the gate of Hans Van Ripper, and it was altogether such an apparition as is seldom to be met with in broad daylight.

Geoffrey Crayon [Washington Irving], *The Sketch Book*, 4th ed., 2 vols. (London, 1821), 2:311.

[8] Part of the letter remains attached to the broken seal, resulting in this and the subsequent gaps in the letter.

[9] Published initially in London in 1790,

a few [cha]pters to see what change 20 years had made on my literary taste. Soon threw this aside for the first vol of the Monestary by Scott.[10] Too tired to read went to bed thought of wife & children slept soundly. At 8 next morning (Saturday) started for the Court-House distant 9 miles reached said place with alternate walks and gallops (trottings out of the question) in about an hour and a half pretty well all things considered. First met with Mr Gibbard[11] & his son[12] visited them seperate at cabinet of minerals. Admired the specimens on which I had before lavished all my praise. Learned something however and was treated with much kindness. Next met Lawyer Hamilton[13] who made inquiries for Stephen. Informed the gentleman and

Susanna Haswell Rowson's (ca. 1762–1824, *DAB*) two-volume novel, *Charlotte. A Tale of Truth*, received an indifferent response from English readers. Americans, in contrast, loved the book. It became America's first best-seller in novel form, requiring at least 136 American editions to satisfy the demand. The most widely read novel in the United States before the publication of *Uncle Tom's Cabin* in 1852, *Charlotte Temple* (as it was titled in later editions) was third in popularity only to the Bible and Benjamin Franklin's *Autobiography* among American readers of the first half of the nineteenth century. It attracted readers because of its combination of bawdiness and sentimentality, melodrama and moralizing, bathos and scandal. Another attraction for American readers was a villain who was easy to hate—the British soldier of the Revolutionary War.

Ellen B. Brandt, *Susanna Haswell Rowson, America's First Best-Selling Novelist* (Chicago, 1975), pp. 52–83; Carl Van Doren, *The American Novel 1789–1939* (New York, 1940), p. 9; Elias Nason, *A Memoir of Mrs. Susannah Rowson* (Albany, 1870), pp. 47–48.

[10] *The Monastery* was Sir Walter Scott's first failure as a novelist. A romance of Scotland during the Reformation, the two-volume work first appeared in 1820. Despite negative reviews and reader reaction, it still sold fairly well. John O. Hayden, ed., *Scott—The Critical Heritage* (New York, 1970), pp. 13, 343–344; James T. Hillhouse, *The Waverly Novels and Their Critics* (Minneapolis, 1936), pp. 34, 110.

[11] John Gebhard (1782–1854) practiced law in Schoharie County. He was Surrogate of that county from 1811 to 1813 and again from 1815 to 1822. He also served one term in Congress (1821–1823). An enthusiastic geologist with considerable knowledge of his own locale, Geb-hard was a member of the American Association for the Advancement of Science from its founding until his death. *Biographical Directory of the American Congress*, p. 1202; Sally G. Kohlstedt, *The Formation of the American Scientific Community: The American Association for the Advancement of Science, 1848–1860* (Urbana, 1976), "Appendix"; John Gebhard, "On the Geology and Mineralogy of Schoharie, (N. Y.)," *Silliman's Journal*, 1835, 28:172–177.

[12] John Gebhard, Jr. (1802–1887), shared his father's interests in politics and science. He was County Clerk for Schoharie from 1828 until 1834 and a delegate to the 1846 State Constitutional Convention. Like his father, he joined the American Association for the Advancement of Science in 1848. He was a sufficiently competent geologist to serve as an assistant on the New York Natural History Survey and was Director of the State Museum from 1849 until 1856. Edgar A. Werner, *Civil List and Constitutional History of the Colony and State of New York* (Albany, 1889), pp. 130, 249, 541; Kohlstedt, *American Scientific Community*, "Appendix"; Michele L. Aldrich, "New York Natural History Survey, 1836–1845" (Ph.D. dissertation, University of Texas, 1974), p. 348; Charlotte Taylor Luckhurst, ed., *Genealogy of Schoharie County Families* (n.p., 1921), n.p.

[13] Perhaps Henry Hamilton (1788–1846), then the Surrogate of Schoharie County. As such he would be involved in the filing of deeds. Hamilton had earlier served as District Attorney of Schoharie (1818–1821) and would later serve two years as Canal Commissioner (1840–1842). Werner, *Civil List of New York*, pp. 227, 497, 502, 514; Luckhurst, *Genealogy of Schoharie County Families*.

his Partner a class mate or college mate of Stephen's of the occurrence witnessed in Albany on the evening of Monday.[14] Best[15] has not paid the remainder of Mr Hamiltons bill on the Webb[16] suit. Started for Middleburgh staid there a few minutes then with the alternations of walks and trotts reached the tavern near Bests at about 6 oclock PM. Capt Fake gone to the *west* with his wife who in all probability had drawn on both legs of the inexpressibles[17] for so important an occasion. Called on Mr Best received his short blunt howdy do. Too late to do business promised to commence on monday morning. Borrowed map of Land returned to tavern too tired to study and almost to eat a bowl of pye and milk with difficulty got to bed could scarcely bend my body. Slept until near 10 oclok on Sunday morning. Found myself very stiff after eating pye and milk returned to room kept the bed nearly all day no church nearer than Middle burgh.

Monday morning tolerably well. Called on Best studied the *Drigg's*[18] affair concluded some of the notes might be collected. Then went with Mr Best *on horse back* !!! over a part of the patent saw several persons who live on the Lots purchased by Driggs. Made good use of pumping system. Spent the afternoon in asking questions apparently about things in general which however related to matters in Particulars. Spent the evening in drawing a map for my own use of the whole patent from the one in the possession of Mr Best. An hour of this or more was devoted to cross questioning a son of Old Driggs about the notes and the possession of his Land succeeded with

---

[14] This is probably a reference to Stephen Alexander's wedding the previous week on Monday, October 3.

[15] Benjamin Best (1785–1868) was the real estate agent for Harriet's mother. Luckhurst, *Genealogy of Schoharie County Families*; Benjamin Best to Maria Alexander, January 28, 1836, Family Correspondence, Henry Papers, Smithsonian Archives. For details of the dealings between the Henry family and Best see the next document.

[16] Webb purchased a lot from Mrs. Alexander. For some details of the dispute see the next document.

[17] The last decade of the eighteenth century and the first three of the nineteenth saw a steady rise in the use of euphemisms in the English language. Usage reached a peak with the coming of Victoria to the throne of England and remained high for the forty years that followed. The United States was especially guilty of substituting rather absurd euphemisms for everyday words.

By 1790 genteel society did not speak of male trousers. Rather, one spoke of inexpressibles. Later euphemisms of the Victorian period for trousers were unmentionables, unwhisperables, and inexplicables.

Henry, however, seems to be using the word to describe women's clothing. He is probably referring to drawers, which during this period were euphemistically known as knickers, panties, or trousers. Thus Henry has used one euphemism to replace a second euphemism in order to avoid a vulgar word.

Eric Partridge, *The Routledge Dictionary of Historical Slang* (London, 1973), p. 475; Eric Partridge, *Words, Words, Words* (Freeport, New York, 1970), pp. 97–100; *Oxford English Dictionary*.

[18] Elisha Drigg had bought a lot from Mrs. Alexander through the agency of Best. Money was still owed for it. Benjamin Best to Maria Alexander, January 28, 1836, Family Correspondence, Henry Papers, Smithsonian Archives. Again, details can be obtained from the next document.

much difficulty in making a straight story from a very crooked affair. Spent the whole of tuesday from 8 AM untill 8 PM in writing off from the statement of Mr Best an account of the situation of each lot sold and unsold. Did not leave my chair the whole day except for a few minutes to take dinner and Tea with Mr B. I returned to the tavern much fatigued and low spirited not so much from the fatigue of manual labour as the exertion during the whole day to meet cunning and *rogery* with apparent unsuspition careless & frankness. I was restless and feverish all the night. I do not know when I shall leave Schoharrie. I think it a duty I owe the family and particularly my wife and children to make myself perfectly acquainted if possible with all the facts relative to this property and to place it in such a situation in future that it will be safe against the system of Fraud which has been in operation relative to it for many years past.

I am obliged to be very circumspect in inquiries and to make sentences and paragraphs from words gleaned from many sources. The Landlord at first appeared very reserved but I have I believe suceeded in convincing him that I am a very good natured man with a little of the Yanky in my composition since I have questioned him about all the concerns of the country for miles around. I have also applied the pumping system to all travellers not of course [to satisfy an idle] curiosity, but that I might collect however remote which might have a bearing on the situation of the property and every person who had ever any connection with it.

TO STEPHEN ALEXANDER
Henry Papers, Smithsonian Archives

Scho[ha]rrie Court House
Friday evening Oct 14[th] 1836

My Dear Stephen

I have again been confined to the house this day by a storm not of snow but of rain so you see there is some variety in the weather in this country since it does not always snow but sometimes rains. I know not when I will leave Schoharrie but will endeavour to be off on monday or tuesday next. I will however remain until I can get the affair of the land in a situation to leave with safety if this be possible. I came to this place to consult with Mr Hamilton yesterday but found that he had gone to Albany, to day it has rained continually and I have not therefore ventured out. Mr Hamilton came up in the stage this evening and will meet me tomorrow morning. I will then return to Mr Bests (12 miles from here) and endeavour to adjust the lines of Lot No 38 preparatory to a sale which I have some prospect of effecting. This is the lot which our *fatheful* agent intended to appropriate to himself at a very reasonable rate. The business has thus far divided itself into 3 heads, The *Driggs affair*, The *Webb cause* and the *Best* agency. As to the first there are several notes amounting to upwards of 300 dollars for a part of which I think the Land is liable but I will determine this point from Mr Hamilton. Three of the Lots are now claimed by two sons of old Driggs and for two of these notes only were given in payment. The inequity of the Father must in this case be visited on the children.

A part of the Webb affair remains to be settled. There is a note in the hands of Best of 50 dollars which has not been collected but which may possibly be considered as an incumbrence on the property which Mr B. of course would not prosecute since he is himself a part owner of the Webb lot. The same line which caused the Webb dispute also cuts off a part of Lot 40, once owned by Dr. Lawyer[1] and which will I fear hereafter make some trouble unless it be settled. I will endeavour to study this matter and try to adjust it in reference also to Lot *38* before mentioned.

The Agency is the most disagreable and most delicate part of the affair to manage. I have had no words of an unplesant kind with Best as yet, have treated him with apparent frankness and unsuspition and have been very guarded in all my remarks relative to him since I find that all my motions have been closely watched and many hints throw[n] out to induce me to express an opinion of the agent. Best is surrounded by Cousins Brothers and Nephews who all consider the Land as a family concern. They speak in the warmest terms of his honesty and zeal in the cause of the "Widdow" but I know him to be a pitifull S_____. Would you believe that he had been offered 20/— per acre as our agent for the Lot which he wished to get last spring from us for 8/— and refused that he might secure it for himself. That he has taken premiums from purchasers for giving the land at a low value. That he has for a mere trifle got the assignment of lots which were about to revert to the estate on account of the failure of the possessor to fulfill his contract and thus got a deed for a Lot by paying about 50 dollars which is now worth 4 or 5 hundred.

I spent all the day of Tuesday last in getting an account of all he [k]new or would communicate of the history of each lot from the time of his agency

[1] John L. Lawyer.

to the present carefully noting down the whole. I think it must have been one of the most unpl[ea]sant days of his life. I observed him closely and was able to tell at once when something was wrong as we came to each Lot in succession by his manner of making the communication. When he came to Lot No 38 I really pitied the fellow; he was fairly put to his witts end. First led me off on another subject for half an hour and when I called him back to it after some hesitation stated that he had sold a part of it to a person who had cut timber and then showed me a map of the part sold dated 1834 surveyed by Vrouman. I took the map and instantly saw that it never had been made by a surveyor. It stated that the contents were 70 acres and being nearly in the form of a right angled triangle. I computed the contents and found it amounted only to about 30 acres. I stated that there was some mistake in the affair, that I marke the Lot unsold and that we would pass on to the next. After getting through the series at about 8 o'clock I left him without any remarkes relative to what I intended to do about No 38 and have not again met with him. I have been frequently asked about this lot and have had several offers to purchase. They all ask if Best has not purchased lot 38. I have given for reply that he had made some offer to my Brotherinlaw and I suppose intended to purchase but that we probably could not agree about the price and that we should sell to the highest bidder. I gave this statement that I might not expose Best publically. I will be obliged however to have a plain talk with the gentleman on the affair of this Lot before I leave. The other charges will be kept secret for the present as rods in pickle[2] for a future occasion. I do not intend to let it be known that we have any charges against him but it is proper that he be brought to an account for the whole and under the terror of a prosecution made to disgorge some of his ill begotten stores. I am sick of the degradation which the affairs of your Fathers estate exhibit of human nature. I ask myself does honesty exist among men in business or is a mere abstraction of the schoolmen. Even our friend J. O. Morse[3] is not immaculate. Do you wish to know why he in so friendly a manner advised Mother to settle the Webb affair. Simply because Webb purchased a farm of his and could not pay for it unless he gained the suit. The friendly gentleman was atorney for himself and not for Webb. *Iam. Satis.*[4]

---

[2] Meaning in reserve, as in "There's a rod in pickle for bad boys like you." *Webster's Third International.*

[3] *Henry Papers,* 1:229n.

[4] i.e., now enough.

A DEMONSTRATION OF DOUBLE REFRACTION
Commonplace Book, Notebook [10615], Page 505,
Henry Papers, Smithsonian Archives

Oct 1836

To exhibit the polarizing cristal of carbonate of Lime[1] given me by Dr
Torrey use the solar microscope or place the crystal in a beam of Light.

J.H.

[1] This appears to be a classroom demonstration of the phenomenon of double refraction. Carbonate of lime, also known as Iceland spar or calcareous spar, refracts incident light into two polarized rays—the ordinary ray, which obeys the usual law of refraction, and the extraordinary, which does not. The phenomenon was discussed in David Brewster, *A Treatise on Optics*, ed. A. D. Bache (Philadelphia, 1833), pp. 125–142. This was the text used by Henry in his class (*Henry Papers*, 2:346). Unfortunately none of the student notebooks from this period are complete, so we do not know if Henry actually carried out this demonstration in 1836–1837. The demonstration does appear as part of lecture 64 in H. C. Pitney's (class of 1848) notebook, Princeton University Library.

TO TRUSTEES, COLLEGE OF NEW JERSEY
Draft, Henry Papers, Smithsonian Archives

[October 1836][1] College of New Jersey

My Dear Sir

Agreeably to your request I state more definitely in writing what I have
communicated to you verbally relative to my wish to visit Europe next
summer.[2] The members of the Faculty have kindly offered to make such an
arrangement of the classes as will enable me to give a full course of Lectures
on Natural Philosophy before the time of my leaving. Mr Stephen Alexander should he continue connected with the college will teach the senior
class in Astronomy.[3] By this arrangement the Institution will incur no ad-

[1] The date is from Henry's file note.

[2] The Board of Trustees had already approved, in principle, Henry's visit to Europe. See the Minutes of September 29, 1836, above.

[3] During the first half of the nineteenth century, the professor of natural philosophy in American colleges was frequently also responsible for astronomical instruction. Henry had taught astronomy to the Seniors during the summer session of his first four years at Princeton (see, e.g., the Faculty Minutes of May 25, 1835 and May 18, 1836, Princeton University Archives), although no notes for this subject survive either among his papers or those of his students.

Henry's suggestion that Alexander might not remain connected with Princeton is a reference to the possibility he might be offered a position with the United States Exploring Expedition (Henry to Harriet Henry, September 28, 1836, printed above). In fact Alexander did teach the astronomy course, and he continued to do so during the next forty years.

ditional expense[4] and the students will suffer no abridgement of the present course of instruction.[5]

[4] Henry's other class during the summer session—architecture—was handled by Albert Dod.

[5] The following sentence appears at the bottom of the draft: "The substance of this letter was furnished by Prof Maclean."

TO MAHLON DICKERSON

Letters Received by the Secretary of the Navy
Relative to the U.S. Exploring Expedition,
1836–1842, RG 45, National Archives

Princeton Nov 17th 1836

Sir

I am informed by my Friend Dr James Eights of albany that he is an applicant for the situation of a naturalist in the expidition now fitting out for the South Seas.[1] In reference to this application permit me to state that I have long been acquainted with Dr Eights and that in my opinion he is eminently well qualified to be a valuable member of the scientific corps of the expidition. He possesses much general scientific knowledge, has de-

[1] Eights, who had already performed competently as naturalist on the 1829 Antarctic expedition (*Henry Papers*, *1*:69n), suffered a troubled and ultimately abortive association with this later enterprise. Although a difficult personality, his problems with the United States Exploring Expedition were symptomatic of ills besetting the venture from the start, especially Mahlon Dickerson's dilatory policies. Although by December 1836 Eights had ostensibly secured an appointment as paleontologist to the Expedition's scientific corps (there was some doubt about Eights's assigned specialty: see below, Torrey to Dickerson, December 3, 1836, footnote 3), Dickerson kept him on tenterhooks for months with evasions and postponements. Finally, on the eve of departure, Secretary of War Poinsett, having taken effective control of the Expedition, and Charles Wilkes dropped Eights and several other appointees in an attempt to scale down and remold the project. The cuts were controversial. Wilkes and Poinsett, a noted amateur naturalist, feared that the participation of too many specialists would pose obstacles to developing a general view of the phenomena and to the harmony of the corps. Also, Wilkes preferred to appoint Navy officers rather than civilian scientists to the Expedition. In Eights's case, there were cryptic mentions of his "habits" not being the best, an allusion perhaps to an argumentative nature. Throughout the affair Eights complained of unfair treatment and later appealed to the Navy Department for compensation for losses in time and money. William R. Stanton, *The Great United States Exploring Expedition of 1838–1842* (Berkeley, 1975), pp. 26, 27, 47, 48, 62, 63, 64. In Letters Received by the Secretary of the Navy Relative to the U.S. Exploring Expedition, 1836–1842, RG 45, National Archives, the following items: Eights to B. F. Butler, August 2, 1836; Eights to Dickerson, January 10, 1837, July 5, 1837, September 4, 1837; Eights to J. K. Paulding, September 21, 1838, November 21, 1838, December 26, 1839.

voted many years to the study of Natural history, is an accomplished Draughtsman and has had much experience in collecting specimens.

> I am sir very respectfully
> Your obedient serv.
> Joseph Henry
>> Prof Natural
>> Phil. College
>> of New Jersey

TO JAMES HENRY

Family Correspondence, Henry Papers, Smithsonian Archives

Princeton Nov 28th 1836

My Dear James

Your letter[1] by William Bullions was received on Saturday or rather friday evening last. I had been expecting for some time a letter from you and was quite anxious to learn the result of the interview with Mr Corning. I regret that you did not feel yourself compitent to take charge of the books but hope that you will yet be able to qualify yourself for the situation before the time will come for going into the business. The affair of bookkeeping is not one of such intricacy as to cause you to despair of soon acquiring it and where so much is to be gained as in this case I think it will be well to make the attempt. I would advise that you call on Peter Shankland[2] and consult with him relative to their business. Ask him to direct you in the course to be persued to acquire the requisite knowledge. I do not believe that you will require much instruction to perfectly comprehend the system of keeping books as practiced by Corning and when you have acquired the requisite knowledge Shankland will speak to Corning. I will write to Shankland on the subject and also at the proper time to Corning.[3] I am extremely anxious you should get into some better business and am confident if you once get started in the right course you will go on not only without difficulty but with credit and profit. I regret that you did not inform me before relative to the result of your interview with Corning as I

---

[1] Not found.

[2] Peter V. Shankland, a close family friend, was Chamberlain of Albany at this time.

[3] Neither letter has been found. Erastus Corning was a personal friend of Henry's as well as an Albany hardware merchant, banker, manufacturer, financier, and, at this time, Mayor. James Henry did not accept whatever bookkeeping position Corning offered. See below, Henry to Corning, February 7, 1837.

would immediately have urged the necessity of your qualifying yourself for the situation and would have requested Shankland to give you information relative to the kind of bookkeeping used by Corning. Do not despair. I know that if you were once started you would succeed and had I been in Albany I would have urged Mr Corning to allow you a trial. You have talents for this kind of business and the character you possess among all who know you for irreproachable integrity must secure you a situation which will render you not only comfortable but I hope will enable you to lay up something for the future wants of a rising Family.

I have been excedingly busy since my return from the north and have scarcely had a leasure houre since. I am now doing double duty in the way of lectures & recitations with the intention of getting through by the 10th or 11th of F^{bry} and starting by the packet of one or other of these dates. I have written to S. Alexander[4] of Rochester asking if he will accompany me. I have not as yet received an answer. I shall not however be without a companion since Linn De Witt the Brother of Richard V Dewitt is now at Princeton attending Lectures &c waiting to accompany me. He and William Bullions lodge in the Hall. Our family at this time is therefore quite a large one. Stephen and his Lady[5] are quite snugly located in the room over the parlor and have become quite like man and wife. We are all well now although the Boy has been quite unwell with a severe cold which still con-[t]inues and appears to have turned into the hooping coughf which has been prevalent here.

I am sorry to learn that Mr Gibson[6] has lost his health but hope his southern residence during the winter will restore him. I will be happy to receive a visit from him on his way to the South should he go by land & should be still more pleased to meet with him next summer in Scotland. Give Mrs[7] & Mr G. my respects and tell them what I say about a visit. I intend to write to Nancy and have commenced a letter but did not get time to finish it before the receipt of yours—I will write to her the next time. I would have written to her relative to her comming to Princeton this winter but did not know what to say. I would have been pleased to have her here but I did not think with all the females of the Family it would be possible for her to get on smoothely we are so much crowded. I do not however wish

---

[4] Alexander Stephenson Alexander (*Henry Papers*, *1*:116) was a cousin of Henry's. We have not located Henry's letter to him.

[5] The newlyweds Stephen and Louisa Meads Alexander.

[6] John Gibson (*Henry Papers*, 2:74).

[7] Isabella Gibson was born in Newburgh, New York, in 1794 and died in Brooklyn in 1889. Hun, "Albany Academy."

you to do all in the way of supporting her and will make you an allowance for her board this winter—

In haste your
Brother

I will write to Shankland this evening so that his letter may accompany this.

JOHN TORREY TO MAHLON DICKERSON

Letters Received by the Secretary of the Navy
Relative to the U.S. Exploring Expedition,
1836–1842, RG 45, National Archives[1]

New York, Dec.ʳ 3rd, 1836

Dear Sir,

On the 23rd. ult. I had the honor of transmitting to you a catalogue of botanical works, prepared by D.ʳ Gray & myself, which it would be desirable to have provided for the Exploring Expedition.[2] We marked such of them as can be obtained in New York, & when you instruct your agent to purchase books in this city, I will point out to him the places where they can be had. Several private naturalists would part with some of their books when they can be replaced in the course of a few months, or even in a year.

I have recently heard what has caused me some uneasiness—viz. that D.ʳ Eights has applied for the situation of geologist instead of a place in the department of zoology. When I gave him a recommendatory letter it was with the express understanding that he was not to apply for the place of geologist & mineralogist, as I knew that it was the general wish of the most intelligent naturalists of the U. States, to have that department filled by Mr. Dana. D.ʳ E. told me to solicit an appointment for him as *one of the zoologists* for which I think he would do very well. His *forte*, however, is *natural-history drawing*, & in this he would be most useful to the Exped.ⁿ provided he would be willing to work out of his own particular branch.[3] If

[1] This letter is printed in *House Executive Documents*, 25th Congress, 2d Session, 1837–1838, No. 147, pp. 201–202.

[2] Torrey enclosed the catalog in his letter to Dickerson of November 24, 1836. Letters Received by the Secretary of the Navy Relative to the U.S. Exploring Expedition, 1836–1842, RG 45, National Archives. The four-page catalog, undated and unsigned, is in Asa Gray's

handwriting and is filed after a letter from Nathaniel Bowditch to Dickerson of November 10, 1836.

[3] In a letter of November 19, 1836, Torrey recommended James Eights for a position with the zoological department. He also, however, commented favorably on Eights's work in geology, concluding the letter with the statement "Dr. E. has labored with great zeal &

you have not full testimonials in behalf of Mr. Dana, I am sure that none could produce what would be more satisfactory to you. In Mineralogy & Geology you are, (or once *were*) capable of weighing the relative merits of persons who cultivate those branches of science. Mr. D. will, I have little doubt, take the place of Cleaveland in Mineralogy.[4] He has an excellent

---

success, for many years, in examining the geological structure of the State of New York." Letters Received by the Secretary of the Navy Relative to the U.S. Exploring Expedition, 1836–1842, RG 45, National Archives. The letters of recommendation for Eights in the same volume support Torrey's contention that the "intelligent naturalists" did not intend that Eights be the geologist. The letters from politicians, however (William L. Marcy, Gerrit Y. Lansing, and John A. Dix, all of November 8, 1836), recommended Eights for the position of geologist, or geologist and naturalist.

[4] James Dwight Dana (1813–1895) was twenty-three at this time and just beginning a long and distinguished career in science. Born and raised in Utica, New York, he attended Charles Bartlett's Utica Gymnasium before entering Yale in 1830. There he became a protégé of Benjamin Silliman. With a recommendation from Silliman following his graduation in 1833, Dana served as an instructor for an eighteen-month Navy cruise in the Mediterranean. A visit to Vesuvius resulted in his first article, published in *Silliman's Journal* (1835, 27:281–288).

Shortly after his return to the United States, Dana became Silliman's assistant at Yale, a position which was an important stepping-stone for Dana as it had been for his predecessor Oliver P. Hubbard and as it would be for his successor, Benjamin Silliman, Jr. During this period Dana prepared his *System of Mineralogy* (New Haven, 1837), a highly successful work both at home and abroad (see the next footnote).

With strong backing from Asa Gray, as well as Torrey and other naturalists, Dana secured the position of geologist for the Wilkes Expedition. He later became responsible for marine zoology, part of Joseph P. Couthouy's duties, when Couthouy was dropped from the corps en route. Following the return of the expedition, Dana worked for the next twelve years with the immense amount of data he had assembled. His first report, *Zoophytes* (1846), introduced and classified hundreds of new species. *Geology* (1849) provided evidence

confirming Darwin's theory of subsidence as the agent in the formation of coral structures, included much new data in volcanology, and strongly supported uniformitarianism. The two-volume *Crustacea* (1852–1854) completed his work on the Wilkes Expedition data.

In 1844 Dana married Henrietta Frances Silliman (b. 1823), one of Silliman's daughters, and moved to New Haven where he spent the rest of his life. In 1846, when Benjamin Silliman, Sr., temporarily gave up the active editorship of *Silliman's Journal*, Dana joined Benjamin Silliman, Jr., as co-editor. Appointed Silliman Professor of Geology (later Geology and Mineralogy) in 1850, Dana did not actively begin teaching until after he had finished the last of the Wilkes reports in the mid-1850s. Dana earned a reputation as an effective teacher. Following years of poor health, he resigned in 1890.

Dana had a nervous breakdown in 1859 and thus did not comment on Darwin's *On the Origin of Species* until years later. Darwin's theories of coral structures had greatly influenced Dana's geological work for the Wilkes Expedition and he later corresponded with Darwin. Dana allowed Asa Gray to use *Silliman's Journal* to refute Agassiz's attack on Darwin's work and by 1874 (*Manual of Geology*, 2d ed.) he had accepted Darwin's theory of evolution.

Although he rarely left New Haven, Dana was active in the national science scene. *Silliman's Journal* gave him an armchair forum. He was a member of the American Association for the Advancement of Science, serving as President in 1854. Dana was associated with the informal but influential Lazzaroni although he was perhaps the most marginal member. He was also an incorporator of the National Academy of Sciences and a Regent of the Smithsonian from 1874 until shortly before Henry's death.

DSB. DAB. For Dana's connection with the Sillimans, see John F. Fulton and Elizabeth H. Thomson, *Benjamin Silliman, 1779–1864: Pathfinder in American Science* (New York, 1947). See William Stanton, *The Great United*

work on the science ready for the press—one which will do him, & his country, great credit. He has introduced a new & simple nomenclature, founded on true natural history principles, &, while it is strictly *classical*, it is very easy to acquire. In the next number of the Annals of the Lyceum of Natural History you will see a first-rate paper of his, on the subject of mineralogical nomenclature.[5]

Some of the most interesting results to be expected from this Expedition will be in the department of Meteorology—particularly in Austral Magnetism. We have a gentleman in our Country who is profound in that branch of science, & has gained for himself solid reputation both in Europe & America. You know, perhaps, that I allude to Prof. Henry of Princeton. I think he would draw up a set of questions, or instructions, embracing the most important experiments & observations which need to be made in order to supply what is defective in our knowledge of magnetic phenomena in the Southern hemisphere. Prof. [H.] is preparing to sail for Europe & I hope you will ask hi[m] for a list of queries before he embarks.[6]

With regard to the matter concerning which I made a confidential request, I beg to be understood that I have no unpleasant feeling towards Mr. Reynolds, nor was I urged to write to you by any gentleman who expects to accompany the Expedition. I knew, however, the sentiments of many of them, & merely gave you the information to make what use of it

---

States Exploring Expedition of 1838–1842 (Berkeley, 1975) for Dana's role in the Wilkes Expedition. See also Daniel Coit Gilman's biography, *The Life of James Dwight Dana* (New York, 1899), which includes a bibliography of Dana's many works, and William F. Sanford, Jr., "Dana and Darwinism," *Journal of the History of Ideas*, 1965, 26:531–546.

[5] In his *System of Mineralogy* (New Haven, 1837), Dana rejected the present nomenclature as "utterly devoid of system" (p. iv), and adopted a system with species designated by a binary name analogous to that used in botany and zoology. His new nomenclature, described in "A New Mineralogical Nomenclature," *Annals of the Lyceum of Natural History of New-York*, 1837–1848, 4:9–34, employed Latin, "the only language fitted for a system of nomenclature, both as regards conciseness and pliability" (p. 102 of *System*). He also introduced, based on Friedrich Mohs's work, a "natural" classification which reflected external characteristics of minerals which he preferred to a classification based primarily on chemical relations (pp. 96–97 of *System*). A glowing review, communicated by "T.," appeared in *Silliman's Journal*, 1837, 32:387–392. This review, probably by Torrey, concluded that "On the whole, we believe this to be decidedly among the best treatises upon this subject that have ever been circulated in the United States . . . ."

Dana's *System* reappeared in several editions during his lifetime. The third edition of 1850 substituted a chemical classification for the "natural" system and dropped the Latin nomenclature. The fifth edition of 1868 was the last edition for which James D. Dana was responsible. The sixth edition (1892) was by Dana's son, Edward S. Dana. (See Edward S. Dana's comments on the editions as quoted in Gilman, *Dana*, pp. 41–43. The first edition is in Henry's Library.)

[6] Dickerson wrote Henry on December 15 (below) asking for a list of inquiries in terrestrial magnetism. We have not located any list by Henry. He met with Dickerson in Washington in December for a long conversation on the expedition (Henry to Harriet Henry, December 28, 1836, below).

you thought proper.[7] I have seen Mr. R. but once, & then only for a few moments, since he sailed from N. York many years ago in the Annawan.[8]

I am, Dear Sir,

Yours with great respect,

John Torrey.

[7] In Torrey's letter to Dickerson of November 24, 1836 (cited in footnote 2), he warned "that if Mr. R. is to *have any control whatever* of the scientific gentlemen, they will (at least the majority of them) abandon the Expedition." Although known as an ardent advocate of a scientific corps in the expedition, Reynolds himself had no training in science. Torrey went on to say that he had no objection to Reynolds having some situation "in the great enterprise in which he has laboured so much."

Jeremiah N. Reynolds (1799–1859) had been advocating a national exploring expedition for years. In 1825 Reynolds appeared before the public as a disciple of John Cleves Symmes, who had been lobbying for a polar expedition to test his hollow earth theory. Reynolds soon dropped Symmes and his theory but continued to press for a national exploring expedition. He came very close to achieving his aim in 1828. In early 1829 the effort was quashed in the Senate. In October 1829, however, he launched a private expedition to the South Seas under Captains Nathaniel B. Palmer and Benjamin Pendleton. Reynolds left the expedition in Chile when his ship turned back. Returning to the United States in 1834, he resumed his advocacy for a national expedition, this time successfully. Although Reynolds was slated to accompany the expedition, he was abruptly dumped before the squadron's departure. For Reynolds's role in the Wilkes Expedition and his earlier activities, see William Stanton, *The Great United States Exploring Expedition of 1836–1842* (Berkeley, 1975), especially pp. 13–33. See also Robert F. Almy, "J. N. Reynolds: A Brief Biography with Particular Reference to Poe and Symmes," *The Colophon*, 1937, n.s. 2:227–245.

[8] The *Annawan*, commanded by Nathaniel B. Palmer, sailed from New York in October 1829 as one of the three ships of Reynolds's private expedition.

TO JOHN TORREY

Gratz Collection, Historical Society of Pennsylvania

Princeton Dec 14th 1836

My Dear Dr.

Your letter of yesterday was received this afternoon and I hasten to answer it by the return mail. I confess that I have been ungrateful in not immediately answering your kind letter of the 19th ult.;[1] but I have to urge in extenuation that my college duties have absorbed almost every moment of my time since the begining of the session. I have lectured every morning

[1] Torrey noted that he received this letter on December 17 and answered it on January 17, 1837. We have not located his reply, or his letters of December 13, 1836, and November 19, 1836.

and heard a recitation every afternoon since my return from New York.

I have given about 30 lectures and wish to finish my course by the first of Fe^by so as to be off according to your advice by the Packet of the 16th. My labours have been very severe and I feel that it will be well for me to relax a little. I therefore propose that as soon as I finish the subject of steam which will be on Saturday the 24th inst. to start for Washington. Can I do anything for you or the cause of science in the Capitol. If so give me directions by letter before the above date.

I will send you my copy of Donevan[2] by the first opportunity and I think Prof. Maclean intends to visit your city in a few days.

As to the Lectures which you are expected to deliver at Princeton in the Spring everything will be done so as to make the affair as convenient and pleasant to you as possible.[3]

Both Mr Maclean and myself will guarantee that you will have as much charcoal as you will wish to use. I have just purchased 40 bushels. The compensation proposed for about five weeks lecturing is $350. The course to commence about the first of march; the term ends on the 10th of april. You can suit your own convenience as to the number of Lectures per week. I have spoken to the President and Prof. Maclean on the subject; nothing however was said on the number of lectures; this I presume will be left as usual to yourself. In reference to the class books, most have been purchased from the former class and I have on hand 16 copies which were left unsold last session so that I apprehend no difficulty or delay on that score. I will most cheerfully deliver to you the key of my little room although it was my intention to put all my articles into it and lock them up during my absence, but I can stow away my articles so that there will be room enough for you. I must however request that you admit no person into it but yourself. I need however scarcely make the request since I know that you would be as careful of my articles as of your own and more so.

I will carefully inspect the case of chemicals and report to you the deficient articles but will it not be well for you to write me what articles

---

[2] Probably Michael Donovan, *A Treatise on Chemistry*, Cabinet Cyclopaedia (London, 1832).

[3] Torrey had previously lectured on chemistry during the summer session. In 1837, and for several years following, he lectured during the spring. According to a letter to Benjamin Silliman of March 25, 1837, it was only at Henry's urging that he continued to lecture at Princeton at all:

I should have declined lecturing any more at Princeton, after my course of last summer was closed, had not Prof: Henry been very urgent to me to remain connected with the College another year, & I delivered my lectures this year, in the early part of the season, as my time will be otherwise occupied during the summer.

Torrey Papers, New York Botanical Garden Library.

will be most necessary that we make sure in particular that they are not deficient?

I will also have the hall well washed and the articles put in as good order as possible.

Mr Maclean has employed a very intelligent young German[4] who will make an excellent servant for the Hall. I have had him with me a few days and find him more active and more disposed to keep things in proper order than any person I have ever before had in Princeton. He will remain during the session and will be employed to assist you. I extremely regret that I have not attended better to your commission to Mr Jaeger.[5] I have seen him but twice this session but inorder to deliver your message more surely I have this evening addressed a note to him which I will send through the Post office—he will get it tomorrow morning.

I am happy to hear that you are about to give a course of Lectures[6] in the way you mention for more reasons than one. It indicates an increasing attention in your enterprising and wealthy city to science and a liberality in reference to it which promises much for the cause. I would that Princeton could afford to pay you for the coming course as much as you deserve. The state of New Jersey is to receive in a short time about one and a half millions of dollars of the Public money on deposit.[7] Now if there were liberal spirit enough in the state the income of a part of this money would be

---

[4] Not identified. Perhaps this is Schmidt, who assisted Henry in 1838.

[5] Benedict Jaeger (*Henry Papers*, 2:55–56).

[6] Torrey had been engaged by the New York Lyceum of Natural History to give a course of lectures on chemistry (Minutes of the Lyceum of Natural History, December 12, 1836). In a letter to Henry of February 10, 1837 (printed below), Torrey commented, "My popular course seems to *take* well." He later reported to Silliman that his course was a success although the lecturers who followed him were hurt by the financial crisis and the public's waning interest at the end of the series of courses. (Letter of April 11, 1837, Torrey Papers, New York Botanical Garden Library.) Henry, tempted by the high fees paid to lecturers, gave a course at the Mercantile Library Association in New York City in early 1839.

[7] On June 23, 1836, Congress had passed a bill, effective January 1, 1837, to dispose of the huge surplus which had built up in the United States Treasury by depositing the money (except for $5 million) with the states according to their representation in Congress. Prior to the effective date, the surplus varied;

New Jersey's share fluctuated between $1,000,-000 and $1,250,000. By January 1 the surplus to be distributed had dwindled to approximately $37,500,000, of which New Jersey received $764,679 in three installments. (The fourth and final installment was cancelled due to the financial crisis of 1837.) The disposition of the money was left to each state. New Jersey deposited its surplus revenue with the counties according to state taxes paid. Most of the interest on the principal was used for schools for many years. The interest added approximately $15,000 per year to school funds until 1852 and $30,000 per year from 1852 to 1877. Edward G. Bourne, *The History of the Surplus Revenue of 1837* (1885; reprint ed., New York, 1968), especially pp. 84–86, 123, 143, 158.

The distribution (technically deposit) of the surplus was an election issue which was hotly debated in the press and among politicians, although the public showed little interest. The Whigs warned that Van Buren and his party would find a way to cancel the distribution. The *Princeton Whig* raised the issue repeatedly throughout the fall and early winter.

given to the College. An effort is talked of but I fear nothing will be accomplished.[8]

> In haste with
> Friendship and Esteem
> Yours &c
> Jos Henry

[8] We have found no evidence that Princeton received any of the money. In Connecticut, Wesley College (Wesleyan) and Washington College (Trinity) petitioned for an annual allowance. Bourne, *Surplus Revenue*, p. 34.

FROM MAHLON DICKERSON[1]

Miscellaneous Letters Sent, Office of the Secretary of the Navy, Volume 23, RG 45, National Archives

Navy Department December 15th 1836

Sir,

As you have bestowed more attention upon the subject of Magnetism than any other person probably in this country it occurs to me that you might propose a series of enquiries, to be made by our Scientific Corps to be attached to the South Sea Exploring expedition that would lead to the promotion of this particular Science. Should you be of opinion with me I would thank you to send me such enquiries as you may think proper.

I am wth gr[t] respect, Mahlon Dickerson.

[1] Also printed in *House Executive Documents*, 25th Congress, 2d Session, 1837–1838, No. 147, p. 205.

FROM JOHN VAN BUREN[1]

Joseph Henry Papers, Library, American Philosophical Society

Albany Dec[r] 20th 1836.

My dear Sir,

It gives me great pleasure to inclose you a letter[2] to my father as you desire & I trust it may further your wishes.[3]

[1] John Van Buren (1810–1866) was educated at the Albany Academy (entered in 1817) and Yale (graduated in 1828). He became a leading figure in the Albany bar and the New York State Democratic party. Considered by some to be the most outstanding orator of his day, Van Buren eventually became a spokesman for the Free Soil movement. *DAB*; Arthur M. Schlesinger, Jr., *The Age of Jackson* (Boston, 1945), pp. 398–400, 461–463, 482–483.

[2] Not found.

[3] Henry wanted Martin Van Buren, the

Wishing you a prosperous & pleasant journey.

I am very truly yours
J. Van Buren

President-elect, to write some letters of recommendation to the American ministers at London and Paris. This Van Buren did. See below, Henry to Torrey, February 4, 1837.

WALTER R. JOHNSON[1] TO STEPHEN C. PHILLIPS[2]
Henry Papers, Smithsonian Archives

Philadelphia Dec 25 1836

My Dear Sir,

Permit me to introduce to your acquaintance and to recommend to your kind regards my esteemed friend Prof Joseph Henry of Princeton New-Jersey. He visits Washington among other objects to receive some letters to Europe whither he will go for a few months in the course of the present season. He is much interested in the success of the Exploring expedition to the South Seas, & knowing your own views of that subject I have ventured to promise him that you would be pleased to make his acquaintance, & would find a congeniality of sentiment respecting its objects and arrangement. Should it be in your power to forward Prof. H.'s views in regard to letters &c. you will by so doing confer a favour on, & lay under a fresh obligation[3]

Your obt servt & sincere friend
Walter R. Johnson

P.S. Will you make Prof. H. acquainted with Mr. Lawrence?[4]

---

[1] Walter Rogers Johnson (for whom see *Henry Papers*, 2:188n–189n) was a professor of natural philosophy at the Franklin Institute and a close friend of Henry's. At the time he wrote this introduction for Henry he had just been appointed to the corps of scientists to accompany the Wilkes Expedition. When Wilkes decided to use naval officers to do the geophysical work, however, Johnson became superfluous and was separated from the expedition. George E. Pettengill, "Walter Rogers Johnson," *Journal of the Franklin Institute*, August 1950, 250:99; Nathan Reingold, ed., *Science in Nineteenth-Century America* (New York, 1964), p. 109.

[2] Stephen Clarendon Phillips (1801–1859)

was a Whig Representative in the Twenty-fourth Congress from the mercantile district of Salem, Massachusetts. He seems to have been a vigorous supporter of the United States Exploring Expedition of 1838. *Biographical Directory of the American Congress*, p. 1678; William Stanton, *The Great United States Exploring Expedition of 1838–1842* (Berkeley, California, 1975), pp. 190–191.

[3] We have not been able to find any letters of introduction by Phillips for Henry. In fact, since this letter was found in the Henry Papers in the Smithsonian Archives, we may assume that Henry did not meet Phillips during his stay in Washington.

[4] Johnson was undoubtedly referring to Ab-

bott Lawrence (1792–1855), Phillips's Whig colleague from Massachusetts in the House of Representatives. Lawrence enjoyed a varied career as an industrialist, an active politician, and a generous patron of science. With his brother Amos, he helped to launch the New England textile industry during the War of 1812. In 1831 he was elected a member of the Boston City Council and served in the Twenty-fourth and Twenty-sixth Congresses. In 1842 he was appointed one of the commissioners to settle the northeastern boundary dispute between the United States and Canada. His interest in scientific research led him in 1847 to grant a $50,000 bequest to establish the Lawrence Scientific School at Harvard University. *Biographical Directory of the American Congress*, p. 1442; *DAB*; Howard S. Miller, *Dollars for Research: Science and its Patrons in Nineteenth-Century America* (Seattle, 1970), pp. 77–81. As with Phillips, we can find no documents indicating that Henry met Lawrence at this time.

TO HARRIET HENRY

Mary Henry Copy,[1] Family Correspondence,
Henry Papers, Smithsonian Archives

Washington Dec. 28. 1836

My dear Wife. I commenced a letter to you last evening but was too late for the mail and since have had no opportunity for writing, since we did not reach this place until yesterday Tuesday afternoon. The Delaware River and also the Bay were obstructed by ice so that the boat did not reach Baltimore until eight o'clock on Monday. We were accompanied from Phil. by R. Horne[2] and Mr. Rogers the geologist.[3] Our arrival in Baltimore was at too late an hour to permit me to visit any of my acquaintances in that city. We therefore passed the remainder of the evening until ten o'clock in visiting the museum.[4] We were in time to see the last part of the performance of the celebrated french juggler M. Adrien: which consisted in making disappear in a very mysterious manner his little plump french wife.[5] Some sage remarks were offered by DeWitt on the importance of the secret

[1] There are two Mary Henry Copies of this letter, one handwritten and one typed. This text is from the handwritten copy, which is more complete.

[2] Or Home. Not identified. The copyist may have misread the name.

[3] Either Henry Darwin Rogers or William Barton Rogers.

[4] The Baltimore Museum and Gallery of the Fine Arts, which had been at the corner of Calvert and Baltimore since 1830, was originally a Peale family enterprise; they lost control in 1833. Its immediate predecessor was Peale's Museum on Holliday Street, which opened in 1814 and was run by Rembrandt Peale. Prior to this the Peales had made several attempts to establish a museum in Baltimore. John Thomas Scharf, *History of Baltimore City and County* (Philadelphia, 1881), pp. 691–694.

[5] Mrs. Adrien's disappearance was the highlight of the show, which included "a great variety of Physical, Mechanical, Magical and Incomprehensible Experiments!" Adrien was billed as "the most accomplished Magician of the present day." *Baltimore Patriot & Commercial Gazette*, December 28, 1836.

to married men &c &c. The museum contains besides a good collection of minerals and other objects of natural history a group of casts among these the Apollo Belvedere. I looked on this with much pleasure also on the cast of the wounded gladiator. These casts give I presume an excellent idea of the effect produced by these [works] of the arts or at least they would do so could we divest ourselves of the fact that they are only plaster and not marble. . . .

We left Baltimore about nine o'clock and reached Washington some time after twelve by the Washington and Baltimore rail road. The car was large and pleasantly heated by a small stove in the middle. We have taken up our lodgings at the principal house Gadsby's Hotel[6] but do not find accommodations as good as in houses of the same class in Philadelphia or New York. We yesterday afternoon visited the Capitol, saw the two houses in session, were introduced to the Library and Rotunda in which the large pictures of Trumbull are exhibited.[7] The effect produced by the Capitol at first sight and from a distance is not good. The pillars of the Corinthian or Composite order are too slender to appear well at a distance. When however the eye is brought sufficiently near to take in the details of the structure the effect is very imposing. The style of architecture is that called the Italo-Romanesque which was much in vogue before the study of Grecian remains introduced a better taste. As far as the architecture is concerned it would scarcely be a loss were the British again to burn the Capitol. In that case I am sure a more imposing and at the same time more simple building would be erected in its stead.[8]

The principal street of the city is that called Pennsylvania Avenue. It is about a mile long and terminated at each extremity by a hill. On one of these the Capitol is placed on the other the "White House." The rear of the Capitol faces this street.

I heard a debate in the house yesterday in which Mr. Adams took part.[9]

---

[6] Also known as the National Hotel, Gadsby's was at the corner of 6th and Pennsylvania Avenue. It was a large, first-class hotel frequented by politicians. In 1856 its popularity suffered when several guests succumbed to the mysterious "National Hotel Disease." W. B. Bryan, *A History of the National Capital . . .*, 2 vols. (New York, 1914–1916), 2:61, 445. Marian Gouverneur, *As I Remember . . .* (New York, 1911), pp. 176–177.

[7] John Trumbull's four panels of scenes from the Revolution for the Rotunda were far from his best works. The *DAB* terms them "heavy-handed, chalky, oversized reworkings of his earlier masterful paintings." Henry had seen Trumbull's work a year earlier at the Trumbull Art Gallery in New Haven (*Henry Papers*, 2:469).

[8] Throughout his life, Henry consistently argued for simple, functional architecture. In 1836, the Capitol was less "imposing" than it is today. Yet to come were the extension of the House and Senate wings, the large dome by T. U. Walter, and the landscaping by Frederick Law Olmsted.

[9] The debate concerned the repeal of laws authorizing protection of American seamen. Adams opposed repeal. *Congressional Globe*, 24th Congress, 2d Session, 1837, 4:55.

He is to my eye totally unlike the portraits of him. He has very little hair and this is not white but sprinkled with black. I am to have an interview with him this evening.[10] I passed last evening with Mr. Calhoun.[11] I was much pleased with his manner his intelligence and the interest he expressed in the cause of science. I called this morning on Mr. Van Buren found him alone with his two sons.[12] He received me with much cordiality and had preparation made to furnish me with all I requested in the way of letters &c. I am to call again tomorrow morning. I also visited the Secretary of the Navy and had a long conversation relative to the Southern expedition. . . .[13] I called on Mr. Butler[14] but did not find him in. I almost forgot to tell you I visited the President's House. The old gentleman cannot be seen but the "White House" is the property of the sovereign people and therefore is open to all comers.

I hope you will be pleased with the bonnet I have bought you. It is not of the colour you mentioned. I chose another which I hope will please you equally. Believe me my dear Harriet as ever your own J.H.

---

[10] We have not located letters introducing Henry to John Quincy Adams or John C. Calhoun. Before leaving for Washington, Henry had solicited letters of introduction. S. H. Porter gave Henry a letter to Senator James Buchanan (December 24, 1836, Henry Papers, Smithsonian Archives) and W. R. Johnson gave him one to Representative S. C. Phillips (printed immediately above).

John Quincy Adams was sixty-nine when Henry met him. His diary does not mention the interview. Adams was heavily involved in the early debates on the use of the Smithson bequest. When Henry became Secretary of the Smithsonian, he consulted Adams concerning the program of the new organization.

[11] John C. Calhoun was a Senator at this time. During Henry's early years in Washing-

ton, he and Calhoun were friends although Calhoun was not fond of the Smithsonian and had opposed acceptance of the Smithson bequest as beneath the dignity of the United States.

[12] Henry had a letter of introduction from John Van Buren to his father, then the President-elect. Martin Van Buren had three other sons, Abraham, Martin, Jr., and Smith Thompson. *DAB.*

[13] The material omitted here by the copyist may have described Henry's conversation with Mahlon Dickerson. We have not located any record of their talk.

[14] Henry knew Benjamin Franklin Butler from Albany. At this time Butler was Attorney General and Acting Secretary of War. *Henry Papers, 1:412.*

⊰ 1837 ⊱

JOURNAL OF JOB M. ALLEN[1]
General Manuscript Collection, Firestone Library,
Princeton University

Jan 25th [1837] Prof Henry commenced his examination to day on Architecture which is to answer for our final examination as he is going to Europe & will be absent at our next fall examination. He goes on business for the college to procure philosophic apparatus &c &c. His lectures this winter have been very interesting, more so perhaps than any part of our college course.

[1] Allen is listed in the *Princeton Annual Catalogue*, 1837, as a member of the senior class from Essex County, New Jersey, and, according to the *Princeton Catalogue*, p. 151, received his A.M. degree from Princeton in 1840.

TO JAMES HENRY
Family Correspondence, Henry Papers, Smithsonian Archives

Princeton Jany 26th 1837

Dear James

I have just finished my course of lectures and am now engaged in the examination of the class. My time has been so completely occupied that I have been obliged to defer writing to you for several weeks past although my conscience has continually reproached me for so doing. I now write to you under feelings of anxiety and pain in reference to our youngest child.[1] She is in a very critical state and but little hopes are entertained of her getting better. She was taken suddenly ill while playing on the floor about two weeks ago and has remained in a state of fever and langour ever since. The Dr[2] attributed her illness to teething. It now appears to be an inter-

[1] Helen Henry was then about nine months old. Her health improved significantly by early February and posed no obstacle to Henry's planned departure.
[2] Unidentified, but possibly George M. Maclean who had given medical attention to the Henry family earlier (see *Henry Papers*, 2: 472). The Henrys' most recent family physician, Dr. A. A. Woodhull, died in 1836 (see above, Henry to Harriet Henry, September 23, 1836).

mitting fever. She was at the first seized with a kind of fainting fit and has had several of the same kind during her illness. Her condition however has not at any time, except at the first appeared very alarming until to day. Yesterday she was apparently much better but this morning was much more feeble and had quite an appearance of change for the worse. About two o'clock she became so bad that Harriet sent for me from the college and the whole family thought that she was in a dying state. The Dr also concluded that she would not recover from the attac; he however gave her some stimulating drops which revived her in an astonishing manner so that she played with a watch for a few moments and called *Pa* sever[al] times. At this time (7 oclock PM) she still continues easy and her pulse has improved.

I can at present inform you nothing definite in reference to my European tour. I have been very actively ingaged in finishing my college duties and intend to devote the remainder of the time to the business of preparation for departure. The whole will however depend on the state of my family. I had concluded to sail on the 20th of next month for London or on the 16th for Liverpool according as I could make my arrangements. Linn De Witt who goes to Albany next week previous to our sailing will call on you for the letters which may be given to you for Scotland &c. I will direct him also to call on Mr Bullions.

In your last letter dated about 2 months since you mention that you had received the amount of Stephen Hayse's[3] note in cash and in Butter and that you intended to send the mony as soon as you could collect some from some other sourse. You need not put yourself to any trouble on this head and may pass to my credit the $100 from Stephen Hayse in part payment for Nancy's board. I can make my arrangements for my tour without that sum.

I hope Nancy will pardon me for not writing as I promised to her. I have compr[essed] the labor of a year into the space of 3 mon[th]s. I will write to her in a few days and to you or her every day after this until the child is better or worse.[4]

In haste your
Brother

---

[3] Stephen Hays (d. 1862), who was married to Joseph Henry's cousin Lydia Alexander (1802–1894). "Alexander Genealogy."

[4] Only one such letter has survived. Henry reported Helen's health "perhaps a little better." Henry to James Henry, January 28, 1837, Family Correspondence, Henry Papers, Smithsonian Archives.

February 3, 1837

TO WILLIAM C. REDFIELD[1]
Letters to Redfield, Redfield Papers,
Beinecke Library, Yale University

Princeton Feby 3rd 1837

My Dear Sir

I hope you will pardon my long silence in reference to the subject of your letter.[2] My time has been so completely occupied in college duties since my interview with you that I have scarcely had a moment to devote to my own affairs.

The account of the Tornado By Prof Johnson has not been published. He informed me lately however that he intended to insert it in some scientific journal[3] previous to his departure for the South Seas.

I am making preparations to sail on or about the 20th inst and will be much indebted to you for some advice relative to the Packets and to a choice between the ports of Liverpool and London or rather Portsmouth. All things being equal I would prefer to sail for London because I wish to reach that city as soon as practicable that I may be in time at least for the close of the Scientific Lectures of the Season and also because I will probably be at Liverpool in the Fall at the meeting of the Scientific association.

May I ask you to drop me a line on this subject as soon as convenient?[4] I will call on you when I come to New York and hope to have some more information relative to Atlantic Storms. I have been informed of a method of producing artificial whirl winds by means of steam from a covered boiler which is said to be an admirable imitation on a small scale of this most interesting phenomin[on].[5]

I will give you a verbal description when we meet.

With Much Respect
Sincerely
Yours &c
Joseph Henry

[1] Redfield (1789–1857; *Henry Papers*, 2:455–456) shared Henry's interest in meteorology.

[2] We have not been able to locate this letter.

[3] The account was published with the title "Observations on the Effects of a Remarkable Atmospheric Current or Storm as Witnessed on the Day Following its Occurrence," *Journal of the Academy of Natural Sciences of Phila-*delphia, 1834–1837, 7:269–281.

[4] Redfield made a notation on this letter indicating that it was received on February 19 and answered on the 20th. The reply has not been located.

[5] We have not found any references to the production of artificial storms through the use of a boiler.

February 4, 1837

TO JOHN TORREY
Torrey Papers, Library, New York Botanical Garden

Princeton Feby 4th 1837

My Dear Dr

I receved Chiltons bill with your letter[1] and have confereed with Professor Maclean on the subject. He has promised to have the appropriation made at the next meeting of the Board of Trustees which takes place at the end of the session the 10th of April.[2]

I have just finished my arduous course of instruction and am now arranging my affairs preparatory to my starting for Europe. I intend if possible to sail in the Packet of the 20th for London. If however the passage to Liverpool is safer and quicker I would wait for the Packet of the 24th. I wish to get to London as soon as practicable inorder to be there in time at least for the close of the scientific lectures of the season. You are no doubt very much engaged in your lectures but you will I hope find time to take my passage as you proposed.

I am to have a companion *de Voyage* Mr Linn DeWitt[3] of Albany a young gentleman who goes under my charge. As there will probably be but few passengers at this season of the year I presume we can each have a state room or a seperat sleeping box.

Nothing new at Princeton. The present college session has been a remarkable quiet one. All the students being confined to the college[4] the chance of irregularity has not been as great as usual.

I hope Mrs T. has interely recovered. We are all well at present but came very near losing our youngest child.[5] She was so ill about 8 days ago that I was called from my class with the expectation that she would survive but a few minutes. She however revived and has since recovered her strength astonishingly although she is still quite weak.

I will give you a list of the chemicals deficient in the case as far as I can make them out. I receved a letter a few days since from James D Forbes[6] of Edinburgh in which he wishes to know if you will permit him to direct packages to your care not only for me but for the Philosophical Society,

---

[1] Not found.

[2] The Board actually met on the 11th and 12th of April; $100 was appropriated to the chemical department and $100 to the philosophical department.

[3] See above, Henry to James Henry, November 28, 1836.

[4] Perhaps because of inclement weather.

Faculty minutes make no mention of a mass disciplinary action, another possible reason for the confinement.

[5] Helen.

[6] The Forbes letter seems to be that of September 22, 1836 (printed above), perhaps long delayed in the mail.

139

Albany Institute and Dr Beck. I directed him to send his packages for me to your care in New-York to obviate the difficulties I have before had in getting them from the city when they happen to arrive in the winter.

Mr Clow[7] will give you the same accomodation you receved when you were here last summer but as the weather in March will be cold and as there is no stove in the lower room it will be perhaps more comfortable for you to lodge in the upper room and use my library for your study. I will have the outer room as well as the others well cleaned and you can then put your settee in one corner.

I have made a visit to Washington and have procured letters from Mr Van Buren to the ministers at London & Paris.[8]

> Most sincerely
> Your obliged
> Friend
> Jos. Henry

PS Joseph the carpenter is just now fitting up your furnace on the side of the large stove.

[7] Henry Clow, Steward of the college. See *Henry Papers*, 2:371.

[8] Andrew Stevenson and Lewis Cass, respectively.

TO BENJAMIN F. BUTLER

Gratz Collection, Historical Society of Pennsylvania

Princeton Feby 6th 1837

My Dear Sir

I have been informed that it will be necessary for me to take a *passport* from this country in order to visit France or any part of the continent of Europe. I was under the impression that the letters I am furnished with from Mr Van Buren[1] would be sufficient to procure for me all the facilities necessary to my purpose and this impression may perhaps be still correct. In order however to be assured on the subject I have concluded to address a line to you and request that if you think it necessary you will procure a passport for myself and Linn DeWitt the Brother of R. V. DeWitt of Albany who is to accompany me on my Tour.

[1] These letters have eluded our search.

The passports can be left blank in reference to the description of the person age &c. These may be filled up by a friend here. I am now making preparations to sail in the Packet of the 20th inst. for London *via* Portsmouth. Should the article not be sent in time to reach me here please direct it to the care of Dr Torrey corner of Charlton and McDugall Street New York.[2] I leave Princeton on 17th inst.

I regret to be under the necessity of troubling you in this affair since I know that you are unduely occupied with the momentous business of your important station.

I intend to be present at the next meeting of the British association which is to be held this year at Liverpool in Sept. and have thought that it might be of some interest to the association and do something in reference to the character of our nation to exhibit an outline map of the United States on which all the canals railways and steam boat routes are delineated in conspicuous lines. I have been engaged for a week past in preparing a large map of this kind but find that my time will not permit me to make it as perfect as I could wish. I have therefore concluded to write to Col. Abert of the Engineer Bureau for some assistance and if you will be so good as to second my application you will oblige me and perhaps serve the cause of the diffusion of Knowledge.[3]

The meeting does not take place untill Sept and the materials I want can be forwarded to me at London during the summer.

With the hiest Respect
I am your ob.t servt
Joseph Henry

[2] The Henry Papers, Smithsonian Archives, has a February 11, 1837, note of Butler's in reply. From an undated, unsigned entry in volume 12 of the Passport Letters, RG 59, U.S. National Archives, the State Department sent the blank forms to the Collector of Customs at New York City for passports nos. 4769 and 4770. To the best of our knowledge, Henry's passport does not survive.

[3] In Butler's reply noted in the previous footnote he says he will speak to Abert. There are no surviving exchanges of letters in this period between Henry and Abert in the correspondence files of the head of the Topographical Engineers in the U.S. National Archives. Because of that we cannot state what assistance, if any, Henry received. The denouement of Henry's talk appears below.

TO ANONYMOUS[1]
The Quill,[2] *April 1895, 1:5–6*

PRINCETON, Feb'y 6th, 1837.

My Dear Sir:

I am making preparations to sail in the packet of the 20th inst. for London, via Portsmouth, and will be happy to be the bearer of any communications to your brother whom I hope to meet on the other side of the wide water.

Please send me his address and an account of his movements as far as you have learned them.

I have just finished my college course of instruction by compressing into the space of three months the usual labours of a college year. I have occupation now for every moment of my time in arranging my affairs, and therefore cannot if I would, trouble you with a long epistle. I will however expect an answer to this of considerable length.

You will please to send your communications to me by Linn DeWitt (the brother of R. V. DeWitt) who is, as you know, to accompany me on my tour, and is now on a visit to his Brother previous to sailing. He will leave Albany to meet me in New York about the 15th, and may be found at his Brother's house near the Academy, Albany.

I intend to spend my time principally in the three great cities of Edinburgh, London and Paris. Neither my time nor my purse will permit me to travel far. I must therefore narrow my field of view within the scope of my means.

My objects are principally the following: 1st. The formation of personal acquaintance with men of science which may be the basis of future correspondence on scientific subjects. 2nd. The study of the modes of instruction in science. 3rd. The methods of making original researches in the different branches of science. In short, to make such attainments as may be useful either in the way of my duties as an instructor or in reference to my own researches and which cannot be obtained from books.

As I feel considerable strength on some subjects of science, I shall not be

---

[1] We have been unable to locate the original of this letter and the newspaper article from which it was taken does not identify the recipient. We speculate that Henry was writing to Julius R. Ames (*Henry Papers, 1*:213), an Albany lawyer. Julius's younger brother Angelo was in Europe at the time. In fact, Henry met Angelo in Europe a number of times (see, e.g., Henry to Henry James, May 23, 1837, printed below).

[2] *The Quill* was the student newspaper of the Albany Academy. This letter is one of a number of Henry letters which the students obtained. It was later reprinted in the New York *Times*. A clipping of the *Times* version is in the Henry Papers, Smithsonian Archives.

ashamed to show my ignorance on others by asking questions even of an elementary nature.

Cannot you, without premeditation, pack up your budget, come to New York with DeWitt and start with us. I know you will not do so if you take a long time to consider on the subject. Your Philosophy will propose so many *pros* and *cons* that the decision will be as tardy as a Chancery suit.[3]

With the highest Respect,
Yours, sincerely,
JOSEPH HENRY.

[3] The English chancery court was infamous for its backlog of cases and the delays involved in obtaining decisions. One member of Parliament remarked in the House of Commons that "a chancery suit was a thing that might begin with a man's life and its termination be his epitaph." Richard Rush to John Forsyth, May 12, 1838, published in William Jones Rhees, ed., *The Smithsonian Institution: Documents Relating to Its Origin and History*, 2 vols. (Washington, D.C., 1901), *1*:54.

TO ERASTUS CORNING

Gratz Collection, Historical Society of Pennsylvania

Princeton Feby 7th 1837

My Dear Sir

I am making preparations to sail in the Packet of the 20th inst for London and must therefore call on you for the funds of which I spoke to you when last in Albany. I will be obliged to make rather a larger call than I intended having been disappointed in receiving money from another source.[1]

I will call on you through Mr R. V. De Witt of albany in about 8 days from this date for the sum of *nine hundred* dollars. I will send Mr De Witt an order on you signed by my brotherinlaw and myself and request Mr D W to give you a receipt for the money.

Mr De Witt will forward the money to me by his Brother Linn De Witt who is to accompany me on my Tour. He has been with me for some time at Princeton and is now on a visit to his Brother in albany previous to his departure.

I have been kindly furnished by Mr Van Buren with letters to our Ministers abroad and have received all the facilities for making such attainments in science as may be useful to myself and perhaps not entirely unimportant to the science of the country.

[1] The money that Henry was to obtain from Corning was part of the estate of his father-in-law; see the next document.

I shall confine my attention principally to the three great cities London, Edinburgh and Paris.

Receive my sincere thanks for your kind intentions towards my Brother. I regret extremely that he does not feel himself competent to take charge of a set of Books and prevents the kind arrangement you had pland for his better support.

> With the highest Respect
> I am sincerely
> Your obt serv
> Joseph Henry

P.S. Should any other situation than the one you thought of for my Brother offer may I ask that you will think of him. He writes me[2] that he has an opportunity of getting the book store of Hoffman and White[3] and is informed by the person who formerly kept there that a good living can be made in the place with a capital of about a thousand dollars. I would willingly assist him to the utmost of my means but am not certain that the affair will be a fortunate one. My Tour to Europe although I apprehend will ultimately cost me but little more than my ordinary living yet now makes a demand on my purse which will render assistance to my Brother at this time rather inconvenient. I am sorry thus to trouble you with my personal affairs and nothing but my anxiety in reference to my Brother would induce me to do so. I do not wish to discourage this attempt to get into better business and yet it does not appear to me to be as good as the situation you had intended for him as with the prospect of a small income he will run the risk of involving himself. As you are intimately skilled in all the business transactions of the city may I ask that you will give my Brother your opinion on this subject and will request him to call on you for that purpose.

> J. H.

---

[2] This letter has not been found.

[3] Benjamin Hoffman and Andrew White ran a printing establishment at 71 State Street in Albany where they published the *Albany Evening Journal*. In the same building there was a bookstore which James Henry did indeed take over in 1837. Albany City Directory, 1837–1838.

TO JAMES HENRY

Family Correspondence, Henry Papers, Smithsonian Archives

Princeton Febry 8th 1837

My Dear James

Your letter[1] would have been answered yesterday but I commenced to late for the mail. I am so intirely unacquainted with the business of Bookselling that I cannot say what will be best in this affair. I am very anxious to see you in better business than you are now in and will do all I can to assist you.

I wrote last night to Mr Corning in reference to my money concerns for Europe.[2] He has money belonging to the estate in his hands and I have made an arrangement with Stephen to transfer to the estate a note I hold against Samuel Pruyne[3] to the estate and a draw on Corning for the same ammount. I added a poscript to my letter stating that you had some thoughts of going into business in the book line and as he is well acquainted with business requested him to give you his advise in reference to the affair. I also thanked him for his kind intentions in reference to you and stated that I would write and ask you to call on him.

I wish you would call as soon as convenient after the receipt of this letter. He has shown himself very friendly to me and will I am confident cheerfully advise with you on the best course and perhaps may have thought on some situation for you which will be ultimately preferable to the one you are now thinking of. My object in wishing you to call on him besides the advise is to acertain if he thinks of giving you another offer.

I am very anxious in reference to the affair and wish you would call on him immediatly and then write me the result. Inform me what I can do for you in the way of getting credit or otherwise.

My tour to Europe although at present it obliges me to call in all the funds I can claim as my own will not in all probability cost me much more than my ordinary living. My Family will board in the country.[4] I receive a commission from the college[5] to purchase apparatus and will get some-

---

[1] Not found.

[2] See the preceding document.

[3] Samuel Pruyn, whose debt to Henry (originally $50) had remained unpaid at least since 1832. See *Henry Papers*, 2:27, 31, 36, 157.

[4] At the home of Mrs. Anthony Van Slyck, in Rotterdam, New York (along the Mohawk River, a few miles upstream of Schenectady).

[5] The alumni resolved to give the money for Henry's purchases, and on February 17, 1837,

Henry received the first installment amounting to $500 (Joseph Henry's receipt, February 17, 1837, Maclean Papers, Princeton University Library). Originally the Alumni Association of Nassau Hall pledged $5,000, but no further funds from the Association reached Henry in Europe. See below, Henry to Harriet Henry, June 28, 1837. Minutes of the Alumni Association of Nassau Hall, September 28, 1836, Princeton University Archives.

thing from DeWitt.[6] Besides this a Friend[7] has offered me the use of his purse which I may draw on in case of accident or otherwise. I cannot advance to you myself at Present but think I could preval on some of my Friends to do so for you. I regret that th[is] happens so near my time of sailing. I wis[h] to be off in the Packet of the 20th inst and will have all my arrangements made accordingly. Harriet and the children will be up about the middle of April and if you can accomodate them with boarding for about three weeks you will be doing a favour to us and render the time less tedious to Harriet.

It will be too early to go to Mrs Van Slyckes (where they propose to Board) before the beginning of May. Write me immediatly. Do not forget the account of our relatives in Scotland. Send me the names and the places if nothing else.[8] Also if you know anything of farther friends write about them. Cornings letter went off last night. The mail coloses at nine and every evening for two weeks past I have been engaged in writing letters.

Love from all to all. Little girl quite smart again. Hope you are all well. Tell Nancy that she must not take trouble on trust; it is bad enough when it comes. I will write a long letter to her before I go. Take care that you and your little Wife do not spoil your big boy.[9] Any packages you wish to send give into the charge of Linn DeWitt who leaves Albany on the 15th.

---

[6] One hundred dollars, according to Richard V. DeWitt's letter to Henry of February 15, 1837 (Henry Papers, Smithsonian Archives).

[7] Either Henry James or James Lenox, or possibly both. That the former may have been the "Friend" is strongly suggested by Henry's letter to Henry James of May 23, 1837 (printed below), in which Henry discusses his use of James's emergency funds.

On the other hand, Mary Henry's "Memoir" (Henry Papers, Smithsonian Archives) quotes from a November 1, 1836, Henry letter to an unidentified recipient (possibly Stephen Alexander in Albany): "I intend to start for New York tomorrow to make arrangements for my long voyage. I wish to have a long talk with Dr Torrey and also to prevail on Mr. Lenox to manage my money affairs during my absence, my letters of credit, &c &c." Mary Henry then writes, "Mr. Lenox not only consented to take charge of Henry's money matters, but placed his private purse at Henry's disposal, earnestly soliciting him to draw upon it to any amount." We have found no corroborating documentary evidence of such a financial arrangement between Henry and Lenox.

[8] No such listing has been found. Henry visited relatives in Ayrshire after leaving Glasgow in early September. No comments on his visit have been found. A letter to one relative, Dr. Robert Ballantine, is printed below, October 2, 1837.

[9] John P. Henry, aged eleven months.

FROM JOHN VAUGHAN
Henry Papers, Smithsonian Archives

Phila. 9 Feb 1837

D Sir

I rejoice that your labors are finished & that you propose paying Phil. a Visit before your departure. You will find the Bed in the same place & the same friend happy to receive you. You can have your interview with Hare,[1] & I shall prepare your letters[2] when better informed of your plans; they will not be long or numerous but such as will I hope serve you & to friends who will be gratified to know you.

Ys

Jn Vaughan

I have been confined some days, but am now completely well.

[1] Henry met with Hare on Saturday, February 11. See below, Henry to Torrey, February 13, 1837, and Hare to Henry of the same date.
[2] We have not located any letters by John Vaughan introducing Henry. He apparently wrote one to his nephew, Petty Vaughan, and his brother, William Vaughan. Henry wrote his wife on March 21, 1837 (see below), that he had called on the Vaughans in London with a letter of introduction and had received several introductory letters from them as a result.

FROM JOHN TORREY
Henry Papers, Smithsonian Archives

New York Feby. 10th 183[7][1]

My dear friend,

I have taken staterooms for two passengers in the splendid ship Wellington,[2] which sails for London on the 20th inst. She is a noble vessel—entirely new—having never yet made a voyage. So you will not be annoyed by bilge-water, nor by the creaking of the masts & joints, the noise of which is so irksome in stormy weather. The state-rooms are very large & all the accommodations of the ship are splendid. I went out in the South America[3] on her

[1] The original letter is erroneously dated 1836.
[2] See below, "Drawing of the Wellington," February 1837.
[3] Built in 1832, the *South America* plied the New York-Liverpool run. It was considered the swiftest and one of the most dependable of the early packets. Robert Greenhalgh Albion, *Square-Riggers on Schedule* (Princeton, 1938), pp. 168, 186, 198.

first voyage & I should always prefer a perfectly new vessel if I could obtain a passage in one. You must not embark later than the 20th. The 16th would have been better, but even then you would be exposed to rough weather in the Channel. Capt Chadwick[4] (who took out D[r]. Cox & Prof Alexander[5]) is a fine fellow. He says he hopes to reach Portsmouth in 18[6] days. You must be here two or three days before the 20th, as I have many things to talk to you about.

I hope you will bring with you the list of desiderata for the laboratory. Can you get an appropriation for purchasing a few hundred dollars worth of app[s] in Europe?

It will always afford me pleasure to take charge of any packages for you from your foreign correspondents & I beg you will allow me to execute all your commissions relating to Custom-house matters.

You are very kind in making every arrangement for my comfort in Princeton. Will you have the goodness to unscrew the top of my settee bed-stead, & see whether I packed up any bedclothes in it.

I am much occupied in my chem[l] lectures this winter. My popular course seems to *take* well. The class is numerous & highly respectable. I take much pains to prepare my expts. on a splendid scale.

The report of Prof[r] Renwick's death is a miserable hoax. The Prof[r] is in good health. He is lecturing for the Apprentices Library Assoc[n][7] at their building in Crosby St.

My kindest regards to all your family.

Truly yours
John Torrey

---

[4] Identified in Henry to Harriet Henry, March 21, 1837, footnote 7.

[5] Samuel Hanson Cox (1793–1880, *DAB*), Presbyterian clergyman and a founder of New York University, and Joseph Addison Alexander (1809–1860, *DAB*), linguist and educator who taught at Princeton and the Princeton Theological Seminary in the 1830s. In April 1833 Alexander and Cox traveled to Europe together in the *Samson* under Chadwick's command. Henry Carrington Alexander, *The Life of Joseph Addison Alexander, D.D.*, 2 vols. (New York, 1870), 1:284, 285, 331.

[6] An inkblot has obscured the reading of this figure.

[7] The Apprentices' Library, opened in 1820, was an establishment of the General Society of Mechanics and Tradesmen of the City of New York. The Society, organized in 1785, also operated a Mechanics' School and, in 1833, inaugurated a lecture course for "promoting and disseminating literary and scientific knowledge." In Henry's day, the library, the school, and the meeting rooms of the Society were housed in a former high school building on Crosby Street. *Historical Sketch and Government of the General Society of Mechanics and Tradesmen of the City of New York, 1785–1914* (New York, 1914), 24 pp., unpaginated.

FROM ALBERT HOPKINS[1]
Henry Papers, Smithsonian Archives

Williams College Feb 10 1837

Dear Sir

Having understood that you were to leave the country on the first of this month I concluded you had probably sailed and accordingly dispatched a letter to Mr Simms.[2] However as my order was not urgent he probably will not execute it before your arrival. I have ordered a dipping needle and some needles suitable for testing the intensity of the earths magnetism. My object is to have instruments perfectly accurate and at the same time as portable as possible for I intend to travel with them. Should you be in London before my ins^s are made you will do me a favor to look a little at the different forms & advise with Mr Simms in relation to them. I enclose a letter to M. Simms. He is a member of the R. Astronomical Soc^y and will be happy I doubt not to introduce you there but you will find no difficulty in getting access to the learned bodies.

Have the goodness to remember me to Dr Torrey. I owe him a letter and intend to pay when the "vines & the tender grapes begin to give a good smell."[3]

Accept dear Sir the assurance of my high regard & best wishes for your success in the interesting voyage you are about to undertake.

Obediently & truly
yours
Albert Hopkins

[1] For Hopkins, see *Henry Papers*, 2:212. A member of the Williams College faculty, he was responsible for the founding of its observatory, the first permanent one in the United States.

[2] Since the death of his partner, Edward Troughton, in 1835, William Simms (1793–1860) was conducting the business of Troughton and Simms, probably the most renowned instrument maker of that period. *DNB*.

[3] Perhaps a play on the words of the *Song of Solomon*, 2.15.

FROM THE SENIOR CLASS OF
THE COLLEGE OF NEW JERSEY
Henry Papers, Smithsonian Archives

Princeton February 13th 1837

Dear Sir.

The members of the Senior Class, aware of your intended departure for

Europe, have appointed (us) a committee to express their kind feelings towards you.[1] We regret exceedingly, Sir, that we could not have remained longer under your instruction, but confidently hope, if your health continues good, that your early departure will prove advantageous to the cause of science. Suffer us, Sir, in behalf of the class, to tender their sincere thanks for your attention as a professor & courtesy as a gentleman. Wishing you a safe voyage, a pleasant visit & a happy return at length to your family & friends.

We remain

Your's most respectfully
Henry A Cram
Joseph H Dukes
William C Storrs[2]

[1] Contemporary and retrospective accounts of Henry as a teacher agree that he was an interesting, informative, even exciting lecturer. His courses were considered by some of the students to be the highlight of their stay at Princeton. He was also sympathetic to and understanding of the feelings of the students. Henry was perhaps the most popular Princeton professor of his day. Weiner, "Joseph Henry's Lectures," p. 79; *Wertenbaker*, pp. 223-224, 243-244; William E. Schenck, preparer, *Biography of the Class of 1838 of the College of New Jersey, at Princeton, N.J.* (Philadelphia, 1889), p. 17.

[2] Cram (d. 1894), Dukes (d. 1875), and Storrs (d. 1873) seem to have been representative Princeton students. Storrs and Cram were from New York City. Dukes was one of the many Southern students at Princeton; he came from Charleston, South Carolina. Storrs and Dukes joined the Class of 1837 during its sophomore year; Cram entered Princeton one year later. *Princeton Catalogue*, pp. 151-152.

FROM ROBERT HARE

Henry Papers, Smithsonian Archives

Philad[a] Feb[y] 13th [1837]

Dear Sir

I have written some letters in which I mention you and make acknowledgements for kindness experienced during my visit to England. You will also find a letter for my Brothers.[1] Should it so happen as that you should be in the same place with my son J I Clark Hare you will need no introduction to him, and I trust you will call on him and M[rs] Hare without hesitation.[2] In London you will find a great number of shops in which

[1] Charles Willing Hare (1778– ?) and John Hare Powell (1786-1850). J. W. Jordan, ed., *Colonial and Revolutionary Families of Pennsylvania*, 4 vols. (New York, 1911), *1*:129-130.

[2] John Innes Clark Hare (1816-1905, *DAB*) would become a notable jurist in Philadelphia. We assume Mrs. Hare is his mother, Harriett Clark Hare.

philosophical instruments are sold. The persons so engaged are generally scientific men and I found no difficulty in making myself acquainted with them. Watkins Charing Cross[3] I found more intelligent than the majority of them. I do not like Newman, N° 122 regent St.[4] He is however much employed. I would advise you as soon as possible after your arrival in London to make out a list of the persons and places which it may be most desireable to see and then with the aid of any person well acquainted with the City adopt some plan of seeking them in succession so as to take as little time as possible. I would get an address book and enter every address as obtain'd.[5] As you ride along the street have your pencil and memorandum book ready and take down every name which you may perchance whish afterwards to find. But I would not trust to pencilling. I would copy the whole in Ink. You may find them of use when you return to America, as well during your stay in Europe.

I will thank you to send to me through Mr Petty Vaughan directed to Jn° Vaughan Esqr for me any new works on Chemistry galvanism and Electromagnetism. Mr Brande offered me an unfinished copy of his work. I have written to him by you requesting him to send me a complete Copy.[6] I would send some copies of the last edition of my text book[7] availing myself of your kindness for the delivery of them did I not know that you would have to pay duty on them at the Custom house and they would be very cumbrous. I have obtain'd a very volatile species of naphtha from caoutchouc but it does not as a solvent of that substance realize all that I was led to expect. I will thank you therefore to send me any account of the process

[3] Francis Watkins (d. 1847), the second instrument maker of that name, was a partner in the firm of Watkins and Hill, 5 Charing Cross, and very active in electricity and magnetism. Henry visited him in London; see the diary entry of March 21, 1837, and other references below. Henry purchased a polarization apparatus from Watkins. E. G. R. Taylor, *The Mathematical Practitioners of Hanoverian England, 1714–1840* (Cambridge, England, 1966), p. 438. Samuel P. Bell, comp., *Biographical Index of British Engineers in the Nineteenth Century* (London, 1975), p. 229.

[4] John Frederick Newman, fl. 1816–1860, third of that family to make instruments in London. He was best known for barometers, having made the Royal Society's standard barometer in 1822. Henry's visit is in the Diary entry of August 1, 1837, below. Henry's accounts disclose the purchase of a few small items from Newman. W. E. Knowles Middleton, *The History of the Barometer* (Baltimore,

1964), p. 148. Nicholas Goodison, *English Barometers, 1680–1860* (New York, 1968), p. 313.

[5] Henry does have an address book for this period among his papers in the Smithsonian Archives (Box 17). The evidence is ambiguous as to whether he proceeded along the lines suggested by Hare, here acting as a solicitous older friend. The address book was used for many years afterwards and contains much useful information about Henry's network of correspondents to the early years at the Smithsonian. As Hare's advice is the conventional wisdom, Henry may have started the address book even before this date. One can wonder why Hare did not suggest keeping a diary.

[6] Possibly a reference to Brande's *A Dictionary of Materia Medica and Practical Pharmacy* . . . (London, 1839).

[7] The third edition of Hare's *Compendium of the Course of Chemical Instruction* . . . appeared in 1836.

of procuring the solvent in question which you may be enabled to procure.[8] I have in my letter to Profr Wheatstone requested him to do the same.

He was so good as to take me to the manufactory of Mess[rs] Enderby by whom the article was first made as I understood.[9] It might be safely shipped in the iron bottles such as are used for mercury in commerce if screwd in with shell lac or sealing wax while hot. I do not however like the idea of putting a substance so volatile and inflamable in ship Board.

I will thank you to bear in mind that I am quite grateful for my reception by the savans of Great Britain at Bristol.[10] My only source of regret is that the shortness of the time and indisposition did not permit of my being personally introduced to many whom I admire and esteem or to make the communications which I was prepared to lay before them.

Sealed letters are required by law to be given up to the Post office. On this account I leave mine open and when you do not hand them yourself you had better seal them as [...][11] are not allowed in England.

---

[8] When caoutchouc (an older term for natural rubber) was subjected to a temperature of about 600°F, the condensation of the resulting vapor was "a powerfully odorous and extremely volatile amber-coloured oil" named caoutchoucine. This chemical could dissolve resins and even natural rubber. It was discovered by William Henry Barnard of Greenwich who received a patent, no. 6466, for the solvent on August 20, 1833.

Its physical and chemical properties understandably interested a chemist like Hare. See the later reference in the entry of April 12–15, 1837. On May 4, 1837, Bache wrote William Hamilton about sending caoutchoucine to the United States for Hare and the Franklin Institute. Some of this shipment was destined for Joseph Henry. At the June 22, 1837, Monthly Conversation Meeting of the Franklin Institute, Robert Hare reported on his experiments with the caoutchoucine sent by Bache. Outgoing letterpress book, Bache Papers, Smithsonian Archives. *Encyclopaedia Britannica*, 8th ed., s.v. "caoutchouc." B.

Woodcroft, *Alphabetical Index of Patentees of Inventions* . . . (London, 1854), p. 26. *Franklin Institute Journal*, 1837, 20:130.

[9] Brian Bowers, *Sir Charles Wheatstone, FRS, 1802–1875* (London, 1975), p. 144, notes that the Enderby firm supplied insulated wires for Wheatstone's telegraphy experiments. Wheatstone also took Henry to Enderby's; see the diary entry of April 12–15, 1837, below. According to one version of a June 13, 1834, Faraday lecture given in the *Franklin Institute Journal*, 1837, *19*:297–302, the firm was notable for its willingness to display the new solvent. Enderby used the material to prepare ropes and cordage impervious to water. The wire furnished Wheatstone may have served for a telegraphy experiment across the Thames, perhaps even under water.

[10] The sixth meeting of the British Association for the Advancement of Science occurred in Bristol in August 1836.

[11] One indecipherable word. We do not understand Hare's advice.

TO JOHN TORREY
Gratz Collection, Historical Society of Pennsylvania

Princeton Feby 13th 1837

My Dear Dr

Your letter of the 10th inst[1] was received this morning. I have made all my arrangements to leave Princeton on Friday and to be with you in the afternoon of that day.[2] I am much indebted to you for your trouble in reference to the passage &c. I have directed several letters to be sent to me directed to your care. Should any of them arrive before Friday please detain them until I come.[3] Keep an account of the postage and I will settle with you for the same.

I have put up all my books and articles and have arranged the little room so that it will answer your purpose. You need not bring on any bed clothes as Mrs Henry bids me say that she will be happy to furnish you with what ever you may want in that line.

I am pleased with the idea of sailing with the capt. with whom Professor Alexander went out. He spoke to me about him sometime since and expressed a wish that I might go with him. No news at Princeton. I saw in a Philadelphia paper the announcement of the death of Professor Renwick but learned in that city that it was a fraud probably invented by some student of the college.

I had a long conversation with Dr Hare on Saturday; he was highly pleased with his reception by Scientific men in England and France but remarked that he had attempted rather too much and thus were he to do the thing again particularly at the association he would bring forward only a few articles and have these well prepaired.

I have been employed a few days in constructing a very large map of the United States on which all the canal, rail way and steamboat routes are delineated in conspicuous lines. I have also procured from Mr Tanner[4] of Philadelphia one of his unpainted maps which also exhibites the same routes on a smaller but more perfect scale.[5] These I intend to take with me

---

[1] See above.

[2] February 17.

[3] Henry and Torrey spent some time together before Henry sailed. An indication of this is the notation "Ans.[d] verbally" which Torrey placed on top of this letter.

[4] Henry Schenck Tanner (1786–1858) and his brother Benjamin (1775–1848), both engravers, established a cartographic firm in Philadelphia in 1811. The younger Tanner soon became the leading American cartographer of

his day. *DAB.*

[5] Probably Henry S. Tanner's "Map of the Canals & Railroads of the United States, Reduced from the Large Map of the U.S. by H. S. Tanner." This map was originally published in Tanner's *A Brief Description of the Canals and Railroads of the United States* (Philadelphia, 1834). It measured 17 by 22½ inches. P. Lee Phillips, *A List of Maps of America in the Library of Congress* (Washington, D.C., 1901), p. 888.

to the association and if an opportunity presents to exhibit them one to the section on mechanics and the other should I find it likely to be interesting to the general meeting.[6] I will however confer with you on the subject when we meet.

Bache is now in London and is highly delighted with the reception he has every where met with. I believe he visited Scotland first. I regret that he did not receive letters from you but if you can find time to write him on the subject I will make all smooth.

I have had a general inventory taken of all the chemicals now in the Hall so that you can determine what are deficient. The amount of each article is given and where the bottle is empty the fact is noted.

In haste yours as ever
Jos. Henry

[6] Henry did exhibit these maps at the meeting of the Mechanical Section of the British Association. See below, Henry to Bache, October 1, 1837.

FROM ERASTUS CORNING

Joseph Henry Papers, Duke University Library

Albany. Feb[y] 15 1837

My Dear Sir

Yours of the 7th Inst was duly received.[1] I yesterday paid Rich[d] V DeWitt Esq Nine Hundred Dollars on your Order.

It would give me great pleasure if I could in any way be of service to you. I could give you letters to some of my friends residing in the Manufacturing towns, say Birmingham & Sheffield. But wether they would promote your object it is doubtfull—and as you have letters of so much more importance than any I could give you I have deferd sending you any. But if you think they will be of service let me know and I will send them by the next Packet. I think rather favorable of the Store occupied by Hoffman & White, and am of the opinion that your Brother with proper exertions would do well there. If I can in any way be of service to him in this undertaking (if he should conclude to embarke in it), it will give me pleasure to promote your wishes.

Wishing you every success in your contemplated tour, I am with much respect

Your Ass[d][2] friend
Erastus Corning

[1] Printed above.   [2] Assured?

FROM WILLIAM C. REDFIELD

Henry Papers, Smithsonian Archives

New York February 18th 1837

Dear Sir

I have taken the liberty to place at your disposal some 30 or 40 copies of my last paper on the Storms of the Atlantic and which was first published in the London Nautical Magazine for April last.[1] As the circulation of that periodical is chiefly among members of the Naval Profession the article has not probably reached a majority of the men of science in Europe, and you may doubtless meet with gentlemen who take an interest in the general subject and to whom our transatlantic views of the case may not be unacceptable. I have therefore designed the bundle of 25 copies for distribution among the gentlemen of the section which includes meteorology, or rather among the meteorologists and geologists at the Liverpool meeting,[2] unless you should otherwise determine. You will have the goodness however to dispose of the whole in such manner as you may think proper, save two or three copies to which I have given a special direction. As you may get taxed with duties at the English Custom house on these papers I propose to place a small sum in your hands to meet this contingency. If I can learn your address in London I shall probably forward you a few copies of my reply to Mr Espy, when the same is in print.[3] Wishing you a prosperous and pleasant voyage,

I am Dear Sir Yours Sincerely
W[m] C. Redfield

[1] "On the Gales and Hurricanes of the Western Atlantic," 1836, 5:199–211. The article was subsequently reprinted twice in the United States. The Henry Library contains one of these.

[2] Of the British Association for the Advancement of Science.

[3] "Mr. Redfield, in Reply to Mr. Espy, on the Whirlwind Character of Certain Storms," *Franklin Institute Journal*, 1837, *19*:112–127.

Redfield continued to use Henry as a conduit to Europe for his writings; see his letter of May 31, 1837, below.

TO NANCY HENRY

Mary Henry Copy, Family Correspondence,
Henry Papers, Smithsonian Archives

New York Feb. 19, 1837

My dear Sister. I know you will pardon me for not writing sooner when you recollect that I have scarcely had a moment to myself this winter, having been obliged to do double college duty previous to my departure. I sail tomorrow at eleven o'clock, in a large new and beautiful ship, and will have in all probability a very quick and safe passage. I would on some accounts have been very happy to have had you in Princeton when I left, but I fear you would not have been a very good comforter for Harriet, and perhaps it is best as it is. Harriet will be lonely, but I hope she will soon become reconciled by my absence, and that she may pass the summer pleasantly among her friends and relatives at the North.

James informs me that you are much troubled about my sailing on account of the dangers of the voyage. It is not proper to make ourselves unhappy in anticipating troubles. The All Wise disposer of events will order all things aright; and whatever happens will be for the best. A voyage to England is now considered a matter of little consequence and the danger in such a vessel as the one in which I sail, is not more than that of a trip to Albany in a steam-boat.[1] Is not the same Providence our protector on sea as on land? We are not sure of our lives from moment to moment, and while we should be prepared at any time to die we should also recollect our lives are in His keeping who holds the winds in His hands and who controls the rage of the elements.

You may expect to hear from me in the course of two or three months. I will write as soon as I reach London, but perhaps a packet may not leave immediately so that some time longer may elapse. I know that you and Harriet will remember me in your prayers. I will join you in beseeching the God of all Mercies—if it be consistent with his will—that I may be safely restored to you and my family and that you may all be under His guidance and protection during my absence. With love and esteem my dear sister

Yours as ever, Joseph

[1] Although transatlantic voyages were still considered hazardous, ocean-going packets set an impressive safety record, suffering proportionally fewer wrecks than ordinary commercial shipping. Albion cites a statistic of only twenty-two wrecks out of almost six thousand transatlantic packet crossings. Passenger risk was statistically low for the New York ocean packets which Henry was to take. The record was especially impressive given the fact that the packets sailed on set schedules regardless of season and weather conditions. Robert Greenhalgh Albion, *Square-Riggers on Schedule: The New York Sailing Packets to England, France, and the Cotton Ports* (Hamden, Connecticut, 1965), pp. 202–203, 228. George Rogers Taylor, *The Transportation Revolution, 1815–1860* (New York, Evanston, and London, 1968), pp. 104–107.

Still, Henry's family was probably comforted by the fact that he paid an extra life-insurance premium of forty dollars to guarantee coverage during the European trip. (The policy was issued on February 18, 1837, by the New-York Life Insurance and Trust Company. Box 50, Henry Papers, Smithsonian Archives.)

TO HARRIET HENRY
Family Correspondence, Henry Papers, Smithsonian Archives

New York Feby 19th 1837
Sunday evening 10 o'clok

My Dear Dear Wife

I have just finished a letter to Nancy and another to James and have reserved the last moments of this evening to be devoted to her who stands nearest my heart. Although much fatigued with my engagements here yet I have not been able to sleep. My wife and little ones are constantly before my minds eye. The Baby in Aunts[1] Arms, the two older ones as I interrupted their merry laugh to give my sad parting kiss and you—you my Dear Dear Wife as I last saw you endeavoring to suppress the Anguish which wrung your breast—all all are continually before me.

I would leave my country on this excursion with pleasure and perfect security were you the companion of my voyage and since my leaving Princeton I have regretted that I did not make an effort to persuade you to accompany me; but then again I have thought it could not be, that you would not leave our children and we could not take them with us.

You know My Dear Harriet that I do not make this voyage for the sake of pleasure and that I do not wish to partake of pleasures which are not enjoyed with my Family. My Dear Wife I cannot express the feelings of tenderness which now swells my breast with the thoughs of you and our Little ones. They appear far more lovely and interesting than ever and you by your conduct in this affair have rendered yourself in my estimation all I ever esteemed you when as the *beau ideal* of your sex I was proud to call you cousin.

My Dear Harriet you have talents; have the capacity of being superior to most of your sex and I most sincerely hope that this seperation will (painfull as it is) be for your good. You will lean on yourself; take charge of your children and also of your Mother who now stands or begins to stand in need of council and support instead of herself being the head and director.

I know you will not give way to despondency but that you will exert your talents for the improvement of your children and the management of your affairs. During the summer you will have a nurse with you. Do not therefore confine yourself to what belongs to her. Take the general management of the whole and make your servers do their part. I hope you will have leasure for reading and also that you will keep the journal[2] of events you

---

[1] Nancy Connor (*Henry Papers*, 2:3n).
[2] We have not been able to find a copy of a journal or diary kept by Harriet Henry in her husband's absence.

157

promised. Register every trifle. It will be important to me when I return. My Dear Harriet you know I have always loved you and you will not be offended when I say that my esteem for you has been much increased by the manner in which you have conducted yourself in reference to my departure. I now feel that you are not only my own Dear affectionate girl but also the woman who when misfortunes assail me will be my comfort and support; Who is not only the most tender and affectionate mother but also the judicious and consistent moniter the wise instructor. My Dear Harriet in this view of our seperation I can almost look on it with pleasure. You wish your Hubby to be happy while abroad. I know you do this. Prove to me by your letters and by those of Stephen that you do not give way to grief that you are too actively engaged to be depressed with unavaling sorrow. I have not forgotten the promise of reading every night and will commence tomorrow evening. I will read about 11 o'clock. This at London will give at Albany about 6 o'clock in the after noon. And now my Dearest on earth I consign you to the protection of Him who never forsakes those who put their trust in him aright.

Kiss the children for me. Ask Stephen to describe the ship in which Papa sails to Bub. Keep before him the stimulous that I am to bring him books and that he must learn to read before my return. Do not however press him to the injury of health. I would prefer that he take much exercise in the open air next summer. I suppose you will attempt something with Miss Mary in the way of letters before next fall. Get your tooth fixed and if that one should happen to break off have another put in. The operation is not in many cases attended with pain and if it were you would not shrink from that. It is now about ½ past eleven. I must therefore stop yet I would willingly continue. When I commenced this letter I was sad but with this conversing I have recovered my spirits. Instead of viewing you as a weeping paralized female I now look on you not only as the wife of my tenderest love but also as my pride and support.

> My Dear Generous Noble Wife
> I am as Ever with the warmest
> Love & highest Esteem
> Your
> Husband

Vessel[3] does not sail until to morrow at 9 o'clock the wind being Easterly. I shall not consequently be at home to morrow *afternoon*. Stephen Feb 20th, 1837 1 o'clock.

---

[3] Stephen Alexander added the following postscript to the cover of this letter.

TO HARRIET HENRY

Family Correspondence, Henry Papers, Smithsonian Archives

[February 22, 1837][1]
Near Sandy Hook
Wednesday 1 o'clock

We left the warf at about ½ past nine in tow of a steamboat are now going dow[n] the bay. We are near the hook. The Pilot will leave us soon and I hasten to give you a parting line. We have just finished dinner. The vessel is under good head way and we are fast sailing from the land with a good wind.

All the canvass is set and every thing appears to give us a prospect of a pleasant voyage.

I was acosted by a gentleman who came with us as far as the steamboat and who made inquiries for Mr. Henry. He is a Brotherinlaw of Gov Throup.[2]

Our Passengers are few in number in the cabin, nine or ten. Among these is a Lady, the wife of the Rev Mr, I have forgotten his name, an english clergiman.[3]

The Lady has a young child and I have thought several times that it would have been practical for you to have accompanied me. We left the warf at New-York with three cheers from the sailors on our ship answered by those on shore. The Pilot has very politely promised to take charge of this epistle. I have much to say but every thing is so new and strange about me that I find it almost impossible to write. My state room is in confusion with all my packages bottles and apparatus scattered about. My first business will be to put this in order and to arrange my papers. There are a number of Pasengers in the Stearage and among them several females.

Before night we will probably be out of sight of Land and will thus as I hope temporarily bid fare well to *Terra ferma*. I have mislaid my pen & am writing with one of De Witt's which is a very poor article and scarcely permits me to make a mark.

        the Pilot   adieu

[1] From the text of the next document we assume this is the date of this brief note dashed off by Henry during his last moments within sight of his native land.

[2] Enos Thompson Throop (1784–1844, *DAB*), a former Governor of New York. We do not know which of his brothers-in-law accosted Henry or why.

[3] The Reverend Charles Luck (1801–1866) was returning to Great Britain with an American wife, Caroline Pine, from a post in Brooklyn, New York. A Cambridge man (St. Catherine's, B.A. 1825, M.A. 1828), we assume Luck was going back to a London parish. Edward John Luck, comp., *A Pedigree of the Families Luck and Lock* (London, 1900), p. 14. *The Clergy List for 1843* (London, 1843), p. 134. *Crawford's Directory, 1865* (London, 1865), p. 404.

TO HARRIET HENRY

Mary Henry Copy, Family Correspondence,
Henry Papers, Smithsonian Archives

Feb. 22, 1837

I sent you a parting line by the pilot but he left so suddenly I had not time to date or sign my letter. When we were left by the steam boat, the wind was fresh and fair but it soon died away and rendered useless the labour which had been expended in hoisting the various extra sails which are pressed on the packets. These vessels are manned by picked sailors and the most experienced seamen are chosen as commanders. The Wellington, being a new vessel, has an additional number of men, the whole crew twenty four. The wind towards evening began to fresh and the sails, which for an hour or more, had been hanging in drapery folds along the masts, soon began to assume the graceful convex and curved outlines which indicate the action of the invisible but strongest element. The ship has but little motion and all on board are as comfortable as regards sea-sickness as if in a parlor. Our dinner was served at four o'clock and was partaken of by all with good appetite. The dishes are placed in a kind of frame-work to prevent sliding. It resembles two ladders placed parallel to each other on the table between the rungs of which the plates on each side are placed and the large dishes in the middle. We had tea about seven o'clock and after that the passengers assembled around the stove and spent a very cheerful hour in lively conversation. I will give an account of our fellow travellers tomorrow or when we have become more intimately acquainted. It was remarked at table that the most disagreeable part of a packet voyage is the first two days before the passengers know each other and particularly if the sea be so rough as to produce sea-sickness.

Before tea the wind had increased so that the ship's progress was about six miles an hour. At nine o'clock the rate was eight knots, with a prospect that the wind would change more to the west, or haul more into the direction of our great [. . .][1] We are now sailing off almost at right angles to the American coast; have lost sight of the Heights of New Jersey and have almost literally bidden "our native Land good night".[2] Very little of moment has occurred since we left New York, except that we were boarded by a small boat from a ship just entering the Bay on her passage from Liverpool,

---

[1] Mary Henry's transcriber has apparently omitted one or more words.

[2] Henry is quoting Lord Byron's *Childe Harold's Pilgrimage*. The line (Canto 1, Verse 13) reads: "My native Land—Good Night!"

which place she left on the 10th of Jan[y]. The object of the visit to our ship was to obtain tobacco, the ship had been so long at sea that the store had run out and the chewers of the weed were in great distress.

HARRIET HENRY TO JAMES P. ESPY
Retained Copy, Henry Papers, Smithsonian Archives

Princeton Feb[y]. 24th 1837.

Sir,

In the hurry of preparation for departure Mr Henry was unable to address all his friends—he wished me to inform you, Sir, that he would "attend to all your affairs in Europe"[1] and that he should be happy to hear from you while in London; any communication will reach him directed to the care of Petty Vaughan, Esq No. 70. Fenchurch Street.

Mr H. was detained at New York by contrary winds untill the 22nd but got safely to sea in the after part of that day. You, Sir, who have become so familiar with the indications of storms as to be able to apprize us of their approach, do I hope see nothing but sunshine and favorable winds in prospect for some time to come.

I expect to spend the summer at the North—shall be gratified to receive a visit from Mrs Espy and yourself on my return. I believe she promised me a visit when I had the pleasure of seeing her at Philadelphia. Remember me affectionately to her and believe me sir.

Yours respectfully
Harriet A. Henry.

---

[1] While we have no direct evidence concerning Espy's affairs, we may venture a guess. Just prior to Bache's departure for Europe five months earlier, Espy had written Bache, requesting him to distribute reprints and deliver some personal communications to European scientists. (Espy to Bache, September 18, 1836, Rhees Collection, Huntington Library.) We assume Espy wanted Henry to do similar things.

CHARLES BONNYCASTLE TO JOHN KNOWLES[1]
Gratz Collection, Historical Society of Pennsylvania

[February 1837][2]

Dear Sir

Allow me to introduce Professor Henry of Princeton College— a gentle-man well known in Europe by his scientific researches. The wide connec-tion which you have always maintained with the savans of the country, and your kindness to all of the corps, make me desirous that Professor Henry should form your acquaintance. He goes to England for the purpose of purchasing instruments, & will I have no doubt meet as much attention as I see by the papers was met by Lieut Wilkes—a gentleman far less known.[3]

With sincerest wishes for your happiness and prosperity

Your much obliged friend
Charles Bonnycastle

P.S. I learned with much regret from John[4] that you were sick. I trust Brighton has restored your health.

---

[1] John Knowles (1781–1841, *DNB*) had been chief clerk in the surveyor's department of the navy office from 1806 to 1832. He published on naval architecture and was elected a Fellow of the Royal Society in 1821. His chief work was a three-volume biography of his close friend, the artist Henry Fuseli. According to the address on this letter, in 1837 he was an actuary for an insurance company in London.

[2] Henry carried this letter with him so it could not have been written any later than February 22. Bonnycastle also wrote letters of introduction to Snow Harris and Peter Barlow; we have not found these letters, which Henry mentions in his diary entries of March 14–16 and April 21, 1837, printed below. Bonnycastle had evidently kept up with his English colleagues after leaving to join the faculty of the University of Virginia in 1825. See *Henry Papers*, 2:419–420.

[3] Mahlon Dickerson had sent Charles Wilkes to Europe with an allowance of $20,000 to buy instruments and books for the U.S. Exploring Expedition. An article on the trip by Doris Esch Borthwick, "Outfitting the United States Exploring Expedition: Lieutenant Charles Wilkes' European Assignment, August–November, 1836," *Proceedings of the American Philosophical Society*, June 1965, *109*:159–172, concentrates on the instruments purchased and Wilkes's contacts with Peter Barlow, William Simms, Francis Baily, and an unknown chronometer-maker.

Wilkes's trip was controversial in several respects. Dickerson had authorized it without consulting Thomas ap Catesby Jones, the commander of the expedition. Nor did Wilkes consult the scientific community to determine what instruments and books were desirable. Reflecting his own interests, he bought only physical science instruments, neglecting items essential for the naturalists such as microscopes. Finally, following arrival in the United States, the instruments were mishandled and scattered, some eventually turning up in Wilkes's house, some with James Renwick's apparatus. See William Stanton, *The Great United States Exploring Expedition of 1838–1842* (Berkeley, 1975), especially pp. 36, 49, 55.

Wilkes offended the chronometer-maker Edward Dent during his trip. See Dent's comment as reported in Bache's diary of April 6, 1837, printed below.

[4] Not identified.

DRAWING OF THE WELLINGTON[1]

Henry Papers, Smithsonian Archives

[February 1837]

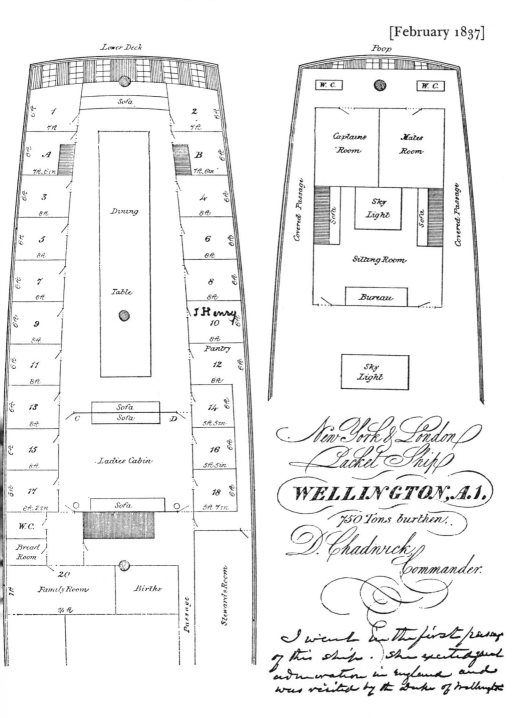

¹ This drawing is in Box 50 of the Henry Papers. We are arbitrarily printing it at the end of the documents for February 1837 although Henry's annotation had to have been made later. The annotation reads:

> I went in the first passage of this ship. She excited great admiration in England and was visited by the Duke of Wellington.

Henry sailed to England on the maiden voyage of the *Wellington*. The ship was built in New York by Christian Bergh & Co., which produced more packets at the time than any other New York shipyard. The *Wellington*

had a long life, serving as a London packet on the Red Swallowtail line until 1850 and as a New Orleans packet from 1853 to 1859. Daniel Chadwick commanded the Wellington until 1845; his brothers Charles and Seth and his son Walter commanded the ship at various times after that date until it was removed from service in 1850. Robert Greenhalgh Albion, *Square-Riggers on Schedule: The New York Sailing Packets to England, France, and the Cotton Ports* (Princeton, 1938), especially pp. 282, 333. For Daniel Chadwick, see below, Henry to Harriet Henry, March 21, 1837.

FROM JOHN TORREY

*Henry Papers, Smithsonian Archives*¹

New York,² March 7th 1837.

My dear friend

Here I am, seated quietly in your room adjoining the laboratory, while you are tossed on 'the Stormy Atlantic.' I am surrounded with every thing to put me in mind of my friend. I arrived here on the 1st, & have already lectured five times. One Sabbath has occurred or I should have lecture six times. I have every thing comfortable about me. My bed is in the larger room where the stove is. Daniell brings my meals with great regularity. Peter makes my fire early in the morning & cleans my boots. Joshua³ never allows the wood-box to be empty, & Joseph⁴ reports himself at 9 o'clock daily to receive orders. So far very well. Bullions⁵ is obliging & improved in manners. My student Douglass,⁶ who came on with me, is amiable & ingenious. He sleeps down stairs in my old room & eats in the refectory. Miller⁷ looks in every day & works some. He is a good fellow, but has not a turn for *soldering*, so I fear he will not come to much. Douglass actually begins to solder already! Is he not a promising lad? But after all you are not here, & when I get through the hardest part of my daily work then I miss you

¹ The letter is addressed to Henry care of Petty Vaughan in London.

² The letter was obviously written in Princeton.

³ Although there were students with these first names at Princeton, Daniell, Peter, and Joshua were probably the steward's helpers.

⁴ Probably Joseph the carpenter.

⁵ William Bullions (*Henry Papers*, 2:274).

⁶ Possibly a private student of Torrey's. We have not been able to identify him.

⁷ John Miller (*Henry Papers*, 2:478), who served as Henry's assistant for a year before entering the Princeton Theological Seminary in 1838.

greatly & I feel sad. I visit none, except at your house & Macleans, for I mean to improve my time & *post-up* many of my affairs that have got behind hand during the winter. I never saw snow on the ground at Princeton before, & this makes the place look strange to me. Thus I have been particular in talking about home—for details on this subject are interesting when we are far away from our native land. I think of you my dear friend, & remember you in my supplications at the throne of Grace. I was affected to hear you commended to the protection of our Heavenly Father at the opening prayer of the Literary Assoc.[n] a few evenings since.[8]

Mr Alexander called in last night to inform me that Maclean would leave at noon to-day for New York, & I embrace the opportunity to forward you a few letters. I forget whether I gave you one for Lindley: if I did not, take the one now sent, & deliver it to him, with the parcels, at the office of the Horticultural Socty, in Regent St.[9] I send a letter to Bache—you will satisfy

---

[8] This may be one of the fortnightly meetings of an informal literary club in Princeton about which we know very little. Joseph Addison Alexander described the club in his journal as a group composed mainly of the faculty members of Princeton and Princeton Theological Seminary. Members either conversed on chosen subjects or read papers to each other. Alexander says the meetings were, "strictly speaking, literary soirées, and were the means of putting in circulation a good deal of scientific and other useful knowledge." At an August 6, 1834, meeting, Henry gave an account of a magnetic needle and promised to present a paper on lightning rods at the next meeting. At a January 1838 meeting at Henry's house, Stephen Alexander discussed the upcoming solar eclipse of September 1838. Henry Carrington Alexander, *The Life of Joseph Addison Alexander*, 2 vols. (New York, 1870), *1*: 338–339, 341, 420, 437.

[9] John Lindley (1799–1865, *DSB*) was an energetic and prolific English botanist and horticulturalist. The son of a nurseryman who could not afford to provide him with a university education, Lindley got his start as a botanist as an employee of Sir Joseph Banks. He soon became associated with the Horticultural Society of London, an association maintained for the rest of his life. In 1828 he became a Fellow of the Royal Society and also Professor of Botany in the University of London.

Torrey and Lindley shared their advocacy of the natural system of classification over the Linnaean system. In 1831 Torrey published an American edition of Lindley's *Introduction to the Natural System of Botany* (New York). Torrey and Lindley met during Torrey's 1833 trip to Great Britain.

Torrey's letter introducing Henry to Lindley indirectly led to an unpleasant situation. We have not located the letter (he apparently wrote only one). Nor have we found any contemporary record of Henry's meeting Lindley. However, in a letter to Asa Gray (in London at the time) of April 3, 1851, Henry provides the following account:

The circumstances as I recollect them were as follows. Dr Torrey promised me a letter to Dr Lindley and gave me a package to deliver to him. He however forgot the letter and when I arrived in London I delivered the package without leaving my address, thinking this unnecessary as I had no introduction to present. Dr Torrey afterwards forwarded a letter of introduction but before this arrived my time had become so completely absorbed in the numerous engagements I had made, that had not the letter contained some matters of business I would not have delivered it. I sent it however to Dr Lindley but unfortunately neglected to state my address. After much trouble he found my lodgings and called upon me at a most unfortunate hour. I was at Dr Baches lodgings, my trunks packed and ready to depart for Paris. I was engaged with Dr Bache in preparing an article for the press. I had no place into which I could invite Dr L. when he called. He mistook

him that I never intended to slight him.[10] By the next packet I will send you two or three letters for France, & in good time you may expect others for the North of England, Scotland & Ireland.[11] As I am to lecture at eleven o'clock & the time draws near, I must be brief & hurried. The Lord bless & keep you my dear friend & permit you to return in peace.

Ever most faithfully yours

John Torrey

Call Lindley—*DOCTOR* Lindley—that is his title.[12] D. Don[13] can be found at the rooms of the Linnaean Society, or at A. B. Lambert's.[14]

---

my embarrassment for a desire not to make his acquaintance and under this feeling I presume wrote a complaining letter to Dr Torrey. I regret the occurrence and certainly under other circumstances would have been highly delighted to have formed a more intimate acquaintance with Dr L. and to have received his attentions with becoming thankfulness.

(Historic Letter File, Gray Herbarium Library, Harvard University). We have not located Lindley's "complaining" letter to Torrey. In his answer Gray advised, "Do not trouble yourself about the contretemps with Lindley. Perhaps I will give him the explanation when I next see him, but it is scarcely worth while" (May 6, 1851, Henry Papers, Smithsonian Archives).

[10] Henry had originally suggested to Torrey that he provide Bache with letters of introduction before Bache's departure for Europe.

Torrey was apparently too busy to make the deadline. Just before leaving for Europe himself, Henry urged Torrey to write and explain, promising that he would "make all smooth." See above, Henry to Torrey, February 13, 1837.

[11] We have not found any of Torrey's letters introducing Henry.

[12] In 1832 the University of Munich had awarded Lindley an honorary Ph.D. *DSB.*

[13] Torrey evidently enclosed a letter for David Don (1800–1841, *DSB*). As Clerk, Librarian and Housekeeper of the Linnean Society of London, Don lived in the Society's quarters. In addition to his positions in the Society, Don was Professor of Botany in King's College, London, from 1836 until his death from cancer in 1841. A. T. Gage, *The History of the Linnean Society of London* (London, 1938), pp. 27–28, 159.

[14] Aylmer Bourke Lambert (1761–1842, *DNB*), a botanist, was a vice-president of the Linnean Society of London at this time.

ALEXANDER DALLAS BACHE'S EUROPEAN DIARY[1]

Bache Papers, Smithsonian Archives

Sunday March 12. [1837] In the morning after service Miss Phillips[2] called upon E.[3] & was very sociable & chatty. Her brother has returned fr. Harro-

---

[1] The extant volumes of Bache's diary, covering the period from November 1836 to March 1838, are in four depositories: Bache Papers, Library of Congress; Girard College; Rhees Collection, Huntington Library and Art Gallery; Bache Papers, Smithsonian Archives. A few of the entries now exist only in copies made by someone other than Bache. The

copies were made for use in preparing Bache's *Report on Education in Europe to the Trustees of the Girard College for Orphans* (Philadelphia, 1839), according to page 603 of the report.

Bache used his diary to record his personal observations and to collect raw material for his report. He was aware of the danger in

gate. Prof. Daniell[4] is here & we are bidden to meet him this evening if M[r] Hincks[5] will spare us an hour to do so.

We went to the afternoon service of the cathedral & were handed up into a gallery behind the wood work of the choir, a position which E. voted a poke–hole but which I was well pleased with as it entitled me to draw the cape of my cloak over the head & make myself as safe as the nature of the cold place would permit. There are air flues to heat the choir of the Minster, but they do little more than barely to temper the roughness of the cold. Prof. Phillips has observations of the interior temperature of this building wh. would be interesting to examine.[6]

The organ here is only second to that at Birmingham the first in the kingdom; it speaks melodiously as well as loudly & the anthem was good though much inferior in the vocal dep[t] to that at Durham. The boys voices are not so good & they do not seem so well drilled. I do not remember the anthem & indeed believe that losing the statement of what it was I could not make out the words as they were sung.

After service we went to M[r] Hincks to tea. M[rs] H. is the mother of a large family the oldest being a youth of nineteen, but appears yet young (the mother). After tea we examined M[r] H's cabinet of shells which is pretty rich in Brit. species &[c] At Prof. Phillips was Rev. M[r] Kenrick,[7] the Rev. M[r] Taylor[8] (Episcopal) & Prof. Daniell. With Prof. P. I had a most interesting con-

---

physically mixing the two kinds of information. In the front of the earliest volume (Library of Congress) he wrote:

What is written in this journal is entirely private & confidential & I charge that in case of accident to me it be held sacredly so, except so far as relates to the schools which I have visited, where the facts tho' not the opinions belong to the public.

We have included occasional excerpts from Bache's diary to supplement Henry's observations, especially on social and cultural topics where Bache's comments are particularly acute. Abroad from September 1836 to October 1838, Bache's extensive itinerary included the countries Henry visited as well as Switzerland, Holland, Italy, and several German states. Our first excerpt finds Bache in York.

[2] The sister of the prominent British geologist and paleontologist John Phillips (1800–1874). Phillips was curator of the museum of the Yorkshire Philosophical Society and also Professor of Geology at King's College, London. One of the founders of the British Asso-

ciation, Phillips was Executive Officer of the organization until 1859. He was known for his contributions to stratigraphy and geological mapping. *DSB*.

[3] Bache's wife, Nancy Fowler Bache, whom he called Ency.

[4] The chemist J. F. Daniell, identified in *Henry Papers*, *1*:213n.

[5] Reverend William Hincks (1794–1871), who was Professor of Natural Philosophy at Manchester College, York, 1827–1839, and taught natural history at Queen's College, Cork, 1849–1853. *DNB*, s.v. "Hincks, Thomas Dix."

[6] See Phillips, "On the Temperature of the Air in York Minster," *British Association Report, 1841* (1842), part 2, pp. 29–30.

[7] John Kenrick (1788–1877), a Unitarian minister, was a tutor in classics, history, and literature at Manchester College. Kenrick was a founder of the Yorkshire Philosophical Society and served as curator of the museum's department of antiquities. *DNB*.

[8] William Taylor (d. 1870) was a member of the Yorkshire Philosophical Society and a Fellow of the Royal Society of London from 1836.

versation about science and its interests. He informed me that pains had really been taken to excite a prejudice against Rogers (H.D.) by the circulation of that vile attack upon his unpublished report: that at first it had done harm but now that the report was in hand all was right. He hoped a continuation of it wh. the Eng. geologists were looking for, & he hoped that the Geol. Soc. of London would duly acknowledge R's merits by awarding a prize to him.[9] As he was in the stream about our science in America I took the opportunity to let him know how harm was done by encouraging such quacks as Featherstonhaugh by membership of the Royal Soc. of Lond.[10] On this body Prof. Daniell passed some heavy [?strictures] alledging that

He was involved in education of the handicapped, according to Bache's next diary entry (not printed), and printing for the blind (Taylor, "Report on the Various Modes of Printing for the Use of the Blind," *BAAS Report, 1837* [1838], pp. 87–102). *Proceedings of the Royal Society, 1870–1871, 19*: 113.

[9] Like Henry, Bache was extremely sensitive to the reputation of American science abroad. Henry Darwin Rogers prepared a report on American geology for the 1834 meeting of the British Association at Edinburgh. Murchison read the report which was well received by Phillips, Lyell, and other geologists in attendance. Murchison prepared an abstract of the paper for the *Edinburgh Philosophical Journal*, 1834, *17*:425–427. The "vile attack" referred to by Phillips was a politically motivated denunciation of Rogers's report by a pseudonymous Amphibole, whom we are unable to identify. The attack, entitled "Remarks on Prof. Rogers' Geological Report to the British Association for the Advancement of Science . . . at Edinburgh," was published in Philadelphia in 1835 and was evidently circulated among Rogers's British supporters. Amphibole was upset that Rogers had obtained the Chair of Geology and Mineralogy at the University of Pennsylvania, claiming that the post had been secretly filled and that Rogers was unqualified as a geologist. Citing the Murchison abstract of Rogers's report, Amphibole accused Rogers of plagiarism and of an erroneous insistence on essential differences between American and European geological formations. While a number of Rogers's American colleagues may have resented his academic success as well as his involvement with the plans for the Pennsylvania geological survey, British geologists backed him strongly and, in fact, asked him to prepare a continuation of his report for the next

meeting of the British Association. The sequel was never written. For information on this episode we are indebted to Patsy A. Gerstner of the Howard Dittrick Museum of Historical Medicine of the Cleveland Medical Library Association. See Gerstner's "A Dynamic Theory of Mountain Building: Henry Darwin Rogers, 1842," *Isis*, 1975, *66*:26–37.

[10] G. W. Featherstonhaugh, the Anglo-American geologist (*Henry Papers, 1*:126), was elected to the Royal Society in 1835. His work was better appreciated in Europe than in America, where he had a mixed reputation. A succession of bitter personal quarrels seriously affected his standing in the community and the reception of his work. Professional jealousies contributed to some of the disputes. As editor of the short-lived *Monthly American Journal of Geology and Natural History* and, later, as a controversial recipient of government support for two geological tours, Featherstonhaugh quarreled with Silliman, C. S. Rafinesque, and W. W. Mather, among others. The latter, who assisted Featherstonhaugh on his government-sponsored explorations, accused him of using his topographical results without attribution. But Mather and other American geologists were particularly upset by Featherstonhaugh's appropriation of the title of "U.S. Geologist" while undertaking his surveys. Mather's protest appeared in the *Naval Magazine* (reprinted in *Silliman's Journal*, 1838, *33*:205–206). Featherstonhaugh wrote a rejoinder, *Official Refutation of a Libel* (Washington, 1837). Featherstonhaugh's survey reports, which began with a speculative overview of geology, came into some scathing criticism. For instance, the reviewer for the Franklin Institute *Journal* (1836, *17*:109–117, 184–190) found much of Featherstonhaugh's theoretical language unintelligible. He accused him also of "continually torment-

Royalty sat heavy upon it & that its slip of royalty in its Pres^ts was this incubus.[11] If a Phys. & Chem. Soc^y were formed it would lose all attraction which remained & this is small. Prof. D. reminds me strongly of Dr Hare, he is just such a heavy mass of matter as to person & moves like the D^r: if he has so good a heart I cannot yet know. He had seen little of Dr H. in Lond. expecting to meet him at the assoc^n & then had been prevented from going there. He mentioned Apjohn as a candidate for "poor Turner's" place.[12] He represents himself as busy "in town" all day & then retiring to his residence which makes coming in to a Soc.^y meeting not agreable, whether the gentle hint about some avocations was meant for me I cannot say until we meet "in town." He impugns Capt. Hall's[13] idea that the Athenaeum[14] is a club for scientific reunions & asserts that such a thing is much wanted: that they miss the old meetings at Sir Jos. Banks'[15] &c. I opened somewhat to Prof. Phillips the differences between my rain results & his, tho' not fully. He says that within the year only he has read Dr Franklin's observations & that they are a complete anticipation of the theory which he has emitted: this statement he volunteered.[16]

For M's amusement Miss P. produced a toy composed of a stone which revolves by capillary action, when placed in a plate the bottom of wh. is covered with a film of water: on the stone are placed two figures in waltzing

---

ing his imagination with the attempt to identify the rocks of this country with European formations, which he seems to consider as the types to which all others are to be referred . . ." (p. 187). Like Bache, the reviewer feared that Featherstonhaugh's publications, receiving the stamp of the federal government, would give Europeans a poor impression of American geology. Yet, while admitting the justice of some of these criticisms, G. P. Merrill felt that Featherstonhaugh's survey reports contained some useful observations and theoretical insight. G. P. Merrill, *The First One Hundred Years of American Geology* (New Haven, 1924), pp. 136–137, 162–163.

[11] The Duke of Sussex was President of the Royal Society until 1838. His election thwarted the attempts of reformers at the beginning of the decade to raise the scientific level of the Society's membership. See L. Pearce Williams, "The Royal Society and the Founding of the British Association for the Advancement of Science," *Notes and Records of the Royal Society of London*, 1961, *16*:221–231.

[12] See below, Henry's diary for April 27, 1837, footnote 9.

[13] Basil Hall. See below, Bache to Hall, July

16, 1837, footnote 1.

[14] See above, Powers to Henry, March 13, 1836, footnote 8.

[15] Joseph Banks (1743–1820), wealthy British botanist best known as a patron and organizer of British science. The dominant figure of the British scientific community, Banks presided over the Royal Society from 1778 until his death. Banks's home in Soho Square was a famous gathering place for scientific London. *DSB*.

[16] In 1833 John Phillips and William Gray presented to the British Association observations on the quantities of rain falling at different altitudes. Finding that greater amounts of rain fell nearer to the ground, the authors explained the results with the hypothesis that raindrops united as they fell to the ground. (*BAAS Report, 1833* [1834], pp. 401–412). In an article for the *Journal of the Franklin Institute*, 1836, *17*:106–108, Bache pointed out that Benjamin Franklin had anticipated their hypothesis. Bache conducted similar experiments in Philadelphia, finding that wind currents seriously affected the results (*BAAS Report, 1838* [1839], part 2, pp. 25–27).

attitude, who go thro' the proper gyrations when once set off. This lady is very like both in appearance & manner to what my friend M^rs. Ingraham[17] once was, tho' not quite so pretty perhaps: quite as free spoken.

Prof. Phillips thinks it unnecessary to swing the wet-bulb hygrometer, but admitted the apparent justice of my reasoning upon it. Espy's essays he has not seen but promises to attend to them.[18] His lectures in King's College are by no means a source of profit & except for the public might be a loss. He is kept about square in his visit to London wh. enables him to act as Sec^r to the Assoc^n without [?bother].

Mr Kenrick stated to me in one walk yesterday that the Assoc^n originated with Dr Brewster & others in Edin who had written to York about it as this was a central place. The merit of Rev. W. Vernon Harcourt was that of taking up the suggestion & by a mind imbued with system, seeing how it could be best followed out.[19] The great offense given by Sir D. Brewster was in decrying the operations of the assoc^n in an article (supposed to be his) in the Edin. Quarterly.[20] In the case of the contest with Forbes both had applied to Prof. Phillips for letters & F. had made some statement which induced Prof. P. to suppose either that he was in the field first or something of that sort & had made some ugly wish, which irritated B. against F. & some merit was now awarded to Sir David for having got over the matter & being upon friendly terms with Forbes.[21]

---

[17] Not identified.

[18] For the bulb hygrometer, see *Henry Papers*, *1*:213n–214n. Early investigators of hygrometry, notably Leslie, believed that the wind had no effect on their readings. Not until the 1840s with the studies of Regnault was the effect of ventilation on hygrometer readings understood. Eventually it was generally conceded that hygrometers had to be whirled for consistent results. James Espy, questioning Leslie's postulate, was an early advocate of swinging. See his "On the Dew-point Hygrometer in Connexion with the Wet Bulb Thermometer," *Franklin Institute Journal*, 1834, *13*:81–85. See W. E. K. Middleton, *Invention of the Meteorological Instruments* (Baltimore, 1969), pp. 126–128.

[19] Brewster first suggested the organization of the British Association for the Advancement of Science in a review of Babbage's *Reflections on the Decline of Science in England*. Reverend William Vernon Harcourt, son of the Archbishop of York, was largely responsible for the decision to hold the first meeting of the Association at York under the auspices of the Yorkshire Philosophical Society. A. D. Orange, "The British Association for the Advancement of Science: The Provincial Background," *Science Studies*, 1971, *1*:315, 316.

[20] See Brewster's "[Review of] *Reports* of the First and Second . . . and . . . Third Meetings of the British Association," *Edinburgh Review*, 1834–1835, *60*:363–394. Brewster objected that the Association did not live up to his original views. Brewster wanted the Association to limit its membership to qualified scientists on the model of Germany's Deutscher Naturforscher Versammlung, organized by Lorenz Oken. Harcourt, who advocated a more general membership, won the dispute. Orange, op. cit., p. 316 and footnote 10.

[21] The reference is to the controversial election in 1833 of J. D. Forbes as Leslie's successor to the Chair of Natural Philosophy at Edinburgh. Brewster, Forbes's early patron, was his chief rival for the position. Some bitterness ensued. *DSB*, *DNB*, s.v. "Forbes."

HENRY'S EUROPEAN DIARY
Henry Papers, Smithsonian Archives

March [14–16], 1837

Henry's European tour began in Plymouth, England, and ended with his departure from Portsmouth on October 2, 1837. His extensive travel diary, which will be printed in its entirety, consists of three small volumes, each devoted to a distinct segment of his journey. The first and most complete of the three diaries documents his experiences in England, centering on London but including visits to Plymouth and Woolwich, the site of the Royal Military Academy. Henry remained in Britain until May 10. Paris is the focus of the second, much scantier volume, chronicling events in the month of June. A trip through Belgium, vividly documented in Henry's correspondence, is absent from his Continental journal. Returning to Great Britain at the end of July, Henry commenced the third volume, devoted to London and Edinburgh, where he spent most of August. The Edinburgh experience is the last to be documented in the diary. Henry had begun a fourth diary volume for the next part of his tour but reported losing it or having it stolen in September. Unfortunately, this volume probably contained Henry's personal account of the eventful meetings of the British Association for the Advancement of Science held at Liverpool in mid-September. Probably lost as well are his impressions of Glasgow, visited in late August and early September. The post-Edinburgh portion of Henry's journey is partially recorded in correspondence and on loose sheets of notes, some of which are printed in this volume.

The neatly written entries of the European diary were usually prepared from rough notes taken on the spot or from memory. Although most entries were made soon after the events described, sometimes a week or two could elapse before Henry formally entered his impressions in the journal. The retrospective character of many entries has introduced some problems in dating and organizing the documents. The array of diary entries presented in this volume is our best reconstruction of the original sequence of events, but some jumping back and forth in time and place is inherent in the documentation and unavoidable.

Henry conceived of his diary chiefly as a scientific and technical record. There is a great deal in his entries on lectures, laboratories, scientific and technical instrumentation, harbor-works and industrial establishments of all kinds. Broader social and cultural phenomena, of which Henry was a keen observer, were generally reserved for personal correspondence. For Henry, the diary was a utilitarian record to be used later in ordering and acquiring apparatus, working up lectures, conducting research, and suggesting new technological approaches. He judged that his diaries would be "of great use to me although scarcely of interest to others," drawing an implicit contrast between his journal style and the grander, more literary effects striven for by other travelers of the period.

Yet Henry's businesslike assessment of his journal is somewhat misleading. He was never an uninvolved observer. Moreover, he knew he had access to unusually good material. As he wrote to his wife from Europe (July 5, 1837, below), "I believe . . . I could furnish more material for sketches in the line of English and French science than anyone who has of late years visited Europe since I have been usually fortunate in gaining admission to intimacy with most of the men actually engaged in science in London and Paris." We are inclined to agree with Henry. Already respected internationally, Henry, we suspect, was able to overcome professional and social barriers that may have confronted less prominent scientific visitors. Laboratories and late research results were open to Henry. Naval establishments, closed to the usual sightseer, were made accessible to him. At such close quarters, Henry could not resist recording candid impressions of scientific personalities and he was ever curious about the politics of science. Although the instruments and ideas he encountered had American counterparts and were familiar to him from the literature, Henry was aware of and curious about the effects of different national and cultural contexts. Such considerations merited explicit notation.

It was the fashion of the nineteenth century to keep diaries and travelers were especially assiduous in doing so. The scientists and early engineers who had begun to go abroad in this period were proving to be conscientious diarists. Despite its limited purposes, Henry's European diary is a special and informed contribution to that literature.

Landed in Plymouth on the 14th of March 1837 after a voyage of 20 days or according to the ship reckoning of 19 days.

Next day[1] viewed the Town and inspected the ship yard or rather Dock yard[2] as it is called. Saw the process of making ropes in the numerous rope walks of the establishment of which there are two each 12[00] feet long.[3]

[1] Since Henry arrived in London on the seventeenth, we guess his visits to the Plymouth dockyards and harbor and with Snow Harris described below occupied two days.

[2] In British usage, dockyard meant naval shipyard. Henry was visiting the Devonport naval yard (formerly called Plymouth Dock). The shipyard at neighboring Plymouth was devoted to commercial shipping and suffered somewhat from the Government's monopoly of the waterside. Devonport's impressive Hamoaze Harbor could handle the largest naval ships and was the deepest of the English dockyards. Henry does not indicate how he gained entrance to the naval yard. According to a contemporary guide, foreigners "cannot be allowed admission without an express order

from the Admiralty." It was customary for one of the naval police to guide the visitor. George Wightwick, *Nettleton's Guide to Plymouth, Stonehouse, Devonport, and to the Neighboring Country* (Plymouth, 1836), p. 75. Richard Nicholls Worth, *History of Plymouth* (Plymouth, 1871), pp. 82, 84. Henry Edmund Carrington, *The Plymouth and Devonport Guide*, 4th ed. (London, 1837), pp. 24–33, 38, 74–75.

[3] This was considered the "finest ropery in the kingdom, consisting of two ranges of buildings, one the laying-house, the other the spinning-house, each being 1200 feet in length, and three stories in height." One of the houses, constructed of stone and iron, was fire-proof. Carrington compared the vista along the length of the rope-houses to that of the Lou-

The machinery although of the most improved kind is very simple. Was much pleased with the realing machine on which several spools were placed and the thread moved up and down over the length of the spool by a guide which received motion from a circular cam thus. The Kings ropes are all marked by a read thread in the middle.

In this yard Mr Snow Harris[4] has the thermometer and rain gague fitted up which are described in the last report of the British association.[5] A regular series of observations has been made on the thermometer every hour in the 24 for the space of 5 years. A similar series is now in progress with the addition of the barometer. We were shown every part of the works and were much surprised at the immense size of the masts and spars of a first rate ship. The main spar of one of them was at least 75 feet long and 20 inches diameter built of pieces joined together.[6]

We were shew a ship in the Dry Dock for copering built of Teak wood in the East Indias.

Sir R Steppings[7] is now no longer director of the yard. He has retired on a pension and his style of ships are now superceeded by that of the new director which differs from the former in making the bough much sharper;[8]

vre. *Encyclopaedia Britannica*, 8th ed., s.v. "Dock-yards," p. 84. Carrington, *Plymouth and Devonport Guide*, p. 30. *Nettleton's Guide*, p. 84.

[4] William Snow Harris (1791–1867) was considered an important local personage, exemplifying the area's "spirit of intelligent enquiry." (Carrington, *Plymouth and Devonport Guide*, p. 9; Worth, *History of Plymouth*, pp. 333–334.) Born in Plymouth, Harris was a medical student at Edinburgh, served as a military surgeon, and then established his practice in Plymouth. Although he did not turn his full attention to electrical research until 1824, he had already, by 1820, invented a method of attaching lightning rods to ships, in which they were permanently fixed to the mast and ran down into the hull. Harris is probably best known for his successful campaign, involving a controversy with Sturgeon over the path taken by lightning flashes, to have his plan adopted by the Royal Navy. In the 1830s Harris presented several papers to the Royal Society on the fundamental laws of electricity, winning the Copley Medal for one on electricity of high tension. In 1860, Harris became the Government's official consultant on electricity. *DNB*. Henry took a great interest in Harris's lightning conductors (see his letter to Harriet of October 30, 1837, below) and acquired many of his writings on lightning and

other aspects of electricity for his Library.

[5] Harris's "First Report on the Hourly Observations of the Thermometer at Plymouth Dockyard," *British Association Report, 1835* (1836), pp. 181–206. Further installments appeared in the *Reports* for 1838 to 1842.

[6] The mast-house was especially recommended to the scientific and mechanically minded visitor. *Nettleton's Guide*, p. 83.

[7] Sir Robert Seppings (1767–1848), leading British naval architect, was appointed Surveyor of the Navy in 1813 and was responsible for ship construction at the dockyards. Seppings was actually stationed at Chatham dockyard, not at Plymouth. When the naval administration was reorganized in 1832, Seppings resigned and was replaced by Sir William Symonds. Seppings was responsible for many basic innovations in ship building, some of which are discussed below. *DNB. Encyclopaedia Britannica*, 8th ed., s.v. "Dock-yards;" "Navy: History and Admiralty Administration." *The Record of the Royal Society of London*, 4th ed. (London, 1940), pp. 346, 557.

[8] Seppings introduced the circular bow in 1807, in response to the damages and casualties suffered on the *Victory* at the Battle of Trafalgar when a shot easily penetrated the boards at the beak of the ship. Seppings replaced the beakhead with timbers running up the side, forming the circular bow. *DNB*.

the ship sails faster it is said but is much less comfortable in regard to stability and dryness.

Steppings is the inventor of a method of trussing applied to ship building known by his name.[9]

A large ship nearly finished is now on the stocks with an eliptical stern.[10] In this I observed an index face like that of a wheel barometer which indicates the position of the rudder to the officer of the lower deck. The buildings are all fire proof with cast iron beams and floorplates of the same metal. The floor plates are about $\frac{1}{2}$ inches in thickness and grooved in two directions to prevent slipping.

The beams are formed according to the solid of greatest resistance with a given quantity of metal.

Among the interesting objects seen in this place is the gallery as it may be called of old figure heads or the carved images which have been preserved from the ships which have been broken up or condemned.

Some of these are of colosal magnitude particularly a figure of Lord Nelson and that from the old ship ocean. They are arranged on either side of an open passage and present a very imposing spectacle which could easily be mistaken for an Indian temple filled with Hindoo gods.[11]

The forging of anchors and the general smith operations of the establishment is an interesting part of the whole.[12] The immense anchors are beaten on large anvils and formed into shape or welled principally by using their own weight instead of a hammer. The anchor being lifted by machinery and suffered to fall on the anvil.

The Dry docks are large excavations faced with stone and furnished with valve gates to admit the largest ship. The water is thrown out by means of steam engines.

The largest of these is called the New Dock[13] (although built in 1789). It is without cover is 240 feet long 85 broad 29 deep. Ships are occasionally taken into it with all their masts and rigging standing. It is unlike the other docks of the yard without a cover and is faced with alternate courses of stone

---

[9] The diagonal truss was Seppings's best-known invention. He replaced the conventional rectangular trusses with a system of diagonal braces in a series of triangles. The design prevented the arching of the keel. Seppings published several articles in the *Phil. Trans.* on his method. *DNB.* For details, see John Knowles, *Naval Architecture* (London, 1822), Appendix A, pp. 6–7.

[10] Perhaps Henry viewed a round stern, also introduced by Seppings as an alternative to the usual square stern. See *Encyclopaedia Britannica*, 8th ed., s.v. "Navy," p. 98.

[11] Local guidebooks we have been able to consult fail to mention this spectacle.

[12] The Anchor Wharf is described in Carrington, *Plymouth and Devonport Guide*, p. 29.

[13] The New North Dock, ibid., p. 26.

and wood. It is the largest dock in Europe. There are in all if I do not mistate 4 docks.

The person who accompanied us said that the yard contained 75 acres.[14] The yard at Portsmouth contains 80 acres but is not as extensive in men and apparatus as this.

The whole number of artizans employed is about [2,200].[15]

In entering the Harbor of Plymouth we passed the celebrated Break water[16] of which a model is in the Albany Institute. It is intended to defend the harbour immediatly in front of the city from the waves of the open sea which but for this would rool in with uninterrupted force and render this position very dangerous in time of a storm. I was surprised to find that the work is not compleated and to learn that it is going on in a languid rate. The appropriations of government are not sufficient for a more vigorous prosecution. The consequence of this slow operation has been that the work has received much injury from several storms and has not as yet afforded the protection which the complete work will furnish.

It is of this form ∿⌐⸝ or rather is intended to have this shape. The whole length of the plan is [57] hundred feet.[17] Of this however about 12 hundred from the east end are finished.

It is formed by throwing large blocks of stone into the water so as to form a sloping dyke or a dyke with sloping sides 36 feet at top and varring at bottom from 3 to 4 hundred feet.

The middle is a straight line of about 3000 feet. Each extremity form an angle of 120° with this line and is 1350 feet long.

The slope on the sea side is 3 to one and on the land side 1½ to one. The estimated expense is £1,171,500. It was begun in 1812 and is constructed

---

[14] The naval station at Plymouth was second only to Portsmouth in size. *Encyclopaedia Britannica*, 8th ed., s.v. "Dock-yards."

[15] Henry wrote, in an obvious slip, "22,000." Carrington, *Plymouth and Devonport Guide*, counts only 2,200 artisans at Devonport. Total employment at the yard fluctuated greatly between peace and wartime. *Nettleton's Guide*, p. 74.

[16] Described as an engineering marvel, "one of the most gigantic, and certainly the most substantial and effective, erections of its kind," the breakwater was built by sinking masses of stone, which became known as Breakstone marble, that found their position by their specific gravities and the force of the waves. The structure was begun in 1812, but was displaced at least twice by gales. Engineers finally

stabilized it by moving the center closer to shore and retaining the natural slope imposed by sea and storms. More than a mile in length, the breakwater consisted of a central line with an arm at each end at 120-degree angles toward the shore. L. F. W. Jewett, *A History of Plymouth* (London, 1873), pp. 665–669. An engineer's view of the breakwater as well as other notable structures in Plymouth is given by P.-C.-F. Dupin, *Narratives of Two Excursions to the Ports of England, Scotland, and Ireland, in 1816, 1817, and 1818; Together with a Description of the Breakwater at Plymouth* . . . (London, 1819?).

[17] Although Henry wrote 17 hundred feet, the figures he gives below add up to 57 hundred feet.

of the beautiful variegated marble which abounds in the immediate vicinity. I forgot to mention that it is faced with large cut stone.

A light house is intended to be erected on each end.[18] We purchased in the city polished specimens of the stone used in the construction and also models of the work made of the same material.

We also visited the citidel[19] the first work of the kind I had ever insp[e]cted. This is an ancient fortification and was erected in the reign of Charles the 2ⁿᵈ.

The whole was strange in its appearance but nothing of special interest attracted my attention except a kettle drum the first I ever saw.[20] It was of this form. A brass kettle the mouth of which was covered with parchement resting on three feet.

In entering the harbour we had an interesting view of the celebrated Eddystone light house[21] situated about 14 miles south of Plymouth a lone tower in the midst of waters which stands a perminent monument of the skill of the Engineer Smeaton.

One object of my leaving the ship at Plymouth was to meet Mr William Snow Harris to whom I had a letter from Prof. Bonnycastle. Mr H is celebrated for his zeal in science and for his researches particularly on the laws of electrical attraction and repulsion made with new and ingenious instruments contrived by himself. He is a practicing Physician of Plymouth in easy circumstances & about 38 or 40 years old has quite an extensive set of apparatus for an amature and devotes all his leisure time to science.

Mr H kindly devoted all his leisure time to me while I continued in Plymouth. He invited us into his *kitchen* the room where he was then engaged in a set of experiments to determine the laws of induction by his *unit measure* and his balance electrometer. He has deduced several laws but they do not appear to me on reflection as much at variance with the theories of electricity as their author supposes. The laws are deduced from the attraction which is produced by a charged plate and another in connection with the

---

[18] A lighthouse was built at the western end and a beacon placed at the east end. Jewett, *Plymouth*, p. 668.

[19] The commanding fortification was begun in 1666 and finished in 1670. R.A.J. Walling, *The Story of Plymouth* (London, 1950), pp. 136–142. Jewett, *Plymouth*, p. 228.

[20] The kettledrum had ancient origins and was certainly a well-known instrument in Henry's day. *Encyclopédie de la Musique et Dictionnaire du Conservatoire* (Paris, 1927), s.v. "Timbale."

[21] After fire destroyed the first lighthouse at Eddystone, the British architect-engineer John Smeaton (1724–1792) erected a new one between 1756 and 1759. It was Smeaton's best-known technical achievement and established his reputation as a civil engineer. Its form likened to an oak tree, Smeaton's creation was viewed as one of the wonders of the world. It had stood for more than 120 years when structural flaws destroyed it. The lighthouse was removed and enshrined at a site in Plymouth. *DSB*, s.v. "Smeaton." J. C. Trewin, *Portrait of Plymouth* (London, 1973), pp. 61–63. R. A. J. Walling, *The Story of Plymouth* (London, 1950), p. 181.

ground and electrified negatively or rendered neutral by the charged plate. He finds that the force is as the area of the plates charged and inversely as the distance of the plates.[22]

This he showed us in a very satisfactory manner by the number of discharges of his unit measure[23] being the same while the weights in the scale were varied inversely as the square of the distance. The unit measure is described in Turners chemistry[24] and can be purchased at Watkins & Hills

[22] Harris's electrical experiments in the 1830s were among the first verifications of Coulomb's electrostatic laws. For this investigation Harris invented two important measuring devices, the balance electrometer and the unit jar, both described below. Harris tested Coulomb's results for more complicated electrical conditions and concluded that Coulomb's inverse-square forces obtained only for simplified conditions. Under such conditions, Harris believed that electrical attraction, given constant electrical quantities, would vary inversely as the square of the surface area and inversely as the square of the distance. However, Harris showed that the shape of the attracting bodies and the distance between them could affect the law of attraction. In some cases, as Henry indicates, the force could vary with the area of the plates and inversely as the simple distance. (Henry may have meant the *square* of the distance. See his next paragraph.) Other results obtained under different conditions. As Harris's measurements progressed he became increasingly convinced that his laws differed significantly from Coulomb's and accepted electrostatic laws. Most commentators, however, found his measurements confirmatory of Coulomb's theories and believed that a careful mathematical analysis, allowing for the more complicated conditions, would demonstrate this agreement. In general Harris was appreciated not for any novel theoretical results but for his instrumentation and careful measurements. Harris pioneered in taking these electrical measurements on charged bodies of different shapes and under different temperature and atmospheric conditions. Harris's laws were developed in several articles for the British Association. See *Reports, 1833* (1834), pp. 386–390; *1835* (1836), pt. 2, pp. 17–18; *1836* (1837), pt. 2, pp. 19–24. His full results appeared in "On Some Elementary Laws of Electricity," *Phil. Trans.,* 1834, pp. 213–246. Parts 2 and 3 of the series appeared in *Phil. Trans.,* 1836, pp. 417–452; 1839, pp. 215–242. For William Whewell's assessment of Harris, see "Report on the Recent Progress and Present Condition of the Mathematical Theories of Electricity, Magnetism, and Heat," *BAAS Report, 1835* (1836), pp. 9–10. (Whewell thought Harris's results in agreement with Coulomb's.) Brewster (*Encyclopaedia Britannica,* 8th ed., s.v. "Electricity," pp. 534–535, 604, 620–621, 622, 624–625) also praised Harris's contribution to electricity but discerned no theoretical heterodoxy, stressing instead the novel instrumentation.

Harris emerged as a supporter of Michael Faraday's electrical theories though he appears to have exerted no significant influence on Faraday's thinking. Harris went into a complex discussion of his electrical force-laws as well as other points of electrostatics in a long letter to Faraday of April 28, 1839, printed in L. Pearce Williams, ed., *The Selected Correspondence of Michael Faraday,* 2 vols. (Cambridge, England, 1971), *1*:337–342.

[23] For many of his electrical measurements, Harris used the unit measure (or jar) in conjunction with the balance electrometer, both introduced and carefully described in his articles. As Henry describes below, the unit measure consists of a small inverted Leyden jar on a glass rod. The inside coating is connected with the electrical machine which charges the jar in the usual way. Brass balls connected with the inside and outside of the jar are set apart at precise intervals. At the same intervals and under similar ambient conditions, each spark represents equal quantities of electricity. The purpose of the unit measure was to charge the Leyden jar with known amounts of electricity. The attractive forces of the known charges were then measured on the balance electrometer, which counterbalanced the force between charged plates against known gravimetric quantities, in grains. The apparatus resembled a common balance.

[24] Edward Turner, *Elements of Chemistry.* In Henry's own American edition (Philadelphia, 1835) this apparatus, as well as the balance electrometer, appears on pp. 82–83.

Charing Cross London. It consists of a tube of glass about one inch in diameter with a wire with balls connected with the inside and also a rod with balls in connection with the outside. The wire connected with the inside is connected with the rubber of the machine and as the tube which is coated on the inside and out like a Lyden Phial is charged the natural electricity of the outside by induction is driven into a jar or any body required to be charged. As soon as the tube is charged a sparke passes between the balls *a b* and the number of these sparkes furnishes the measure of the quantity thrown into the jar or other body. The apparatus is supported on a slender glass tube.

Turner (p. 85) also sees Harris's work as reinforcing rather than deviating from accepted electrostatic theory.

HENRY'S EUROPEAN DIARY

Henry Papers, Smithsonian Archives

Arived in London Friday March 17th 1837. Stoped at the Bull and Mouth Tavern.[1]

[1] A corruption of Boulogne Mouth, the name commemorated the capture of the mouth of the harbor of Boulogne by Henry VIII in 1544. H. E. Popham, *The Taverns in the Town* (London, 1938), p. 121.

HENRY'S EUROPEAN DIARY

Henry Papers, Smithsonian Archives

[March 20, 1837] Spent saturday in getting Lodgings and on Monday visited the Adelade[1] gallery principally for the purpose of seeing Mr Per-

[1] Founded in 1832 to educate and entertain the public, the Adelaide Gallery (formally the Gallery for the Illustration and Encouragement of Practical Science) was originally both a museum displaying the arts and sciences of its day and a forum for popular scientific demonstrations and lectures. Over the two decades of its existence, however, the Gallery underwent tremendous changes. Like Peale's Museum in Philadelphia, a natural history analogue (*Henry Papers*, 2:182n), the entertainment side eventually overshadowed the educational side. Music and magicians began to replace scientific demonstrations. In 1852

kins[2] to whom I have a letter from Dr Hare.[3] Mr P is not at present in London but is engaged in some experiments on a rail way in reference to his steam generators.

I intend to visit this institution again[4] and therefore will not give a detailed description at this time. One of the first objects which attracted my attention when I entred the gallery was one of my magnets by March[5] of Woolwich. It is formed of a pice of square iron of about the diamater of my first magnet but the legs are too long and the whole arrangement not proper to produce the greatest effect. It is supported on a Tripod and has a hollow[6] lifter which one of the attendants informed appeared to work better than a solid *pice* of *iron of the same* size. (Try some experiments on this in connection with the magnetism of hollow bars.)[7] It is surrounded with 10 coils each 90 feet weighs 34 lbs and supports between <3> 4 and 500 lbs. My small magnet weighs 21 lbs and supports 1000.

There are several magneto electrical apparatus for giving shocks one a very large article constructed by Mr Sexton[8] for intensity and quantity with

---

the Gallery was converted into a marionette theatre. Greville Bathe and Dorothy Bathe, *Jacob Perkins: His Inventions, His Times, & His Contemporaries* (Philadelphia, 1943), pp. 152–154, 166–167.

At the time of Henry's visit, the Gallery consisted of nine rooms, housing some six hundred exhibits—paintings, sculpture, technological improvements, anthropological specimens, and scientific apparatus. Society for the Illustration and Encouragement of Practical Science, *Gallery for the Exhibition of Objects Blending Instruction with Amusement, Adelaide Street, and Lowther Arcade, West Strand*, 14th ed. (London, 1836), hereafter cited as *Adelaide Gallery Catalogue*. There is a copy of this catalogue in the Henry Library. *The Magazine of Popular Science* (vols. 1–4, 1836–1837), published under the auspices of the Society, also contains information on the Gallery.

[2] Jacob Perkins (1766–1849) was the founder of the Adelaide Gallery and an inventor. One area of special interest to Perkins was the high-pressure steam engine. For Henry's early knowledge of Perkins's work, see *Henry Papers, 1*:83, 89–91.

[3] Not found.

[4] Henry does not mention a later visit to the Adelaide Gallery in either his European Diary or in any of his extant correspondence.

[5] James Marsh, an English experimenter (*Henry Papers, 1*:317). The electromagnet in question is described in the *Adelaide Gallery Catalogue*, pp. 14–15.

[6] C. Payne, the manager of the Adelaide Gallery, had suggested using a hollow keeper. William Sturgeon, "An Experimental Investigation of the Influence of Electric Currents on Soft Iron, as Regards the Thickness of Metal Requisite for the Full Display of Magnetic Action: and How Far Thin Pieces of Iron are Available for Practical Purposes," *Annals of Electricity, Magnetism, & Chemistry*, 1836–1837, *1*:476.

[7] Henry had conducted experiments with magnetized hollow bars as early as 1834 (see, e.g., *Henry Papers, 2*:225–234). References to experiments made with or upon hollow magnets appear in his "Record of Experiments" through at least October 1839. Another experimenter with similar interests was William Sturgeon. He had begun a series of experiments in 1829 comparing solid and hollow pieces of iron. Sturgeon's work was somewhat limited, however, until he had read Henry's "Contributions II: Spiral Conductor." Finding the spiral conductor very useful in conducting these comparative experiments, Sturgeon greatly increased the quality of his work in this field. Sturgeon, "An Experimental Investigation of the Influence of Electric Currents . . . ," *Annals of Electricity, Magnetism, & Chemistry*, 1836–1837, *1*:472–483.

[8] For Joseph Saxton's (*Henry Papers, 2*:159n–

two pairs of coils one for each purpose. The magnet is about 2 feet long and consists of [. . .][9] plates.

The assistant [. . .][10] informed me that he had discovered a method of procuring the two gases seperate by taking off one of the points of the spur which dips into the small cup of mercury.[11] The French use the bascul[12] for the same purpose but I did not suceed in producing the result with Pixiis[13] apparatus belonging to the N Y University.[14]

I witnessed the interesting exhibition of the cutting of a steel file by a re-volving wheel of soft iron.[15] The effect was truely astonishing. The wheel of iron was made to revolve at the speed of 180 miles an hour by means of a large wheel and pinion moved by a steam engine. When the iron was at its highest speed the file was pressed against it and instantly the most brilliant stream of cintillations were produced which reached to the height of 6 or

---

16on) apparatus, see: *Adelaide Gallery Cata-logue*, pp. 15–16; Arthur H. Frazier, "Joseph Saxton at London and His Magneto-Electric Devices," unpublished xerox copy in Joseph Henry Papers files, pp. 21–22. Henry later met Saxton in London. See below, Henry's Euro-pean Diary, April 17, 1837.

[9] Henry left a blank at this point. The mag-net was composed of twelve plates. *Adelaide Gallery Catalogue*, p. 15.

[10] Another blank left by Henry.

[11] Ways of modifying the magnetoelectric machine in order to decompose water into hydrogen and oxygen gas were exhibited in the Adelaide Gallery in 1833. Frazier, "Joseph Saxton at London," pp. 18–20.

[12] We earlier reported our inability to lo-cate a contemporary description of the bascule (*Henry Papers*, 2:96). Invented by Ampère, the bascule was a device for quickly changing the direction of a current. Four cavities and two grooves were made in a wooden table, then filled with mercury. A wooden bar fitted with four metallic arches was placed on the table over the cavities. The bar acted like the pivot of a seesaw. The arches would either complete or interrupt a circuit, according to whether they were in or out of the cavities. The direc-tion of the current would be determined by which pair of arches was in the cavities. Eng-lish language sources call the bascule an "elec-tripeter," the name E. M. Clarke gave to his variation of the bascule. Antoine-César Bec-querel, *Traité expérimental de l'électricité et du magnétisme, et de leurs rapports avec les phénomènes naturels*, 7 vols. (Paris, 1834–1840), 3:9–10; *Encyclopaedia Britannica*, 8th ed., s.v. "Voltaic Electricity," p. 643.

[13] Antoine-Hippolyte Pixii (1808–1835), the son and grandnephew of instrument makers, invented the magnetoelectric machine which bears his name in 1832. His father, Nicolas Constant Pixii-Dumotiez (1776–1861), was con-sidered one of the finest makers of instru-ments in nineteenth-century Europe. While in Paris Henry purchased a considerable amount of demonstration apparatus from the firm of Pixii, Père et Fils (see the Appendix at the end of this volume). Maurice Daumas, *Scien-tific Instruments of the Seventeenth and Eigh-teenth Centuries*, trans. Mary Holbrook (New York, 1972), pp. 287–288.

[14] This apparatus was probably purchased in Europe by John Torrey during his trip there in 1833. One of Torrey's purposes for going overseas was to purchase apparatus for the University of the City of New York. Andrew Denny Rodgers, *John Torrey: A Story of North American Botany* (Princeton, 1942), p. 104. We have no record of when Henry used this apparatus.

[15] Visitors were invited to bring old steel files to be destroyed by the iron wheel. This was considered one of the great attractions of the gallery. The apparatus had been invented by Perkins to demonstrate the effect of high ve-locities on metals. *Adelaide Gallery Catalogue*, pp. 13–14; Eugene S. Ferguson, ed., *Early Engi-neering Reminiscences (1815–40) of George Escol Sellers* (Washington, D.C., 1965), p. 133.

7 feet above the wheel. At the same time a number of sparkes
appeared to follow the circumference intirely around and to present the appearance of a ring of fire around the circumference of
the wheel. The thickness of the wheel was about ¼ of an inch. Fire
enough under some circumstances may perhaps be generated in
this way to be applied to some useful purpose where motive power is cheap.
The file appeared blue where it had been cut by the revolving disc.

From the gallery I passed into the shop of Mr Clark[16] Phil. inst. maker
whoes form of the electro. magn. machine has been described in the Phil
Mag.[17] He was very polite. Was making a machine on a large scale for magneto-electrical exp. Said that he had many orders for my magnets and that
he always gave them by my name. I introduced myself after asking several
questions by pointing to my name as heading an article[18] in the Electrical
and Magnetic Journal which happened to be lying on his counter at the
time. He showed and explained to me his method of fitting up the Elec.
mag. appr. and also gave me several items of interesting information.
Among these a method of making a hole in a thick plate of glass by means
of a rat taild and a drop of spirits of turpentine. The former being constantly wet by the latter. He also showed me that there are two vapours of
ether a heavy one and a light one the latter will not fire while the heavy one
does.* [19]

* This fact was shewn Mr C. by Mr March of Woolwich and is of some
importance in exps with the vapour of ether. Thus a tube of ether held
below a sparke of electricity will not give of[f] a vapour which will fire but
one that is held above produces the effect. The two vapours seperate one
falls the other rises.

[16] Edward Montague Clarke (fl. 1804–1846)
had a shop at 11 Lowther Arcade. Both he and
Saxton claimed priority for the magneto-
electric machine. E. G. R. Taylor, *The Mathematical Practitioners of Hanoverian England,
1714–1850* (Cambridge, England, 1966), p.
359; *Henry Papers*, 2:160n, 165. Henry later
bought one of Clarke's machines; see below,
Henry to James Henry, September 15, 1837,
footnote 3.
[17] "Description of E. M. Clarke's Magnetic
Electrical Machine," *Phil. Mag.*, 1836, 3d ser. *9*:
262–266.
[18] Probably William Sturgeon, "On the Electric Shock From a Single Pair of Voltaic
Plates, by Professor Henry, of Yale College,
United States," *The Annals of Electricity,
Magnetism, & Chemistry*, 1836–1837, *1*:67–75.

Sturgeon admits in his paper that he obtained
his knowledge of Henry's work (and his institutional affiliation) second-hand. What
Sturgeon received from his informant was an
account of Henry's "Contributions II: Spiral
Conductor."
[19] This was quite a trick, since one of the
characteristics of an ether was its inflamma-
bility. Because ether was a generic term in
early nineteenth-century chemistry, embracing alkyl chlorides and nitrates as well as true
ethers, we suspect that Marsh had created a
compound other than ether. We have been unable to locate a published account of his experiment, either by him or in the contemporary chemical texts. Information from Jon B.
Eklund, National Museum of History and
Technology.

A particular account of his machine is given in the Journal of Mr Sturgeon.[20]

Mr C also showed me a compound batery on the retaining principle. The metals are surrounded or rather seperated by an animal membraine, bladder, or parchment, and excited by a solution of sulp[hate] copper on the principle of Dr Daniels battery.[21] This apparatus will continue in action for a whole day and is applied in the Adelade Gallery to give motion to Dr Richies rotatory apparatus.[22]

Mr C is about to apply it to the continued ignition of charcoal in a vacuum to produce a vivid and constant light in his window. The battery consisted of 20 gallipots of about a pint each with copper cylenders covered with bladder and the zinc on the out side. Mr Clarke introduced me to Mr Wm Leithead[23] operative chemist 22 Compton Street Brunswick Square. I accompanied this gentleman to his house for the purpose of seeing the operation of a small elementary battery[24] composed of an English <*shilling*> sixpence between two connected plates of zinc. The zinc was first cut into the form here represented one face covered with bladder and the other with cealing wax. The sixpence was placed between these after they were bent at the connecting pice so that the plane of each was parallel to that of the other. This battery was excited by a strong solution of *lunar caustic*.[25] It required some time to get into action and indeed appeared to increase in intensity while I remained which was more than an hour. Its power was tested in producing rotation in one of Richies machines. The motion was so rapid that the revolving magnet of soft iron could scarcely be seen and the motion shook the whole table. It was moving with increased rapidity when I left which was more than [. . .] hours[26] after its excitation.

It would be highly interesting to make a series of experiments with dif-

[20] E. M. Clarke, "A Description of a Magnetic Electrical Machine," *The Annals of Electricity, Magnetism, & Chemistry*, 1836–1837, *1*: 145–155.

[21] Daniell showed Henry his battery at King's College. See below, Henry's first European Diary for March 23, 1837.

[22] Henry would later watch Ritchie (*Henry Papers*, 2:162) demonstrate his electric motor during a lecture at the Royal Institution. See below, Henry's European Diary, April 27, 1837.

[23] An active experimenter in electricity during the closing years of the 1830s, William Leithead became Secretary of the newly founded London Electrical Society in 1837. "First Report of the Committee of the London Electrical Society," *Annals of Electricity, Magnetism, & Chemistry*, 1836–1837, *1*:504.

[24] One of Leithead's major research interests was the efficiency of batteries, attempting to get the most power out of the smallest possible battery. He eventually developed a battery only two and a quarter inches in length, yet powerful enough to rotate Ritchie's apparatus. His batteries used very little copper, but relatively large amounts of zinc. William Leithead, "An Account of Various Arrangements of the Voltaic Apparatus, and Remarks on the Limited Extent of Metallic Surface, Sufficient for Electrical Excitation; With a Few Observations on Electro-Chemistry," *Annals of Electricity, Magnetism, & Chemistry*, 1836–1837, *1*:216–223.

[25] Silver nitrate.

[26] Henry left a blank in the manuscript.

ferent salts[27] to determine the action of each. The only objection to the use of the nitrate of silver is that it is too expensive an article.

Mr Leithead also showed me an experiment which at first sight appeared like an electro magnetic effect but which is nothing more than an ordinary electrical action. A prime conductor placed in the direction of the meridian and on this a magnetic needle supported on a metal pin. The needle turns at right angles to the axis of the conductor when the machine is turned. The needle becomes electrified and is repelled by the conductor and every point seperates as far from it as possible.

I suggested to Mr Leithead that this arrangement might be applied to the construction of an electrometer on a new plan. Thus or thus *a* a bent wire supported on a glass stem and terminated by a ball at each end; above this supported on a pin from the middle place a magnetic needle also terminated by a ball at each [end]. When the apparatus and the wire nearly in the direction of the magnetic meridian repulsion will take place. The instrument may be made more sensible by partially nuteralizing the directive force of the needle.

[27] Another of Leithead's interests was finding the best solution for a sustaining battery. He spent the early part of 1838 conducting a series of experiments, the results of which were reported at the March 17 meeting of the London Electrical Society. Unfortunately, the experiments had not been carried out to a conclusive result and we have been unable to locate the "future papers" that Leithead promised. "London Electrical Society," *Annals of Electricity, Magnetism, & Chemistry*, 1838, 2:303–304.

TO HARRIET HENRY

Mary Henry Copy (in part),[1] Family Correspondence
Henry Papers, Smithsonian Archives

London March 21st 1837

My Dear Harriet

We arrived in this city of wonders on the 17th inst via Plymouth instead

[1] The first six paragraphs of this letter are based on an incomplete original in Henry's handwriting. The remainder is from a Mary Henry Copy presumably made from the part of Henry's letter which no longer survives.

In the Family Correspondence there is a second version of the letter in Henry's handwriting. It ends in the middle of the second page and was obviously never complete. It covers basically the same subjects as the first six paragraphs printed here but differs in the amount of detail and the order given to various subjects. There is also a second Mary Henry Copy which is merely a composite of materials from the two letters in Henry's hand.

of Portsmouth after a passage of 19 days from land to Land. The voyage was a very plesant one for the season of the year. The thermometer was sometimes at 60° and except for a few hours on the banks and when we arrived in the english channel was scarcely ever below 50°. The temperature of the water in the mid ocean was 55°. We had several days of almost dead calm with delightful sunshine but when we came into the english channel we met a violent easterly or head wind which rendered the last four days of our passage the most disagreeable part of the voyage.

I did not suffer quite as much from sea sickness as I had expected although I was scarcely well at any time and quite uncomfortable during a wind. Still the time passed very rapidly & I was interely void of any apprehensions relative to safety. Indeed there appeared much more security on board a good ship even when the waves are running mountains high than in a steam boat exposed to accidents from bursting boilers. Sea sickness however has a tendancy to produce a state of apathy incompatible with fear or anxiety about personal safety.

There were in all 8 cabin passengers. The Rev. Mr Luck and his Lady with a child of eleven months old.[2] He had been a few years in America and had married an english girl Miss Caroline Pine of New York, had been pastor of the episcopal church at Brooklin and was now returning to England on account of his health. He was a very well disposed and amiable person but appeared not to be much acquainted with the world. The Lady was well informed and apparently very good natured. Her situation was rather unpleasant being the only lady on board except a scotch woman in the stearage who from appearance might be intitled to the appelation. The next person was a Mr Savage a Batcherlor and merchant of Wall Street New York.[3] He had several times crossed the ocean, was well informed on subjects of english literature. The next person was an english man who had resided a number of years at Jamaca in the west Indias. His name was *Scacole*[4] a good sort of a negative body always in good spirits and very civil. The next was a picture merchant[5] going from New York with a number of old Pictures to sell in London. He was also very good natured and afforded us considerable sport in the way of remarks on pictures, politics &c. The last Pasenger which it is necessary for me to mention was Mr Blake of Boston[6] a

[2] See above, Henry to Harriet Henry, February 22, 1837.

[3] Possibly Joseph W. Savage, listed in the 1837 New York City Directory as a broker at 149 Second Street.

[4] Not identified. Henry's spelling is unclear —the name may be Seacole. In the other version of this letter Henry describes him as a "withered Batchelor of about 45 or more who has made a fortune in the West Indies and now is returning to England probably to begin the world by marrying a girl of 15."

[5] Not identified. In the other version, Henry gives his name as Rical.

[6] In the other version Henry wrote that Blake's first name was George, that he was

young merchant of about 30 years old who was well acquainted with England this being his ninth passage across the atlantic.

He was a fine specimen of a Boston gentleman, was acquainted with Mr Vaughan of London. I put myself under his directions in reference to sea sickness and found much relief from his advise. He was also sick at every rough sea but made sport of his infermity. Not so however with Mr Savage who appeared to be mortified with the idea of being so weak as to give way to the malady.

Our Captain was one of the best natured and pleasant men I have ever traveled with. He is a yanky from Lyme on the Conecticut river, has a wife and four children, has been married 15 years and in that time has not spent more than three years with his family.[7] Including the capt. we had 5 married men, two old Batchellors and one young one (De Witt). The first saturday night according to custom we drank in bumpers of soda water [to] wives and sweethears. The capt then informed us that he had been educated in connecticut and that it was always his rule if a clergyman was on board to ask him to officiate on the sabath. I was accordingly deputed to wait on Mr Luck and request that he would officiate. This he agreed to do but the weather not proving very favourable he did not preach on deck but gave us a sermon attended with the prayers of the episcopal church in the cabin.

---

married, and that he was "acquainted with all the scientific men of Boston and Cambridge."

This is probably George Baty Blake (1808–1875), a Boston dry goods merchant. In 1833 he married his cousin Ann Hull Blake. In the early 1850s, having left the dry goods business, he became a banker. One of his ties to the scientific community was through his cousin George Smith Blake (1803–1871, *Appleton's Cyclopedia of American Biography*), at this time an assistant on the U.S. Coast Survey and later Superintendent of the U.S. Naval Academy. *A Record of the Blakes of Somersetshire, Especially in the Line of William Blake, of Dorchester, Massachusetts* . . . (Boston, 1881), pp. 36, 39, 42–44, 47. *The New-England Historical and Genealogical Register* (Boston, 1877), *31*:343.

[7] Henry describes the captain in greater detail in the other version:

In person he is the beau ideal of a sailor, stout and well formed but not very tall. A native of Lyme in connecticut 39 years old and been on the sea since the age of 16—has made more than 40 voyages across the Atlantic. Has the ease and manners of a person long used to good society mingled with the frankness and generosity of a sailor. He is ¼ owner of the ship of which (the ship) he is quite prowd every plank having been put together under his immediate inspection and the form modeled according to his experienced views.

Daniel Chadwick (1795–1855) was a veteran packet captain who had begun commanding London packets in 1825 and who ended his career over twenty-five years later. According to Albion, an ocean packet command was very prestigious and lucrative. A packet captain had to be "a courteous gentleman . . . with a sort of a bluff amiability, to inspire confidence in passengers" (p. 153). It was common practice for owners of a line to grant shore leave to a captain of a packet under construction so that he could suggest changes and supervise the building: "There are recorded instances, which may have been a general practice, of the captain's initialling every stick of timber which went into the hull" (p. 82).

Robert Greenhalgh Albion's *Square-Riggers on Schedule* (Princeton, 1938) is an excellent source of information on the packet captains. For Chadwick, see p. 333.

The next sabath Mr Luck was too unwell to leave his state room and I officiated by reading a number of chapters from Mason on Self Knowledge.[8] The third sabath was spent in the English Channel while the ship was rooling so violently that most of the passengers myself and Mr Luck among the number could not leave their berths.

Very little occurred to break the monotony of a sea voyage. We did not see a vessel for more than 10 days until within about ¾ of the way to england when one morning we were cheered with the intelligence that a large ship was to be seen far to the north of us. She appeared like a Packet but wether the French or Liverpool we could[9]

I do not intend in my letters to give you a detailed account of my tour. I commenced (yesterday) a journal of scientific observations and also a register of observations intended solely for my dear little wife. I will devote the last portion of time before going to bed to the latter and will send it by the packets in succession as they sail.[10]

My first night in London was not a pleasant one. We were obliged to take the outside of the coach as all the inside seats had been taken. I became very much chilled and when we stopped at the *Bull and Mouth* I was stiff and was apprehensive of being very ill. I however put myself under the direction of the female directress of the establishment, who prescribed a warm bath, a warm bed, and warm tea. With these I was restored the next day Saturday to health.

I delivered my letter to Mr. Vaughan and his uncle,[11] Mr. Vaughan's of Philadelphia brother, and met with a very warm reception. They directed me to lodgings and gave me several letters of introduction.[12] De Witt and I are to dine at Mr. Vaughan's and to meet Mr. Rush, the former american minister on Saturday.[13] Our lodgings are in a very pleasant and fashionable

---

[8] The extremely popular work by the nonconformist divine John Mason, *Self-Knowledge: A Treatise*, first published in 1745. An 1853 New York edition is in the Henry Library.

[9] This is at the bottom of the second page of the original; we have not found the remainder. The text which follows is based on a Mary Henry Copy.

[10] Henry's "journal of scientific observations" is his diary. The first diary entry refers to his landing in Plymouth on March 14. That entry and those up to March 20 were apparently written in retrospect.

As far as we know Henry did not keep a separate register of observations for Harriet unless he is refering to the series of very long letters he wrote to her; these are printed below.

[11] John Vaughan's nephew Petty Vaughan and his brother William Vaughan (*Henry Papers*, 2:108, 429). William Vaughan, in particular, was an important contact for Henry's purposes. He was a Fellow of the Royal Society, the Linnean Society and the Royal Astronomical Society. He had been active in London's business community for many years and was an authority on London's port facilities. *DNB*. His *Tracts on Docks and Commerce* (London, 1839), which includes an autobiographical memoir, is in the Henry Library.

We have not located the letter of introduction to the Vaughans; it was probably by John Vaughan.

[12] Not found.

[13] See Henry's diary entry of March 25, printed below.

part of the city; they were not chosen on account of the latter circumstance however, but because convenient to the Royal Institution. We have a suite of two bedrooms, a sitting room handsomely furnished. We are supplied with muffins bread and tea by the servant of the house and pay only the cost of what we eat. We are obliged to make our own tea, a part of the arrangement somewhat perplexing at first. We did not know the exact quantity to be added to a given amount of water in order to produce a proper strength of decoction. The difficulty has however been overcome by experience.[14]

My reception thus far in England has surpassed my most sanguine expectations. Every person I have met has treated me with the greatest kindness and attention. I have as yet delivered but one letter and believe I could gain access to every thing I could wish without further introduction than the mention of my own name. At Plymouth Mr. Snow Harris, who has made some interesting experiments on electricity devoted a day to me and almost persuaded me to remain longer with him. Of the wonders of London, of this modern Babel, I must speak in my next. I deeply regret that circumstances did not permit you to accompany me. I could then enjoy my visit unalloyed. I now feel I must devote myself almost exclusively to science and give only a hasty glance at other matters of interest.

You promised to keep a journal and transmit to me every circumstance relative to yourself and our dear little one. Do not fail to write often and I hope you will find pleasure in the act.[15] The hour I have just passed in penning this letter is one of the pleasantest I have passed in England and were it not for the mail I would gladly fill another sheet. I recall to my mind's eye the expression of our boy's sweet face, I look at your miniature[16] and although it is not as good as I could wish, it assists my imagination in bringing before me what you are and what I hope and trust to find you when I return.

[14] Henry later wrote a humorous account of his newly acquired skill in his first letter to Harriet of July 5, 1837, printed below.

[15] We have not found any letters from Harriet Henry to Henry while he was abroad.

[16] Unknown to us.

HENRY'S EUROPEAN DIARY
Henry Papers, Smithsonian Archives

March 21st [1837] Visited this evening Mr Watkins optician Charing cross[1] —was received by him with much politeness.

[1] See above, Hare to Henry, February 13, 1837, footnote 3.

I am to meet him tomorrow. He showed this evening the apparatus used for exhibiting the horizon rotation of a chain and other bodies by a thread *6* The only peculiarity worthy of notice is that all the articles *are coloured dead white* by using a great quantity of sperits of terpentine which destroys all glossiness. The revolution of a cone and also of a cylender produces beautiful optical effects.

Leaving Mr Watkins we gave a shilling for admittance to the astronomical Lecture of a Mr Adams in the Kings Theatre.[2] The house was well filled and would yeald at least 200 dollars to the Lecturer. The illustrations were tolerable well got up but the Lecturer was but very imperfectly acquainted with the subject. I did not glean a single idea either in reference to the subject or the methods of exhibiting illustrations except it be that a stand with movable circles to represent the different orbits and their nodes may be improved on and applied to some advantage. Charlatanism is this country as well as in America meets with the best encouragement.

[2] The *Times* of March 21, 1837, reported: "The King's Theatre. Last Four Nights of Mr. C. H. Adams's orrery. This evening, March 21, and during the week (Good Friday excepted), Mr. Adams will deliver his lecture on astronomy, illustrated by new and transparent apparatus which he will have the honour to present on the stage of the Italian Opera house." King's Theatre, Haymarket, was built in 1704 and rebuilt in 1789 after it burned. The Theatre was primarily an opera house, having been granted the only license by Parliament in 1737 to perform Italian opera. Daniel Nalbach, *The King's Theatre* (London, 1972), pp. xi, 18, 39, 153.

HENRY'S EUROPEAN DIARY
Henry Papers, Smithsonian Archives

[March] 23[1] [1837] Started this morning to deliver my letters at the Royal Institution in Albemarl Street. Mr Faraday was just leaving town on an excursion during the holydays therefore did not see him. Delivered my letter to the Librarian was well received and by an other Gentlemen shewn into the museum, the lecture room and the Philsoph cabinet but as I am to visit these rooms frequently will not describe them here.[2]

Next called at Somerset House[3] and delivered my Letter to Mr Robton

[1] Henry originally wrote "24th" but changed the date.

[2] The Keeper of the Library was William Mason. *List of the Members of the Royal Institution of Great Britain, 1836* [London, 1836], p. 5. We have not located the letter. For later visits to the Royal Institution, see especially Henry's diary entries of April 18, 22, and 24, printed below.

[3] Somerset House was the third home of the Royal Society (after Gresham College and Crane Court). The Society occupied rooms there, provided rent-free by the government, from 1780 until the move to Burlington House in 1856–1857. *The Record of the Royal Society of London*, 4th ed. (London, 1940), pp. 27, 48–49, 64–65.

assistant secretary of the Royal society.[4] This gentleman is about 30. Received very politely and spent several hours in showing the several rooms and objects of interest about this establishment so celebrated in the history of the science of the human race in latter times. Among the articles which was viewed by me with peculiar interest was the original telescope of Newton constructed by his own hands.[5] It is as we all know a reflector with the eye glass in the side. The tube appears to be of paper about <9>10 or 12 inches long 3 inches in diameter and supported by a very simple contrivance namely a large ball fixed to a stout wire supporting the tube and this ball clasped by two pieces of brass one on each side which permits of a universal motion simple and efficient.

A still more interesting relique of this great man was shewn me and which I was not aware was in existance, the copy of the Principia from which the work was printed in Newtons handwriting corrected and interlined.[6]

It is in good preservation and about the size of a common ledger. Besides this, interesting objects the original air pump of Mr Boyle[7] and the condensing apparatus of Hook[8] were shown me. Als[o] the great Theodolite of Ramsden.[9] The clock used by Capt. Parry,[10] the fluid lense tellescope of Prof Barlow[11] & &c.

---

[4] John David Roberton was Assistant Secretary of the Royal Society from 1835 until his death in 1843. *The Record of the Royal Society of London*, 4th ed. (London, 1940), p. 344.

[5] The Royal Society became aware of Newton's work in optics through the exhibition of this telescope in 1671. The following year Newton was elected a Fellow. *DSB*. The telescope was presented to the Royal Society in 1766. *The Record of the Royal Society of London*, 4th ed. (London, 1940), p. 165.

[6] The manuscript is actually in the hand of an amanuensis, Humphrey Newton. Henry is otherwise correct. This is the manuscript copy, with corrections and interlineations by Edmond Halley and Isaac Newton, that was sent to the printer. For a physical description of the manuscript, see Alexander Koyré, I. B. Cohen, and Anne Whitman, eds., *Isaac Newton's Philosophiae Naturalis Principia Mathematica*, 2 vols. (Cambridge, Massachusetts, 1972), *1*:ix, xi–xiii.

[7] After reading of Otto von Guericke's air pump, Robert Boyle (1627–1691, *DNB*, *DSB*) instructed his assistant Robert Hooke to construct an improved pump. Completed about 1658 or 1659, "Boyle's engine" was the first modern air pump.

[8] We are unaware of any condensing apparatus particularly associated with Robert Hooke (1635–1702, *DNB*, *DSB*).

[9] In 1784, Jesse Ramsden (1735–1800, *DSB*) was commissioned by William Roy to build a theodolite thirty-six inches in diameter. Upon completion in 1787, Roy used it in the triangulation to determine the difference in longitude between the observatories at Greenwich and Paris. The instrument was later used by the Ordnance Survey in the Principal Triangulation of Great Britain and Ireland. *The Record of the Royal Society of London*, 4th ed. (London, 1940), p. 167.

[10] Perhaps the Parkinson and Frodsham chronometer (#259) used by William Edward Parry on his 1819–1820 Arctic expedition and later bought by the officers for Parry as a token of their esteem. Parry considered this chronometer to be the most reliable of the fourteen taken on the expedition. Parkinson and Frodsham, *A Brief Account of the Chronometer, With Remarks on Those Furnished by Parkinson and Frodsham to the Expeditions* . . . (London, [1832]), pp. 3–4, 13. For Parkinson and Frodsham, a firm specializing in chronometers, see E. G. R. Taylor, *The Mathematical Practitioners of Hanoverian England, 1714–1840* (Cambridge, England, 1966), p. 401.

[11] See Henry's comments in his account of a visit to Barlow at Woolwich in his diary

In the room where the meetings are held the walls are covered with portraits of the most distinguished philosophers of modern times, Bacon, Newton, Tico Brahee[12] and among which I recognise as being the paintings from which the likeness published in the library of useful knowledge have been taken.[13]

One circumstance was pointed out by Mr Roberton in reference to the portrait of Tico Brahe entirely new to me. He had a false nose made from the skin of his face or forehead which gives a peculiar appearance to his countenance.[14]

I also saw the meterological instruments of the society. They are kept in a litle room and out of a window of the same in the upper story. The place appears badly chosen for observations on temperature being too much confined. It may answer for the barometer.[15]

The standard barometer[16] is a good instrument but one lately constructed and now used is a better looking article; it consi[s]ts of two tubes, one of flint and the other of crown glass each $3/4$ of an inch or more in diameter. The register is made by sliding down a pice of brass which embraces both sides of the tube until light cannot be seen between it and the convex part of the mercury. Mr R thinks this as good as a microscope attached.[17]

---

entry of March 24, 1837, below.

[12] A listing of the portraits in the Royal Society appears in *The Record of the Royal Society of London*, 4th ed. (London, 1940), pp. 154–161. The portrait of Francis Bacon was by the studio of Van Somer. Two portraits of Newton would have been there at this time, one by Charles Jervas and one by J. Vanderbank. The portrait of Tycho Brahe was by M. J. Mierevelt. Plate 18 of the *Record* shows the meeting room and the portraits.

[13] A reference to *The Gallery of Portraits: With Memoirs* . . . , 5 vols. (London, 1833–1835), published under the superintendence of the Society for the Diffusion of Useful Knowledge, with biographical sketches by Thomas Malkin.

[14] Tycho Brahe lost part of his nose in a duel in 1566. When his tomb was opened in 1901, a green stain at the nasal opening indicated that his false nose had been largely copper. *DSB.*

[15] Francis Baily addressed this problem at the end of his article "Description of a New Barometer, Recently Fixed Up in the Apartments of the Royal Society. . . ," *Phil. Trans.*, 1837, pp. 431–441. He concluded that the barometer and hygrometer were in acceptable positions. On the thermometer and rain gauge, however, he quoted (almost verbatim) an earlier remark by Cavendish (*Phil. Trans.*, 1776, p. 376), "that, on the whole, the situation is not altogether such as could be wished, but is the *best* the house affords."

[16] Made for the Royal Society in 1822 by J. F. Daniell and John Newman. Daniell gives an account of its construction in *Elements of Meteorology*, 3d ed., 2 vols. (London, 1845), 2: 251–282 (reprinted from the second edition).

[17] Most barometers with two tubes were intended to protect against an undetected defective vacuum. Francis Baily designed this barometer, with one tube of flint glass and one of crown glass dipping into the same cistern, to also show which material had a greater chemical effect on the mercury over time. The movable brass rod had a scale on one end and an agate point on the other to make the point of contact between the rod and the mercury readily perceptible. Francis Baily, "Description of a New Barometer, Recently Fixed Up in the Apartments of the Royal Society. . . ," *Phil. Trans.*, 1837, pp. 431–441. W. E. K. Middleton, *The History of the Barometer* (Baltimore, 1964), pp. 250–251.

I was also shewn a barometer constructed on the continent with a sliding microscope with cross hairs to read off the altitude.[18] The thermometer to indicate the temperature of the mercure was plunged with its bulb into the large basin. The altitude of the mercury in the basin was regulated by skewing it up by some means so that its surface touched a fine point. The contact of the surface and point are observed by a tube with a diagonal eye piece.

In the stair way going up into the rooms of the Royal Society is placed Mr Daniels water barometer, nearly 40 feet long. The instrument is not now in order. The surface of the reservoir was covered with oil which suffered a kind of decomposition and let in a small quantity of air. No observations are now made with it.[19]

I was also shewn the large magnet given to the society by [Gowin Knight] and which is mentioned in the papers of Mr Faraday and Prof. Christie. It is nearly as large as a barrel and is placed in an outer room in bad condition from rust.[20]

From the rooms of the Royal Society I was conducted to the Laboratory & Lecture room of Prof. Daniels of Kings College the building of which forms a wing of summerset house.

I had forgotten my letters to the Professor one from Dr Hare and the other from Prof Renwick.[21] I was however received with much cordiality

[18] Middleton mentions that two German firms of this period made barometers with microscopes for reading the height of the mercury column: Pistor and Schiek, and J. G. Greiner, Jr., of Berlin. Middleton, *Barometer*, p. 202.

[19] Daniell constructed the water barometer, commissioned by the Royal Society, in 1830. With what Middleton considers poor scientific judgment, he intended to use it to investigate atmospheric tides and the variation of vapor pressure of water with temperature. Overcoming technical problems, the barometer tube was drawn in one piece to a length of forty feet, with an internal diameter of one inch. The water in the cistern was covered with a one-half inch film of castor oil to prevent communication with the air. Within two years, however, comparison with a mercury barometer indicated that communication had taken place. The barometer was abandoned until 1844 when the Royal Society commissioned its refilling. Substituting caoutchouc in naphtha for the castor oil, Daniell was still not successful. Although refilled again after Daniell's death, the barometer did not function successfully for long. It was destroyed in a fire in 1866. Daniell gives a full account of the construction and defects in "On the Water-Barometer Erected in the Hall of the Royal Society," *Phil. Trans.*, 1832, pp. 538–574. A posthumous account of the refilling, based on Daniell's notes, is given in Daniell's *Elements of Meteorology*, 3d ed., 2 vols. (London, 1845), 2:208–214. For a later account by Henry, see "Account of a Large Sulphuric-Acid Barometer in the Hall of the Smithsonian Institution," AAAS *Proceedings*, 1857, 10:135–137. See also W. E. K. Middleton, *The History of the Barometer* (Baltimore, 1964), pp. 366–368.

[20] Henry evidently couldn't remember the name of the donor. In his First Series of "Experimental Researches in Electricity," *Phil. Trans.*, 1832, p. 135, Faraday mentions using the magnet, given to the Royal Society by Gowin Knight (1713–1772, *DNB*). It consisted of 450 bar magnets, each 15 x 1 x ½ inches. S. H. Christie mentions it in "Experimental Determination of the Laws of Magneto-electric Induction in Different Masses of the Same Metal, and of Its Intensity in Different Metals," *Phil. Trans.*, 1833, p. 97.

[21] Neither letter has been found Henry mentions finally delivering them on a later visit to Daniell in his diary entry of April 12-15, 1837, printed below.

and assured that my name was a sufficient introduction. Prof D showed me his Laboratory his lecture room & study. I am to visit these again and will then describe them more minutely. The laboratory is below the lecture room and the articles are sent up by a dumb waiter.

Prof D also showed me his new battery of continued action which is excited by sulphate of zinc and the metals seperated by a pice of ox gut or bladder. The cause of the rapid diminution of the power of a common battery is in a great measure owing to the deposition on the copper or platina of a quantity of metalic zinc acid.[22]

Prof D is a large man of about 55 very plesant constantly laughs—commenced the study of science at an early age. His principal work is the Essays on Meterology but does not now confine himself to this subject.[23]

Expressed himself much pleased with the views of Mr Redfield—was unacquainted with the theory of Mr Espy.[24] Showed me his decected battery

[22] Daniell had announced his new "Constant Battery" in early 1836 in a letter to Faraday entitled "On Voltaic Combinations," *Phil. Trans.*, 1836, pp. 107–124. Experimenting with his "Dissected Battery" (see footnote 25, below), he reported finding that the primary cause of erratic and declining output in batteries was the deposition of metallic zinc on the conducting plates, caused by the combination of zinc oxide formed at the zinc generating plates and hydrogen from the conducting plates. Henry had earlier made the comment when trying to maximize sparks from a battery that "a rapid evolution of hydrogen is unfavorable to the effect" (*Henry Papers*, 2:323).

For each cell of his battery, Daniell used a glass cylinder with an ox gullet or bladder suspended in it to form an exterior and interior cavity. The zinc electrode in the interior cavity was charged with dilute sulfuric acid. Fresh acidulated water was added to the top of this cavity to force the newly-formed zinc oxide out the bottom through a siphon. The bladder enabled Daniell to charge the copper electrode in the exterior cavity with a second electrolyte, copper sulphate, which did not cause the evolution of hydrogen as did the dilute sulphuric acid. The bladder thus prevented the deposition of metallic zinc on the copper electrode while still permitting a current of electricity to pass.

Having attained a steady current, Daniell next concentrated on making his battery more powerful. He presented his results, shortly after the first letter to Faraday, in "Additional Observations on Voltaic Combinations," *Phil. Trans.*, 1836, pp. 125–129. Daniell received the Copley Medal of the Royal Society in 1837 for his two 1836 papers on voltaic combinations. The continuing investigation resulted in four more papers, the last one appearing in 1842. Presentation copies of these four are in the Henry Library.

At the time of this visit by Henry, Daniell was just about to send the third installment to Faraday. Henry was at the Royal Society on April 13 to hear the concluding part of this paper, which dealt primarily with the effects of temperature on the voltaic current ("Further Observations on Voltaic Combinations," *Phil. Trans.*, 1837, pp. 119–139).

The constant battery proved to be a valuable experimental tool. Henry constructed one for himself in March 1840 ("Record of Experiments," March 25 and 27, 1840, Henry Papers, Smithsonian Archives). He used the battery extensively for the experiments reported in "Contributions IV:Electro-Dynamic Induction," crediting it with the solution of some previous anomalies caused by the erratic and declining output of a Cruickshank battery.

[23] John Frederic Daniell, Professor of Chemistry at King's College since 1831, was only forty-seven at this time. His early work was largely in chemistry and meteorology. His *Meteorological Essays* was first published in 1823; the posthumously published third edition of 1845, entitled *Elements of Meteorology*, is in the Henry Library. In 1835 Daniell turned to researches in electricity, particularly electrochemistry. *DSB*. See *Henry Papers*, 1: 213.

[24] For Espy and Redfield, and their theories, see *Henry Papers*, 2:195–196, 456.

by which quantity is converted into intensity and the converse. Also all the products of the action are caut in glass jars and can be seen by the class. The gas from the zinc and copper is collected in a vessel inverted over the plates in the vessel which contains the acid. The production of the decomposition collected from the platina decomposing plates is also detained.[25]

Speaking of Meterology he stated that America was setting the example to the world in reference to observations. He also directed my attention to the labours of a society established many years ago in Manhim (?) which furnished instruments and directions to individuals in almost every part of the world. He regretted that something of the kind was not done at the present time. The observations now made are of little or no use because regulated by no system. The observations of Manheim are noticed in Mr Daniel's work and the curves of the barometer protracted from them.[26]

---

[25] The dissected battery was designed as a tool to investigate Faraday's electrochemical theories. When experiments with it led Daniell to a realization of the causes of unstable and declining battery output, it was superseded by the constant battery. Daniell's description of the dissected battery precedes that of the constant battery in "On Voltaic Combinations," *Phil. Trans.*, 1836, pp. 107–124.

Flexibility was stressed in the design of the dissected battery. Ten glass cells in a circle allowed easy connection of the cells in various combinations. Each cell consisted of an easily removable platinum and amalgamated zinc electrode. A graduated glass jar could be suspended over either plate in a cell to act as a voltameter.

Daniell began by arranging the battery for quantity and then for intensity. He then varied the plates, substituting different metals for the zinc and platinum. Next he studied the effect of changes in the electrolyte, and while doing this, noticed erratic output which jeopardized the comparability of the results from different arrangements. When he pinpointed hydrogen as the cause of the erratic output, he designed the constant battery to prevent its formation.

[26] The Meteorological Society of the Palatinate, with headquarters in Mannheim, was founded in 1780 by the Elector Charles Theodore and his private confessor, Johann Jakob Hemmer (1733–1790). Observations from a network of meteorological stations ranging from the Ural Mountains to Cambridge, Massachusetts, and from Greenland and Norway to Rome, were published in the Society's *Ephemerides, 1781–1792*, 1783–1794. Following Hemmer's death in 1790, the Society began to decline. Daniell praised the scope of the observations and claimed that this Society "might, undoubtedly, afford the most perfect model of a similar institution at the present day for promoting the Science of Meteorology." J. F. Daniell, *Elements of Meteorology*, 3d ed., 2 vols. (London, 1845), *1*:305–307, 310 (quotation from p. 305). W. E. K. Middleton, *The History of the Barometer* (Baltimore, 1964), p. 134.

In the published observations of the Meteorological Society, Daniell found "the first exemplification of the method of representing the oscillations of the barometer by a curved line upon a scale. . . ." Drawing upon the extensive data, Daniell extended this method to prove that "within certain limits, the movements of the barometer coincide by some general law over large portions of the surface of the globe." Daniell, op. cit., *1*:307–308.

HENRY'S EUROPEAN DIARY

Henry Papers, Smithsonian Archives

[March] 23rd [1837] Spent yesterday in arranging my papers. This week and the next are festival weeks and the several societies have no meetings. This afternoon went [to] Carie's[1] in the Strand who makes the oxyhidrogen blow pipe & microscope. For most optical experiments this instrument answers as well as sun light but does not give quite as good a spectrum. The experiments on polarization can be shewn with it on a screen to a class and also those of interferences.[2] At Cares I also saw a globe about 4 feet in diameter the cost of which is about 200 dollars.

In the evening I went to an exhibition in the strand Theater of various entertainments. The first exhibition was one imported from the continent and called the *Tableau vivant* or *living picture*. The design was to represent a picture or a scene by means of persons arranged in peculiar attitudes and dressed in appropriate costume. At the sound of a drum or a sudden stamp the whole was changed. The characters through themselves into an other position and thus represented an other picture or rather group belong to the same set; in this way the story of the murder of Abel was represented by a number of pictures.

The effect was very striking and the accompanyments of musick and lights of different colours increased the delusion.

After this was a representation of the most celebrated Grecian statues by a man dressed to resemble marble and placed on a pedistal. Some of the atitudes was very good but the effect was not equal to the other exhibition.

---

[1] George Cary (d. 1859) and his brother John (d. 1853) had taken over the businesses of their father John (1754–1835), a cartographer and globemaker, and of their uncle William Cary (1759–1825, *DNB*), an instrument maker. They kept the name and address of their uncle's shop at 181 Strand. E. G. R. Taylor, *The Mathematical Practitioners of Hanoverian England, 1714–1840* (Cambridge, England, 1966), entries 695, 810, 1290. See also Sir Herbert George Fordham, *John Cary: Engraver, Map, Chart and Print-Seller and Globe Maker, 1754 to 1835* (Cambridge, England, 1925). A card advertising the shop is in Box 50, Henry Papers, Smithsonian Archives.

[2] The oxyhydrogen or lime microscope was a variation of the solar microscope, a popular instrument used to project magnified images on a screen. Thomas Drummond's lime light, a small ball of lime ignited by oxyhydrogen gas, was substituted for the sun as the source of light. A lens added to the solar microscope converted the divergent rays from the lime into parallel rays like those from the sun. The oxyhydrogen microscope was used mostly for public lectures and classroom demonstrations. Unlike the solar microscope, it could be used on cloudy days and at night. A major disadvantage, however, was the explosiveness of the oxyhydrogen gas. In the *Encyclopaedia Britannica* (8th ed., s.v. "Microscope," p. 793), David Brewster endorsed his own suggestion of substituting an oil or gas lamp supplied with oxygen.

HENRY'S EUROPEAN DIARY

Henry Papers, Smithsonian Archives

[March] 24[th][1] [1837] Started this morning to visit Woolwich. For this purpose took a steamboat at Hungerford Market and proceeded down the Thames. The vessel was quite small and propelled by two engines on the same shaft. These were of the vibratory kind with strokes of about 2½ feet and as they had no parallel joints they occupied very little space.

The several parts were highly polished & the engines worked very smothely.

The objects along the river are highly interesting. The vessels which are not under sail are placed in large plattoons as it were on either side of the stream and thus make an imposing show.

The fare to Woolwich about 10 miles from London is 1/— for the back part of the boat and 8[d] for the fore, perhaps 6[d].

We passed Greenwich hospital and had a distant glimpse of the Observatory.[2]

When we arrived at Woolwich I inquired for the military academy[3] and was directed immediatly to the place but when I asked for the house of Professor Barlow[4] or rather Mr Barlow for he occupies the situation of third

---

[1] This entry was apparently written on the 25th.

[2] See below, Henry's diary entry of August 7, 1837, footnote 32.

[3] Founded in 1741, the Royal Military Academy at Woolwich was for over two hundred years the main cadet training establishment for officers in the Royal Artillery and the Royal Engineers. It was informally known as "The Shop," a designation probably deriving from its location in Woolwich Warren in the Royal Arsenal. The Academy provided, in addition to its military studies, a good scientific and general education, with heavy emphasis on mathematics. Like its counterparts elsewhere in Europe and in America, Woolwich was an important early home for science and mathematics. The mathematics staff was particularly illustrious, including some of the best pure and applied mathematicians in England. Charles Hutton, Peter Barlow, John Bonnycastle, Olinthus Gregory, S. Hunter Christie, and J. J. Sylvester were all associated with the school at one time or other. The Woolwich mathematical tradition was especially noted for contributions to applied mathematics and mechanics, subject-fields closely related to

problems in ballistics. The chemistry staff of the Academy enjoyed the services of Michael Faraday, who lectured there for twenty-nine years. Faraday was assisted by the noted chemist and electrical physicist James Marsh. In 1947, the Woolwich Academy merged with the Royal Military College at Sandhurst, founded in 1799 to train Army staff officers, to form the present-day Royal Military Academy at Sandhurst. F. E. Guggisberg, *"The Shop:" The Story of the Royal Military Academy* (London, 1900), pp. 1, 2, 65–67, 106, 260, 263. John Smyth, *Sandhurst* (London, 1961), pp. 17, 19, 20.

[4] Peter Barlow (1776–1862) had long been an important scientific influence on Joseph Henry. Like many of his Woolwich mathematical colleagues, Peter Barlow was self-educated in mathematics and science. A protégé of Charles Hutton, he won the post of Assistant Mathematical Master at Woolwich in 1801, later becoming Professor. (In an apparent contradiction to his statement here, Henry later in this entry will designate Barlow as "2nd Master.") Barlow's scientific interests ranged over mathematics (number theory), magnetism, electromagnetism, and optics, but

Mathematical Master in the seminary I could not without much difficulty find his residence.

One person of whom I inquired for Prof B. said no such man belongs to our regiment. Another said I am sure he is not a member of the 79th. A third I have heard of the person but do not know where he is to be found. I was much surprised to find tha[t] a person who[se] name is know[n] where ever science is cultivated should not be better known in his own village. But this was accounted for by the Prof by his stating that the village is principally made up of trancient Persons belonging to the army and it was only of such persons I had happened to inquire. Mr Barlow received me with much kindness introduced me to his wife and daughter and gave me an invitation to a family dinner. Made many inquiries of my friend Mr Bonnycastle.[5]

Mr B is a short stout person of a very plesant aspect about or nearly 60 years old. Has been connected with Woolwich about 30 years. Has according to his own statement had several hobbies each of which he has road with success. He is at present engaged in the study of rail roads and is one of the commissioners to establish a line in Ireland.[6]

He informed me that railroads are very expensive in this country. Stated the cost of the one from greenwich to London 3½ miles long at the enormus rate of £200,000 per mile.

---

some of his best-known achievements were in associated scientific technologies. For instance, his *Essay on the Strength of Timbers*, based on extensive experiments in the Woolwich dockyard, brought Barlow his first notice. Similarly, his famous *Essay on Magnetic Attractions*, a study of the deviation of the compass due to iron used in ship construction, was based on fundamental investigations of magnetic induction. His solution of compensating local attractions by the placement of an iron correcting plate was adopted by the Admiralty and won him the gold medal of the Society of Arts. Barlow was subsequently (1825) awarded the Copley Medal of the Royal Society for a sequence of theoretical and experimental studies in electricity and magnetism—studies which had greatly interested Henry. Below, Henry will comment on Barlow's important work on optical instruments and his involvement in steam locomotion. In several instances Barlow secured government aid for his researches, especially from the Board of Longitude. He was consulted frequently by govern-

ment and industry on technological matters. He was always a prolific contributor to the encyclopedia literature in mathematics, science, and technology. *DNB, DSB*.

For more on Barlow and his apparatus, see Henry's Diary of April 21, 1837, printed below.

[5] Charles Bonnycastle, who was educated at Woolwich and taught at the University of Virginia (*Henry Papers*, 2:419n–420n), was the son of the prominent Woolwich mathematical professor and textbook author, John Bonnycastle (*DNB*).

[6] In the 1830s, Barlow began to conduct experiments with important practical results for railway construction and steam locomotion. He served on railway commissions in 1836, 1839, 1842, and 1845, and "two reports addressed by him in 1835 to the directors of the London and Birmingham Company on the best forms of rails, chairs, fastenings &c., were regarded as of the highest authority both abroad and in this country." *DNB*.

This rail way however is built the whole way on a high arcade which rests at bottom on a series of inverted arches.[7]

Prof. B showed me a globe on which he had traced all the lines of magnetic variation and also the magnetic equator.

The globe was first procured the lines drawn on it and then varnisheed. It formed a very interesting article as all the lines are continuous and not broken as on the map. It gives a much better idea of their relative position.

Also showd me his observatory for experimenting with his fluid lense telescope.[8]

[7] The estimates for the cost of railway construction could vary wildly depending on what was counted in the cost and when and where the railway was built. In what appears to be a balanced presentation, D. K. Clark (*Encyclopaedia Britannica*, 8th ed., s.v. "Railways," p. 786) reported that up to 1857 the average cost of British railways was about £35,000 per mile, a figure which included not only the rails, but rolling stock, price of land, and other financial considerations. (Clark's figure roughly accords with that of Dionysius Lardner's *Railway Economy* [London, 1850], p. 496.) However expenditures would skyrocket for railways in or around major cities where land values were highest and construction made more difficult, requiring viaducts, tunnels, high embankments, and the like. According to Clark, the London and Blackwall Railway was the most expensive (until 1857) at £311,912 per mile. And early railroads tended to be more costly than later ones, which benefited from more favorable financial conditions and more efficient construction practices. Barlow's high figure for the Greenwich-London Railway, which was by all accounts an impressive and elaborate piece of engineering, was therefore not implausible. (Bache's European Diary for March [27], 1837, describes just how impressive the railway was.)

Americans were always impressed by the far greater amounts spent on English than on American railroads. Railroads on this side of the Atlantic tended to be constructed quickly and cheaply, with an eye toward gradual future improvement. The English built for permanence according to the highest engineering standards, producing "efficient" railways of high initial investment. However, the vastly higher British expenditures (five to six times as expensive per mile as those in the United States between 1830 and 1860) also were due to higher English land values reflecting the relative states of development of Britain and the United States in that period. John H. White, Jr., *The American Locomotive, An Engineering History, 1830–1860* (Baltimore, 1968), p. 3. John B. Jervis, *Railway Property* (Philadelphia, 1888), p. 42.

[8] English experiments on fluid-lens achromatic telescopes, which had begun in the eighteenth century, were made imperative by ever-rising duties on crown and flint glass in the period 1750–1825. Opticians and scientists felt that the high levies put the English effort at making achromatic refractors at a great disadvantage, especially in comparison with German instrument makers who had ready access to superior glass. The British Government attempted to finance glass manufacturing in England (in which Faraday was involved). When that effort proved disappointing, opticians turned to the alternative of the fluid lens. Early fluid lenses were quite successful in eliminating both chromatic and spherical aberration, but opticians feared for their permanency since the acid liquids used were thought to be corrosive to the lens surface.

Around 1827, Peter Barlow picked up this line of experimentation, using a combination of an ordinary crown-glass objective with a fluid lens further down the tube, as Henry will describe below. Instead of acid, Barlow used carbon bisulfide, which Brewster had studied in 1813 for its high transparency, dispersive powers (about twice that of flint glass), and absence of color. In 1827, Barlow built a 6-inch fluid-lens telescope and two years later, one of 7.8-inch aperture. The lenses proved long lasting and Barlow thought his astronomical observations with the fluid-lens device compared well with those from the best British conventional refractors. Encouraged, Barlow

He showed me one of the lenses filled with sulphuret of carbon. The lens was not interely filled with the liquid but contained a small bubble of air which is necssary to prevent the glass from breaking by a change of temperature.

The glass showed to me was intended to be placed part down the tube, and not at the end which contained another glass. The tube of the tellescope was about 6 inches diameter and 7 or 8 feet long. He did not appear to be very well satisfied himself with the performance and said that admirably when the object was in the middle of the field of view but that a slight obliquity of the ray gave a prismatic spectrum.

The observatory I think as well as the telescope and its mounting is described in the transactions of the Royal Society.[9]

The observatory is made of wood and resembles externally a circular tent of about 12 feet or more in diameter. In the cover or top of the tent a
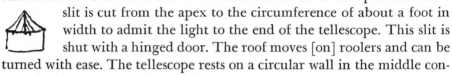
slit is cut from the apex to the circumference of about a foot in width to admit the light to the end of the tellescope. This slit is shut with a hinged door. The roof moves [on] roolers and can be turned with ease. The tellescope rests on a circular wall in the middle connected with the floor of the building.

Gave Mr B an account of my experiments on the magnetism of hollow bars[10] with the results of which he appeared interested.

A company of visitors came to see the family. I then took my leave after having spent several hours with the Prof. He accompanied me over the green or as it is called Woolwich common and pointed to me the house of Prof. Christie and also of Dr Gregory. Prof. Christie was not at home.[11] I left my letter and then proceeded to Dr Gregory's.[12] The Dr was at home

---

obtained financial support from the Royal Society for the construction of an 8-inch fluid telescope. Completed in 1832, the instrument was examined by Herschel, Airy, and Smyth, who in a lengthy report praised the light-gathering qualities of the lens but declared it a failure because of problems with chromatic and spherical aberration at higher magnifications. Barlow objected and determined to continue, but essentially abandoned active experimentation on a fluid-lens telescope after 1832. Henry C. King, *The History of the Telescope* (London, 1955), pp. 188–191. King is especially good for disclosing the imperatives of political economy behind the fluid-lens effort in England. See also *DSB, DNB.*

[9] "An Account of the Preliminary Experiments and Ultimate Construction of a Refracting Telescope 7.8 Inches Aperture, With a Fluid Concave Lens. . . ," *Phil. Trans.*, 1829, pp. 33–46.

[10] See above, Henry's diary for March 20, 1837, footnote 7.

[11] Henry met him later. See the diary entry of April 12–15, 1837, below.

[12] Olinthus Gregory (1774–1841). Like Barlow, Gregory was self-taught and a protégé of Hutton, his predecessor at Woolwich. He began teaching at Woolwich in 1802 and held the Professorship in mathematics from 1821 to 1838. Gregory's most important work was *A Treatise of Mechanics*, 3 vols. (London, 1806), a compilation of knowledge in applied mathematics and mechanics (contained in the Henry Library). Deeply concerned about the relations between science and religion, Gregory wrote *Letters to a Friend on the Evidences, Doctrines, and Duties of the Christian Re-*

but in the midst of a company of friends and strangers. He insisted on my going up with him in to the room above and again taking dinner. I consented and was introduced to the company. His two Daughters a Nephew a Tutor from Cambridge and several young persons sons and relatives of the Dr. I was soon made at ease and entered into conversation with the Dr. until the dinner was anounced. One of the gentlemen handed Mrs G and another Miss G to the dining room. The other young lady was unwell and remained in the sitting room. Mrs G took the upper end of the table the oldest son the lower. The Dr next his wife a seat he claimed as he said as an old man. I was placed next him. The Tutor opposite with the young Lady next him. In the course of conversation I was informed that Mr Patter[13] who has written on the subject of Light in the Phil Mag. is an under graduate of Camb. or perhaps Oxford will graduate this year is not however very young.

The subject was that of the tides at first. Dr G said that he was very happy to see that the tides had at length attracted the attention they deserved that he had once given the subject much attention had made a seriees of observations on the Tames but could get no person to join him. Found two tides in some places in the river which at first much perplexed him.[14]

---

ligion, also owned by Henry, in the New York, 1826 edition. A scientist of stature and a prominent Dissenter, Gregory was one of the founders of London University. *DNB. DSB.*

[13] Probably W. Pater, author of "On Vision," *Phil. Mag.*, 1816, 48:353–354.

[14] Long a matter of great scientific interest, chiefly to astronomers, the problem of tidal motions received renewed attention in Britain during the 1830s. For the *Encyclopaedia Metropolitana*, Airy produced an important mathematical formulation of tidal phenomena; in the same period, the British Admiralty and British Association launched an international effort to test existing tidal theories with systematic observations. The foremost competing theories, both extensions of Newton's ideas, were the equilibrium theory advanced by Daniel Bernoulli and the hydrodynamical theory of Laplace. William Whewell and John Lubbock took the lead in organizing this effort, collecting and recording tidal data from around the world. Explicitly applying his "Methods of Induction," Whewell stressed the particularities and the great variations in tidal motion, focusing on problems posed by the Liverpool and London tides for which he derived new laws. Asserting that the main tide-producing forces of sun and moon were insufficient to explain the complexity of variation, Whewell maintained that local hydrographic features determined the extent and frequency of tides on particular shorelines. It was later found that each body of water has a natural period of oscillation dependent on two factors: the oscillations in water level caused by the sun and moon and the period of oscillation due to the configuration of the basin. Tidal estuaries like the Thames showed very complicated patterns, caused by the resistance of the banks, the river bottom, and the drainage water. See John William Lubbock, "On the Tides in the Port of London," *Phil. Trans.*, 1831, pp. 379–416; "On the Tides at the Port of London," *Phil. Trans.*, 1836, pp. 217–266, and 1837, pp. 97–140. *DSB*, s.v. "William Whewell" and "John William Lubbock." Whewell's "tidology" as an application of his inductive philosophy is treated in Michael Ruse, "The Scientific Methodology of William Whewell," *Centaurus*, 1976, 20:227, 233–237. Robert Grant, *History of Physical Astronomy* (London, 1852), p. 162, writes of the renewed attack on the problem of tides in the 1830s. Several works by Henry A. Marmer are authoritative for the patterns of tidal phenomena: "The Variety in Tides," *Annual Report of the Smithsonian Institution for 1934* (Wash-

We next conversed on the Drs experiments on projectiles: he stated that no experiments on this department of science made at Woolwich were alowed to be published. They were made at the expense of the government and belonged to them.[15]

Some of his exp were published by Dupan[16] who came to Woolwich with introductions to the officers of the place. He was then about 25 years old was a *protuger* of Carnot the 2nd consul[17] & wrote the work for the purpose of raising himself into notice in his native country. He was says Dr G. the most indefatagable person he ever knew would not be put off on any pretence but percevered until he gained the desired information. He came 4 times to Woolwich to get an account of a planing instrument; every time he was put off by the superintendant of the machine. At length he wrote stating that he had seen enough to make out the description and that he could get an order from the heads of department for a detailed account if the officer refused any longer to grant his request. He at length succeeded.

He published some libells on the nation, amoung the rest the manner of floging the English soldiers naked. He showed the* drawing of this and the burlesk English officer superintending the punishment to Dr G and excused himself for inserting it by declaring that he had said so many good things of the English that his book would not be sold in France or be believed unless something of the kind were inserted. He also purposely gave an exagerated account of the treatment of the French prisoners at Greenwich. The balistic pendulum[18] used by Dr G is described by Du-

* (See plates of Force comercial of Dupans)

ington, D.C., 1935), pp. 181–191; *The Tides* (New York and London, 1926), chapters 4–6; *The Sea* (New York and London, 1930), pp. 207, 217. The assistance of Harold Burstyn of the U.S. Geological Survey, Reston, Virginia, is gratefully acknowledged.

[15] *The Royal Society Catalog* lists only two articles by Gregory on ballistics. The first volume of his *Treatise of Mechanics* deals extensively with the theory and practice of ballistics and includes lessons on practical gunnery (pp. 193–217).

[16] Pierre-Charles-François Dupin (1784–1873), the French mathematician, economist, and educator. Employed as a naval engineer, Dupin visited England in 1816 to study its arsenals and technical installations. *DSB*.

[17] The mathematician and engineer Lazare-Nicolas-Marguerite Carnot (1753–1823, *DSB*) played a very prominent political role in the French Revolution, as a military leader, a member of the Committee of Public Safety, and the leading figure of the five-member Directory. However, although serving in high positions under Napoleon in the Consular government, Carnot was never second Consul. Dupin supported Carnot when Carnot was exiled from France after Napoleon's downfall. See Robert Fox, "Scientific Enterprise and the Patronage of Research in France, 1800–70," *Minerva*, 1973, *11*:467, footnote 125.

[18] The ballistic pendulum measured the velocity of military projectiles and the force of the fired gunpowder. It consisted of a large block of wood fixed to the end of an iron stem, which was capable of oscillating like a pendulum. Initially at rest, the block of wood was fired at and set in motion according to the velocity of the projectile. The amplitude of vibration was recorded on a ribbon attached

pan and the results of some experiments made I believe at the time.[19]

Dr G. is the person who used the method of the revolving discs of paper to determine the initial velocity. The discs were about 10 feet in diameter and placed on an axis about 30 feet long so that the distance of the discs could be lessened or increased.

This apparatus worked well in a still day. The ball in passing through did not tear the paper but cut a round hole through as if made by a sharpe knife. In my lectures I have been in the habit of giving the credit of this arrangement to Robbins.[20] It is simply this Two discs of paper placed on an axis and made to revolve with a known velocity by means of a train of wheels and a fly and then a ball shot through both when placed parallel with the axis. The amount of deviation of the direction of the two holes from the parallelism of the axis gives the velocity.

Dr. G. also devised an ingenious method to get the form of the curve described by the ball. A number of paper screens were placed at equal distances along the path. The ball perforated each and thus gave the abscissa (*a*) of the path and also the ordinates of each point *b b* &c. The paper was very thin. The ballistic pendulum is a very expensive article being required to be made of large blocks of wood. A piece of sheet lead was nailed over the face & when the ball struck the pendulum a flash of fire was seen in the day time and this made to explode a quan[ti]tey of gun powder placed in a hole bowered in

---

to the lower end of the pendulum. The ribbon passed through steel edges which acted like drawing pens. *Encyclopaedia Britannica*, 8th ed. For Gregory's description, see *Treatise of Mechanics*, 2:109–110.

[19] The work referred to by Gregory was apparently Dupin's *Force commerciale de la Grande-Bretagne* (Paris, 1824), part three of his multi-volume account of his 1816 British travels: *Voyages dans le Grande-Bretagne entrepris relativement aux services publics de la guerre, de la marine, et des ponts et chaussées, au commerce et à l'industrie depuis 1816* (Paris, 1820–1824), which generated a multitude of spin-off volumes by Dupin in French and in English translation. We were unable to find Dupin's "libells" in *Force commerciale* . . . , but they do appear in two other related works by Dupin, which we have found in English translation. His *Narratives of Two Excursions to the Ports of England, Scotland, and Ireland, in 1816, 1817, and 1818* . . . (London, 1819?) refers to Gregory's large-scale ballistic

pendulum (p. 14), to Dupin's meeting with Gregory at Aberdeen (pp. 41–42), and to Britain's alleged cruelty to prisoners of war (pp. 17–18). Dupin's *A Tour Through the Naval and Military Establishments of Great Britain, in the Years 1816–17–18–19 and 1820* (London, 1822) resumes the issue of the treatment of military captives in England (pp. 24–32) and the military punishments meted out by the English to English soldiers (pp. 103–104), with sensational accounts of mutilation. The plate depicting flogging in the British army is on p. 105. Dupin extolled the treatment of war prisoners in his native country (p. 25) in words only a Frenchman would believe.

[20] Benjamin Robins (1707–1751; *DSB*) is credited with the invention of the ballistic pendulum and known generally for his work on the principles of gunnery. Robins figures prominently in A. R. Hall's *Ballistics in the Seventeenth Century* (Cambridge, England, 1952), pp. 51, 55, 65, 142.

the face of the pendulum. The Dr supposed the flash to be produced by the compression of the air between the ball and the face of the pendulum. I informed him that this could not be the case since no light has ever been produced by the compression of air. The condencing cyringe produced fire and light by combustion of the oil. When carbonic acid or hydrogen is used no light is produced. (try this exp)[21]

Dr G. is Prof of Math and Lecturer on Nat Phil. Mr Christie is 1st Math. Master and Mr Barlow 2nd Master. Dr G must be nearly 60 years old but does not appear of that age. He is one of the most plesant persons I have met with in my intercourse thus far with English Philosophers. He resembles in person and stature Mr Stansbury[22] appears to abound in good feelings made me promis to call again a promis which I intend to keep when he recommences his experiments on projectiles and this will probably be in a few weeks as he has his pendulum made and all prepared for a new series as soon as the weather and his own health will permit.[23]

From Dr G's I went to the residence of Mr Sturgeon the electrician who as well as Mr March[24] resides in this place. After some difficulty I found the house and was introduced into Mr S's study. He was not at home but returned soon. I was on the whole well pleased with him and found that he is a man of great industry has a strong mind but the want of early disipline has rendered him not as clear in his conceptions as an other course of education would have rendered him. He informed me that he had spent most of his life in the army had been a bombarder & had studied mathematics and natural philos while a soldier. He has brought himself into considerable notice and is now making a very good living by lecturing to several schools in the neighbourhood.[25] He is a strong vigerous man apparently about 40

---

[21] For the electrical syringe, see *Henry Papers*, 2:239, and for the relationship between the spark and the condensation of air, see *Henry Papers*, 2:292. It is not known whether Henry attempted to reproduce Gregory's results.

[22] Arthur J. Stansbury, an Albany friend. *Henry Papers*, 2:443–444.

[23] See below, Henry's diary entry of April 21, 1837.

[24] Henry's usual misspelling of the name of James Marsh.

[25] Compare these remarks with those in Henry's European Diary, April 22, 1837 (see footnote 11 of that document). Sturgeon started to pick up his notable mechanical skills during his youthful apprenticeship to a shoemaker and began to acquire book-knowledge in science on his own during his subse-

quent career in the Artillery. According to Sturgeon, his attentions were abruptly turned to electricity by a spectacular thunderstorm he experienced in Newfoundland, where he was stationed with the Artillery. After retirement from the Service, Sturgeon moved to Woolwich and resumed his trade as a bootmaker, supplementing his income by lecturing at schools in the area and teaching officers' families. Sturgeon established close associations at Woolwich with Marsh, Barlow, Christie, and Gregory. *DNB.* Silvanus P. Thompson, *William Sturgeon, The Electrician: A Biographical Note* (Privately Printed, 1891). James P. Joule, "A Short Account of the Life and Writings of the Late Mr. William Sturgeon," *Memoirs of the Literary and Philosophical Society of Manchester*, 1857, 2d ser. *14*:53–57.

years of age but informed me that he is turn of 50. I stoped with him until after 10 o'clock and then took breakfast with him in the morning. After this he accompanied me to London and very freely gave me much interesting information relative to magnetic experiments.

He showed me a very simple method of forming a battery with the zinc and copper very very near. This is merely by rapping the zinc in a piece of cloth—silk perhaps would be best as not so readily acted on by the acid—and then bending the copper around this. The cloth prevents contact however near the metals. The whole is then plunged into a gallipot of dilute acid.[26]

He next showed me an apparatus for revolution by thermo electricity by a pile made of a thick piece of bizmuth 6 inches long ½ an inch diameter of a cylindrical form. Around this a pece of copper wire was twisted at each end a break in the middle of the wire served to form the communication with the revolving apparatus (a). (Try This)[27] The revolving apparatus was made of bell wire and about 5 inches high.

Also showed me a small battery of 130 11½ or 2 inch plates very near together charged with water by means of which, and a battery of coated glass with a revolving wheel to break connection, he produ[c]es intence shocks. The plates are about as near together as those of my little battery.

(Try an experiment of this kind with one pair and the coil used with the coated glass.)[28]

When[29] the wheel is used a shock is produced with 300 feet of wire and a single battery formed of two wires one of zinc & the other of copper.

The piece of bizmuth which Mr S has described in the Phil Magazine[30] is in the form of a cone about 4 inches high and weighing about a lb. It is

---

[26] Many of Sturgeon's experiments were directed toward the simplifying and cheapening of apparatus with an eye toward making them practical for use in scientific industries. *DNB.*

[27] Experiments on electromagnetic rotations were the subject of Sturgeon's first scientific publications. Sturgeon operated the rotating apparatus with thermoelectric as well as voltaic currents in order to demonstrate equivalences between the two varieties of electricity. His "Electro-Magnetical Experiments," *Phil. Mag.,* 1824, *63*:95–100, was the first of a series of articles relating to this subject. As yet we have not come across any evidence of Henry's repeating this experiment.

[28] For a description of Sturgeon's apparatus in the context of his other electromagnetic

work see Joule's "Sturgeon," p. 64. It was already known that a voltaic battery could charge a Leyden jar.

In Sturgeon's apparatus, the toothed wheel, connected to a Cruickshank's trough, charged and discharged a Leyden battery rapidly enough to present the sensation of continuous shock. Again, any Henry experiments along this line have yet to be located.

[29] Henry put an X in the left margin next to this passage, perhaps for emphasis.

[30] Probably Sturgeon's "On the Thermo-Magnetism of Homogtneous Bodies," *Phil. Mag.,* 1831, 2d ser. *10*:1–24, 116–124. However, the article deals with the thermoelectric properties of a piece of antimony rather than bismuth.

very crystaline in its structure and when heated at the apex will deflex a needle for sometime afterwards shewing a current from the apex to the base of the cone.

(To produce a current of thermolectricity of any quantity a large piece of metal should be used. This is my own opinion.)

Mr S. also explained to me his method of producing a continued electrical current by magnetic induction which is very ingeneus but has not as yet been published.[31] It consists in using 4 cams for making and breaking the connections. No mercury is used but the wires rubb on the surface or circumference of the cams and produce at proper intervals the change required in the connections to constitute a continuous current. The magnet consisted of two batteries or compound horshoes one within the other and before the ends of these two cylenders of iron are made to revolve and these are the axes of the coils of wire in which the electrical induction takes place. The change in the connection to produce a current constanly in one direction is effected by four cams placed on the axes of revolution and connected to the wires which form the terminations of the coils by soldering.

The arrangement of these cams may be stud[ied] out by a little reflection by reccollecting that the nutral point or that at which the current begins to change its direction is that where the soft iron cylenders are in the same

---

[31] The memoir describing this early generator equipped with a primitive commutator was, according to Sturgeon, read before the Royal Society on June 16, 1836, but (for unspecified reasons) was not printed in the *Phil. Trans.* Sturgeon later published it under the title "Researches in Electro-dynamics, Experimental and Theoretical," in his own *Annals of Electricity, Magnetism, and Chemistry*, 1838, 2:1–24; 1838–1839, 3:16–24. A hymn of praise to the magnetoelectric machine (with or without iron armature), Sturgeon's memoir came forth with assertions like:

The magnetic electrical machine, whose exhaustless powers, free of expense and ever ready at command, when brought even to a moderate state of perfection, can hardly fail of becoming a powerful engine of analysis, and an useful and economical implement in the hands of the experimental enquirer.

Annals of Electricity, 2:2.

Of particular interest were the pointed comparisons made between the magnetoelectric machine and the voltaic battery in which Sturgeon opted decidedly for the eventual superiority of the former. In his biographical memoir on Sturgeon, Joule seconded this prediction with the following argument:

It has been shown by Liebig, and also demonstrated by my own experiments, that the production of force by the oxidation of zinc, is at least one hundred times as expensive as that derived from the combustion of coal in the steam engine. Therefore, admitting that half the effect is wasted during the conversion of ordinary force into that of current electricity, and also that half the useful effect is wasted in the production of force by the voltaic battery, we arrive at the conclusion that the zinc requisite to produce a current of given intensity is at least twenty-five times as expensive as the coal which, consumed in a steam engine working a Sturgeon's magneto-electrical machine, would be able to effect the same result.

(p. 66.) Such considerations were pertinent to the mounting debate about the practicality of electric power. The dynamo would drastically alter the terms of the debate over the competition between steam and electric power. See *Henry Papers*, 2:448n.

plane with the magnet. At that moment the iron begins to loose its magnetism and it must be reccollected that a current is produced only when the
iron is receiving magnetism or loosing it. In the act of changing its magnetic
 state there is also a current produce[d]. Let *a c* represent the
poles of a horseshoe magnet then the keeper revolving from *a*
will begin to produce a current the moment it begins to move
off from *a* since its magnetism will be decreasing and will
continue to produce a current in the same direction until it has revolved on
to c. Since the decrease of magnetism of one polarity and the taking on of
an opposite polarity may be considered as a constant dimininution of the
magnetic intensity in one direction.

Also for the same reason a constant current will be produced while the
keeper revolves through the arc from *c* to *a*.

Mr S thinks that he will be able to produce with this machine electricity
sufficient to perform all galvanic experiments; with an apparatus which he
exhibited to Prof Hare the effect was so great in decomposing that the Dr
concluded it was equal to the action of a battery of 40, 4 inch plates.

HENRY'S EUROPEAN DIARY
Henry Papers, Smithsonian Archives

[March] 25th [1837] Returned from Woolwich and dined with Mr Vaughan
met at his table Mr Rush former minister to the court of St. James.[1]

[1] Richard Rush (1780–1859) was in London
to negotiate the transfer of the Smithsonian
bequest to the United States government. According to the will of the British chemist
James Smithson, his half-million dollar estate
went to the United States if he and his nephew
died without heirs. Henry's dinner with Rush
was, as far as we know, his first direct contact
with the bequest that in ten years would
change his career from professor of natural
philosophy to the nation's foremost scientific
administrator. As Henry later recalled the dinner to Rush's son Benjamin (letter of February 11, 1860, Rush Papers, Princeton University Library):

I had the honor to form his acquaintance in
London, while he was on his mission in regard to the Smithsonian bequest; and although at that time nothing was farther
from my thoughts than ever to be intimately

associated with him in carrying out the intention of the founder of this Institution,
yet his friendship for Princeton College
with which I was then connected, and his
kind attention to me as well as his fund of
information on various subjects with which
I was but little acquainted, made an impression upon me which was deepened, and rendered permanent by our subsequent official
connection.

Third child of the well-known Philadelphia
physician Benjamin Rush, Richard Rush was
educated at Princeton and admitted to the
bar in 1800. He moved up rapidly in Pennsylvania and then national politics, first as Attorney General of the United States. Rush
enjoyed an illustrious career as Minister to
the Court of St. James from 1817 to 1825,
where he showed exceptional skill and tact at
negotiating the many disputes arising from

the War of 1812. Rush played an important role in the negotiations leading up to the Monroe Doctrine. The urbane and learned Rush moved easily in British social circles and was one of the most capable and best-liked Ministers to the Court of St. James. These attributes certainly recommended him to the delicate task of procuring the Smithsonian bequest, to which he was appointed in July 1836. Smithson's estate was tied up in the Court of Chancery for two more years. At the date of Rush's meeting with Henry, the Court was still seeking possible heirs of Smithson and his nephew. Rush saw the estate through these legal barriers, finally obtaining it for the United States in May 1838. The estate was in the form of securities, which Rush was extremely successful in selling and converting to gold coin, amounting to over £104,000, which he shepherded to the United States Treasury. Future volumes will chronicle Rush's role as a Smithsonian Regent and in deciding how the trust would be used to fulfill Smithson's call for an institution for the "increase and diffusion of knowledge." Rush later carried on a correspondence with Henry and emerged as one of the strongest supporters of Henry's policies at the Smithsonian. *DAB*. Cyrus Adler, "The Relation of Richard Rush to the Smithsonian Institution," *Smithsonian Miscellaneous Collections*, 1910, 52:235–251.

ALEXANDER DALLAS BACHE'S EUROPEAN DIARY
Copy,[1] Bache Papers, Smithsonian Archives

Monday Mar. [27, 1837] This morning I called at the Bank of Messr's Barings[2] & was disappointed in not getting letters & in not finding the address of Americans whom I wanted to see. The newspapers retained for me were two old political papers, one contained an account of the Penna election &c and the other a long speech apropos to I forget what. I had a first glimpse of London town—such a concourse too & fro in the strand—such lines of vehicles at the Poultry & in Fleet St. The moving tide certainly exceeded any thing I have ever seen. Advertisements are posted up three stories high & such as are duly imitated in New York. Clerical advertisement about when the Rev Mʳ so & so is to preach &c. Appointments by the Bishop of London to preach during Lent occupy certain church doors. At the Bank of England the formula for getting a note exchanged is an [...] one. You endorse it with name & residence then pass to the cashiers up stairs [...] & [...] a second door also, then down stairs it is paid in gold if you please. Passing on to Mʳ Wᵐ Vaughan's I found just the ditto as to kindliness of manner & purpose of his brother Mʳ John Vaughan & in his nephew Mʳ Petty Vaughan a gentleman who emulates both. They tell me it is high fair today at Greenwich & returning home for Ency & Maria we set off forthwith for Greenwich fair. I have learned Prof. Henry's address but did [not] find him at home to

---

[1] Apparently, the blanks in the text were left by the copyist where Bache's handwriting was illegible. In an obvious slip of the pen, the original gives the 26th as the date. The ellipses represent the gaps in the copy.

[2] Founded by Sir Francis Baring (1740–1810, *DNB*); various sons and grandsons were part of the firm.

invite with us. The stream of people down Greenwich road is surprizing all wending to the fair. The omnibus coaches run full, the pedestrians are a continuous line, the steamboats run every quarter of an hour for 6^d & the railroad cars run every ten minutes for 6^d & 1^s according to place. London seems pouring out & yet the crowd is not missed from the thronged streets. This has surprized us. Wherever we go there is a crowd & yet in approaching the place few persons are seen crowding towards it, so it was at the Foundling hosp^l church & so at St Paul's. After passing along a [. . .] we reached the fair. Children with holiday faces all agog made the road a pleasant sight & occasionally we met punch & judy & jugglers performing in the open street. Venders of oysters & scallops &^{c} &^{c} lined the side ways & the tempting gingerbread "six a penny" and the gilt gingerbread in all sorts of shapes, cakes & oranges, all sorts of eatables & drinkables exposed on temporary stands. In the main line of the fair, the scenes was [?most] new & racy. Booths were on both sides with all the before mentioned matters & various others. Tents under which circus riders & rope dancers were at work, while on a stage in front "the company" were playing all sorts of antics. Punch & Judy his wife, harlequin &^{c}. [. . .] seemed to take mightily. One real african was cracking his jokes in regular "nigger tongue" & a white Jim Crow with blackened face was imitating him. By the help of a 6^d each we made the way into one of these places & were glad to get out again. We occupied part of the boxes & hither the poor devils of performers resorted to rest themselves & to make repairs of garments. Women rouged from eye to chin with tawdry over clothes & dirty under ones & men with be-floured faces & dirty finery composed this horrid assemblage, one out of the many of various pretensions wh. lined the street, Fagh! After a little performer had excited admiration on the tight rope she was carried round on the shoulders of a fellow to pick up pennies "all for the little Miss" in a hat wh. the bearer offered to the company individually. "Six a penny, very nice, very nice, pray Miss just taste, six a penny" "Try only a penny." Pies all hot ha' penny a throw all hot "only a penny two knives, two forks only a penny." "Oranges two a penny, nice sweet oranges" a penny a swing get in, get in, only a penny— two a penny, two a penny—one for ha'pence—3^d to the pit gentlemen come forward—ladies enter only 3^d—all alive— all alive admission only 3^d thirty animals—only 3^d. Pray Miss allow me to assist you to a cake—six a penny— three a penny—choice cockles—three a penny. Such a confusion of cries, one might say a babel if they were not all in the same tongue. Mix this up with the music from the booths & the shouts of the spectators. The swings of various descriptions, the up, up, up, & down, down, down, single swings, ships going round & slightly rising & falling. Then rouge et noir tables were at hand. Whirligigs to turn for pies where foolish boys took a chance for a half pence of what they might have come honestly by for a penny at most, & what would have been dear at that. A little off the crowded part of the fields was throwing for various objects "three throws for a penny—three throws for a penny, only a penny for three throws." Several sticks are stuck up with articles such as pincushions, snuff-boxes, & the like upon their upper ends thus, there is a hole about the foot of each stick. The thrower stands off at some distance & with a short stout stick tries to knock these things down. If he succeeds in hitting any one of them & the object upon it does not fall into the hole (which it must unless he strikes high) the thrower has the object. This rarely happens except with a dexterous few. Sometimes a tempting bait in the way of a heavy jack-knife is put upon one of the sticks, & this being hit almost always fell *plump* in the hole below. Advertisements on the windows of tea, coffee, & hot water within. "Sandwiches two a penny, nice am sandwich" &c. We jostled our way thro' this dense moving mass of the lower orders passing from one end of the street to the other, highly amused. No rows were going on & but for the squeeze & pulling it was all well. I never saw such a collection of people better behaved, indeed they were all intent upon amusement & drink had not yet interfered. Long booths with all sorts of viands & drinks invited & successfully it seemed, with some. We saw but one fight & that was between an omnibus conductor & a man whom he had brought to the fair & who wanted to get off without paying. Among other contrivances for making money were tolls taken on the RR. company's bridge to shorten the distance to the fair & there stood a fellow crying "a full & particular account of the Greenwich Railway, of the arches, of the engine with all the dimensions of the road & interesting particulars of its construction, & a map, all for a penny, all for a penny—only a penny with the map." After a visit to the Naval Asylum which we ignorantly took for the hospital[3] we returned in the railway train. The Wellington police had here all the management of people & did their duty well. About ten minutes took us to the London bridge. This rail way is a remarkable one.[4] It is wholly raised above the level of the soil upon high arches,

[3] The Naval Asylum, a school for the orphans of deceased seamen, was close to Greenwich Hospital, which cared for old or disabled seamen. *Encyclopaedia Britannica*, 8th ed., s.v. "Greenwich."

[4] The Greenwich Railroad, a six-mile line from London Bridge to Greenwich, had been completed only from London to Deptford. The expensive, elevated railroad had numerous critics. Henry Fairbairn, citing estimated construction costs of £85,000 per mile, considered it "amongst the most monstrous abortions that

folly ever yet has caused to be brought into the financial world." Fairbairn, *A Treatise on the Political Economy of Railroads* (London, 1836), pp. 25–28. Peter Barlow had told Henry the line cost £200,000 per mile. See Henry's diary entry of March 24, above, especially footnote 7.

Despite criticism, the line was popular with the public. The day of Bache's trip (Easter Monday), ridership was 24,125. John Herapath, ed., *The Railway Magazine*, 1837, 2:273.

with piers; passing thro' Southwark you are upon a level with the third stories of the dwellings. There are two tracks laid, & a parapet walk on either side, which is so near that the cars cannot much incline from the vertical, keeps all safe. It is proposed to make houses of these arches & one is actually fitted up to show the practicability of the scheme. For fire they must use gas so as not to smoke the passers by the railroad. The passage of the train is said to make for a very brief time, a noise resembling the rumbling of distant thunder. What with excitements, an empty stomach, bad gingerbread, & omnibus riding I was made quite "sea-sick" & for the first time in my life in the awkward predicament of cascading in the street for I left the omnibus in time to prevent a scene there. While very sick at home Prof Henry came in & I had the additional discomfort of hearing his voice without being able to go & see him. After plenty of warm water & a nap I joined the party in the next room & heard of and from home.

HENRY'S EUROPEAN DIARY
Henry Papers, Smithsonian Archives

[March] 27[1837] Spent this day in getting my baggage through the custom house. Whole cost about 2 £. When I returned in the evening found Professor Bache's card on my table. He arrived in London on the 24th and accidentally took lodgings within a few steps of me. We agreed to spend the next few days in seeing together some of the Lions of the city.

HENRY'S EUROPEAN DIARY
Henry Papers, Smithsonian Archives

[March] 28th [1837] Visited with Prof. and Mrs Bache the Tower of London was much gratified with the exhibition of ancient armour and the arrangement of the different implements of war.[1]

---

[1] Many of the specimens of arms and armor at the famed fortress-prison originated with Henry VIII, who was a great amateur of military art. Drawn upon and dispersed during the English Civil War, the collections were partially reconstituted after the Restoration in 1660. An especially great number of additions were made in the early nineteenth century. Quite a few of these later additions proved bogus. Viscount Dillon, *Illustrated Guide to the Armouries, Tower of London* (London, 1910), pp. iii–iv.

Returned and in the evening went to see Forest[2] in Magbeth was pleased with the performance but did not experience as much pleasure as formerly in the amusement of the stage.[3]

[2] Edwin Forrest (1806–1872) is considered to be the earliest American-born actor of first rank. Forrest became famous for the passion and vigor of his acting. The Albany of Henry's day provided the scene for the evolution of Forrest's athletic style of acting, which he is said to have acquired from co-starring with Edmund Kean in that city in 1825. Presumably, Henry attended some of these performances. Forrest received high acclaim for his London performances in the 1830s, although Macbeth was not thought to be one of his stronger interpretations. His stage presence was only a reflection of a tempestuous, disastrous personal life. A bitter personal rivalry with nationalistic overtones with the English actor W. C. Macready climaxed in a riot of opposing claques in New York in 1849, leaving twenty-two killed and thirty-six wounded. *DAB.*

[3] This is one of the rare mentions made by Henry of his early love for the theater, long since displaced in his heart by science.

HENRY'S EUROPEAN DIARY
Henry Papers, Smithsonian Archives

[March] 29 [1837] Visited the chambers of the House of commons and also of the house of Lords, was surprised to find that the Lord chancellor and the Judges really set on a large wool sack of the size and shap[e] of a bail of cotton placed on the floor.

The chamber of the house of commons is now in progress of being fitted up for the session of next week and we had an oportunity of seeing Dr Reeds plan of warming the building by a false floor through which the warm air is passed by an innumerable number of gimblet holes. The floor is covered with hair cloath which permits the air to pass up through its meshes. The ventilation is produced by a flue through which a stream of heated air is passing. The plan is said to succed well.[1]

[1] David Boswell Reid's system is described in *Brief Outlines Illustrative of the Alterations in the House of Commons, in Reference to the Acoustic and Ventilation Arrangements* (Edinburgh, 1837), a copy of which is in the Henry Library. The system was installed as a test in the temporary House of Commons which was used following the 1834 burning of the Houses of Parliament. Later, the system was adopted for the new Houses of Parliament, constructed between 1840 and 1860. In 1844 Reid published a further explanation of his principles, *Illustrations of the Theory and Practice of Ventilation*. Reid worked on the Houses of Parliament until 1852 when he was discharged due to disagreements with the architect. According to Reid, his system was completely carried out in only one building—St. George's Hall in Liverpool.

Reid was born in Edinburgh and attended the University of Edinburgh. Pursuing an interest in chemistry, Reid taught private

From the chambers we went across the street to Westminster abbey. This most interesting edifice is an english cathedral as all others in the form of a cross and on the end of the shorter arm is placed the chappel of Henry the 7th a gorgeous structure of the florid gothic kind.

We noticed amoung the number of monuments two of interest recently erected, one to the memory of Davey and the other to Dr Thomas Young. They however were only small slabs of marble against the wall in an unoccupied spot while the monuments of martial valor were so lofty that the tops in many cases were 50 feet high.

The original marble statu of Watt by Canova is also highly interesting. The monument to Newton represents his various labours amoung the others that of weighing the sun against all the planets with a steelyard.[2]

---

classes in the subject before returning to the University where he received an M.D. in 1830. During his medical studies, Reid served as an assistant to Thomas Charles Hope, Professor of Chemistry. Following friction with Hope and the University's failure to institute a chair of practical chemistry at his suggestion, Reid again became a private lecturer, teaching sanitation as well as chemistry, and was very successful. It was apparently the recognition he achieved in this capacity that earned Reid the commission to test his principles in ventilation and acoustics in the temporary House of Commons.

In 1855 Reid took up permanent residence in the United States. Henry invited him to give an eight-lecture course at the Smithsonian, "Progress of Architecture in Relation to Ventilation, Warming, Lighting, Fire-Proofing, Acoustics, and the General Preservation of Health," during the winter of 1856–1857. In these lectures, Reid commented further on his work on the Houses of Parliament. Despite successful lectures at the Smithsonian and elsewhere, Reid had trouble finding a post that would utilize his various abilities. In 1863 he became an inspector of military hospitals, but died shortly afterwards. *DAB* (the *DNB* account differs substantially in chronology). Smithsonian Institution, *Annual Report for 1856* (Washington, 1857), pp. 46, 147–186. Henry reports meeting Reid in his diary entry of April 27, 1837 (below).

Other examples of Henry's interest in ventilation will appear below in this volume and in subsequent volumes.

[2] Monuments to scientists are scattered throughout Westminster Abbey. Those of Humphry Davy and Thomas Young, both by Sir Francis Legatt Chantrey (1781–1841, *DNB*), are in St. Andrew's Chapel. The huge, and thus controversial, statue of James Watt is not by Antonio Canova (1757–1822), an Italian sculptor, but by Chantrey. Arthur P. Stanley, *Historical Memorials of Westminster Abbey*, 4th rev. ed. (London, 1876), pp. 313, 314–315, 317, 319.

Newton's monument, in front of the choir, is by John Michael Rysbrack (1693?–1770, *DNB*). In front of a sarcophagus with a reclining figure of Newton are a number of figures holding symbols of Newton's major discoveries. Henry singled out the figure weighing the sun and the planets. In his 1826 inaugural lecture at the Albany Academy, Henry termed the accurate determination of the weight and density of the earth "astonishing" (*Henry Papers*, *1*:171). Henry was fascinated with this problem throughout his life. For a description of the monument to Newton see David Brewster, *Memoirs of the Life, Writings, and Discoveries of Sir Isaac Newton*, 2 vols. (Edinburgh, 1855), 2:393–394.

HENRY'S EUROPEAN DIARY

Henry Papers, Smithsonian Archives

[March] 30th [1837] Called in the morning on the American Minister Mr Stephenson.[1] He was not at home. Left our cards stated that we would call again. After this went to the rooms of the Royal Society. Mr Roberton gave me a copy of the abstracts of the society.[2] Also a copy of Queteslets papers on the Lat. and Long of Brussells.[3]

Called with Bache on Prof Daniels, was by him introduced to Prof. Royle[4] of Kings College a young gentleman perhaps 30. He is Prof of Materia Medica, showed us his arrangement of articles which are kept in wide mouth vessels with ground stoppers. All the substances of similar kinds are placed together. Dr R has a large collection of the native medicines of the East-Indians collected by himself during a residence of some years in that country.

In this institution (Kings college) much use is made of drawings and a person is constantly kept imployed in making them. Every part of anatomy and physiology is illustrated by them. They are made on corse paper and coloured. The method of preserving these deserves notice; a large table or rather a box like a [?table top] is place on the floor and contains about 8 or 10 shallow drawers and into these the drawings are put.

---

[1] Henry had a letter of introduction to Andrew Stevenson (1784–1857, *DAB*) from Martin Van Buren. Born in Culpepper County, Virginia, Stevenson was educated at the College of William and Mary and was admitted to the bar in Richmond. After serving twelve years in the Virginia House of Delegates, he was elected to the United States Congress in 1821 and in 1827 elevated to the Speakership. An ardent Jacksonian, he soon became embroiled in controversy for his extreme partisanship in committee selections and his opposition to Nullification. As a result of political antagonism, his appointment in 1834 as minister to Great Britain was delayed for two years. Finally confirmed in 1836, Stevenson remained in Britain until 1841. Retiring from politics, he settled in Albemarle County, Virginia.

[2] See Henry's letter to Stephen Alexander, April 10, 1837, footnote 17, printed below.

[3] In 1836 and 1837 Quetelet published three such papers.

[4] John Forbes Royle (1799–1858, *DNB*) had only recently joined the faculty of King's College. After attending the East India Company's military academy at Addiscombe, Royle joined the Company as an assistant surgeon and returned to India, his birthplace, in 1819. During his medical service there, he made extensive botanical collections, studied and collected local drugs, and made meteorological observations. Royle returned to England with his collections and enough material for several books on Indian medicine, plants, and manufactures. The first, *Illustrations of the Botany and Other Branches of the Natural History of the Himalayan Mountains*, was published in London in 1839.

A member of the Royal Society (1837), the Linnean Society, the Royal Geological Society and the Royal Horticultural Society, Royle was a prolific contributor to the journals of these societies and to other scientific periodicals.

These tables for there are several about the room answer the purpose of an ordinary table and are quite ornamental. They are painted like oak. A door at the end opens to expose the end of the drawer. From the room of materia medica we were taken to that of anatomy and physiology. In this there is a large collection of wax preparations for illustrating morbid anatomy.

We next visited the Geological Society rooms,[5] were kindly receved and shewn many articles of interest in this establishment. The curator[6] is employed to attend and give every person an opportunity of studying the science. They appear much interested in American rocks and the curator stated that it would be of great importance to the cause of the science if some of our young geologists would come to England and study the English formations the science would be much benefited.[7]

The specimens are all placed in drawers and fastened to small pieces of board. Thus They are fastened by a mixture of gum and brown sugar. Gum arabic alone would crack. The sugar is added to toughen it.

---

[5] The Geological Society of London, founded in 1807, was also in Somerset House. Its apartments included a meeting room, a library, and a museum divided into British and foreign collections. The Society was known for its interesting meetings, particularly the oral discussions which followed the presentation of papers. Horace B. Woodward, *The History of the Geological Society of London* (London, 1907).

[6] William Lonsdale (1794–1871, *DSB*) was Librarian and Curator from 1829 to 1842. Unlike most of the other members of the Society, Lonsdale, retired from the army, was not independently wealthy and had no other profession. He was the general factotum of the Society, overseeing its publications, preparing catalogues for the library, and arranging and naming specimens in the museum. Lonsdale became an authority on British fossils, particularly shells. His hypothesis, from fossil evidence, of a distinct intermediate strata between the Carboniferous and the Silurian in the Devonshire deposits was later confirmed by Roderick Murchison and Adam Sedgwick and led to their Devonian System. This finding, which confirmed the validity of using fossils to correlate strata, was an important contribution to stratigraphical geology. M. J. S. Rudwick, "The Devonian System: A Study in Scientific Controversy," *Actes du XII e Congrès*

international d'Histoire des Sciences (Paris, 1971), 7:39–43.

[7] An American who shared Lonsdale's opinion was Richard Harlan, whom Patsy Gerstner considers the leading American paleontologist at the time. Harlan recognized the need for international cooperation in paleontology and responded both by summarizing American work for British readers and by visiting Europe twice. Following his first trip in 1833, Harlan published "Critical Notices of Various Organic Remains Hitherto Discovered in North America," *Transactions of the Geological Society of Pennsylvania*, 1834, *1*:46–112, and *Medical and Physical Researches* (Philadelphia, 1835), and then contacted friends in England to distribute the works. During a more extended trip from 1838 to 1840, Harlan delivered a paper to the Geological Society and worked with Richard Owen in interpreting the Stonesfield fossils.

According to Gerstner, by the 1830s American contributions to vertebrate paleontology had won acceptance and respect in Europe. American or other foreign work could provide confirmation of British work based on local evidence. See *DSB*, s.v. "Harlan," and Patsy A. Gerstner, "Vertebrate Paleontology, an Early Nineteenth-Century Transatlantic Science," *Journal of the History of Biology*, Spring 1970, *3*:137–148.

HENRY'S EUROPEAN DIARY
Henry Papers, Smithsonian Archives

[March] 31 [1837] Visited in company with Prof Bache the editors of the Philosophical Magazine, delivered my letter from Dr Hare to Mr R Philips,[1] found him a very plesant old gentleman. Said that he had the minute before come across my name in a german journal. Showed me the article which stated that there were many discussions in the Philosophical Magazine on subjects which had been long settled by Henry in America.[2] He was very kind offered any assistance in his power in the way of introduction to institutions or scientific men.

In the evening I delivered my letter also from Dr Hare to Professor Wheatston of Kings' College—found him at the music store No 20 Conduit Street. He is a partner with his Brother in the music line. Devotes however most of his time to philosophical persuits.[3] Has lately taken out a patent for

[1] The editors of the *London and Edinburgh Philosophical Magazine and Journal of Science* were David Brewster, Richard Taylor, and Richard Phillips. Editor of the *Annals of Philosophy* which merged with the *Phil. Mag.* in 1827 and also an editor of the succeeding series, the *London, Edinburgh, and Dublin Philosophical Magazine and Journal of Science*, Phillips (1778–1851) was a Quaker mineralogical and pharmaceutical chemist with extensive publications to his credit. Elected a Fellow of the Royal Society in 1822, he lectured on chemistry at several schools, including Sandhurst. From 1839 until his death, he was a curator at the Museum of Practical Geology in London. *DNB*.

[2] The German article was an editorial comment by Poggendorff appended to abstracts of recent British articles on electromagnetism printed in his journal *Annalen der Physik und Chemie* (1836, n.s. 39:410). Poggendorff commented that the articles were interesting but lacked novelty. The Henry reference, somewhat less emphatic than Henry indicates, appeared in connection with an article by George Rainey, "On the Feeble Attraction of the Electro-Magnet for Small Particles of Iron at Short Distances," *Phil. Mag.*, 1836, 3d ser. 9: 72–73. Rainey attempted to explain why a soft iron armature in contact with the poles of an electromagnet is magnetized far more strongly than when the armature is near but not touching the electromagnet. Poggendorff stated that, while Rainey's observations were interesting, they had already been noted by "Henry and Ten Eyck" in America, a reference to Henry and [Philip] Ten Eyck, "An Account of a Large Electro-Magnet, Made for the Laboratory of Yale College," *Silliman's Journal*, 1831, 20:201–203.

Poggendorff's critical remarks about Rainey's and other electrical articles in the *Phil. Mag.* were mentioned by the latter journal in its issue of June 1837, 3d ser. 10:463–464.

[3] Charles and his brother William Dolman Wheatstone inherited the musical instrument manufacturing business from their father and an uncle. The business sustained Charles Wheatstone economically, despite his reputed disinterest in its commercial aspects and his preoccupation with the philosophical aspects of sound-making. The music shop spawned Wheatstone's fascination with the practical and theoretical aspects of sound, which in turn engendered much of his subsequent work in science and invention, including his electrical researches (see Henry's next diary entry). Constructing practical music devices and researching the science of sound were interpenetrating aspects of Wheatstone's early work, resulting in both patents and published articles. His contributions to sound ranged from the invention of a keyed *flute harmonique* and a concertina to subtle demonstrations of Chladni figures. Brian Bowers, *Sir*

a variety of musical instruments all on the principle of producing sound from a stringed instrument by means of a blast of air.[4] A violin can be played by a bellows on each side of the strings. The instrument for shewing the principle in the most simple manner consists of a silk thread streached across a sounding board with a portion of the middle enclosed by two slips of wood and the wind forced between these Thus or a view of the underside.

Prof. W also showed me an instrument called the Lyre by which the vibrations of a column of air may be measured when they are so rapid as scarcely to produce an audible sound.[5] It consists of a cylindrical reservoyer into the bottom of which the air is forced and passes out at the top of the cylender by a row of holes placed around the circumference of the top of the cylender.

These holes are not perpendicular to the plane of the top plate but a little oblique. Over the top plate and parallel to it is placed an other movable plate with the same number of holes in it which are also pierced oblique and by this means the plate is caused to revolve with great velocity by the pressure of the escaping air.

The movable plate is connected with a trane of wheels which serve by two indices to register the number of turns it makes. There are 25 holes in the plate and the same number in the top of the cylender therefore every

---

Charles Wheatstone (London, 1975), Chapters 2–4. W. G. Adams, "On the Musical Inventions and Discoveries of the Late Sir Charles Wheatstone," *Proceedings of the Musical Association*, 1875–1876, 2:85–93.

[4] Wheatstone was interested in the vibrations of rods and strings and the modes of setting them in motion. In July 1836, Wheatstone and John Green, a musical instrument maker, obtained a patent for musical devices in which " 'strings, wires or springs' were set in vibration by a current of air directed upon a limited portion only of the length of the string, wire or spring, and also instruments in which the string, wire or spring was struck mechanically as well as blown when the corresponding key was pressed." Bowers, *Wheatstone*, p. 37.

[5] With the instrument here described, Wheatstone provides a means of graphically illustrating the harmonic vibrations of a column of air. The device was similar to previous ones designed by Wheatstone to produce acoustical figures on sounding plates.

Another technique Wheatstone used to show the vibrations of air columns was to place the open end of a flute on or just above a liquid. The vibrational patterns were observed on the liquid surface. His writings and lectures on the harmonics of sounding air columns included "On the Resonances, or Reciprocated Vibrations of Columns of Air," *Quarterly Journal of Science*, 1828, *1*:175–183; "On the Vibrations of Columns of Air in Cylindrical and Conical Tubes," *Athenaeum*, March 24, 1832, p. 194.

We have not further identified the device described below. It is not to be confused with Wheatstone's publicly exhibited *Acoucryptophone*, or enchanted lyre, which illustrated the linear transmission of sound through thin wires. Wheatstone was fond of embodying basic principles in amusing devices, feeling that such demonstrations made the principles popular and memorable.

Bowers, *Wheatstone*, pp. 7–8, 17, 18, 24, 27–31.

turn of the plate gives 25 stops and opening of the holes or the same number of pulsations of air are produced.

I promised to meet Prof W tomorrow at [10 a.m.].[6]

---

[6] The appointed time is unclear in the manuscript.

HENRY'S EUROPEAN DIARY
Henry Papers, Smithsonian Archives

April 1ˢᵗ [1837] Called with Prof Bache on Prof Wheatstone that the former might deliver his letters. Was favoured with the reading of several letters from eminent Philosophers among the number was one from Herchel[1] another from Orested[2] and also one from Quetellet.[3]

Prof W also read to us an unpublished paper on the light from the long wire as analyzed by the prism and also by the revolving mirror. His experiments in the general corroborate the results of Fusinieri that the light of electricity is the result of the incandesence of ponderable matter but not in any case of a combustion.

Different metals produce different lines in the spectrum. He does not intend to publish this paper until he can get an instrument for the accurate measurement of these lines on the plan of Fraunhofer.[4]

---

[1] John Herschel (1792–1871; *DSB*) lent early encouragement to Wheatstone's scientific career and became his frequent correspondent. See Brian Bowers, *Sir Charles Wheatstone* (London, 1975), pp. 14, 15, 54, 55.

[2] Hans Christian Oersted (1777–1851; *DSB*), the Danish physicist, helped introduce the young Wheatstone to the scientific world. Bowers, *Wheatstone*, pp. 14–16.

[3] The Belgian scientist Adolphe Quetelet (1796–1874; *Henry Papers*, 2:261) was a friend of Wheatstone and a promoter of his work on the Continent, especially his experiments on the electrical telegraph and on the velocity of electricity. Bowers, *Wheatstone*, pp. 49, 145.

[4] Wheatstone's paper apparently remained unpublished; however, similar experiments were described in one of his earlier communications, "On the Prismatic Decomposition of Electrical Light," *British Association, Report, 1835* (1836), part 2, pp. 11–12, in which it was stated:

Fraunhofer having found that the ordinary electric spark examined by a prism presented a spectrum crossed by numerous bright lines, Professor Wheatstone examined the phaenomena in different metals, and found that these bright lines differ in number and position in every different metal employed.

Wheatstone concluded that "electric light results from the volatilization and ignition (not combustion) of the ponderable matter of the conductor itself; a conclusion closely resembling that arrived at by Fusinieri from his experiments on the transport of ponderable matter in electric discharges." Possibly Henry inspired Wheatstone to extend his experiments to (self-inductive) sparks from long conductors.

Numerous natural philosophers in the 1820s and 1830s were concerned with the light of the electric spark as yielding possible clues to the basic nature of electricity. Some theorized that the light was a modified form of the electrical fluid itself, electricity made visible. Others interpreted the light, not as the elec-

He finds some curious results on analysing by the revolving mirror the spark from a battery which is produced in breaking contact and also the spark on making contact. The first has all the appearance of the spark produced by common electricity; the 2[nd] is composed of several sparkes or is of longer duration. The first is instantaneous.[5]

Called this evening at Kings College to see Prof Wheats[t]one. He showed us several interesting instruments. 1[st] an article to illustrate the vibrations of a glass goblet.[6] The goblet is placed on a board from which rises an upright piece of wood or stiff wire *a* which supports a circle of wood which carries 8 arms desposed in equal angles and from each arm a small ball is suspended down the side of the glass. These balls are paired red and black alternately. When the glass is rubbed by the finger so as to cause a vibration the balls at equal angles or every other ball is thrown off, showing that the glass divides into 4 parts of vibrat[ion]s. He also exhibited to us his apparatus for measuring the velocity of electricity.[7]

The whole apparatus is quite small. The board on which it stands is not more than 12 or 14 inches long by 6 or 7 wide. The large wheel figured in the Phil Transactions[8] (Wheatstone's paper) is not more than 5 inches in diameter. The spark board is also about 5 inches in width and is placed at the distance of 10 feet from the mirror.

We were also shewn an apparatus for the same experiment made from an old watch with the ballanc[e] taken off. The revolving mirror being placed on the pivot of the second hand. Above this is placed a stationary mirror

---

tric fluid, but as an excited state of ponderable matter. In the experiments cited by Wheatstone, Ambrogio Fusinieri came to the latter theory, asserting that the electric spark carries with it particles of the conductor from which it issues. The incandescence of these metallic particles causes the electric light. Contrary to Wheatstone's account, however, Fusinieri believed that the particles are emitted in a group such that interior particles are in a fused state while exterior particles are indeed in a state of combustion because of exposure to oxygen. "Sopra il trasporto di materia ponderabile nelle scariche ellettriche," *Giornale di Fisica, Chimica, e Storia Naturale,* 1825, 8:450–461. Fusinieri's elegant experiments were widely reported in the English language. *Silliman's Journal* communicated some of his results in 1832, 22:355–357. Henry saw an extensive discussion of Fusinieri's work in the *Encyclopaedia Britannica* and took notes in notebook [23894], p. 115, which

remain undated but may have been prompted by Wheatstone's results. For Henry's experiments along these lines see the first notebook entry, above, of March 15, 1836.

Several scientists applied the prism to the electrical light. Wollaston and Biot were among the earliest, followed by Joseph Fraunhofer's thorough spectral analysis of sparks. For a discussion of Fraunhofer's techniques and a history of other inquiries into the electrical light, see *Encyclopaedia Britannica,* 8th ed., s.v. "Electricity," pp. 546–549.

[5] In his studies to determine the velocity of electricity, Wheatstone had perfected the revolving-mirror technique of analyzing the form and duration of electrical sparks. See *Henry Papers,* 2:125n–126n, 292, 491–493.

[6] Wheatstone's experiments on acoustical figures and modes of vibration are examined in Bowers, *Wheatstone,* Chapter 2.

[7] See *Henry Papers,* 2:491–493.

[8] *Phil. Trans.,* 1834, pp. 583–591.

and at a distance of about 10 feet the spark board is placed and near to it and immediatly behind it is placed a card on which lines are drawn corresponding to ½ degrees of the circle of which the distanc[e] of the card from the eye is the radius.

Several interesting experiments of the kind can be made by a common glass mirror of about 4 inches in diameter mounted as in the figure and put on a common whirling table.

Prof. also showed us the method used by the german Phil.[9] for the purpose of getting accurate results from the galvanometer. The coils of the instrument insted of being placed in the plane of the magnetic meridian are placed at right angles to it. The needle is first caused to ocillate by the action of the earth and then by the combined action of the earth and the coils which also tend to make the needle ocillate on each side of the meridian. The action of the earth is then eliminated from the last and the action of the galvanic current accurately determined. This method was first used by Biot.[10]

Prof. W. is now engaged on some experiments relative to the galvanic Telegraph by a number of galvanometers and as many wires.[11] He has

[9] Probably the Leipzig electrical physicist and philosopher Gustav Theodor Fechner (1801–1887), best known in science for his experimental refinement and verification of Ohm's Law. Fechner's oscillatory technique for neutralizing the earth's magnetic effect on the galvanometer is treated in H. J. J. Winter, "The Work of G. T. Fechner on the Galvanic Circuit," *Annals of Science*, 1949, 6:199. Fechner's *Elementar-Lehrbuch des Elektromagnetismus* (Leipzig, 1830) is in the Henry Library.

[10] Fechner introduced much of J.-B. Biot's physics into Germany. Biot's oscillatory method is discussed in Winter, "Fechner," p. 199.

[11] Wheatstone's invention of the electromagnetic telegraph was a direct outgrowth of his interests in sound transmission and closely related to his experiments in the velocity of electricity—aspects of Wheatstone's work carefully noted by Henry. In 1840 Wheatstone summarized the development of his interest in telegraphic communication. Since the 1820s he had conducted experiments on sound transmission over long distances through solid wires and rods but found distance a difficult barrier to clear communication. He then turned to electricity as the communicating agent. Feeling that earlier experimenters on electrical communication had failed to develop a practical device because of insufficient knowledge of electrical propagation, Wheat-

stone set out to investigate basic electrical properties, especially the velocity of electricity. When his experiments indicated a velocity approaching that of light, Wheatstone became convinced of the possibilities of electricity for telegraphy. His insulated circuits were particularly efficient enabling him " 'to ascertain that magnetic needles might be deflected, water decomposed, induction sparks produced, &c., under properly arranged circumstances, through greater lengths of wire than had ever yet been experimented upon.' " (Bowers, *Wheatstone*, pp. 104–105.)

According to Wheatstone, his first experiments using several miles of insulated wire began in 1836, although his first published announcement of an electromagnetic telegraph was not made until a month before Joseph Henry's visit, in the March 1837 issue of the *Magazine of Popular Science*. In 1837, Wheatstone formed a partnership with the entrepreneur W. F. Cooke for patenting and developing a practical telegraph. Their patent was obtained in June 1837, the first English patent for an electric telegraph. Bowers, *Wheatstone*, pp. 105–114. The device was a "five-needle telegraph" which required multiple wiring and indicated letters by the simultaneous deflection of two of the five magnetic needles. The signaling system was very easy to learn and use, requiring no special code,

suspended 4 miles of wire around the building and showed us decomposition through this long surcuit with a Wollaston battery of 20 pairs of 4 inch plates. For a conducting wire to be used with his Tellegraph he intends to use a small rope or cord about the size of that used for beads and to place a wire in the centre or axis of this. The rope being covered with tar will be impervious to water and may be used in any situation.

Prof. W has a method of communicating force to a great distance by means of the electrical wire. His project is the following. A long wire gives motion to a galvanometer needle placed at the further end of the route and this swings against two pins which are connected with the wires of an electromagnetic magnet which is thus set in action. The plates are immersed in diluted acid and are amalgamated so that no action or very little takes place until the circuit is completed.[12]

---

but the need for many wires made the apparatus extremely difficult to install. Bowers gives a complete history and technical account of the Wheatstone-Cooke device in chapters 9 and 10 of *Wheatstone*.

The business partnership between Wheatstone, the scientist-inventor, and Cooke, the businessman and amateur electrician, foreshadowed many aspects of the Henry-Morse relationship over the next two decades. Similar disputes arose over the amount of credit due to the natural philosopher as opposed to the practical man. At issue were questions of the patentability or accessibility of fundamental scientific discoveries. See Bowers, *Wheatstone*, pp. 103, 130.

[12] In modern terms, Wheatstone had incorporated a relay device into his telegraph to compensate for the weakening of the signal over long distances. Henry, at this point, does not seem especially surprised at Wheatstone's relay, but tradition has it that Henry invented an electromagnetic relay in 1835 when setting up a telegraph at Princeton. *Coulson*, p. 107. In an 1849 deposition in the case of *Morse* v. *O'Reilly*, Henry's recollection of his visit to Wheatstone corroborates the attribution. After giving a description of the Wheatstone relay essentially as it appears in the present entry, Henry added:

I informed him that I had devised another method of producing effects somewhat similar. This consisted in opening the circuit of my large quantity magnet at Princeton, when loaded with many hundred pounds weight, by attracting upward a small piece of moveable wire, with a small intensity magnet, connected with a long wire circuit. When the circuit of the large battery was thus broken by an action from a distance, the weights would fall, a great mechanical effect could thus be produced, such as the ringing of church bells at a distance of a hundred miles or more, an illustration which I had previously given to my class at Princeton. My impression is strong, that I had explained the precise process to my class before I went to Europe, but testifying now without the opportunity of reference to my notes, I cannot speak positively. I am, however, certain of having mentioned in my lectures every year previously, at Princeton, the project of ringing bells at a distance, by the use of the electro-magnet, and of having frequently illustrated the principle of transmitting power to a distance to my class, by causing in some cases a thousand pounds to fall to the floor, by merely lifting a piece of wire from two cups of mercury closing the circuit.

The object of Prof. Wheatstone, as I understood it, in bringing into action a second circuit, was to provide a remedy for the diminution of force in a long circuit. My object, in the process described by me, was to bring into operation a large quantity magnet, connected with a quantity battery in a local circuit, by means of a small intensity magnet, and an intensity battery at a distance.

Quoted in *Smithsonian Institution, Annual Report, 1857* (Washington, 1858), pp. 111–112. Class notes taken by Henry's students prior to the European trip are incomplete and do not

A battery of several pairs will be required to <*complete*> be attached to the magnet on account of the imperfect connection formed by the needle and the pins.

I was surprised to see that Prof W in making his experiments took no precaution relative to good metalic contact and that he did not even scrape the wires or amalgamate the ends.

Prof W. loaned me a pamphlet by M H *Jacobi* (*Mémoire* sur *L'application de Electro Magnetism au Mouvement des* machines) (printed at Berlin) which contains an exposition of the theory of Ohm (1827). The following is a translation.[13]

1) In a voltaic circuit shut the same quantity of electricity passes across each section perpendicular to the direction of the current whatever may be the form or the matter of the divers parts of the circuit. (The battery forms of course a part of the circuit)

2) Whatever change we make at one part of the circuit this change affects the entire action of the pile and is not confined to the place where the change takes place.

3) The voltaic action, measured in any manner whatever (either by the deflection of the needle the decomposition of a fluid or by any other opera-

---

provide documentary proof of his recollections. Those which survive from after the European trip do record class discussions of the Princeton telegraphs and electromagnetic relays. See Weiner, "Joseph Henry's Lectures," pp. 197–198. Henry, in any case, nowhere denies, to our knowledge, Wheatstone's independent discovery of the telegraphic relay. Coulson's complaint that Wheatstone "never publicly acknowledged his indebtedness to Henry for information about the relay" (p. 120) appears unjustified.

[13] The pamphlet, by Moritz Hermann von Jacobi, was published in Potsdam in 1835 and later translated in Taylor's *Scientific Memoirs*, 1837, *1*:503–531. The latter was owned by Henry and bears his markings. However, the translation from the French which appears below was probably made by Henry himself. The original French version of the Jacobi article was reprinted by A. A. De La Rive, in *Archives de l'électricité*, 1843, *3*:233–277. In that easily accessible printing of Jacobi's article, which we have used, the passages translated by Henry appear on pp. 247–249, 251, 252. The bulk of the passages translated (or paraphrased) by Henry consist of Jacobi's

summary of Ohm's principles as laid down in *Die Galvanische Kette, Mathematisch Bearbeitet* of 1827. Although Henry had heard of Ohm's theories previously and had even demonstrated an intuitive sense of the law in his electrical experiments, Wheatstone apparently provided Henry with his first direct knowledge of Ohm's mathematical principles, a point considered in *Henry Papers*, 2:299.

Wheatstone was instrumental in introducing Ohm's ideas to English-speaking scientists. Although his full treatment of Ohm did not appear until the publication of his Bakerian lecture of 1843, "An Account of Several New Instruments and Processes for Determining the Constants of a Voltaic Circuit," *Phil. Trans.*, 1843, pp. 303–327, he had utilized Ohm's results much earlier in experiments on the electric telegraph. Wheatstone, in fact, attributed his success with the telegraph to his understanding and application of Ohm's theory. See Bowers, *Wheatstone*, pp. 87–88, 122–123. On Wheatstone's verification of Ohm's Law, see H. J. J. Winter, "The Significance of the Bakerian Lecture of 1843," *Phil. Mag.*, 1943, 7th ser. *34*:700–711.

tion) is in the direct ratio of the electro-motive force and inversely as the resistance which is opposed to the passage of the current or

$$A = \frac{E}{R} \qquad \begin{array}{l} E = \text{Electro motive} \\ R = \text{Resistance} \end{array}$$

4) This resistance is composed of a 1) the resistance of the partial conductor or of the conjunctive wire. For the same substance this resistance is in the direct ratio of the length of the wire and inversely as the transverse section.

b 2nd) of the resistance of the liquid conductor. This is in a ratio direct of the thickness of the liquid stratum which seperates the positive and negative plates <and> or inversely as the transverse section of the battery which coincides in most cases with the surface of the plates.

During the action of the pile this last resistance increases and in the same time the electro motive power E is affected. The chemical effect changes by degrees the nature of the liquids the surface of the metals and consequently the electrical tension.

The difficulty of expressing the electro-magnetic actions comparable amoung themselves and the still greater difficulty of arriving at an absolute measure consists for the most part in the continual changes of these several elements.

Thus in expressing by r the resistance of the conjunctive wire we will have $\frac{rl}{d}$ for the resistance of the wire of the length l and thickness d

also $\frac{r'l'}{d'}$ will be the resistance of the liquid conductor of which the thickness and surface are expressed by l' and d'. Then the action of the current or the quantity of electricity passing through the pile will be expressed by

$$A = \frac{E}{\frac{rl}{d} + \frac{r'l'}{d'}}$$

5) The electro-motive force is the direct ratio of the number of (cupples) plates and at the same time the resistance r' increases in the same proportion.

Having a pile of n' couples the force of the currant will be expressed by

$$A = \frac{n'E}{\frac{rl}{d} + \frac{n'l'r'}{d'}}$$

6) If the electrical current is divided into many branches of which the lengths reduced in the inverse ratio of the diameters are expressed by $l\ l'\ l''$

l''' &c the total action will be the same as if there were but a single wire of which is expressed by the equation

$$\frac{1}{L} = \frac{1}{l} + \frac{1}{l'} + \frac{1}{l''} \, \&$$

Having then n wires of the same length the total force of the currant will [be] expressed by

$$A = \frac{n'E}{\frac{rl}{nd} + \frac{r'l'n'}{d'}} = \frac{nn'dd'E}{rld' + r'l'nn'd}$$

As we can profit by the power developed by each unit of length of the conjunctive wire plied around the bars of soft iron of the same dimensions (or around different needles of the same strength) the total force developed by the conjunctive wire of the length l will be

$$A = \frac{lnn'dd'E}{rld' + rl'nn'd}$$

From the last formula we can deduce the limits of the action of the current which can be augmented but by the number of the number or the surfaces of the voltaic couples, by the length of the wire, the number of the branches and the diameter of the same.[14]

In increasing the surface of the plates d' the limit of the total force of the currant will be

$$A = \frac{nn'dE}{r}$$

In augmenting the number n' this limit is

$$A = \frac{ld'E}{r'l'}$$

In augmenting the length l

$$A = \frac{nn'dE}{r}$$

The thickness d

$$A = \frac{l'dE}{r'l'}$$

---

[14] Henry has mistranslated and confused the sense of this sentence, which should read, "From this formula one can deduce the limits of the action of the current which cannot be augmented by the number or the surface of the voltaic couples, by the length, the diameter and the number of conjunctive branches." De La Rive, *Archives*, 3:249.

the number of branches n

$$A = \frac{ld'E}{r'l'}$$

In general to augment the force of the current as much as we wish it is necessary to increase the surface of the couples and in the same time the thickness of the conjunctive wire or the number of branches.

The increase of the length of the wire requires an increase of the number of couples to attain the same end.[15]

The experiments made by Fechner on this subject and published in his work *Maassbestimmungen über die* galvanische Kette (1831)[16] leaves no doubt of the truth of this law which expresses very simply the divers elements which constitute the voltaic pile.

The same author[17] states that the primative state of a battery is sooner restored after action by exposing the negative element to a current of air until it be perfectly dry. Both elements should be so exposed but particularly the negative one.

The galvanic effect is much more constant if the distance between the troughs or I should say the width of the sels be considerable so as to contain more acid.

(Could not the retaining battery be formed of pourous wood instead of bladder or porcelan as the intermediate substance.[18] JH)

Where galvanic action is required for hours and days copper cannot be used with advantage. The negative element should be of platina or of silver. Perhaps plates of copper plated with either of these metals may be found to answer. The solution of the copper in the acid however slight it may be and its subsequent reduction by the hydrogen in its nacent state gives place to partial galvanic effects (or produces small galvanic circles) by which the principle galvanic action is much impeded.

In some cases the author found that when the apparatus[19] ceased to act the deposition of copper or iron from the negative element formed a coting to the wood which seperated the plates and thus produced a metalic communication which discharged the battery at least in part.

---

[15] A line in the left margin of the original draws attention to this passage.

[16] For the importance of this work and the techniques used by Fechner in his verification of Ohm's principles, see H. J. J. Winter, "The Work of G. T. Fechner on the Galvanic Circuit," cited in footnote 9, above.

[17] i.e., Jacobi. This passage was marked in Henry's copy of the English translation appearing in Taylor's *Scientific Memoirs*.

[18] Here Henry inserts his own idea, relating to the constant battery of Daniell. See above, Henry's first diary entry of [March] 23 [1837], footnote 22.

[19] i.e., the electromagnetic motor which is the subject of Jacobi's article. This passage, too, is marked by Henry in the *Scientific Memoirs* translation.

HENRY'S EUROPEAN DIARY
Henry Papers, Smithsonian Archives

April 2nd [1837] Sunday. Went to St James church.[1] The service in the true english stile. The clergiman who read the prayers did not officiate in the pulpit as a preacher. The sermon was pronounced by the rector.[2]

The Beedle is designated with a coat trimed with gold lace. The gallery is the fashonable part of the house at least I judged so from the number of servants in liver[y] standing behind the pews. Observed a method of ventillating the house without permitting the cold air to incommode the audience. Several panes of glass are removed from the middle of a window and the part closed by a frame of glass resembling in form a cellar door. The upper part shuts with a cover and this is occasionally opened.

The air is thus deflected upwards and does not come in contact with the persons near the window.

The end of the church was decorated with flags.

[1] One of the over fifty churches built by Sir Christopher Wren (1632–1723, *DNB*) in the wake of the Great Fire of London of 1666, St. James, Piccadilly, was consecrated in 1684. Wren thought the interior of St. James, with its regular and straight lines, should be the model for English churches. St. James contained an organ donated by Mary II, crimson velvet hangings given by the Prince of Wales in 1738, and wooden carvings by Grinling Gibbons (1648–1720, *DNB*). George H. Birch, *London Churches of the XVIIth and XVIIIth Centuries* (London, 1896), pp. 94–96; Albert E. Bullock, ed., *Grinling Gibbons and His Com-*

peers (London, 1914), n.p.

[2] A communion service in the Church of England required three clergy: the Priest or Celebrant, the Deacon or Gospeller, and the Subdeacon or Epistoler. The prayers were read by the Priest. Any of the three clergy might deliver the sermon. On the other hand, the preacher could be an individual other than the three clergy. Frederick George Lee, ed., *The Directorium Anglicanum*, 3d ed. (London, 1866), pp. 45–59; *A Directory of Ceremonial*, Alcuin Club Tracts no. 13, 4th ed., 2 vols. (London, 1950), *1*:37–46.

HENRY'S EUROPEAN DIARY
Henry Papers, Smithsonian Archives

April 3rd [1837] Went with Prof Wheatstone to see Mr Babage.[1] Was ushered into the house of the Professor by a servant in livery.

[1] The English mathematician Charles Babbage (1792–1871, *DNB*, *DSB*) had served as one of Henry's early models for scientific methodology and the role of the professional scientist (*Henry Papers*, *1*:342–343), but this was the first meeting between the men. It led to a relationship which, as later Henry correspondence indicates, remained warm into the 1850s.

Found Mr B a very plesant person much younger in appearance than I had anticipated. Appeared not more that 40 although he has a son[2] grown up and engaged in the business of an engineer.

We were informed (Prof. Bache and my self) that the celebrated calculating machine was to be exhibited to Mr Hume[3] the radical member of parliament from Middlesex and his Brotherinlaw[4] who is about to sail for america.

The principal object of the request that the machine might be exhibited at this time is that the Brotherinlaw of Mr Hume might know something of the machine before visiting America as he had been informed that every person comming from England would be required to explain the machine.

Before the company arrived Mr B took us into an other room apparently his work shop to explain to us the general principles of a new machine[5] of which he is now making the drawings and which will far transend the powers of the first machine[6] even were it compleeted according to the original plan.

[2] Benjamin Herschel Babbage (b. 1815) was the eldest of Babbage's eight children. An assistant to M. I. Brunel during the construction of the Great Western Railway, Herschel (as he was usually known) then accompanied Brunel to Italy to survey for the Genoa-Turin railway. He later became a surveyor in Australia, eventually settling there. Maboth Moseley, *Irascible Genius: The Life of Charles Babbage* (Chicago, 1964), pp. 126, 167, 232.

[3] Joseph Hume (1777–1855) was a former surgeon and administrator with the East India Company and the army. He had entered Parliament in 1812 as a Tory, but crossed over to the Radicals in 1818 and served as their leader for the next thirty years. In Parliament he agitated for the repeal of the Corn and Combination laws and advocated Catholic emancipation, the end of flogging in the military, and the abolition of imprisonment for debt. *DNB*.

[4] Unidentified.

[5] This is Babbage's analytical engine, the automatic calculating machine which resulted from his study of the punch cards used for weaving machinery. Babbage realized that the cards could be adapted for use in an advanced decimal computer. His design included a storage area, a "mill" for arithmetical operations which could handle up to one thousand numbers, and printed or punched output. Three different sets of cards were necessary for the operation of the engine: one set would supply the given numbers or constants for the particular problem; a second would direct the engine, supplying the overall program; the third set would indicate the particular arithmetical operation to be performed. The analytical engine was very impressive, but never obtained the needed financial backing. As a result, it remained on the drawing-board. *DSB*; H. P. Babbage, "The Analytical Engine," *Charles Babbage and his Calculating Engines*, eds. Philip and Emily Morrison (New York, 1961), pp. 331–344.

[6] It was around 1820 that Babbage began designing calculating engines using the calculus of finite differences. In theory he had found a practical method of reducing the drudgery of producing accurate tables. In practice, however, he failed. Partly this was due to his overambitious goals. He kept enlarging the capacity of his engine, which in turn meant higher costs. The required funds were not obtainable. But his failure to bring "Difference Engine Number One" to fruition was primarily due to his infatuation with the analytical engine. Work on the difference engine had been stopped in April 1833 and was not resumed. By the Fall of 1834 Babbage had begun concentrating on the more sophisticated version of the calculating machine. Yet during Babbage's lifetime less ambitious versions of the difference engine were successfully built by others. One ended up in the Dudley Observatory in Albany, New York. *DSB*; H. P. Babbage, "Analytical Engine," p. 332; Moseley, *Irascible Genius*, pp. 65–81, 113–118.

The explanation given us was confined to the *modus applicandi* of the machine and to some very general principles of action. This machine is divided into two parts one of which Mr B calls the store house and the other the mill. The store house is filled with wheels on which numbers are drawn. These are drawn out occasionally by levers and brought into the mill where the processes required are performed. This machine will when finished tabulate any formula of an algebraic kind. It will also calculate the numerical value of an integral when the same is expressed approximately by an infinite series. Besides calculating all Logarithmetic functions it also will be of great use in calculating the mean results of astronomical and meterological observations.

Before Mr B had finished his exposition the important person Mr Joseph Hume the member from middlesex his Daughter[7] and his Brotherinlaw were anounced. We then adjourned to an upper parlor where the machine 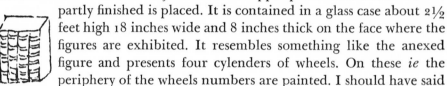 partly finished is placed. It is contained in a glass case about 2½ feet high 18 inches wide and 8 inches thick on the face where the figures are exhibited. It resembles something like the anexed figure and presents four cylenders of wheels. On these *ie* the periphery of the wheels numbers are painted. I should have said that each colum or cylender is composed of 4 wheels thus figured.

The operation of calculating by this instrument is by an application of the principle of differences. For an account by Dr Lardner see Edinburgh Review No 120.[8] The machine of which Mr B is now making the drawings is of a totally different nature and operates on interely different principles.

We were favoured by a most admirable exposition of the use of the machine and of its importance in producing perfect accuracy without the possibility of committing an error.

---

[7] One of six children. We have uncovered no further information.

[8] Dionysius Lardner, "Babbage's Calculating Engine," *The Edinburgh Review*, 1834, *59*: 263–327. This highly favorable review of five of Babbage's writings on the calculating machine and two considerations of the machine by others was the first popular exposition on the subject. In it, Lardner argued for the necessity of such a machine, pointing out the importance of the accurate tables which the machine would generate. He also attempted to convince the general reader of the practicality of Babbage's concept by discussing both the mathematical principles behind it and the mechanical operation of the machine. The conclusion of the review was a history of the construction of the machine, with suggestions on reaching a rapid and successful conclusion to the project.

HENRY'S EUROPEAN DIARY
Henry Papers, Smithsonian Archives

[April 4, 1837][1] Visited Prof Wheatstone and was favored by him with an exposition of his speaking machine which is the most perfect thing of the kind ever produced by man.[2]

The mouth part is formed of Indian rubber and he workes the lips by hand. There are also tubes leading into the mouth to perform the office of the nostrils. Could a toung be formed or any contrivance to supply the office of that organ the machine would be perfect. It is worked by a bellows and articulates with startling accuracy the words *Papa Mamma Mother Father thumb plumb* and some other sounds. It also laughs and cryes most admirably.

A child does not at once learn to speak correctly but utters a few words after a considerable time so Prof Ws ofspring will it is hoped in due time extend its power of speech. We were also shewn a variety of other instruments and experiments by the same ingenious gentleman. An apparatus for the interferences of sound by means of a bent tube of lead about one inch caliber and forming a ring 5 or 6 inches in diameter.[3] This ring has a joint at the middle (a) by which the two mouths (c) (d) can be turned aside from each other. When a plate of glass is made to vibrate between the extremities scarcely any sound is produced because the waves are sent in opposite directions into the tube and are half a vibration apart and thus form an interferance. They are half a vibration a part because the movement of the plate in one direction throws in a wave at one end and the movement of the plate in the contrary direction gives a wave to the other end. If now however the tube be bent at the point of juncture so that the two branches be not in the same plane and the mouthes not opposite and a plate be made to vibrate between them then the

---

[1] This undated entry appears in Henry's diary immediately after the entry of April 3 and before those to which we have assigned the date of April 8. Partly given in Reingold, *Science in Nineteenth-Century America: A Documentary History* (New York, 1964), p. 77, with a few misreadings.

[2] Wheatstone's speaking machine was an improvement of an earlier device by von Kempelen. In a presentation before the British Association in 1835, Wheatstone pointed out the importance of such devices for the analysis of speech. He apparently made no further improvements on the machine. *British Association Report, 1835* (1836), part 2, p. 14. Brian Bowers, *Sir Charles Wheatstone* (London, 1975), pp. 33–34.

[3] Wheatstone presented the following experiment to the acoustics section of the British Association at the 1832 meeting. He was giving an experimental proof of Bernoulli's theory that "in the fundamental sound of a tube, open at both ends, the portions of air on opposite sides of the centre of the tube move in contrary directions to each other." *British Association Report, 1831–1832* (1833), p. 556.

ocillations will coincide and a loud sound be produced. The plate will then throw the waves in at the two ends so that they will conspire with each other to produce a loud sound.

We were also shewn the kaledrophon[4] and Mr W. promised to give me some of the beads for producing the phenomina of this most beautiful toy.

He also exhibited to us the vibrating plates of glass with sand strewed on them.[5] The glass should be of very uniform thickness and thin. The form on which the most interesting figures can be made is the octagon about 5 inches in diameter. Besides this circular plates and also triangular as well as square ones can be used but require care and practice to produce striking results. The vibrations produced by these plates with the fiddl bow are of the kind cald normal.

 If a [g]lass tube of a broken thermometer be cemented by cealing wax to the middle of a circular glass plate and the bow be drawn along the perpendicular tube then the vibrations called tangential will be produced. The sand will not be thrown up as in the other case but will appear to creap along the surface of the glass.

In connection with the caledrophon and also the velocity of electricity Prof W exhibits a revolving machine with a flat prism on it which rotates with great velocity by means of a circular wheel on friction rooles. The wheel (b) drives the smaller wheel a which is supported by the small friction wheels and thus gives rotatory motion to the prism withough obstructing the light through the axis.

To shew this instrument in operation caus the prism to revolve while looking at a candle. A circular ring will be seen by the refraction of the Light as it passes through the prism. If the bead on the caledrophon be viewed in the same way a beautiful combination will be shown.[6]

---

[4] See Wheatstone's "Description of the Kaleidophone or Phonic Kaleidoscope; a New Philosophical Toy, for the Illustration of Several Interesting and Amusing Acoustical and Optical Phenomena," *Quarterly Journal of Science*, 1827, *1*: 344–351. Inspired by Brewster's kaleidoscope and a specially prepared piano of Thomas Young, Wheatstone's instrument was designed to show the vibratory patterns of a sounding body. It basically consisted of a metal rod fixed at one end and with a reflecting bead at the other. When viewed by a point-source of light, the vibrating bead, due to persistence of vision, created regular oscillatory patterns. In its more elaborate form, the instrument consisted of four rods. Bowers, *Wheatstone*, pp. 24–25.

[5] The following experiments illustrated the acoustical phenomenon known as Chladni figures. See Wheatstone's "On the Figures Obtained by Strewing Sand on Vibrating Surfaces Commonly Called 'Acoustical Figures,'" *Phil. Trans.*, 1834, pp. 583–591.

[6] This device was a forerunner of Wheatstone's instrument for determining the velocity of electricity. In 1830 Faraday delivered a lecture on Wheatstone's use of a rotating mirror, rather than a prism, to count the vibrations of the kaleidophone. The principle was that the speed and direction of motion of the illuminated bead could be determined by combining its image with another moving image whose motion and speed were known. See Bowers, *Wheatstone*, pp. 36–37, 39.

To exhibit the sand exp to a class place the glass after the figure is formed on a black cloath. The figures may be drawn by holding the glass on which they have been formed over a paper and trace the outline with a pencil stuck at right angles to a pece of stick.

Mr W also exhibited to us some exp with the effect of a vibrating goblet on a membrane streatched over a common bowl. For this exp the best kind of substance is French tracing paper. No regular figure can be produced but for an instant. The constant change in the hygrometric state of the paper and also in the temperature of the same instantly derange the figures as fast as they are formed. This fact is shewn by breathing on the paper when the changes are seen to be more rapid.

In the afternoon visited Mr Richie.[7] Was shown several interesting articles of apparatus amoung others a small thermoelectric pile of a cheap construction for shewing some of the experiments on heat to a class. It consists of 30 pairs and blackened.

Prof Richie is a Scotchman and speeks quite broad. Promised to attend his Lecture on Wednesday.

On the same day visited Dr Roget. Was receved very politely by the gentleman. Informed him that his books had a wide circulation in America.[8] Asked if he had not studied Dr Robisons treatise on electricity before writing the article in the Library of U K[9] on that subject. The reply was that he had been a pupil of Dr Robison and had received his first lessons on that subject from the Dr.

Called at the British Museum. Was introduced to Mr Gray[10] by my letter

---

[7] William Ritchie.

[8] Peter Mark Roget (1779–1869), best known for his *Thesaurus* (1852), held an M.D. from Edinburgh and was a prominent member of the London medical community. A contributor to numerous scientific fields as researcher, compiler, and popularizer, Roget was secretary to the Royal Society from 1827 to 1849. Henry found Roget's *Treatises on Electricity, Galvanism, Magnetism, and Electro-Magnetism* (London, 1832), part of the Library of Useful Knowledge, extremely useful both as a guide to current knowledge in his field and as a source of inspiration for further investigation. *DNB*.

To our knowledge the *Treatises* did not appear in American editions. However, Roget's contribution to the Bridgewater series, *Animal and Vegetable Physiology, Considered with Reference to Natural Theology*, first published in London in 1834, appeared in at least three Philadelphia editions.

[9] i.e. the Library of Useful Knowledge. Roget's compilation did draw on Robison's *Mechanical Philosophy*.

[10] John Edward Gray (1800–1875), whom Henry met through a letter of introduction from his friend Jacob Green (see Henry to Gray, June 13, 1849, J. E. Gray Papers, American Philosophical Society Library), came to the British Museum in 1824 to assist in the cataloging of the collection of reptiles. In 1840 he became keeper of the Museum's zoological department. Although Gray published extensively in zoology, his main contribution to his field was the maintenance, organization, and cataloging of his collections at the British Museum. *DNB*. For the British Museum in this period and Gray's active role in promoting zoology at the institution, see Albert Edward Gunther, *A Century of Zoology at the British Museum Through the Lives of Two Keepers, 1815–1914* (London, 1975).

from Dr G of Philadelphia. Was kindly received. But learned something in reference to the science of our country which gave us pain. No naturalist of any reputation in the U S and those who pretend to the science continually quarrel amoung themselves. Make much out of little. Immagine themselves intitled to immortal honor for having described a new species when things of this kind are of every day occurrence. There are now in the Museum 72 hundred species of animals not described and hence on this principle as many naturalists may be immortalized.

One naturalist (Dr M)[11] came from America to see a particular animal described by Cuvier[12] and brough[t] with him some specimens in bottles and [a]moung these the very one he so much desired to behold. When told it was the animal he laughed at the assertion, gave the specimen to the museum. Cuvier afterwards himself stated it to be a genuine specimen of the animal in question.[13]

Some of the naturalist[s] who have visited Europe have got up a reputation out of the corps by making communications to different societies. Thus a person with a smattering of a knowledge of shells makes a speech on the subject to the geological section is much aplauded by those who know but little about the affair and in this way cheets himself and the american public into the belief that he really knows something. On the strength of this [erroneous] character he goes home commences to publish and looses the little reputation he really had amoung those who have especially attended to the subject.[14]

---

[11] The naturalist is unknown to us.

[12] Georges Cuvier (1769–1832), the great French paleontologist and dominant figure of the Muséum d'Histoire Naturelle in Paris. *DSB*.

[13] The essentially philosophical debate between the "lumpers" and "splitters" was perennial in natural history. We do not know what standards Gray applied to his American colleagues. Ironically, although criticizing the Americans for an alleged tendency to split, Gray's own later zoological research was considered "detrimental to the science on account of the needless number of genera and species which he introduced." (*DNB*).

One obvious reaction of sophisticated U.S. scientists was to establish institutions with the type of specimens and literature required to make the judgments involved. Henry's friends Torrey and Asa Gray were engaged in doing this in later years. It is what the Smithsonian Institution started under Henry and Baird—and still does.

Joseph Henry was very sensitive about the good name of his nation's scientific community. This frank talk by John Edward Gray must have pained him; the stiff final sentence on the visit given below, with its statement of agreement after the mild assertion of exaggeration, is a typical Henry understatement when confronted with an important painful matter. Even though Henry was sensitive himself about priority credit, the disputes were distasteful to him and to other scientists. In this encounter Henry may reflect the attitudes of a physical scientist to the natural historians' urge to name, with all its attendant possibilities for squabbles over possession of specimens and the glory of having a Latin version of one's name tacked onto a place in the order of nature.

[14] In this discussion with John Edward Gray, Henry is clearly aware of and sensitive about European standards of good science. They were *the* standards, after all. At this point a particular issue arises—the need for speciali-

These remarkes were made with perfect freedom and although an exageration may perhaps contain some truth.

We were shewn the rooms of the museum and were particularly pleased with those containing the Elgin Marbles[15] and the Egyptian Hirogliphics. The rooms containing the mummies and other specimens of Egyptian art are not at present open to the Public although we were introduced to them by Dr Gray.

I was much surprised with the perfect preservation of these remains particularly with the beautiful appearance of the gilt on the mummy cases. I however intend to spend some days in this most delightful retreat of science and English librality and shall not therefore at present stop to attempt a formal description.[16]

---

zation. In the United States, even more than in Great Britain, specialization was linked with the development of professionalization. In his later career Henry firmly pushed for a refereeing by qualified specialists of scientific writings. What John Edward Gray here describes Henry frowned upon and moved against with all the prestige he acquired in the course of a long life.

[15] See below, Henry to Rogers, December 5, 1837, footnote 2.

[16] Although he makes no mention of meeting Robert Brown (1773–1858), head of the botanical department at the British Museum

from 1827 to 1858, Henry jotted down sketchy notes elsewhere on the phenomenon which became known as "Brownian movement":

Brown moving molecule any substance produces which will seperate into very small parts [...] heat not essential. Mr Brown has made exp on this head not many—does not he ....

These notes, made about the same time as Henry's visit to the British Museum, are in Notebook [13269]. Brown had investigated the erratic motion of particles suspended in fluids, for which see *DSB*.

ALEXANDER DALLAS BACHE'S EUROPEAN DIARY

Rhees Collection, Henry E. Huntington Library and Art Gallery, and Bache Papers, Smithsonian Archives[1]

Thursday April 6 [1837] Went this morning according to arrangement to Sir Jas South's observatory.[2] The owner is a short thick-necked sanguine

---

[1] The first part of this entry, describing a visit to James South, is taken from the original in the Huntington Library (RH 809). The remainder, for which no original survives, is based on a copy in the Smithsonian Archives. Henry also visited South; his much briefer account is printed below, ca. September 20–30, 1837.

[2] James South (1785–1867), the eccentric astronomer, was known for his superb collec-

tion of instruments and for his accuracy as an observer. According to T. R. Robinson, he had "a keen eye, a steady hand, great power of bearing fatigue and want of sleep, prompt decision in catching a bisection, and boundless enthusiasm."

Following his marriage to the wealthy Charlotte Ellis in 1816, South abandoned a large surgery practice to devote himself to astronomy. He set up an observatory at his home

Jno. Bull—hates frogs & Frenchmen—& abuses right & left. Nevertheless he was exceedingly kind to me tho' disliking republicans & loving ultra tories. He is rough & uncouth[. . .][3] positive but I doubt not has a good heart beneath the rough exterior: so we got on famously. He began by letting me know that his large equatorial by Troughton & Simms was "not worth a damn" & then carried me thru his obs.[y] It consists of a range of low buildings without attention to ornament, & placed in his garden at Kensington two miles to the W. of London & out of its veil of carbon. The first room is a transit room. A four & a half foot transit[4] & the usual clock arrangements are here & besides a loud ticking time keeper with wooden pendulum which can be set going with the clock & thus may [be] used even in a noise or for

---

in Blackman Street, Borough, moved temporarily to Paris in 1824, and finally settled at Campden Hill, Kensington.

South's best known work was a reexamination of the double stars first described by William Herschel. South and John Herschel, using South's telescopes, worked together from 1821 to 1823 and produced a catalog of 380 double stars. South moved to Passy near Paris in late 1824 where his continued observations of double stars resulted in a second catalog of 458 stars. During this period South also examined the problem of errors in the solar tables and concluded that discrepancies between the observed and calculated solar right ascensions were not due to heating of the instruments as some had thought but to errors in the solar tables. For this work and his work on double stars, South received the gold medal of the Royal Astronomical Society, the Copley Medal of the Royal Society, and the grand prize of the Institut de France.

Although South's astronomical work was distinguished, it was largely overshadowed by his conflicts with the scientific establishment. South was a prolific writer of critical articles. In 1822 he published an attack on the *Nautical Almanac*. He eventually headed a committee of the Royal Astronomical Society which recommended reforms in the *Almanac*. An 1830 attack on the Royal Society was coldly received and officially ignored. South, like Babbage, warned of a decline of science in England, and considered moving permanently to France. He decided to remain in England after being awarded a knighthood by William IV and an allowance of £300 per year for his astronomical work. Another conflict occurred in his association with the Royal Astronomical Society, of which he had been a founder. When a Royal charter was granted in 1831 during

South's presidency of the Society, a dispute arose over whether South could remain in office. Babbage supported South while Richard Sheepshanks and G. B. Airy opposed him. South immediately withdrew from the Society.

An almost total alienation from institutional science and from many of his colleagues resulted from a trial between South and Troughton and Simms over a defective instrument (see footnote 11, below). Charles Babbage alleged that the trial was merely a pretext for South's enemies, particularly Sheepshanks and Airy, and that the persecution continued after the trial.

After 1838 South virtually abandoned astronomy, except for meridian observations, the study of clocks mentioned by Bache, and an analysis of the effect on astronomical observations of vibrations from nearby trains. In his last years, South became ill as well as almost totally blind and deaf.

DNB, DSB. T. R. Robinson, "Sir James South," *Proceedings of the Royal Society of London*, 1868, *16*:xlvii. J. C., "Sir James South," *Monthly Notices of the Royal Astronomical Society*, 1867–1868, *28*:69–72.

[3] One illegible word.

[4] Although South may have had a 4½-foot transit, it is not mentioned in any of the accounts we consulted. He did have a 7-foot transit made by Troughton in 1820. The instrument, which was similar to a larger one made by Troughton for the Royal Observatory, Greenwich, is described in detail by South in "On the Discordances Between the Sun's Observed and Computed Right Ascensions. . . . Also a Description of the Seven-Feet Transit with Which the Observations were Procured . . . ," *Phil.Trans.*, 1826, part 3, pp. 423–432.

an observ out of doors. I forget what Sir Jas. S. called it. It strikes every minute. The slits are arranged to lift & held vertically by iron rods, with a joint, which slips into a ⌐ & is fastened betw joints. A chair with a back inclined by wheel & pinion work affords a comfortable posture for the observer. There is no meridian mark "but nature's." This, as well as the other instruments, is painted with green paint upon the iron working parts & then varnished smoothly. In the next room is a very nice equatorial mounted by Capt. Huddart[5] "an old Sea Capt & as steady as a rock." The telescope is about 3 ft. No clock work is attached. The small dome turns by hand. This tho' an ugly is a most steady instrument. The general aspect of the polar axis work is this but how it is braced within "no mortal man knows"—probably by a series of edge bars supporting the arches which form the frame & which are of sheet iron tinned or otherwise. The telescope circle is thus braced by edge bars on the under side. Thru' the glass I saw Capella near noon moving with perfect steadiness between the two equatorial wires. Envious cumulus clouds occasionally covering up the sky. In the next room is a Troughton Circle[6] wh. is always used by Sir J.S. by direct & reflected vision so as to get rid of [. . .][7] errors. Further on is a small room in which some elaborate experiments are going on as to the effect of variation of atmos^c pressure on the going of a clock.[8] A clock is placed in an app^s similar to that used in the pendulum expt's of Capt. Sabine. It has a mercurial pend^m & the means of heating the room is at hand in a small stove with a long pipe. Sir J.S. gave an off hand opinion that the influence of pressure would be proved. He has in another place some clocks

---

[5] According to several sources, it was Joseph Huddart and this five-foot equatorial that influenced South to become an astronomer. Huddart (1741–1816, *DNB*), a sea captain and hydrographer, became wealthy manufacturing cordage. He had an observatory in his house, which was near that of South's father. When Huddart died, South bought the instrument for his observatory on Blackman Street. It is described in detail in J. F. W. Herschel and South, "Observations of the Apparent Distances and Positions of 380 Double and Triple Stars. . . ," *Phil. Trans.*, 1824, part 3. Huddart himself superintended the construction, which was completed in 1797. The object glass of 3¾ inches aperture was by Peter Dollond. The brasswork was by Troughton.

T. R. Robinson, "Sir James South," *Proceedings of the Royal Society of London*, 1868,

16:xliv–xlvii. Henry C. King, *The History of the Telescope* (London, 1955), p. 160.

[6] Troughton made the four-foot transit circle in 1806 for Stephen Groombridge. The telescope had a 3½ inch aperture, 5-foot focal length. South bought it for his Campden Hill Observatory where it remained until after his death. Henry C. King, *The History of the Telescope* (London, 1955), p. 234 and figure 97 (a photograph of the circle, now in the Science Museum, London).

[7] One illegible word.

[8] South never published the results of these experiments. According to Robinson, op. cit., the purpose was "to ascertain their performance in *vacuo*, the air's resistance to pendulums, the influence of various modes of suspending them, and the effect of screens in their vicinity."

on trial as to the compensating qualities of their pendulums. The taste of the observer is shown by sundry caraicatures which adorn the walls of the observatories, but there are also busts of LaPlace, & Faraday, and a picture of Wollaston &c. The *pure* mathematicians according to him are a very useless race & he seems to think also a very supercilious one.[9] In a structure erected for the purpose is the great equatorial containing the 12 in (11.9) object glass purchased fr. the French gov.[t] by Sir J.S. & mounted by Troughton & Simms. After a careful examination of the mounting with its imperfections pointed out by the [. . .][10] eyes of its disapp.[d] possessor I wonder at the scandalous way in wh. the whole thing is got up & would actually if a thriving instrument maker pay the cost rather than have this excited man to show off the job.[11] The muskmelon form is assumed by the whole affair. Its joints gape, its sides bend in & out as the instrument is moved, it wiggles when moved, & by clamping the altitude circle & turning the instrument half a circle the circle was changed nearly 10°—Capella shook like an aspen leaf a figure wh. my host insisted should be put down in his observation book. The dome was made by Brunel & like the rest appears to be a job.[12] Sir J.S. went to Dorpat to satisfy himself that Struves great equatorial was steady[13] & that

---

[9] South himself was not proficient in mathematics and was a purely observational astronomer. As Henry reported to Stephen Alexander, "South it is said has scarcely enough mathematics to make the simple calculations of astronomy but is as you know celebrated for his skill as an observer" (Henry's letter of April 10, 1837, printed below). South's opinion of the "pure mathematicians" was shared to a certain extent by other observers and experimentalists who found their work considered suspect by the theoreticians whenever it conflicted with previously established theory. William Snow Harris complained to Faraday that in a contest between mathematical laws and the laws of nature, mathematics would win. See his remarks and similar ones by Faraday in L. Pearce Williams, ed., *The Selected Correspondence of Michael Faraday*, 2 vols. (Cambridge, England, 1971), especially *1*:211, 292, 295, 339, *2*:628, 885.

[10] One illegible word.

[11] In 1829, after buying an 11.7-inch object glass, one of the largest then available, from Cauchoix of Paris, South engaged Troughton and Simms to provide an equatorial mounting. When the mounting proved defective, South refused payment and Troughton and Simms sued him. Arbitration dragged on from 1833 to 1838 with Richard Sheepshanks and G. B. Airy advising Troughton (who died in 1835) and Simms, and Charles Babbage supporting South. Although corrections to the instrument failed to satisfy South, the arbitrator (Sir William Henry Maule) ruled against him. In 1838 South smashed the mounting and sold it as scrap metal; he saved the lens and later gave it to Trinity College, Dublin.

South emerged from the trial bitter and alienated. According to the *DNB*, "it wellnigh unhinged his mind."

Two accounts sympathetic to South are T. R. Robinson's sketch in the *Proceedings of the Royal Society*, 1868, *16*:xliv–xlvii, and Babbage's *Exposition of 1851* . . . , 2d ed. (London, 1851), pp. 156–164. Unsympathetic accounts are Henry C. King, *The History of the Telescope* (London, 1955), p. 236, and Sophia E. DeMorgan, *Memoir of Augustus DeMorgan* (London, 1882), pp. 61–64.

[12] According to Robinson, "The dome was also a failure; in general it required four or five men to move it; sometimes it stuck fast!" The dome was designed and constructed by Isambard Kingdom Brunel (1806–1859, *DNB*), son of M. I. Brunel.

[13] F. G. W. Struve's equatorial, which South saw in 1832, was one of Joseph Fraunhofer's

his dome, covered merely with canvass, had stud the weather completely. How he depreciates even the dividing of his countrymen! The law suit about this great instrument is not yet settled. 1500£ are charged & he has had four years of hot water & a deep disappointment besides the non use of his great lens for all that time & may after all have to pay the piper. That individual had better been paid first unless indeed the state of excitement is agreable. He keeps an autograph book & a book of remarks by guests, which seem to amuse him. He alleges that many people used to come to his place & make a tavern of it eating & drinking their fill & then report what was going on about the instrument &c. to his detriment, so now he is chary of admissions. The stories were almost endless & if I charged every thing as a job which he represents as such there would be no end to them hardly. A lunch being ready I was introduced to Lady S & to Miss S. *his* sister. Two dogs, a black curly [. . .]¹⁴ & a black & yellow Spaniel (?) formed an important part of the family establishment. The latter got a seat upon its master's lap & he kissed it more than once—*on the mouth.* Afterwards in town he got biscuits for the wretches remarking that he never returned without something for them & that he could do nearly as well with out his wife as without his dogs. They watch for his return at the window & frisk about when he approaches. The yellow & black suffers no caresses but his, while curly is the lady's favorite. Some minced meat being brought up for their dinner, the pampered favorites would not eat it because they smelt ham wh. they preferred! To chronicle the ill I heard of the poor Frenchmen would be useless. Connecting the meridians of London & Paris they are accused of having cooked the results or indeed of not measuring angles but deducing them from the Eng. angles communicated to them in the rough while they breaking faith gave only means.¹⁵ As to the great base it was but

most famous telescopes. Henry C. King describes this refractor, then the largest in the world, in *The History of the Telescope* (London, 1955), pp. 180–184. To his later regret, South had turned down an offer by Fraunhofer to construct his large telescope because he wanted the mounting done by Troughton. T. R. Robinson, "Sir James South," *Proceedings of the Royal Society*, 1868, *16*:xlvi.

¹⁴ One illegible word.

¹⁵ We have not verified South's allegation of French "cooking" of results. He is probably referring to the 1787 British-French triangulation to determine the difference in longitude between Greenwich and Paris. The cooperative geodetic survey resulted from a proposal by Cassini de Thury (1714–1784), who alleged

that the astronomically derived difference was in error by 11 seconds. In 1784 William Roy measured a base at Hounslow Heath, using deal rods, steel rods, and finally glass tubes. Roy received the Copley Medal of the Royal Society in 1785 for the measurement, which was considered very accurate.

Further work was delayed until 1787 when Jesse Ramsden completed a three-foot theodolite commissioned for the survey. The connection by signals across the English Channel and most of the land measurements were completed later that year. After completion of the survey in 1788 the difference in longitude was given as 9m20s.

The French team consisted of Cassini IV, P.-F.-A. Méchain, and A.-M. Legendre, all re-

a series of botches fr. beginning to end. As we came in this Sir Anth[y] Abso-lute[16] gave me sundry specimens of his character with the omnibus boys & altera simili. With all this he holds a deference to rank wh. is amazing & called to inquire after his *grace* the Duke of Northumberland's[17] health: his g. being gouty & living behind the huge wall at charing cross where the lion passant does or does not wag his tail.

Apropos[18] to the Atheneum club,[19] he mentioned that some young frenchman had got access there and amused himself with writing articles lampooning the tories in the club room & by introducing demi[?mondes] to see the place. They smoked him finally as he was not able to keep his own counsel. What a glorious chance for a Trollope[20] to pick up scandal! and so kind was he as to go continually out of his way to take me to places; one of these was the United Service club[21]—a splendid building to which I was admitted by Gen (?) Reeves[22] wounded at Bidassoa, Waterloo & every where else that he had been. He now wears a belly pad to keep in certain intestines that have an ugly way of protruding. He mentioned a curious fact that while a musket shot wound in the hand hurt him so that he wished it bound up, he did not know that he was hit in the abdomen. The surgeon saw blood upon the white pants & cutting them open to examine the wound it bled so profusely as to produce fainting.

In this club house are many pictures, some good, some bad in different degrees. Their loyalty is shown by a suite of Kings & Queens of Eng. some of whom rather seem (?treasonable) pictures [...].[23] Most of them pre-sented by the Earl de Grey[24] & many of them originals. Old George III

---

spected scientists. In the early 1820s, a second cooperative survey was made to verify Roy's results. The work was led by T. F. Colby and Henry Kater for the British, and Arago and C.-L. Mathieu for the French. South was in Paris in 1824 and may have heard rumors about the French methods on this second survey.

Charles Close, *The Early Years of the Ordnance Survey* (Chatham, 1926), pp. 12–24. Eric G. Forbes, et al., *Greenwich Observatory: The Royal Observatory at Greenwich and Herstmonceux, 1675–1975*, 3 vols. (London, 1975), *1*:147–150. Roy's report on the first triangulation is in *Phil. Trans.*, 1790, pp. 111–270. Kater's report on the second is in *Phil. Trans.*, 1828, pp. 153–240.

[16] The stubborn and dominating Sir Anthony Absolute of Richard Brinsley Sheridan's play *The Rivals*.

[17] Hugh Percy, third Duke of Northumberland (1785–1847, *DNB*).

[18] From this point our text is based on the copy.

[19] For a brief description, see Titus W. Powers to Henry, March 13, 1836, footnote 8.

[20] After Frances Trollope, the author of *Domestic Manners of the Americans* (1832), an exposé of society in the United States.

[21] A gathering place for army and navy officers. The Club occupied a large building, designed by John Nash, in Pall Mall. Louis C. Jackson, *History of the United Service Club* (London, 1937).

[22] Perhaps Lt. Col. George James Reeves (1767–1845), who was severely wounded in Spain, although his military record does not exactly match Bache's account. Obituary in the *Times*, March 26, 1845, p. 5.

[23] The copyist left a long blank space.

[24] Thomas Philip de Grey (1781–1859, *DNB*) donated a collection of Royal portraits in 1834. Jackson, *United Service Club*, p. 31.

seemed the favorite of these two good old tories. A picture of the battle of Trafalgar beautifully done hangs on one side of the grand staircase & one of Waterloo on the other. The land fight is confused. The staircase in itself is no mean affair. The statue of the Duke of York which stands on its first landing was denounced as a Scotch job. The statue in particular with a [. . .][25] before it. The kitchen & offices are here on the same floor, with the coffee room but all fumes are disposed of by a ventalator wh. effectually carries them out with the warm air containing them, so that not a snuff escapes thro' the passage door. One of the S[t] James Sq[r] clubs Sir Jas. S. says is known currently as the "cheap & nasty" or Cle*ar*ance club—the Clarence,[26] the clearance from their having had a general clearing out, in consequence of malconduct which excited the other clubs against them.

Next to Arnolds & Dent's where I saw M[r] D. He is preparing to lecture at the Royal Ins[t] tomorrow on chro[r] making.[27] He tells me the glass springs do not take up a permanent elast[y] under two or three years, & hence a good capital would be locked up in their manufactory. They are not flat like the steel springs. Different materials he thinks take different times to acquire this normal state. Hence to M[r] Newman's[28] Regent St. In passing I was taking from Leicester Sq[r] anciently "Leicester fields" down [. . .][29] street to see Newton's house which remains exteriorly as he left it. The interior is used for an infants school. The raised roof for his observatory is still as in days of yore. Newman is a much older man than I imagined. As in the shops there are few instruments on hand. An air pump with a Smeaton pump[30] attached to effect the last degree of rarifaction & part of one of his Robinson[31] Barometers were all I saw. There was a [?shocking] rain gauge intending to be self registering made by Carey & put here for repairs. I did not fancy it. All sorts of jobs were denounced at the U. Service Club. A statue of the Duke of York cost 2000 guineas—pictures jobbed &c. M[r] Dent complains of my countryman M[r] Wilkes that he was too knowing & tho' he got instruments from M[r] D. he would not get information, but knew all about chron[s].[32] On dit that the way to get instruments was to go to some one person who ordered them all about town. Henry being missing I went solus to the club of the Royal Soc[y][33] After D[r] Roget came in, he introduced me to

---

[25] Left blank by the copyist.
[26] A club in Waterloo Place. *Penny Magazine*, 1837, 6:139.
[27] For Dent and his lecture, see Henry's diary entry of April 7, 1837, especially footnote 2.
[28] See Hare to Henry, February 13, 1837, footnote 4.
[29] Left blank.
[30] A detailed description is given in *Encyclo-*

paedia Britannica, 8th ed., s.v. "Pneumatics," pp. 37–41.
[31] Henry and Bache later visited Robinson's shop. See below, Henry's diary entry of April 17, 1837.
[32] See above, Bonnycastle to Knowles, February 1837, footnote 3.
[33] The Royal Society Club dates from the early days of the Royal Society. At first, the

several gentlemen present one of whom said "Mr Backey you are author of a recent paper on the effect of colour on radiation &c." He entered into the full stream of discussion: I explained the objects of the paper & what I considered the results which had been misstated by the author of the abstract which the gent. had seen. He quoted to me all Prof. Powell's ideas & as I had attempted to refute some of them I proceeded to explain how the absolute radiation power of any surface had been determined by increasing gradually the thickness of the coating of the substance forming the surface &^{c} He agreed to my position. When we came to a stoping place I went to inquire who the gent. was & learned him to be Prof. Powell! [34] I of course shook him anew by the hand feeling much complimented by his remarks. He stated that recently in a lecture that they had called upon him to give at Tunbridge wells he had given an acct of these experiments, that he regretted not being able to refer to the original paper which he had not seen. We now adjourned to the dining hall, a company of twelve. Sir John Stanley of Anglesea whose one son is Sec^y Treasury & M.P. & another M.P.[35] was in the chair. On his left Sir _____ Barrow[36] of the admiralty; on his right

---

practice of Fellows dining together after a meeting was quite informal. Geikie (p. 1) sees it as a natural outgrowth of the common scholarly interests and personal friendships of the Fellows: "The intimacy thus created could not be restricted to the meeting-room or the laboratory, but would necessarily demand the genial intercourse of the table. It was the Age of Taverns." In 1743 the organization, then called the "Club of the Royal Philosophers," was somewhat formalized. After 1795 it was known as the Royal Society Club. The Crown and Anchor, a tavern, served as the meeting place between 1780 and 1848.

In the early years, most Club members were Fellows of the Royal Society, although this was not required for membership. In addition to offering informal discussion the Club promoted contacts with foreign scientists, who were allowed to attend the dinners as guests of members.

Sir Archibald Geikie gives a chronological account in *Annals of the Royal Society Club* (London, 1917). T. E. Allibone, *The Royal Society and its Dining Clubs* (Oxford, 1976) brings the history of the Club to 1974. The dinner registers of the Club are in the Library of the Royal Society.

[34] Baden Powell (1796–1860, *DSB, DNB*) was Savilian Professor of Geometry at Oxford, a post he held from 1827 until his death. Ordained in 1820, he began his researches on

radiant light and heat while still earning a living as a vicar.

Bache and Powell were discussing Bache's "Inquiry in Relation to the Alleged Influence of Colour on the Radiation of Non-Luminous Heat," *Silliman's Journal*, 1836, *30*:16–28. Bache's paper was a response to one by James Stark and an endorsement of it by Powell, "Remarks on a Paper by Dr. Stark, 'On the Influence of Colour on Heat,' &c . . . ," *Edinburgh New Philosophical Journal*, 1834, *17*: 228–243. Bache contended that Stark erred in equalizing the thickness of various colored coatings on a radiating surface to compare what effect each had on radiation. After repeating some of Stark's experiments himself, with different thicknesses of coatings, Bache concluded that the influence of color on radiation had not been proven and should be the subject of further experiment.

[35] John Thomas Stanley (1766–1850) became a Fellow of the Royal Society in 1790. Edward John Stanley (1802–1869, *DNB*) was at this time patronage secretary of the treasury and M.P. from North Cheshire. His twin brother William Owen Stanley (1802–1884) represented Anglesey. Frederick Boase, comp., *Modern English Biography*, 6 vols. (1892–1921; reprint ed., London, 1965), *3*:711.

[36] Sir John Barrow (1764–1848, *DNB*) was Second Secretary of the Admiralty from 1804 to 1806 and 1807 to 1845. In addition to being

a dandified Sea Capt. Sir G. Staunton.[37] The dinner went off without much talk to be recorded. M[r] Millman[38] was near me but he did not come out much. It seems that the admiralty have by a circular letter forbidden the mast-heading of midshipmen,[39] so much for their opinion of this most execrable punishment in favour of wh. Capt. Hall[40] testified to me. The prohibition is said to have been caused by the mast-heading of a passenger on board of one of the mediterranean fleet recently. Henry never came to the dinner having been exhausted by going without breakfast & other food until 5 P.M.! The club adjourned to the Soc[y] Hall where I had the pleasure of meeting several interesting men. Mr Children[41] who was very polite on the score of a letter from Mr J.C. Biddle[42] to him. Capt. Jas. Ross[43] to whom I have a letter from Mr Lloyd[44] & who is a younger man than I had imagined. Mr Davies[45] of Woolwich, Mr Miller[46] of Cambridge &[c]. An old gen-

---

an expert on the British navy and Arctic exploration, Barrow was a scholar of Chinese language and culture, and an author of numerous literary and scientific works, including *Sketches of the Royal Society and Royal Society Club* (1849; reprint ed., London, 1971).

[37] George Thomas Staunton (1781–1859, *DNB*), writer on China and for many years a Member of Parliament. He was not a sea captain.

[38] The copy clearly reads Millman, presumably Henry Hart Milman (1791–1868, *DNB*), rector of St. Margaret's, Westminster, and later dean of St. Paul's. According to the dinner register, however, Milman was not present. The copyist may have misread the name of Henry Hallam, the historian.

[39] i.e., sending midshipmen to the top of the mast as punishment.

[40] Basil Hall. See below, Bache to Hall, July 16, 1837, footnote 1.

[41] After early researches in galvanic electricity, John George Children (1777–1852, *DNB*) became a librarian at the British Museum, first in the department of antiquities and later in the department of zoology. Elected a Fellow of the Royal Society in 1807, Children served as a foreign secretary from 1826 to 1827 and 1830 to 1837. After resigning from the British Museum in 1840, Children dabbled in astronomy.

[42] James Cornell Biddle (1795–1838), a Philadelphia attorney, and a member of the Girard College Committee on Scholastic Education. M. M. Odgers, *Alexander Dallas Bache: Scientist and Educator, 1806–1867* (Philadelphia, 1947), p. 33. Philadelphia City Directory, 1837.

[43] James Clark Ross (1800–1862, *DSB*, *DNB*). From 1818 to the early 1830s, Ross accompanied his uncle, John Ross, and W. E. Parry on numerous Arctic explorations; in 1831 he located the magnetic north pole. Under Ross's leadership, the 1839–1843 British Antarctic Expedition was a model of a comprehensive scientific survey, producing valuable observations on magnetism, geology, and marine life in addition to geography.

[44] Humphrey Lloyd (1800–1881, *DSB*) spent most of his life at Trinity College, Dublin. Having graduated from there in 1819, he remained as a member of the faculty, eventually rising to the rank of Provost (1863).

Although Lloyd made significant contributions to the field of optics, especially in support of the wave theory of light, he was probably better known to Bache and Henry through his work in terrestrial magnetism. He was a member of the committee appointed by the British Association to coordinate observations of the intensity of the earth's magnetic field. An experienced observer who had made magnetic observations in Ireland with Sabine, Lloyd established a magnetic observatory at Trinity in 1837 which became a model. In 1838 the British Association asked him to supply instructions and training for observers of magnetic intensity.

According to Bache's diaries for November 1836 (Bache Papers, Library of Congress), he saw Lloyd frequently when he was in Dublin.

[45] Thomas Stephens Davies (1795–1851, *DNB*) taught mathematics at Woolwich. With Olinthus Gregory, Davies edited and revised several of Charles Hutton's mathematical

tleman who resided in America just after the late war (or before?) & who remembers every body & every place, took great notice of me on the score of my descent. He occupied "Solitude"[47] on the Banks of the Schuylkill & remembered Grandpa Dallas'[48] family Mr Suthist[49] &^{c} &^{c}.

A paper by Mr Daniel was read.[50] The jun^r Sec^y reading while the scr. (Dr Roget) makes the abstract. It was on the new constant battery & some modifications of form &^{c} of exciting fluid &^{c}. It was only in part read. It is said that Mr D. is to be appointed Sec^y to the new London University with a good salary (1500£) & thus that King's College will have the benefit of his services.[51] The reading was frequently interrupted by the announcement of the results of balloting. They were all successful this evening. Indeed there is no doubt that a man who is entirely unknown & can get some friend to propose him is sure of a place as a resident member. I heard the question asked if my countryman Dr Mott[52] now at Paris could be proposed & the answer of the Sec^y was affirmative. Thus it is that Featherstonhaugh & Audubon[53] are members by paying 70£ which I am told the honor costs. How a man who refused Mr Vaughan the 5 dollars contribution his arrears to the Philos Soc. of Philad. can muster the 70£ I know not nor if he has done so. Mr Bailey[54] occupied the chair & conducted the proceedings in a dignified way. The galaxy of great men who hung on canvass around the walls of the meeting room cannot fail to strike a stranger who knows anything of the history of science, Newton & Flamsted, Tycho Brahe, Halley, Davy, Wollaston &^{c}.

---

textbooks. He also wrote frequently on science for scientific and popular periodicals.

[46] William Hallowes Miller (1801–1880, *DSB*, *DNB*) was Professor of Mineralogy at Cambridge, having succeeded William Whewell in 1832. Miller published influential texts in crystallography and mineralogy as well as numerous articles on these and other subjects. He was elected a Fellow of the Royal Society in 1838.

[47] The mansion was built by John Penn (a grandson of William Penn) in 1785 and remained in the family until 1874 when it became the home of the Philadelphia Zoological Society. From 1810 to 1850 none of the Penn family was in residence. Thompson Westcott, *Historic Mansions of Philadelphia* (Philadelphia, 1877), pp. 437–448, and Richard J. Webster, *Philadelphia Reserved* (Philadelphia, 1976), p. 139.

[48] Bache's maternal grandfather was Alexander James Dallas (1759–1817, *DAB*), a prominent Philadelphia lawyer and Secretary

of the Treasury from 1814 to 1816. [Alexander James Dallas], *Dallas . . . of Philadelphia . . .* (n.p., 1877), pp. 12–13, 15.

[49] Our reading of the name is tentative.

[50] "Further Observations on Voltaic Combinations," *Phil. Trans.*, 1837, pp. 119–139.

[51] Most of the faculty of King's College did not receive a salary but had to depend on erratic student fees, of which they received a percentage. F. J. C. Hearnshaw, *The Centenary History of King's College, London* (London, 1929), p. 89.

[52] Valentine Mott (1785–1865, *DAB*), an American surgeon with an international reputation, lived in Europe from 1834 to 1841. He was never elected a Fellow of the Royal Society.

[53] Bache had previously criticized Featherstonhaugh's election. See his diary entry of March 12, 1837, printed above. Audubon had been elected a Fellow in 1830.

[54] Francis Baily. See below, Henry's diary entry of April 21, 1837.

After the meeting tea was served in the library & conversation goes on until a variable hour. Mr Wheatstone as usual was with us. He is not a member[55] but I believe is now "up" for ballot. They can hardly refuse to be honoured by his admission.

[55] Wheatstone had been elected a Fellow of the Royal Society on January 21, 1836. Royal Society *Proceedings*, 1830–1837, 3:366.

HENRY'S EUROPEAN DIARY
Henry Papers, Smithsonian Archives

[April 7, 1837]

I attended on thursday[1] evening a lecture by Mr Dent[2] of the firm of Arnold and Dent on the construction of chronometers. The room was well filled with an attentive audience. The lectures in the evening and also those given to the popular class on saturday after noon are in the Theatre or large lecture room of the Institution. The morning lectures to the students of medicine and others are given in the room below.[3]

Mr Dent is an intelligent man and one of the very first in his line in England. He is however not much of a lecturer and exhibited his drawings in rather an odd manner. While he read the description a young man with a long pole pointed out the figures and letters after the manner of the

[1] This should be Friday, April 7; our dating of this entry is based upon the date of the lecture described below.

[2] Edward John Dent (1790–1853) was the leading chronometer maker in London. His chronometers were renowned for their accuracy. At various times, the Admiralty, the East India Company, and the Greenwich Observatory employed his skills. Dent conducted long-term experiments on steel, gold, palladium, and glass springs and authored several articles on these and other horological investigations. Henry later acquired for his Library Dent's pamphlet on *Chronometers, Watches, and Clocks* (London, 1842), which pictures and explains the workings of many of his devices. In 1830, Dent went into partnership with John Roger Arnold to form the firm of Arnold and Dent at 84 Strand. *DNB.*

Dent's Royal Institution lecture was reported in the *Magazine of Popular Science*, 1837, 3:316, and in the *Literary Gazette*, April 15, 1837, p. 242.

[3] Henry was attending one of the famous Friday Evening Discourses of the Royal Institution, instituted by Faraday in 1825, in which scientists and nonscientists lectured to lay audiences. The lectures did much to further public knowledge of science in England. L. Pearce Williams, *Michael Faraday, A Biography* (New York, 1965), p. 329.

In addition to its popular lectures, the Royal Institution also developed a tradition of giving private lectures to students. The tradition began with William Thomas Brande, Professor of Chemistry at the Institution, who gave morning lectures in his laboratory to medical students. Faraday also gave many such lectures, and in 1826 a Committee of the Royal Institution recommended that other professors adopt the practice. Edward Ironmonger, "The Royal Institution and the Teaching of Science in the Nineteenth Century," *Proceedings of the Royal Institution*, 1958, 37:138–147.

ancient actors in which a person behind the scenes spoke the part while another in front with a mask on acted the part or rather suited the action to the words. The lecture however was interesting. The drawings were acurately and well made. The different escapements were illustrated by drawings and models. A watch was taken a part and all its parts placed on the table. On a paper against the wall the number of parts of a watch was mentioned and also the several trades employed to construct each part. Mr Dent has promised me a copy of this table which is a curiosity and illustrates the great division of labour which is required to produce cheap and good articles where the labour saving machine is not used or cannot at present be applied.[4]

Mr Dent exhibited to me after the lecture one of his glass hair spring chronometers. It is a very beautiful article and performs well but the glass requires a long time, some years to take up a regular rate which is an objection to their use since much capital must on this account be unemployed. Mr D has described his researches on glass springs in the 58th No of the Nautical magazine Dec 1836 (Nautical and Naval).[5] He finds that glass and all substances used for springs of a solid kind decrease in elasticity on two accounts. 1st by an increase of length and 2ndly by a decrease of elasticity from the seperation of the particles. The latter effect produces the greatest amount of decrease of elasticity as was shewn by gradually shortening a hair spring in proportion as the heat was increased from 32° to 100° by the quantity due to the expansion. The decrease of time as shewn by the watch in an hour whould in this way give the diminuntion of elasticity due to the molecular change.

It was also found that the glass spring did not change its elasticity but by a small fraction of that of steel. Thus a steel spring caused the watch to loose 6m 25″ in 24 hours while the glass one under the same circumstances of a change of temperature from 32 to 100 changed 40″ so that a glass spring requires less compensation than metal. In order to shew the change of elasticity by heat a lamp was placed under a bell which was struck 1st cold and then the time of audible vibration noted, then the time when the bell had

---

[4] Dent's list showed 992 pieces, employing 43 tradesmen. *Magazine of Popular Science*, 1837, 3:316. At this time in America great strides were being taken toward the machine production of precision devices, such as clocks, locks, and firearms. By mid-century, British engineers were surprised by the extent to which Americans had replaced craftsmen by special tools and machinery capable of producing interchangeable parts. The British were very slow in adopting American labor-saving techniques. For these comparisons, see Nathan Rosenberg, "Introduction" to *The American System of Manufactures* (Edinburgh, 1969).

[5] "On the Application of Glass, as a Substitute for Metal Balance Springs in Chronometers," *Nautical Magazine*, 1836, 5 (no. 58): 705–717. Dent's article does not go into the molecular theory of elasticity Henry describes below.

acquired a considerable increase of temperature. The difference was very perceptable.

Large drawings of the Duplex,[6] the horizontal and the lever escapement were exhibited.

In the Library of the Institution a collection of very old watches were exhibited shewing the progress of this art for the last 200 years and more. I should have mentioned that in Mr Dents chronometers the springs are made in a cylindrical spiral form. This form gives a more acurate motion than that of the spring of a common watch which is a flat spiral and is thrown into a warped surface at each vibration.

The ballance of one of the chronometers is also made of glass and is compensated by two small slips of compound metal brass and platina placed perpendicular to the plain of the ballance.

By an increase of temperature the spaces[7] of metal are bent outwards or inwards and consequently the rotatory motion altered. These pieces of metal are adjusted by cutting off small pieces until the watch does not vary for any change of temperature. Mr D. for his best chronometers uses the best kind of common salad oil. From long experience he finds this better than any prepaired oil and has known chronometers to run 9 years without cleaning or renewing of the oil.

I was shewn at Mr D shop one of the 1st chronometers used. It appeared like a large clock and occupied a case nearly 20 inches square.

---

[6] The duplex movement employed a dual action escapement wheel having both cogs and teeth. This and other escapements are described in Dent's *Chronometers, Watches, and Clocks*, pp. 15–18.

[7] Henry meant "pieces."

ALEXANDER DALLAS BACHE'S EUROPEAN DIARY
*Bache Papers, Smithsonian Archives, and Rhees Collection,
Henry E. Huntington Library and Art Gallery*[1]

Friday April [7, 1837][2] This morning I rose heavy from the reaction of over excitement, still I determined to work & had a note written to Henry to join me in a visit to the gas works,[3] when lo! in came Mr Yarrell[4] & sat until

---

[1] The first paragraph of this entry exists only in a copy in the Smithsonian Archives. The remainder of our text is based on the original in the Huntington Library (RH 809).

[2] Bache erroneously dated this April 8.

[3] See Henry's diary entry of April 18, 1837, printed below.

[4] William Yarrell (1784–1856, *DNB*), a newspaper agent and bookseller, devoted his leisure time to zoology. He belonged to the

after the time appointed to meet the Eng.ʳ Mr Low[5] at the works: so there was an end to that. To Mr Y. I brought a parcel from Dʳ Harlan.[6] Mr Y. is in business (   )[7] & states that such is usually the case with British naturalists who thus have but little time to their science & thus are obliged to take quite a limited department in general.[8] After a shop visit with Ency, I went in search of Mr Morgan[9] who is to be in town today. They had not heard of him at his store (stationers) but returning home he came up to see me. I do not make him out quite yet. He is well to do in the world residing at Ham Common near Richmond & coming in only occasionally to attend to business. His pamphlet to the Trustees of the London University College,[10] finds fault with the management of the college as far as Moral Philos. & Political Econ. are concerned & he is probably interested in these sciences. He has written to Mʳ Biber[11] the biographer of Pestalozzi who conducts a school M. M's vicinity & will make me welcome. He profess also to renew an invitation which he gave me to Hanwell school. He is a *dryish* sort of body.

I determined this afternoon to make my appearance at the Athenaeum Club[12] & see how things were managed there. After scanning the news which

Royal Institution, the Linnean Society, and the Zoological Society. Besides contributing numerous articles to natural history publications, he authored a *History of British Fishes* (1836) and a *History of British Birds* (1843), both of which went through many editions and were considered standard works.

[5] George Lowe (1788–1868), for many years an engineer at the Chartered Gas Company. Elected a Fellow of the Royal Society in 1834, Lowe held numerous patents related to gas manufacturing and machinery. Frederick Boase, comp., *Modern English Biography*, 6 vols. (1892–1921; reprint ed., London, 1965), 2: 512.

[6] Richard Harlan, the Philadelphia physician and naturalist. *Henry Papers*, 2:265n.

[7] Left blank by the copyist.

[8] Yarrell's statement is ambiguous to modern eyes. In all probability the meaning is not that part-time scientific work forces amateurs to specialize. Rather, the implication is one of superficiality within a narrow compass. David Elliston Allen's *The Naturalist in Britain, a Social History* (London, 1976) does not take up this point; the assumption for this period is that very few naturalists were professional. He does note (p. 82) that naturalists (even naming Yarrell) benefited from "the counting house mentality, with its punctilious sense of order and its skill in executing business with

complete correctness and dispatch, that made it well suited to the ceaseless roster of minor, yet demanding and somewhat back-breaking tasks in the intellectual housekeeping that forms so large a part of the work of natural history."

[9] John Minter Morgan (1782–1854, *DNB*), a wealthy stationer and philanthropist, wrote extensively on social reform, religion, and education. Morgan unsuccessfully advocated the establishment of self-supporting Christian communities.

[10] *Address to the Proprietors of the University of London* (London, 1833).

[11] George Edward Biber (1801–1874, *DNB*), born in Würtemberg, later became a naturalized British citizen. Following a university education, Biber headed a Pestalozzian school in Switzerland. He later published two works on the Swiss educator: *Beitrag zur Biographie Heinrich Pestalozzi's* (St. Gallen, 1827) and *Henry Pestalozzi and his Plan of Education* (London, 1831). Moving to England, Biber headed a school at Hampstead and later at Coombe Wood. In 1839 he was ordained by the Church of England and became very active in church affairs.

[12] For comments on the Athenaeum Club, see above, Titus W. Powers to Henry, March 13, 1836, footnote 8.

does not amount to much I ordered dinner. This is done by a little bill in wh. you enter from the lists what you want. My dinner turned out as might have been expected from being ordered by an ignoramus thrice too much & thus heavily did I pay & bought a nine shilling experience. The little tables spread in diff^t parts of the room were many occupied by single persons, some by two. The single fellows read & ate many of them & seemed to enjoy the morceaux as they went by the palate. That the mock turtle soup & [?sop] were too much for me was the cooks fault, but I had ordered in addit^n cutlets, tomates, spinach, sweet omelet & tarts, an a *pint* of sherry which were my own faults. The liveried waiters of which there is half a dozen are exceedingly atentive. The presiding genius in [?black] keeps all right & the mode of serving & appliances are very neat & convenient. The eau de cologne & water & tooth pick are among these appliances. This is a nice bachelor establishment but be it recorded for my spouse's edification that I would rather have her society & a shilling dinner than gourmandize at nine without her. This values the soc^y at 8s. ? This evening we went to a lecture at the Royal Instit^n or rather their so called Friday ev^g conversazione, E. & M. having tickets fr. Mr Vaughan. Ladies are kept in the gallery, while gentlemen visit the library & are upon the floor to hear the lecture. Mr Dent is no doubt skilled in his vocation wh. however is *not* lecturing. . . .[13]

After the meeting I met Dr Arnott[14] who is a very agreable man in conversation. He invites me to meet Wheatstone & a small club on Tu. They meet for a discussion of questions in Mechs. & Nat. Philos.

Faraday was exceedingly busy in saying a word to every body & is plainly the genius loci. He devotes himself in fact to this institution & is its atlas. Ency wondered he had time to attend the lecture, but he is here extravagant of time & economises it elsewhere to be lavish here. This is necessary it seems to the upholding of the Instit^n which was in a sad way when he under-

[13] We have omitted Bache's account of Dent's lecture.

[14] Neil Arnott (1788–1874, *DNB*). Following medical training and two trips to China as a surgeon with the East India Company, Arnott practiced medicine in London from 1811 to 1815. A facility with languages led to positions as physician to the French and Spanish embassies; he was also a physician to Queen Victoria.

Even before abandoning his practice in 1855 to devote himself to science, Arnott had published a popular physics text which went through many editions, invented a stove and a water bed, for which he declined patents, and written on heating and ventilation.

Arnott was active in London scientific society, particularly the Royal Institution. He was elected a Fellow of the Royal Society in 1838. Declining health after 1859 limited his social activities although he continued to update his physics text, authored *A Survey of Human Progress* (London, 1861), and published tracts on education.

Copies of the first American (1829) and sixth London edition (1865) of Arnott's *Elements of Physics* are in the Henry Library; the former has numerous Henry annotations. A copy of *A Survey of Human Progress* is also in the Henry Library.

took it. Being wholly supported by voluntary contribution it may languish at any moment from a falling off of the subscribers.[15]

[15] Clearly reflecting experiences in the United States, Bache's observation is part of the orientation leading him and others to seek governmental support for research.

HENRY'S EUROPEAN DIARY
Henry Papers, Smithsonian Archives

[April 8, 1837][1]

During this week I have attended several lectures by Mr Faraday in the morning on the metals.[2] The subject is one of the dullest in the whole course of chemestry but by his manner and the many new facts he gives the lectures are quite interesting as well as highly instructive. He is assisted by a Person named Anderson[3] who was formerly a soldier but being picked up by Mr Faraday is rendered a very eficient person and makes a most admirable help to the active and rapid manipulations of the lecturer.

M Faraday in his lecture on the means of detecting the presence of arsenic insisted on the necsity of much practice before an opinion be given in the case of suspected poison by means of this metal or its oxide.

He then detailed the several processes which are given in the books but said nothing of that recently invented by Mr March of Woolwich. I asked his opinion of it after the lecture and gathered from the answer that the method would answer as one of the proofs but that it could on[l]y be made by a person well skilled in the use of instruments and without proper pre-

[1] The date assigned is that of Faraday's discussion of arsenic, which occurred on the morning of April 8 according to Bache's diary entry of that date (printed immediately below).

[2] Probably an 1837 version of the 1835 lecture course at the Royal Institution listed in Jeffreys. The course consisted of eight lectures on the chemical and physical properties of "iron, gold, platinum, lead, copper, zinc, mercury, tin and silver." Manuscript notes are at the Royal Institution. Alan E. Jeffreys, *Michael Faraday: A List of His Lectures and Published Writings* (London, 1960), p. 31.

[3] Charles Anderson (ca. 1790–1866) had been a sergeant in the Royal Artillery for over twenty years when he was hired by the Royal Society in 1827 to assist in the experiments which Faraday and others were conducting at the Royal Institution on the manufacture of glass for optical purposes. Anderson's duties included keeping the furnaces at a constant temperature. In 1832 Faraday hired Anderson as his assistant at the Royal Institution. Described as faithful and obedient, Anderson assisted Faraday until his death in January 1866. Bence Jones, *The Life and Letters of Faraday*, 2 vols. (London, 1870), *1*:398–401, 2:476, 478. L. Pearce Williams, ed., *The Selected Correspondence of Michael Faraday*, 2 vols. (Cambridge, England, 1971), *1*:171, 348, 2:1022–1023. Silvanus P. Thompson, *Michael Faraday: His Life and Work* (New York, 1898), pp. 96–97.

cautions the whole of the metal might escape without being caught. I afterwards saw the apparatus for collecting the gas or rather generating it in the case of apparatus at Kings college and was informed by Prof Daniell that he considered the process a good one but that it is difficult to procure zinc in commerce which does not contain in itself some arsenic but this can always be known by testing the liquid or a liquid with zinc by the apparatus itself before using the suspected fluid.[4]

In the Lecture on lead Mr F gave a table of the different tenacities of the metals and also one of their relative hardness. To shew the softness of lead an impression of a seal in wax was placed on an anvil and a piece of sheet lead of the thick kind laid on it. A blow was then struck with a hammer and an impression made which would again give many new impressions of the wax. He then spoke of the alloys and the amalgams of metals and stated the fact that they are all definite compounds. When the metals are mixed in any other proportions than those proper to form the relative atomic weights a definite compound takes place among parts of the materials and the remainder form mecanical mixtures which in some cases maybe seperated by simple means. Thus in a compound of lead and bizmuth if not in the proper proport[ion]s the excess may be melted out or rather I should say the fusible alloy will first melt and the other metal which is in excess will remain in a solid state and thus seperated by a little precaution in managing the heat. The silver on the back of the looking glass is a definite compound and the fluid metal which runs out the quantity of metal in excess.[5]

---

[4] Faraday's omission of James Marsh's process must have seemed strange because Marsh was Faraday's assistant at the Royal Military Academy at Woolwich and his new method of detecting arsenic had won the gold medal of the Society of Arts. Although Marsh's process was widely accepted, many commentators agreed with Faraday that the sensitive test should only be made by skilled investigators.

Marsh's process is described in "Account of a Method of Separating Small Quantities of Arsenic from Substances With Which It May Be Mixed," *Edinburgh New Philosophical Journal*, 1836, *21*:229–236. The apparatus consisted of a siphon tube with a stopcock and jet on the shorter leg. A piece of zinc was inserted in the short leg and then the test solution mixed with dilute sulfuric acid poured in. If the test solution contained arsenic, arseniuretted (rather than pure) hydrogen was produced. When the gas was released from the jet and ignited, arsenic was deposited on a piece of glass held in the flame.

Marsh and others later recommended improvements in the process. A modification by Berzelius to permit quantitative analysis resulted in the Marsh-Berzelius test. W. A. Campbell, "Some Landmarks in the History of Arsenic Testing," *Chemistry in Britain*, May 1965, *1*:198–202. See also J. R. Partington, *A Text-Book of Inorganic Chemistry*, 6th ed. (London, 1950), pp. 854–855.

[5] Little was known at the time about the chemical nature of alloys and amalgams (alloys of mercury). Some chemists considered any combination of metals an alloy. An alloy could thus be a mixture, a definite compound or a definite compound mixed physically with an excess of one of the metals. Faraday seems to be restricting the definition of alloy to those combinations which are definite compounds. We have not examined Faraday's manuscript notes of the lecture (see footnote 2) which might clarify his remarks.

For examples of the variant theoretical interpretations at the time, see Edward Turner, *Elements of Chemistry*, 5th American from the 5th London edition (Philadelphia, 1835),

The fusible metal[6] may be used for taking casts from imbossed paper from the surface of any substance not easily altered by a heat less than the temperature of boiling water. A quantity of the metal being poured over a surface of music on which the type had left a projection similar to that on the paper used for the Blind[7] a cast was taken which could be used as a plate for the multiplication of the copies of the music. The plates of this compound metal possess considerable hardness.

Under the head of mercury it was mentioned that this metal does not expand like ice and cast iron in the act of passing into the solid state. A beautiful exp. was shewn to illustrate the burning of mercury in chlorine. The retort was exausted and filled with chlorine. A small quantity of mercury placed in *a* was heated by a spirit lam[p] and ignition produced.

It was stated that the combination of all metals produce heat like any other chemical union. This was shewn in an extreme case by the union of potass[ium] and mercury which entered into union with heat and light.

(This general action of metals gives an explanation of the phenomenon observed when zinc and platina are burned in contact J H)

In lecture on the metals Mr F always puts on a black board behind him a table of the several compounds of the metal and constantly refers to this. The figures and letters appear to have been made by a tin marking plate. I must make inquiries of this and endeavor to procure some articles of the kind.

The precipitating glasses used by Mr F. are of this shape about 6 inches deep and 3 inches in diameter.

The amalgams of mercury are all very easily decomposed and on this fact may depend the motions observed on mercury.[8]

Mr F spoke of the experiment of Berzelius for forming something like an alloy of nitrogen, hydrogen and mercury by mixing a strong solution of muriate of ammonia with muriate of ammonia and into this pouring a quantity of mercury. An action takes place, the mercury swells, and assumes a buttery appearance. Mr F in this exp made a large hole in a piece of muriate of ammonia put the mercury into this and on it poured a quantity of liquid ammonia.

p. 415, J. F. Daniell, *An Introduction to the Study of Chemical Philosophy*, 2d ed. (London, 1843), p. 427, and W. A. Miller, *Elements of Chemistry*, 2d ed., 3 vols. (London, 1860–1862), 2:297.

[6] An alloy of lead, tin, and bismuth used for taking casts for electrotyping. The alloy fuses at 212°. *Encyclopaedia Britannica*, 8th ed., s.v. "Chemistry," pp. 484, 496.

[7] Some of the early printing for the blind used the regular alphabet but embossed the letters. *Encyclopaedia Britannica*, 8th ed., s.v. "Printing," pp. 553–554.

[8] For a discussion of the motions of mercury, see above, Henry's "Record of Experiments," March 16, 1836, footnote 2.

The exp. was not in this way a very striking one. It has been supposed that the swelling is due to a gas given off which rising through the mercury throws the whole up in form. I wished to ask Mr F if this opinion had ever been tested by making the mixture in a vacuum but did not that morning get an opportunity. Mr Solley however informed me that he had tried the exp thus and the result favoured the supposition that the swelling was due to a froathiness. I do not however see how this can be produced. Does it not indicate an action through[ou]t the whole mass of the metal and is there not something in this peculiar?[9]

The silver of the old english coin always contains a small quantity of gold which may be seen in a dark powder after the action of nitric acid on the coin.[10] To determine the nature of any white precipitate thrown down by common salt from a solution in nitric acid pour on this a small quantity of ammonia if the precipitate be dessolved it is the oxide of silver.[11]

Mr Faraday introduced [me] to Mr Edward Solly Jun quite a young man who has made some experiments of an interesting kind on the conducting power of Iodine, Bromine and chlorine which he finds not to be conductors of electricity. The conduction of a body for electricity is a very important test of the nature of the substance. A very good conductor may in almost every case be considered as a metal. Mr Solly is now engaged in translating some papers for the scientific memoirs. He is well acquainted personally with some of the German chemests who have visited England and I find his paper published in the German journal of science.[12]

[9] Henry's description is confusing, especially where he writes "muriate of ammonia" twice. Although departing considerably from Berzelius's preparation, Faraday seems to be producing a substance that had perplexed chemists for some thirty years, the mysterious "ammonium amalgam." A rapid decomposition followed the swelling of the mercury; the proportions of the hydrogen and ammonia gases given off implied the existence of an ammonium radical, which chemists had hypothesized but could not isolate. The reaction of the presumed ammonium amalgam, whose precise chemical nature had eluded chemists, was therefore seen as important indirect evidence for the "ammonium theory," proposed by Berzelius and others. Humphry Davy, involved in the early investigations of the ammonium amalgam, was fascinated and mystified by its behavior. According to his brother John Davy,

The more he scrutinised this extraordinary compound, the more mysterious it appeared;

it proved a complete chemical Proteus,—a mystery throughout; and, were it possible for human ability to invent a thing to perplex the understanding, and unsettle systems, it would be difficult to imagine a more successful effort.

Memoirs of the Life of Sir Humphry Davy, 2 vols. (London, 1836), 1:400.
See J. R. Partington, *A Text-Book of Inorganic Chemistry*, 6th ed. (London, 1950), p. 707.

[10] "Goldsmith's silver commonly contains copper and traces of gold, the latter appearing in dark flocks when the metal is dissolved in nitric acid." Edward Turner, *Elements of Chemistry*, 5th American from the 5th London edition (Philadelphia, 1835), p. 400.

[11] Henry probably meant silver chloride. J. R. Partington, *A Text-Book of Inorganic Chemistry*, 6th ed. (London, 1950), p. 738.

[12] Edward Solly (1819–1886, *DNB*) was only seventeen at this time. Having studied chemistry in Berlin, in 1836 he published "On the

Mr Solly informed me that Mr Sturgeon first became dissatisfied with the Royal Institution by a harshe remarke of Sir H Davey who when Mr S shewed him some exp. on magnetism said he had better mind his last than be dabling in science.[13]

Mr S also said that he had been with Mr Faraday when he made the exp^s on the long wire coil that very strong acid was used. Mr Jenkins whoes name is mentioned in Mr Faradays paper on this subject is a young engineer.[14]

Conducting Power of Iodine, Bromine, and Chlorine for Electricity," which appeared in the *Phil. Mag.*, 1836, 3d ser. 8:130–134, 400–402, as well as in three German journals: *Journal für praktische Chemie*, 1836, 7:411–416; *Annalen der Chemie und Pharmacie*, 1836, 20:124–125; *Annalen der Physik und Chemie*, 1836, 27:420–422. A reprint from the *Phil. Mag.* is in Henry's Library.

The "Scientific memoirs" is Richard Taylor's new journal which featured translations from German articles. Solly translated articles by Carl Löwig, Henry Rose, and R. Schulthess for the first volume. Following his return to America, Henry expressed his support of the journal and encouraged Taylor to continue publishing in a letter of August 9, 1838 (Henry Papers, Smithsonian Archives, to be printed in the fourth volume of the *Henry Papers*).

Solly was subsequently Chemist to the Royal Asiatic Society, Lecturer in Chemistry at the Royal Institution, and Professor of Chemistry at the Royal Military College of Addiscombe.

A presentation copy to Solly of Henry's "Contributions I: Battery" is in the Dibner Library of the History of Science and Technology (in the National Museum of History and Technology).

[13] For other comments on Sturgeon, see Henry's diary entries for March 24, 1837 (above), and April 22, 1837 (below), especially footnote 11.

[14] The paper is Faraday's Ninth Series of *Experimental Researches in Electricity*, "On the Influence by Induction of an Electric Current on Itself:—and on the Inductive Action of Electric Currents Generally." Paragraph 1049 reads:

> The inquiry arose out of a fact communicated to me by Mr. Jenkin, which is as follows. If an ordinary wire of short length be used as the medium of communication between the two plates of an electromotor consisting of a single pair of metals, no management will enable the experimenter to obtain an electric shock from this wire; but if the wire which surrounds an electromagnet is used, a shock is felt each time the contact with the electromotor is broken, provided the ends of the wire be grasped one in each hand.

According to Faraday, Jenkin's contribution was unique among the suggestions offered by "volunteers," or amateur scientists:

> The number of suggestions, hints for discovery, and propositions of various kinds offered to me very freely, and with perfect goodwill and simplicity on the part of the proposers for my exclusive investigation and final honour, is remarkably great, and it is no less remarkable that but for one exception—that of Mr. Jenkin—they have all been worthless.

Henry Bence Jones, *The Life and Letters of Faraday*, 2 vols. (London, 1870), 2:45.

ALEXANDER DALLAS BACHE'S EUROPEAN DIARY
Copy,[1] Bache Papers, Smithsonian Archives

Sat. April [8, 1837] Rose by times today i.e. by 8 o'clock to get to Mr Faraday's morning lecture at the Royal Inst. It was upon arsenic, chromium,

---

[1] The copyist left blanks in the text at several places which are indicated here by ellipses in brackets. The date was also left blank.

tellurium, &c and their compounds. The arsenic contained in ar[seniu-retted] hydrogen was beautifully shown by passing up a few bubbles of chlorine into a small quantity of the former gas. He stated that this sometimes produced an explosion. He did not pretend to go minutely into the detection of arsenic but spoke of the best way to get oxide from the stomach to put the contents into water, & pick out the white heavy particles which would subside. He did not mention Hume's[2] method tho' he is his assist. at Woolwich why? He mentioned it I was told last year, Don't it work? In regard to Vanadium he had not the history right as I understand it, Del Rio's claims being mixed up as to time with those of [. . .].[3] Having forgotten the rationale (?irrationale) of the name he confesses quite gracefully his forgetfulness. In making the ars^d hydrogen his flask fell [. . .] and broke which disconcerted him for a moment but not more. His manner is exceedingly rapid & his experimenting is likewise & yet neither appears to be at all hurried. His arrangement is clear, & the fire which he throws into his manner keeps up the interest of the lecture even on a dry subject. His class was forty or fifty, & several grey heads spotted it. After the lecture he was detained at least half an hour obligingly answering questions. Henry had met Mr Whitwell[4] the editor of the journal of Pop. Sc. which he believes to be the author of that rascally review of our Institute expts. on explosions.[5] I went in search of him to feel his pulse but found that he had left his

---

[2] Probably an error by the copyist. The method was that of James Marsh; see Henry's first diary entry of this date (above), especially footnote 4.

[3] Vanadium was first discovered by Andrés Manuel Del Río in Mexico in 1801. Alexander von Humboldt brought a specimen back with him to Europe but lost Del Río's accompanying description of the new metallic element. When Collet-Descotils mistakenly concluded that the element was chromium, Del Río reluctantly accepted the conclusion. Nils Sefström later discovered vanadium in Sweden and was accorded priority for the discovery. *DSB*, s.v. "Río, Andrés Manuel Del."

[4] Stedman Whitwell, the editor of the *Magazine of Popular Science* according to Bache, is listed in BAAS membership lists as an architect (*BAAS Reports, 1831–1832, 1835, 1837*). The address given, 22 Sussex, is the same as Joseph Saxton's. Despite Saxton's derogatory remarks about him further on in this entry, Saxton's London notebooks (Saxton Papers, Smithsonian Archives) indicate he spent a great deal of time with Whitwell, meeting him at the Adelaide Gallery, taking walks

with him, frequenting coffeehouses together. Although the falling-out that Saxton mentions is confirmed by the paucity of references to Whitwell in the later notebook entries, Whitwell chaired a farewell dinner given for Saxton (see below, April 26, 1837).

In Henry's eulogy of Saxton, he lists Whitwell as one of the "celebrated engineers and mechanicians" with whom Saxton worked at the Adelaide. We have not, however, been able to locate any further information on him. The *Magazine of Popular Science*, published by the proprietors of the Gallery, lasted only two years. No editor is given on the title pages or elsewhere in the four volumes which appeared.

[5] The unsigned "Prevention of Explosion in Steam-Boilers," *Magazine of Popular Science*, 1836, 2:114–124, was a review of Bache's subcommittee report on the causes of explosions, *Report of the Committee of the Franklin Institute . . . on the Explosions of Steam-Boilers. Part I. Containing the First Report of Experiments Made by the Committee, for the Treasury Department of the U. States* (Philadelphia, 1836). The reviewer made many critical

lodgings, & lighted upon my former acquaintance Mʳ Saxton, who was living hard by. His den was small a turning table & tools took up a goodly share of the disposeable space. I passed the morning with him highly attracted by his naive account of his difficulties & of the jealous feelings of the men among whom he has mingled & who are any thing but favourable disposed according to his account towards our country & its science. The Journ. of Popular Sc. originally came out under Prof. Powell's auspices, then Mʳ [. . .] brother in law was to take it, but Mr Whitwell who had been sort of editor managed to secure it. So there was a split in the household. He thinks the article above referred to like Mʳ Whitwell who is self opinionated & quarreled with Mr Saxton first because he objected to an article which he made for the gallery being discribed & afterward because Saxton insisted on his having erroneously discribed the appˢ by which the motion of the ship in a storm as shown by a French machine in the gallery, was produced.[6] Saxton states that he was juggled out of the diagonal tracer used in Bate's machine for medal ruling.[7] It seems that there is now pending before a Com. of the house of Commons an application by a Frenchman for ruling copies from the medals in the British Museum, the right to do which or the job as they call it Mr Bates desires to have. Mʳ B's partner in the affair a Mʳ _____ called on Saxton to explain the machine to him fully the night before he went to give evidence before the Com. of the house & next day never mentioned S's name.[8] His account of the treatment by Prof. Ritchie

---

and sarcastic comments. Henry's copy of the review is annotated with such comments as "False see report," "not necessary," "show this." In May 1837 Henry wrote a review of the committee's general report for the *Magazine of Popular Science*. See below, Henry to Harriet Henry, May 9, 1837, especially footnote 6, and Bache to Henry, June 7, 1837. A bibliography of the committee's reports is given in Henry to Bache, June 4, 1836, footnote 3, printed above.

[6] The apparatus is described in the unsigned article "Automatic Ship and Sea," *Magazine of Popular Science*, 1836, *1*:190–192.

[7] Medal ruling machines mechanically produced drawings of three-dimensional coins, medals, and other relief objects. Saxton had long been familiar with the first such American machine, made by Christian Gobrecht in 1817, and had tried to find a way to eliminate distortions which were particularly evident when tracing from high relief. Shortly after arriving in London, Saxton solved the problem by using a diagonal, rather than horizontal, tracing arm. John Bate saw Saxton's

improvement and, without Saxton's knowledge, took a patent on it in 1832 (no. 6254). The invention of the daguerreotype in 1839 made medal ruling machines virtually obsolete.

After returning to the United States, Saxton made two more models of his machine. The second, used at the United States Mint, was steam-powered and, after being adjusted, did not require an operator.

Arthur H. Frazier, *Joseph Saxton and His Contributions to the Medal Ruling and Photographic Arts*, Smithsonian Studies in History and Technology, No. 32 (Washington, 1975). Henry describes Saxton's machines in his eulogy of Saxton, National Academy of Sciences, *Biographical Memoirs* (Washington, 1877), *1*:306–309.

[8] An author had petitioned the House of Commons to let a French company copy the medals for his book. The company owned the French patent for a medal ruling machine invented by Achille Collas. The hearings, which included as witnesses the artists William Brockedon and Francis Chantrey, centered on

Henry James, Sr. (1811–1882), n.d., anonymous miniature oil portrait.
By permission of the Houghton Library, Harvard University.

Michael Faraday (1791–1867), published 1849, lithograph by W. Bosley
from daguerreotype by A.F.J. Claudet (1797–1867).
Courtesy of the Smithsonian Archives.

William Sturgeon (1783–1850), engraving.
Reproduced from *The Electrician*,
September 13, 1895.

John Frederic Daniell (1790–1845).
Courtesy of the Royal Society Library.

Joseph Louis Gay-Lussac (1778–1850).
Courtesy of the Smithsonian Archives.

Macedonio Melloni (1798–1854), 1846,
engraving by Angelo Rossena from
1839 drawing by Giuseppe Naudin.
Courtesy of the Biblioteca Palatina
di Parma.

Charles Wheatstone (1802–1875), 1837,
drawing by William Brockedon (1787–1854).
Courtesy of the National Portrait Gallery,
London.

Charles Babbage (1792–1871), 1840,
drawing by William Brockedon (1787–1854).
Courtesy of the National Portrait Gallery,
London.

Peter Mark Roget (1779–1869), 1835,
drawing by William Brockedon (1787–1854).
Courtesy of the National Portrait Gallery,
London.

William Whewell (1794–1866),
published 1835, lithograph by
W. Drummond from painting by E. U. Eddis
(1812–1901).
Courtesy of the Royal Society Library.

Edward Sabine (1788–1883), 1850,
by Stephen Pearce (1819–1904).
Courtesy of the National Portrait Gallery,
London.

Peter Barlow (1776–1862), circa 1853,
engraving by Samuel Cousins from
painting by William Boxall (1800–1879).
Courtesy of the British Museum.

Olinthus Gilbert Gregory (1774–1841),
published 1846, engraving by
H. Robinson from painting by
Richard Evans (1784–1871).
Courtesy of the Library of Congress.

James David Forbes (1809–1868)
by W. H. Townsend.
Courtesy of the Royal Society Library.

Mary Somerville (1780–1872),
engraving from painting by Chappel.
Courtesy of the Smithsonian Archives.

David Brewster (1781–1868),
engraving from photograph
by A. F. J. Claudet (1797–1867).
Courtesy of the Smithsonian Archives.

throws that gentleman in a very bad light. The effects produced by the revolving keeper magnet & the arrangements were shown by Prof. R. from apparatus lent him by Saxton & so shown that his auditors believed them to be his own.[9]

---

the quality of the copies produced by each machine. Much of the testimony, with additional statements by Bate and the opposition, is printed in *The Literary Gazette* (London, 1837), pp. 89–95. Bate mentions Saxton only as having designed a machine similar to his at about the same time.

[9] Saxton didn't publish a description of his magnetoelectric machine (*Henry Papers*, 2: 159n), which was on public exhibition at the Adelaide Gallery from August 1833, until November 1836 (*Phil. Mag.*). Although Ritchie was primarily interested in developing a motor, he also claimed a generator. See *Henry Papers*, 2:162n. See also Arthur H. Frazier, "Joseph Saxton at London and his Magneto-Electric Devices," unpublished manuscript in Joseph Henry Papers files.

HENRY'S EUROPEAN DIARY
Henry Papers, Smithsonian Archives

[April 8, 1837][1]

On saturday attended a lecture the first of a popular course by Mr Faraday in the theatre of the Royal Institution. The room was crowded by ladies many of whom were very busily engaged in taking notes.

The subject was rather a singular one if we judge only by the title. *Earth air fire* and *water* the four elements of the ancients.[2] I did not much admire the title although it afforded the lecturer a wide range particularly with the help of a little immagination.

He first stated the size of the earth relative to the sun and the other planets also the weght as derived from the experiments of Cavendish.[3] Then spoke of the three principle earths which made up the bulk of the materials of the solid crust of the globe. Geologist[s] are not yet agreed on the condition of the interior. All that is known referes to the surface or to a depth of about 100 miles.

A large sectional drawing was exhibited shewing how by the dipping of the strata this depth is determined.

The three principle earth[s] above alluded to are *Lime, Silex*[4] and *Alu-*

---

[1] This entry has been given the date of the opening lecture of Faraday's series, discussed in footnote 2.

[2] Faraday delivered his lectures at the Royal Institution over six successive Saturdays, April 8–May 13. His manuscript lecture notes survive at the Royal Institution. Alan Jeffreys, *Michael Faraday: A List of His Lectures and Public Writings* (London, 1960), p. 34.

[3] Henry Cavendish's experiments on "weighing the earth." *DSB.*

[4] An equivalent term for silica.

mina. These are very different substances all though to the eye in the pure state they appear the same. The one insoluable in water (silex) the other soluable with heat &c (Lime) the other slightly so.

In a subsequent lecture on the same a very large drawing was exhibited of a segment of the earth and on this the relative quantity of matter forming the atmosphere was exhibited and thus although the globe was (or would have been if completed) 12 feet in diameter, only about ¼ of an inch in depth. I should have mentioned that the Professor gave a good illustration of the relative size and distance of the earth and sun by exhibiting a small globe to illustrate the latter & referring to the dome of St Paul in size and in distance from the lecture room to give the relative magnitudes required.

Some interesting remarkes were made on the subject of falling stones. They do not appear to belong to the earth and yet cannot be refered to any of the planets on account of the great specific gravity which exceedes that of any of the planets near our earth.

While on this subject I was shewn by Prof Daniel a specimen of meteorolite lately sent from the East Indies. It was very similar to that which fell in Connecticut[5] and contained small specks of native iron diffused through the mass. On the subject of the air Mr F. showed some experiments to illustrate the operation of air as a supporter of combustion by putting a piece of phosphorous on a plate and covering it with a glass jar a few inches in height. He also exhibited the use of the same *"element"* in the process of germination by a glass vessel in which a small quantity of soil was placed and some wheat planted in this. A candle put in was immediately extinguished. The effect of breathing the air in the generating of carbonic acid

was pleasingly illustrated by an apparatus of this kind *a b* are two tubes. When the short one *b* is put into the mouth and the air drawn in through the water[6] no effect is produced on the lime water contained in the vessel but when the long tube *a* is put in the mouth and the air blown through the water from the lungs then the liquid of course became quickly milky. The weight of the air was shewn by the process of Gallileo by giving 12 strokes with a cyringe into a copper vessel and then suspending this from the end of a ballance to which it had been also attached previous to the condensation.

The equilibrium was then made by placing in the other scale a number of *corks* as weights. The extra air was next let out under a tall glass jar and

[5] The meteors which fell in 1807 on Weston, Connecticut. The stones were analyzed by Silliman and others. See *Henry Papers*, 2:469n.
[6] It must be assumed that the top of the vessel was sealed around the tubes so that when *b* was drawn upon air entered the water through tube *a*.

the quantity which produced the increase of weight shewn.[7] He next stated the weight of the air in the lecture room as equal to about 2 tons. I think this estimate too high. Mr F is deservedly a very popular lecture[r] but does not surprise or strike one with the depth of his remarkes or the power of a profound mind but more by his vivacity of manner & his hapy illustrations as well as inimitable tact of experimenting.[8]

On Friday evening last I attended a lecture on the application of capiliary attraction to venering and cabnet work. The lecturer was a Mr *Grifin*[9] a protege of Mr Brand.[10] Although the subject from its name did not promis much yet it proved very interesting and to me instructive.

The most obvious facts of capiliary attraction were stated and illustrated by experiment.

A large parallopiped of about the size of a brick of fine salt was placed on end in a dish of coulered water. The action commenced and the dark fluid was seen to rise 5 or 6 inches. This is a good class exp. Another illustration was also very striking. A piece of Honduras Mahogany of about 4 inches long was placed on end in a basin of spirits of turpentine. The fluid rose by capiliary action and was fired at the top. The action of the same principle in shortning ropes was also alluded to and its application pointed out in the case of covering a block of wood with a thin sheet of Mahogany. A strong piece of canvass is lightly drawn around the cylender of wood and then fastened by screwes. It is then wetted by a spunge which causes the cloath to shrink with great force. To illustrate this shrinking and consequently titening of the pours of cloath by wetting a large globe was exhibited of linen. This was blown into by a pair of revolving bellows but in its dry state no inflation could be made but by wetting the whole it was expanded

---

[7] This account of Galileo's experiment from the First Day of the *Dialogues Concerning the Two New Sciences* (1638) is incomplete. What Galileo actually determined was the specific gravity of air as compared with water. To do this he filled the tall receiving jar with water, a certain amount of which was displaced by the air escaping from the first vessel. His intention was to disprove Aristotle's notion of the "levity" of air. We have used the Dover edition of the *Two New Sciences*, trans. Henry Crew and Alfonso de Salvio (New York, 1954), pp. 77–81.

[8] Faraday himself was well aware of how important his experiments and manner of presentation were to his popular lectures. He was always reluctant to publish them, knowing how much they would lose in being reduced to the printed page. Jeffreys, pp. xvii–xviii.

Faraday worked very hard at becoming a leading popular lecturer of his day. He had taken private lessons in elocution and took care to rehearse his demonstrations beforehand, being "particular about small and simple illustrations." Silvanus P. Thompson, *Michael Faraday, His Life and Work* (New York, 1898), pp. 231–233.

[9] Probably a lecture at the Royal Institution by the chemist John Joseph Griffin (1802–1877), who ran a bookselling, publishing, and chemical apparatus business in Glasgow. An author of several chemical books, Griffin excelled in the popularization of chemistry and in introducing chemical methods into commercial processes. *DNB.*

[10] William Thomas Brande (1788–1866), Professor of Chemistry at the Royal Institution. *DNB.*

into a ball of 3 feet in diameter and remained inflated until the end of the lecture. The subject was rendered interesting by the operations being carried on before the audience by a number of workmen introduced for the purpose.

The process of gluing the thin veneer on a board was shewn; the preliminary opperation of stopping the holes so that the glue might not be absorbed by the pours. The method of expelling the air and so on were all exhibited and explained.

Jar covered by cloth at top holds water when the cloth is wetted.

Lectures of this kind might be made very interesting in New York and Philadelphia but would require some attention in getting up inorder that the right kind of man should be engaged.

ALEXANDER DALLAS BACHE TO
SOPHIA BURRELL DALLAS BACHE

Retained Copy,[1] *Bache Papers, Smithsonian Archives*

London April [9]th[2] 1837

My dear Ma

The pack ship Wellington left here yesterday & I send this to meet the mail which she carries at Portsmouth next, to report health & safety for such a whirl as I am in just now is highly unfavourable to any thing like rational writing. By good advice of that most amiable of all travellers save one Capt. Basil Hall R. N. we took some days to see the lions before delivering letters & well it was so. So far from finding the Londoners inaccessable & too busy to treat one well, I will answer for one portion of the society, viz: the men of science, who most of them work double tasks being also men of business, that they are much more attentive than I would have asked. As to the [. . .], & the [. . .][3] having neither desire to mingle with them, nor claim I am content to think them as reported the most artificially simple people in manners & intercourse (?mind) in the world. To give you some idea of what I mean last evening we dined at Mr. Vaughn's (all) & then I went to a soirée at Mr Babbages. So many clever people were there as to

---

[1] This three-page copy is not in Bache's hand. The first page is a letterpress copy.

[2] Although dated April 7, internal evidence shows that Bache could not have written this letter any earlier than the morning of April 9.

[3] In each case the letterpress copy contains an illegible word.

confuse me, you will know best, Hallam[4] & Milman[5] & Chantry[6] but I prized most Powell[7] Wheatstone Ritchie (Profs) & Taylor[8] &. Mrs. Somerville[9] was there also pleasing both men & women, the latter you will admit a most difficult task for so [. . .][10] a lady, but she is without affectations as much at home in the occupations & amusements of the ladies as in the study of the men & withal too amiable to avail jealousy. But I shall tell you more about her after the visit which Henry & myself are to make to Chelsea, to Doctor Somerville.[11] During the day attended two lectures by Mr Faraday at the Royal Institution, one to his regular class, & another to a mixed audience of ladies & gentlemen. It is pleasant to see the collection of grey headed men which he has at his popular lectures. His manner & matter we shall have over when we meet. Both are excellant & varied to suit his audience with much apparent ease. I take his popular manner to be the result of great study. Bye the bye never speak again of "a Mr Dalton"[12] if you love me—even Maria[13] was shocked. This "old Mr Dalton" is one of the first of living philosophers, the author of the atomic theory as now understood which has opened up more original views than even the discoveries of Davy[14] have done. His praise is worth the clamour of a thousand throats of common intellect so just be good enough to be highly flattered that he should have said any one of us was intelligent. At Mr Babbage's soirée there was quite an odd looking lady past thirty "for the least"—in grass green velvet gown & flaring turban: the rumour went about that it was Mrs Trollope[15] & next a sensation as it quietly spread & the old lady sailed about with this unknown companion! It was no such *thing*. As all our American friends (except *of course* good republican selves) seem bitten with the Aristocracy

[4] One of the founders of the English historical school, Henry Hallam (1777–1859) had withdrawn from legal practice around 1808 to devote himself to the study of history. He published three major works on the history of Europe; they continued to be the standard works in the field well into the twentieth century. Well known in scholarly and literary circles, Hallam was both an officer in the Statistical Society and the Society of Antiquaries and a frequent attendee at the soirées of his day. *DNB.*

[5] Henry Hart Milman.

[6] Sir Francis Legatt Chantrey (1781–1841) was one of the leading sculptors in England during the last three decades of his life. Elected a member of the Royal Academy in 1818, he was knighted in 1835. *DNB.* Henry would later admire Chantrey's work while in Edinburgh. See below, Henry's European Diary, August 5, 1837.

[7] Baden Powell.

[8] Richard Taylor (1781–1858), a London publisher and naturalist, was one of the editors of *The Philosophical Magazine. DNB.*

[9] Mary Somerville (1780–1872) was one of England's great woman scientists of the nineteenth century. See *Henry Papers,* 2:186–187.

[10] Another illegible word.

[11] For Henry's account of this visit, see below, Henry's European Diary, April 19, 1837.

[12] A reference to John Dalton (1766–1844, *DSB).*

[13] Maria Fowler, Bache's sister-in-law.

[14] Humphry Davy.

[15] Frances Trollope.

mania (our minister inclusive & our good friends the Miss Pattersons[16]) it may be just as well to say that if the invention of the calculating machine & being a successor in his Professorship to Newton does not warrant our host as "good society," his standing will appear from the presence of Lords & Honorables. Two real Lords—one no doubt of a very antique tittle Lord Cole,[17] as the exterior of the Ark was probably carbonized for preservation sake & thus tittles & all may have been preserved by the powers of this time & air & water visiting agents. If the honorable Mrs S. had not screwed her fine black eyes, not being near sighted, nor stuck out her chin she would have been a right pretty woman, but I grow scandalous. Such a conglomeration of Trollopiana as I have heard since I have reached this modern Babel, & mixed up so with science, then when I want a fact a joke is present.

On Friday Ency[18] & Maria went with me to the Royal Institution to the conversation meeting. The lecture was about chronometers by a chronmaker[19] & tired M. very much, but she was repaid according to our account by seeing Mr Faraday for whose character she thinks second hand, she has a high respect, "& Sister actually shook hands with him." What a practical satire upon all aristocracy. The son of a blacksmith, the book binders apprentice is the greatest man, saving the politicians honour who if you believe what each says of the other are very small men in the nation, followed by "nobles by courtesy" & "dining no where but at the palaces of two Royal Dukes" his most royal masters, nominally because President of the *Royal* society[20] & of the *Royal* Institution.[21] Who is the exclusive? To this the Prof is actually forced for 313 dinners in the year would spoil his profession.

On Thursday I went to Kensington to see Sir Jas. South's observatory.[22] I met with a most capital specimen of the English man one reads of in books; the man who has a holy horror of French men & a great contempt withal for their doings & their *nasty* way of living. Practically a democrat as

---

[16] Unidentified.

[17] John Willoughby Cole, Earl of Enniskillen and Baron Grinstead (b. 1768). John Debrett, *The Peerage of the United Kingdom of Great Britain and Ireland*, 7th ed., 2 vols. (London, 1809), *1*:747–749; *The British Almanac by the Society for the Diffusion of Useful Knowledge for the Year 1838* (London, 1837), p. 40.

[18] Bache's wife, Nancy.

[19] An account of this lecture appears above, Henry's European Diary, April 7, 1837.

[20] Augustus Frederick, Duke of Sussex (1773–1843), was the ninth child of George III. He was elected President of the Society of Arts in 1816 and served as President of the Royal So-

ciety from 1830 through 1838. His personal library, a reflection of his deep interest in intellectual activities, contained more than fifty thousand volumes. *DNB*.

[21] The President of the Royal Institution was Edward Adolphus Seymour, Duke of Somerset (1775–1855). *DNB*.

Faraday's self-imposed limitation on dining away from home was widely publicized, presumably to forestall invitations. For another reference see below, Henry's European Diary, April 19, 1837.

[22] A more detailed account of Bache's visit appears above, Bache's European Diary, April 6, 1837.

far as he a component part of the people will have his own way, but theo-
retically a fierce tory, opinionated, self-will'd & yet kind hearted withal. It
would never do to tell on paper all I heard but if not pushed out by something more amusing, you shall hear what he said of the Frenchmen. In the
afternoon to dine at the Royal Soc^y club, & in the eve^g to the meeting of the
Soc^y At the club I was introduced to a gentleman who on hearing my name
or rather an attempt at it for verily it cannot be English, asked if it was Mr
Backey who had made exp^s on the radiation of heat &^{c} & we fell to talking
without my having the advantage of knowing him. I successfully combatted
Prof. Powell's views which were singularly familiar to this gentleman &
after bringing him over to my own enquired of my introducer who it was—
Prof. Powell of Oxford![23] The rest of the week was filled with the like but
the sheet is full. Good bye love to *all* from *all*, all well. The Miss Pattersons are not half a mile from us. How could you let the Wellington &
Mr Henry come out without a letter. Your letters are sent by the London
not Liverpool packet.

Yrs ever
ADB

[23] An expanded version of Bache's meeting with Powell may be found above, Bache's European Diary, April 6, 1837.

TO STEPHEN ALEXANDER

Family Correspondence, Henry Papers, Smithsonian Archives

London April 10th 1837

My Dear Stephen

As soon as possible after my arrival in London I wrote to acquaint Harriet[1] and all of you that we had safely landed at Plymouth after a pleasant
voyage from land to land of 19 days and that we came to London on the 17th
had taken lodgings and were comfortably settled in a pleasant and fashionable part of the city within a few steps of the Palace of St. James and about
the same distance from the Royal Institution.

I have as you may suppose often visited the latter but do not intend to
pay court to the former. Queen Adelade[2] is not quite as interesting a person

[1] See his above letter to Harriet, March 21,
1837.

[2] Adelaide (1792–1849), Queen of William
IV. *DNB*.

to me as Mrs Summerville and I have derived more pleasure and profit from several interviews with Mr. Babbage than I could possible do from kissing the hand of his most greacious and *illiterate* majesty.[3]

My reception thus far has been cordial and kind beyond my most sanguine expectations and every facility has been given me to prosecute the object of my tour. I have received more than politeness from Daniel, Faraday, Wheatstone, Dr Roget, Mr Babbage, and Mrs Summerville.[4] Mr Wheatstone has spent nearly a week with Professor Bache and myself in going over his interesting experiments on the velocity of electricity and also inducting me into the mystery of the late discoveries in sound. Mr Babbage spent several hours with us in explaining his calculating machine and gave a small party that we might meet Mrs Summerville. I was much disappointed in his character; he appears very amiable and has nothing of that causticity of manner which we might infer from his writings.[5] The calculating machine as you know is only partially finished some misunderstanding having occurred between Mr Babbage and the government and it is now probable the one commenced will never be finished. Mr B is now engaged in making the drawings of a machine on an intirely different principle which he says will be far more extensive in its operations than the first as he can apply it to the calculation of any algebraic formula what ever and even to the integration by approximation of the most involved algebraic functions.

We are to meet Mrs Summerville at her own house sometime next week.[6] She is the most agreeable and unpret[end]ing person we have as yet met, has a strong scotch accent and is a native of the south of scotland. I was not aware of this circumstance and claimed kindred with her as having descended myself from the land of lakes. She is now preparing for the press the fifth edition of her work on the connection of the sciences.[7] I am attending a course of lectures by Mr Faraday in the mornings, am much pleased with his method of treating the dulest part of the course of chemistry namely the metals.

He is also engaged at present in giving a popular course once a week on the four elements of the ancients earth air fire and water. The street leading to the Royal Institution at the time of his lecture is crowded with the car-

---

[3] William IV (1765–1837), King of England since 1830, had a reputation for being "unversed in courtly etiquette" and for being prone to delivering rambling, foolish-sounding speeches. *DNB*, pp. 328, 330, 331.

[4] A large portion of what follows repeats material in preceding documents, to which the reader is referred for commentary and identifications.

[5] For example, from Babbage's *Reflections on the Decline of Science in England*, discussed in *Henry Papers, 1*:342n–343n.

[6] Below, Henry's diary for April 19, 1837.

[7] The fifth London edition of *On the Connexion of the Physical Sciences* appeared in 1840. Henry obtained this edition for his Library.

riages of the gentry. Mr Faraday has given me free access to all the privileges of the Institution while I remain and almost persuaded me to give a lecture on the mathematical principles of the theory of Electricity.[8] I have however declined as I come to London as a student not an instructor.

My time as you may suppose is much occupied so thus I can scarcely find leasure to note down my scientific observations. I however endeavour to keep an account of the experiments and objects which will be of most value to myself and the cause of science in our country. Professor Bache had not arrived when I first came to London. I was therefore disappointed in not meeting with him but about 10 days after I was agreably surprised to find his card on my table directing me to his lodgins within a few doors of our own. We are thus accidentally plesantly situated near each other and have been constantly associated in our intercourse with men of science. He is busily engaged in collecting materials for a report relative to the plan of education for Girard college. I have given a visit to Woolwich and was kindly received by Mr Barlow and Dr Gregory. Professor Christie was not at home but has since called on me but we did not meet. Professor Bache and myself will again go to Woolwich to witness some experiments of Dr G on projectiles which he intends commencing as soon as the weather will permit. Prof Barlow shewed me his observatory and also his fluid lense telescope. I am also invited to see the observatory of Sir James South[9] on the first clear evening and will make a note of any thing which I may see that will be interesting to you. The advantages for successful cultivation of science are by far more ample in this country than in ours but still I think we can do much more than we have done. The persons with [whom] I have as yet met are men of the first order of scientific character but yet they do not pretend to all knowledge and in general take a less wider range of subjects than men of science with us. Division however of mental as well as mechanical labour leads to perfection.[10]

---

[8] What Faraday expected of such a lecture is unclear. Although Henry rarely put his electrical researches in mathematical language and included very few mathematical formulae in his lectures at Princeton—in large part because his nonscience students lacked the sophistication (see *Henry Papers*, 2:365, footnote 7)—he was well read in the mathematics of his field and generally subscribed to prevailing formulations in electrostatics and electrodynamics. In "Contributions II: Spiral Conductor," for instance, Henry developed a qualitative explanation of self-induction from the mathematical investigations of Poisson and others. While not a mathematical physicist, Henry was capable of speaking knowledgeably on the subject to a general audience. Faraday, self-consciously and notoriously nonmathematical in his approach to physics, perhaps wanted Henry to deliver a popular introduction to those mathematical aspects of electrical physics in which he himself was least comfortable. That Faraday would delegate such a lecture to Henry is illustrative of one of the notable differences in scientific style of the two electrical physicists.

[9] Documented in Henry's diary entry of September 20-30, 1837, below.

[10] The virtues of specialization were taken for granted by Henry and growing numbers of

Sir James South it is said has scarcely enough mathematics to make the simple calculations of astronomy but is as you know celebrated for his skill as an observer.[11] I am also promised an introduction to the Royal observatory. Mr Babbage offered to procure one but our Minister Mr Stephenson had previously undertaken to do the same.[12] The Minister to St James has been very attentive to us thanks to the letter from Mr Van Buren.[13] Prof. Bache and myself left our cards at his house when he was not at home and stated that we would call again. He however immediatly returned the call and has been quite generous in his offers to afford us any facilities in his power. He is a good sort of a man whose head is a little turned with the style of the court. Of this however I must say nothing although I could give you a sketch of a scene witnessed by Prof B and myself which would produce some meriment on the other side of the water. (Do not mention this)[14]

We have been introduced to several of the Professers in the scientific line at Oxford and Cambridge and have promised a visit to those ancient and celebrated seats of Learning.[15] I must inform you that I have constant access at all hours of the day to the rooms of the Royal Society & have been shewn all the curiosities of the place.[16] The original telescope of Sir Isaac Newton, the air pump of Boyle, the condensing apparatus of Hook, and the gallery of portraits. Amoung the most interesting Articles however shown me is the original copy of the Principia from which the work was printed. It is in the hand writing of Newton with the erasures and interlineations. There is also deposited here the great theodolite of Ramsden and a variety of Philosophical apparatus used in extending at different periods the boundaries of science. Mr Children has promised me a copy of the abstracts of the society and will transmit the same to me as they are published.[17] You know that I

---

scientists of the period. This belief was a central aspect of a process we now call professionalization. It is important to point out, however, that Henry's notion of specialization was far less narrow than the modern concept. The degree of specialization could vary from country to country. Although Henry considered his American colleagues "behind" the British in this respect, it has been pointed out that the British in this period were less specialized than the French. Maurice Crosland, "History of Science in a National Context," *The British Journal for the History of Science,* 1977, *10*:103–104.

[11] See above, Bache diary, April 6, 1837, footnote 9.

[12] Henry did not visit the Greenwich Observatory.

[13] See above, Henry to Torrey, February 4, 1837. Van Buren's letter has not been found among Stevenson's papers in the Library of Congress.

[14] Henry's diary makes no further mention of the incident, nor does Bache's diary provide any clues. For similar observations by Bache, see Bache's letter to his mother of April 9, 1837, above.

[15] Henry's notes on his Cambridge visit of September 18–20 are printed below. He did not visit Oxford.

[16] The visit to the Royal Society is documented above in Henry's first diary entry of March 23, 1837.

[17] In 1832 the Royal Society determined to print abstracts of papers appearing in the *Phil. Trans.* The first two volumes of the *Abstracts of the Papers Printed in the Philosophical Transactions* covered the years 1800 to

have already in my library a copy of the two published volums which I will present to you should Mr Children not forget his promis.

I attended a lecture by Mr Dent on the construction of chronometers and was afterwards introduced to the gentleman. He took great pains to show and explain to me the construction of his ballance and hair spring of glass. The only difficulty in applying the glass is that it requires about two years to get a constant rate. The loss on the capital thus long unemployed is the objection. He showed me the chronometer which obtained the large prize.[18] His lecture was quite interesting. It gave a clear exposition of the principles of the different escapements illustrated by large drawings and working models.

Mr Faraday introduced me to the particular attention of Mr Dent and I am to call on him and his Partner for further information relative to the Philosophy of the subject. He belongs to the Firm of Arnold and Dent of whom you have probably heard.

Amoung other things I must not forget to mention that I was shewn the great water barometer of Prof Daniel.[19] It is now some what out of order but is shortely to be repaired. It is placed in the axis of the wide winding stairs which lead to the rooms of the Royal Society in Summerset House.

Mr Wheatstone of whom I have before spoken as having devoted much time to me is the most "talented" person as far as my observation extends in London. He is not more than 30 years old and has more new projects than will suffice for the labour of a long life. He is highly esteemed by men of science in London and also on the continent. He wants however stability and does not finish one thing before he begins another.[20] You know his most ingenious method of measuring the velocity of electricity. Sir John Herchel proposes to make a series of experiments with Mr Wheatstone when he returnes from Africa to determine by the same means the velocity of light and thus, establish an *experimens crucis* to descide between the rival theories of

---

1814 and 1815 to 1830. A change began with the third volume which printed, in addition to the usual abstracts of papers, brief accounts of the meetings in which the papers were read. *Record of the Royal Society of London*, 4th ed. (London, 1940), pp. 178–179. The Henry Library contains several volumes from this series.

[18] In 1829, the Royal Observatory awarded Dent first prize for his chronometer no. 114, which Dent claimed to be one of the most accurate on record. The chronometer was tested at the observatory for thirteen months in a public chronometer competition instituted by the Admiralty. Edward J. Dent, *Chronometers,*

Watches, and Clocks (London, 1842), pp. 11, 14. E. G. R. Taylor, *Mathematical Practitioners of Hanoverian England* (Cambridge, England, 1966), p. 389.

[19] See Henry's first diary entry of March 23, 1837, above, footnote 19.

[20] Although known for an encyclopedic grasp of the scientific and technical literature, Wheatstone was not considered a "deep investigator." While admitting this deficiency in Wheatstone, Bowers traces a continuous thread of ideas and interests through Wheatstone's wide-ranging researches. Brian Bowers, *Sir Charles Wheatstone, 1802–1875* (London, 1975), pp. 216–217.

undulation and emission by causing the light to pass through different media. If the velocity is the greater in the denser medium the experiment will favour the latter hypothesis and if in the rarer the former.[21] Prof. W has instructed me in many beautiful experiments on sound and shown me a whole class of instruments of his own invention for playing stringed instruments by wind. The most surprising production of this individual is a speaking machine[22] which without the aide of any deception from dress or other auxiliary circumstances to help the dec[e]ption startles you with the utterance of several words so planely and distinctly that you can scarcely persuade yourself that a person is not concealed under the table. The part which performs the part of the mouth is formed by a half bag of Indian rubber which is compressed and opened so as to produce the sound of the *labials*. It says *Papa Mama Mother Father Thumb Plumb* and many other words of like sound as distinctly as I can do. It also laughs and cryes with a perfect imitation of nature.

Mr Watkins of Charing Cross[23] has taken much pains to show me some of the more recent and difficult experiments on light. Prof Powell[24] of Oxford has promised if I visit that Place to go over with me his methods of repeating the experiments of interferences polarization &c. My visit to Europe is attended with many sacrifices of feeling in reference to absence from my Family and the sojourn among strangers in case of sickness but I have almost

[21] We have found no record, published or unpublished, of any such joint experiment, nor can we explain how Herschel proposed to adapt Wheatstone's method, except to suggest that he proposed to apply Wheatstone's revolving mirror technique to optical measurements. Herschel's long-standing interests in physical optics have been inadequately studied (except for his contributions to photography). At first an advocate of emission theory, Herschel converted to the undulatory hypothesis, which he attempted to support by experiments on the transmission of light through different media. In one of his major articles on the subject, Herschel cited Wheatstone's experiments on sound transmission as analogical evidence in favor of a wave theory of light. "On the Absorption of Light by Coloured Media, Viewed in Connexion With the Undulatory Theory," *Phil. Mag.*, 1833, 3d ser. *3*:401–412, especially p. 411.

While Herschel's proposal cannot be documented, François Arago was in fact inspired by Wheatstone's rotating mirror method of measuring the velocity of electricity. In 1838,

he suggested adapting the apparatus to terrestrial measurements of the velocity of light in order to make a definitive comparison of the velocities in water and air—a "crucial experiment" for deciding between the wave and particle theories. Arago never completed the experiments, but his suggestion was taken up by Fizeau and Foucault. Using a rotating mirror technique, Foucault declared in 1850 that light traveled faster in air than water, a vindication of the undulatory hypothesis. *DSB*, s.v. "Arago," "Foucault."

For Herschel's work in Africa, see below, Henry's diary entry of August 10, 1837, especially footnote 2.

[22] See Henry's diary for April 4, 1837, above.

[23] See above Hare to Henry, February 13, 1837, footnote 3.

[24] See above, Bache's diary entry of April 6, 1837, footnote 34. We do not know where Henry met Baden Powell. He may have encountered him at the Royal Society. The Henry Library contains a number of Powell's published works on physical optics and the philosophy of science.

already seen enough to compensate for these and to repay the loss of time and expense of the voyage.

Linn DeWitt appears much pleased with his visit has greatly improved in his deportment and will I hope receive much benefit from his tour. He has been entered as a student at the British museum and after seeing most of the *"Lions"* of the city is now engaged in studying the elgin marbles and the other antiquities of the place.

I have made inquiries relative to the map of the moon[25] but learn that there is not a copy for sail in London. Several have been ordered by the German Book seller but they were ordered for individuals. The nautical almanac for 1839[26] is not yet published but will be out in a few weeks. Mr Roberton assistant secretary of the Royal society has promised to get from amoung the loose papers a copy of the paper on the stars which you mention in your list.[27] In a package which I sent off yesterday in a great hurry from the rooms of the Royal Society directed to the Albany Institute and which contains a bundle of papers for that Institution there are two packages directed to Mrs Harriet Henry, one of these contains a dress for each of the little girls and a scarf for Harriet. The other contains some items for Beck,[28] and a paper for you from the author on the observations on the tides.[29] I have also put into the general bundle copy of a prospectus of a set of tables for working differences by one of the secretaries of the astronomical society which will be published as soon as about a doz subscribers more

---

[25] We assume this to be the great collaborative effort of the German astronomers Wilhelm Beer and J. H. Mädler, *Mappa selenographica totam lunae hemisphaeram visibilem complectens* (1836), considered a milestone in moon mapping. In 1837, the astronomers produced a companion volume for their map: *Der Mond nach seinen kosmischen und individuellen Verhältnissen, oder allgemeine vergleichende Selenographie. DSB*, s.v. "Beer," "Mädler."

[28] The *Nautical Almanac and Astronomical Ephemeris for the Year 1839* (London, 1837). The English nautical almanac was reformed in 1834 after falling into disrepute following the death in 1811 of its first editor, the Astronomer Royal Nevil Maskelyne. In 1837 it was under the independent superintendence of Lt. W. S. Stratford who restored its accuracy and general reputation. John L. E. Dreyer and H. H. Turner, eds., *History of the Royal Astronomical Society, 1820–1920* (London, 1923), pp. 56, 61. *Man is Not Lost, A Record of Two Hundred Years of Astronomical Navigation with the Nautical Almanac, 1767–1967* (London, 1968), pp. 12–13.

[27] Alexander's list has not been found, but, presumably, he desired a recent paper from the *Phil. Trans.* In that journal, one of the more prominent papers on the stars published during the decade was J. F. W. Herschel's "Observations of Nebulae and Clusters of Stars, Made at Slough with a 20-Feet Reflector, Between the Years 1825–1833," 1833, pp. 359–506.

[28] T. R. Beck.

[29] Possibly an article by William Whewell. It was Whewell's paper on tides that Henry conveyed to Gibbes. See below, Henry to Gibbes, December 27, 1837. Whewell's tidal work is treated above in Henry's diary for March 24, 1837, footnote 14. Henry himself was presented by Whewell with two articles on tides: "Researches on the Tides (6th and 7th series)," *Phil. Trans.*, 1836, pp. 289–341; 1837, pp. 75–85.

are obtained.[30] I have directed your name to be put down for a copy. The two packages are directed to Harriet, are bound together and with the other parcels are made up into one large bundle and directed to the care of Dr John Beck[31] New York. I was so long detained by Mr Roberton at the Society that the ship had started 5 minutes before I arrived at the dock with the package. I therefore sent it to O. Rich[32] who will forward it to Pourtsmouth by coach when it will arrive in time for the ship and will accompany this letter. This letter will probably not reach you until after a month from date and as the vacation is now about commencing at Princeton I will direct it Albany where I hope it will meet you and your good [. . .][33] amid the enjoyments of friends and the blessings of health.

I will be anxiously expecting a letter by some of the Packets which are now due and will open it with much anxiety. I hope all things have gone on smothely, that you have settled about your summer residence that Harriet and you all have been well that my Dear Little wife has become recconciled to my absence and that she is now comforted by the presence of her friends in Albany and cheered with the prospect of my safe return. I cannot realize that I am so far removed from home and since the arrival of Prof Bache and his good Lady we scarcely think of being in a foreign country. My Love to Mother, Aunt, Louisa, Nancy, James and his Family, Mr Meads and Family. I will not be able to send books home but must keep them until I return the difficulty in sending bundles through the custom house will be an objection.

---

[30] We are unable to identify the proposed publication. No mention of it is made in the *Monthly Notices* of the Royal Astronomical Society. If it was to be an official publication of the Society, it may have been an attempt to publish a new edition of the handbook to accompany the *Nautical Almanac* originally published in 1766 by Nevil Maskelyne, *Tables Requisite to be Used with the Astronomical and Nautical Ephemeris*. The handbook was designed for the use of navigators and other practical astronomers who needed a practical mathematical guide for reducing Greenwich observations to their locality. An attempt was made in the early 1830s to produce a new edition of the work, but, for some reason, it failed to appear in 1833, its tentative publication date. Dreyer and Turner, *Royal Astronomical Society*, pp. 65–66. The attempt may have been revived in 1837.

None of the secretaries, to our knowledge, personally compiled a set of tables in this period.

[31] John Brodhead Beck, identified in *Henry Papers, 1*:284.

[32] Obadiah Rich (1783–1850), American bibliographer and bookseller, operating in London since 1829. Rich specialized in early books and manuscripts pertaining to the United States. *DAB.*

[33] The manuscript is torn at this point.

TO HARRIET HENRY

Mary Henry Copy, Family Correspondence,
Henry Papers, Smithsonian Archives

London April 10th. 1837

My dear Harriet. I have just finished a letter to Stephen[1] which will afford him some amusement if not information of interest. In this letter to you I will endeavor to give matter of another kind so that those most interested in whatever concerns my welfare may be gratified. We are most comfortably lodged at no 37 Jermyn Street near St. James Church, in the West end of the city. We have two rooms and a parlor handsomely furnished. We pay two and half guineas[2] per week for the rooms and take our breakfast before going out; we dine about five o'clock wherever we may chance to be at the time. Mrs. and Prof. Bache arrived about ten days after we came to London, and accidentally took lodgings in a street within a few steps of our house. They were highly pleased to meet me. I call for Bache every morning and we pass the entire day together visiting scientific and other institutions. The first week in London was the Easter vacation, and little was doing in the way of science. I took advantage of this time to kill off a few of the lions of the city. I visited the Tower, St. Pauls, Westminster Abbey and other places of interest. The tower is an object of much interest carrying one back. St. Pauls also is of great interest, not the exterior. To my surprise every building in London is as black as if formed of cast iron.[3] The terraces, which look so well on paper, in reality are as if powdered with a thick coat of lamp black which is washed off in places and thus the black surface is variegated with irregular stripes of white. The effect is such as to interfere very much with the pleasure in the building. The inside of St. Pauls however is magnificent. The lofty dome, circulary whispering gallery midway [up] the

---

[1] See above.

[2] This was equal to 52½ shillings or about $12.60 in United States money of that period.

[3] The problem of the pollution of London's air by coal smoke was a very old one. Coal burning in London was prohibited as early as 1273, but this and subsequent acts and proclamations against coal burning were either ignored or not enforced. Wood was too expensive, and there was no third alternative. It was not until the Clean Air Act of 1956 that the English began serious attempts to end air pollution.

St. Paul's was a particularly unfortunate victim of smoke pollution. The great edifice was blackened with coal smoke even before it was completed. Sir Christopher Wren had to arrange for a special cleaning of the exterior walls before holding a Thanksgiving service in the presence of Queen Anne in 1702. But as Henry's description indicates, such cleanings were at best temporary measures. It was not until 1968, when new cleaning technology was available and London's air cleansed, that St. Paul's exterior was given the elegance that Sir Christopher Wren had imagined it should have.

Terence McLaughlin, *Dirt: A Social History as Seen Through the Uses and Abuses of Dirt* (New York, 1971), pp. 102–103; John P. Lodge, Jr., *The Smoake of London* (Elmsford, New York, 1969), pp. x–xii.

concave, the high aisles, and the tesselated pavement all conspire to produce an overwhelming effect on the beholder at the moment of entrance. The walls are studded in almost every part with statues and monuments to the departed greatness of the English people. It is however a commentary upon the character of the two last centuries of this people that there are but three or four monuments to men of literature or science, while the walls are covered with monuments of military and naval heroes. It is the same in Westminster Abbey—while the poet occupies a small corner and is commemorated by a small stone, the hero of barbarous war lies in a marble tomb reaching in many cases almost to the vaulted roof, and many names unknown to general fame live only in this manner immortalized thus by friends or circumstance.

HENRY'S EUROPEAN DIARY
Henry Papers, Smithsonian Archives

[April 11, 1837][1]

We attended a Lecture at the Society of arts[2] room on the recent improvements of Paper making by Mr Cowper[3] an engineer who has made several improvements in this business himself and also is the Patentee of the latest Printing presses by steam. The whole art of paper making was most admirably illustrated and great interest given to the subject.

He commenced by exhibiting the several kinds of letters received by a

[1] We have assigned this date from the date of Cowper's lecture. In the original diary, this entry appears between those which we have dated [April 7, 1837] and [April 8, 1837].

[2] The London Society of Arts was founded in 1754, part of a general European movement to establish technical societies (the American Philosophical Society was in part derivative of this same movement). Its full title was "The Society for the Encouragement of Arts, Manufactures, and Commerce." In the beginning its sole purpose was the awarding of prizes for inventions and significant advances in arts, manufactures, and commerce. The chemist Arthur Aikin was responsible for a shift away from prize-giving to the dissemination of knowledge in the industrial arts and sciences. In 1829, Aikin initiated the lectures on manufactures, such as Cowper's. Also, papers began to be read and discussions held at the Society's regular meetings. Henry Trueman Wood, *A History of the Royal Society of Arts* (London, 1913), pp. 2, 17, 19, 336–337.

[3] Edward Cowper (1790–1852) made several important improvements in printing and paper making. He invented a new method for distributing the ink, and, in partnership with his brother-in-law, advanced machine making. In 1827, the two partners invented the "four-cylinder machine," which greatly accelerated the process of printing. Cowper is described as the "improver" of the steam printing machine as Watt was for the steam engine. *DNB.* Cowper's April 11 lecture is summarized in the *Athenaeum* for April 15, 1837, p. 267.

person and the impression made by the mere quality and folding of the letter. He then exhibited a model sheet of paper to illustrate the construction of the ancient papyrus. I had before no conception of this substance or how sheets to answer the purpose of modern paper were formed. It appears that the papyrus was formed by making strips of bark into a kind of checker work like the bottom of a split chair and these were fastened together by a paist formed from the gum of the plant or perhaps by flower.

The paper is formed into continued sheets on the improved process by causing the pulp to flow on the surface of a gause wheel the upper part of which is connected with an exausting pump by which the moisture is sucked from the pulp and the sheet formed instantaneously. It is then carried off by roolers and wound around cylinders until it forms in some cases a sheet of more than a mile in length. On the occasion of the visit of the Duke and Dutches of Southerland to the establishment of a celebrated paper maker the avenew to the works was covered by a sheet 3/4 a mile long which served as a carpet for the tread of the aristocratic visitors.[4] Attempts have been made to form paper of new linen but with little success since although the paper was very strong it cracked and formed white lines like those produced on bladder parchement.[5]

After the lecture on paper an exhibition of insects was given by the oxyhydrogen microscope.[6] The effect was highly interesting. The dessections of the insects among which was the american cricket and the bed bug was very minute and exhibited the structure with great clearness.

The apparatus for turning the lime consisted of a train of wheels connected to the lime spindle by a universal joint. Behind the lime was placed a concave reflector for condensing the light which the exhibitor said was a great improvement. The Society of arts possess a very interesting collection of machines which have been deposited at different times and which are exhibited in a large room fitted up for the purpose.

[4] Probably George Granville Leveson-Gower, second Duke of Sutherland, and his wife Harriet Elizabeth Georgiana Leveson-Gower (*DNB*). The story was recounted by Cowper.

[5] Henry made further comments on this lecture in his diary entry of April 22, 1837, printed below.

[6] According to the *Athenaeum* (April 15, 1837, p. 267), the lecture was delivered by A. Goadby. For the oxyhydrogen microscope, see Henry's second diary entry, above, of March 23, 1837, footnote 2.

HENRY'S EUROPEAN DIARY
Henry Papers, Smithsonian Archives

[April 12–15, 1837][1] On Saturday afternoon I visited Mr William Christie Jun.[2] of Clapham road about 3 miles over the river. Found a very plesant family with several guests.

Spent the evening agreeably. One of the gentlemen was a Brother of Sir James South[3] who offered to introduce me to the astronomer. Stated that his Brother is a great Tory but only so in politics not in science. Was originally a physician but much attached to astronomy, had an observatory. Now engaged in a law suit with the successor of Troughton, Mr Sims, in reference to the mounting of the large telescope with the lens purchased in France. It is now useless on account of the tremour of the instrument from as it is said defective mounting. Another gentleman was Alderman Anible with whom I have promised to go to hear the bishop of London preach. This person I was informed is the [late][4] Lord Mayor of the city. He appeared pleased to refer to his former dignity and defended with considerable eagreness the procession &c which had struck us [as] being so ridiculous.[5]

I also last week attended part of a lecture by Prof Daniel. I brought letters to him from Dr Hare and Professor Renwick.[6] He has been very kind to me and gave a general invitation to come in at any time to his lecture.

[1] We do not know when this entry was written. The Royal Society Club dinner and Royal Society meeting which Henry says he attended "on Thursday last" took place on April 13. We are assuming that Henry's Saturday visit to Christy was on April 15 and his Wednesday visit to the Greenwich factory was on April 12.

[2] William Christy, Jr. (1805–1839) was a Quaker botanist whom John Torrey had contacted concerning Henry's visit. Christy became a Fellow of the Linnean Society in 1828. The *Royal Society Catalog* lists five articles by him from 1833 to 1838. James Britten and George S. Boulger, comps., *A Biographical Index of Deceased British and Irish Botanists*, 2d ed. revised and completed by A. B. Rendle (London, 1931), p. 63. Christy to Torrey, March 16, 1837, Torrey Papers, New York Botanical Garden Library.

Christy was the eldest son of William Miller Christy (1778–1858), a banker, hatmaker, and Turkish towel manufacturer. One younger brother, Henry Christy (1810–1865, *DNB*), be-

came a noted ethnologist. Information on the Christy family from the Library of the Religious Society of Friends, London.

[3] John Flint South (1797–1882) was a younger half-brother of James South. Unlike his elder brother, he remained a surgeon, practicing, teaching, and writing on the subject. *DNB*. For James South and his ill-fated telescope, see Bache's account of his visit to South's observatory of April 6, 1837, printed above. For Henry's account of his visit, see September 20–30, 1837, below.

[4] Unclear in the original. We think this is the sense of the text.

[5] Henry's rendering of the Alderman's name is erroneous; this is William Venables (ca. 1786–1840), Alderman of Queenhithe and Lord Mayor of London in 1826. Charles Welch, *Modern History of the City of London* (London, 1896), pp. 159, 183. A. B. Beaven, *The Aldermen of the City of London*, 2 vols. (London, 1908, 1913).

[6] Not found.

The subje[c]t was not one of much interest the salts of crome. Dr Daniel is rather a plesant lecturer, appears a gentlem[an] of good feeling, about 50 years old. Is much engaged in the chemical action of the battery.[7] Shewed me his large scale of chemical equ[i]volents which is made of pieces of board 15 feet high. The divisions and numbers are permanent[l]y put on but the names of the substances are added from time to time as the course progresses.[8] He has a fine collection of wooden models for illustrating christology.

Among the apparatus is a model to represent a common beam of Light formed of a number of waves of the different coulors which when blended makes white.

Prof D[s] Laboratory is in a room directly under his lecture room. There is a communication by means of a trap and dumb waiter.

A thick wire (1/5 inch) is suspended around the room to shew the effects of galvanism namely the magnetism, heating &c.

Prof D gave me a very ingenious theory of the sharpening of a raisor by means of dipping it into hot/cold[9] water. The edge is serated by cracks. When heat is applied the whole metal expand but the thick back remains heated while the thin edge is cooled and is thus slightly curved in the plane of the length of the blade and this causes the serated parts to close and become a smooth cutting surface. This might be tested by making a blade without a thick back. The exp is almost worth the trouble of testing.

I have not yet mentioned that on thursday last I dined at the club of the Royal Society at the old stand the crown and ancer.[10] Several distinguished gentlemen were at the table among the number Sir H Parry,[11] Mr Christie of Woolwich,[12] Comand. Ross of the northern expedition,[13] Mr Talbot the

[7] Henry had met Daniell several weeks earlier and been given an explanation of the constant battery. See Henry's first diary entry of March 23, 1837, especially footnote 22.

[8] Henry and his Albany colleague L. C. Beck had designed and sold a scale of chemical equivalents in 1827. See *Henry Papers*, *1*:191–194.

[9] In the original, the word "hot" appears above "cold."

[10] The dinner register of the Club for April 13, 1837 (Royal Society Library), shows that Henry attended as a guest of Francis Baily; Bache was also present, as a guest of P. M. Roget. Not mentioned below by Henry, but also in attendance, were the members John T. Stanley, Lord Teignmouth, Charles Hatchett, Sir John Rennie, Thomas Phillips, Herbert Mayo, W. H. Smyth, and the Treasurer, Joseph Smith. The other guests were Mr. Rodd, Ge-rard Vrolik, Monsieur Mannoir, Mr. Vaughan (probably William), and W. H. Whitbread.

[11] Although Henry wrote "H Parry" this is William Edward Parry (1790–1855, *DNB*), the Arctic explorer. *Henry Papers*, *2*:251.

[12] This may have been Henry's first meeting with Samuel Hunter Christie (1784–1865, *DSB*), although Henry had attempted to see him at Woolwich and Christie had tried to return the call. Christie taught mathematics at the Royal Military Academy from 1806–1854. Most of his researches and publications were in terrestrial magnetism, although he also published on magnetoelectric induction.

Christie's father was James Christie (1730–1803, *DNB*), founder of the famous London auction house.

[13] For James Clark Ross, see Bache's diary entry of April 6, 1837, printed above.

writer on light,[14] Mr Children[15] the companion of Davey and now one of the curators of the British Museum, Mr Pepys the author of the original experiment which proved the nature of the diamond.[16]

After the dinner we adjourned to the Rooms of the society where the reading of Mr Daniel's paper on galvanism was concluded.[17] The members then adjourned to the library where tea was served. In this place I had a very agreable interview with Ross, Davies[18] and Prof Christie on the subject of terestrial magnetism. Prf Bache and myself are to visit Woolwich together sometime this week.[19]

On Wednesday of the same week went with Prof Wheatston to visit a manufactory at Greenwich ware a number of processes are carried on by a company. The principal works are those for the construction of rope imbued with Indian rubber. The rubber is desolved by a substance called caouchicine which was discovered at this place by one of the firm named Enderby (?).[20] It is made by distilation from the Indian rubber in the form of a very volatil and pungent liquid the vapour of which is very heavy like

[14] William Henry Fox Talbot (1800–1877). Talbot came from a well-to-do family. After attending Harrow, he received a B.A. from Trinity College, Cambridge, in 1821. Shortly thereafter he began publishing papers in mathematics. In 1826 he started investigations in light and optics. In 1834, frustration in attempts to sketch scenery with the aid of a camera lucida led him to experiment with ways of capturing the camera images on chemically sensitized paper. He presented his findings to the Royal Society in January 1839, a few days after Arago communicated an account of Daguerre's process to the Paris Academy of Sciences. Talbot continued to make improvements in photography, including a method for taking instantaneous pictures and one for giving a gloss to prints. His "talbotype," originally "calotype," was a forerunner of modern photography.

Although remembered primarily for his work in photography, Talbot continued his early mathematical researches and also published on astronomy, history, and philology. He was a member of the Royal Astronomical Society and a Fellow of the Royal Society. He dabbled briefly in politics, serving as a member of Parliament from 1833 to 1834. *DSB*. *DNB*.

Henry visited Talbot several weeks after this meeting (see the first diary entry of April 25). Talbot's 1839 article announcing his photographic process, "Some Account of the Art of Photogenic Drawing," Royal Society

Proceedings, 1839, 4:120–121, is in the Henry Library.

[15] John George Children. See Bache's diary entry of April 6, 1837, above.

[16] William Hasledine Pepys (1775–1856) and William Allen published "On the Quantity of Carbon in Carbonic Acid, and on the Nature of the Diamond," *Phil. Trans.*, 1807, pp. 267–292, which confirmed earlier findings that diamonds consisted of carbon. Pepys was a Fellow of the Royal Society and was active in a number of local scientific organizations. He is best known for his invention of apparatus, including a mercury gasometer and a water gasholder. *DNB*.

[17] "Further Observations on Voltaic Combinations," *Phil. Trans.*, 1837, pp. 119–139. A presentation copy is in Henry's Library. For further information on Daniell's series of articles, of which this was the third, see Henry's first diary entry of March 23, 1837, footnote 22.

[18] Thomas Stephens Davies, also on the faculty at Woolwich. See Bache's diary entry of April 6, above.

[19] Bache and Henry visited Woolwich on Friday, April 21. See their diary entries for that date, printed below.

[20] The firm of Enderby, one of the principal manufacturers of Greenwich, made rope and sailcloth. Henry S. Richardson, *Greenwich: Its History, Antiquities, Improvements, and Public Buildings* (London, 1834), p. 130. For caoutchoucine, the powerful chemical solvent produced from caoutchouc, or India rubber, see above, Hare to Henry, February 13, 1837.

that of ether. The mouth of a botle being held over a tube closed at the bottom will be filled and this may be fired. Another way of shewing the same thing is to pour the heavy vapour into a long tube inclined to the horizon and light it as it passes out at the lower end by a taper.

When a rag is tied around a thermometer bulb and this moistened with the liquid while a stream of air is blown on it by a bellowes the thermometer shrinks in a few moments to −10 and the caouchicine converts into little white masses like hoar frost.

A very curious property was mentioned of this substance namely it will desolve the Rubber of the same kind as that from which it is procured but does not act on that from another country. The caouchin which has been prepared here was made from the East India gum and this will not desolve that which we have in America from the West Indias. This circumstance has given some trouble to Dr Hare who did not effect the solution. The desolved gum may be mixed with any coulering matter and this will be left in the resolved state when the spirit evaporates.

We were shewn the process of planing iron, also the several operations in the art of making canvass. I here observed a singular method of reversing the motion of a circular movement by causing the axle of the part to be reversed to rool on the out side during a complete revolution of the driving wheel and then by a litle stop causing the same to revolve on the inside.

We also saw an engine in which the whole cylender was caused to reciprocate. Something new perhaps but not good.

The engine which caused the works of the Factory to move was a beautiful specimen of English taste in such matters. Every part was kept perfectly bright. All the offensive parts b[e]low the flo[or] which around the upper part was covered with figured oil cloath. Among the interesting articles seen at this factory I must not forget to mention the naptha Lamp a new invention for burning one of the products of coal tar. It consists of a fountain like that of an argand burner which supplies a large tube *a* through which passes a smaller tube bebe[21] connected with a forcing pump attached to the engine for giving a strong blast of air. Over the burner is placed a hood of this form the mouth of the inner tube being a litle above the level of the naptha in the burner. A most brilliant and cheap light is given by this apparatus which perhaps may also be applied to the combustion of other substances.[22]

---

[21] Unclear in original.

[22] Various fuels could have been used in the design Henry describes. Naphtha was inexpensive but also dangerous and was never widely used as a lamp fuel. William T. O'Dea, *The Social History of Lighting* (New York, 1958), pp. 229–230.

HENRY'S EUROPEAN DIARY
Henry Papers, Smithsonian Archives

April 17$\underline{\text{th}}$ [1837] visited to day in company with Professor Bache Mr Saxtons room. Was shewn a small instrument made by Mr S for cutting thin wood shavings for the microscope. It consisted principally of a disc of metal with a hole in the centre through which the wood is gradually forced up by a screw from beneath so that the shaving may be cut by a raizor knife very thin and of uniform thickness.

 Also a circular plate of copper and zinc forming a battery which can be renewed and which may be attached to a magneto-electric machine and be moved by the power generated.

We also saw a specimen of looking glass for carriages covered on the back with lead instead of amalgam of <*mercury*> tin.[1]

Mr Saxton is about to return to America after an absence of 8 years. He has been appointed balance maker to the mint at Philadelphia.

With Mr S we went to the workshop of Mr Ross[2] a manufactorer of Phil. Instruments. Saw a dividing engine every part of which is capable of adjustment, an engenious instrument but which would probably require great care in the management. The motion is given by a spiral moving into teeth in the circumference of the limb which are formed by projecting screws having a lateral motion by which they are adjusted. The surface of the spirals tangent screw is composed of a series of screw heads which are also adjustable.

This instrument is described in the transactions of the Society of arts for 1832.[3]

---

[1] The backing of mirrors was usually an amalgam of tin and mercury, but in 1835 Liebig discovered that pure silver could be used instead. A coating of red lead was placed over the silver to protect the latter from tarnish. It was this coating that Henry noticed. By 1840 the silvering process had become commercially feasible. Geoffrey Wills, *English Looking-glasses: A Study of the Glass, Frames and Makers (1670–1820)* (London, 1965), pp. 63–64.

[2] At a time when English microscopes were second to none in design and workmanship, Andrew Ross (d. 1859) was one of England's leading craftsmen in the construction of microscopes. Ross's reputation seems to have been built upon his ability to translate the designs of others into reality, although he did **make** original contributions to the design of micro-

scope tubes and focusing devices. His first important microscope was built in 1831, using the design of W. Valentine, and won for Valentine the large silver medal of the Society of Arts. Beginning in 1837 he constructed lenses for Joseph Jackson Lister (1786–1869, *DSB*), the man usually credited with changing the microscope from a toy into a piece of scientific apparatus. S. Bradbury, *The Evolution of the Microscope* (Oxford, 1967), pp. 194–195, 203, 207–211; W. Valentine, "Microscope for Botanical Dissections," *Transactions of the Society of Arts*, 1831, *48*:413–423.

[3] "Dividing Engine," *Transactions of the Society of Arts*, 1831, *48*:302–332. Ross won the Gold Isis Medal from the Society for this invention, which partially depended upon high power microscopes—which Ross excelled at—for its accuracy.

We were next shewn by the same person several acromatic object glass microscopes. The instruments had rather a common appearance but performed most admirably. It appeared as if I had for the first time in my life seen a minute object in the microscope so supperior was this instrument to those I had before seen. Every part of the field of view was clear and the quantity of light from an opeque object astonishing. We were shewn several test objects and among others the down on the wing of a peculiar butterfly also the scales of the wing of a moth. These were so perfectly distinct that objects much smaller could apparently have been easily distinguished. The globules of the blood are an interesting object and when viewed with a good instrument exhibit no central nucleus which is thus proved to be an optical illusion. If the focus be a little deranged by touching the adjusting screw the central spot appears. The object glass consists of two pieces. The focus is not very short. Mr R thinks that it is impossible to apply a power higher than 800 on account of the limit of the diameter of the pencil. Instead of placing the objects between plates of mica as in the old method he fastens them between bits of plain glass the surfaces of which adhere by a little canada balsam. This artist is one of the most sucessful constructors of this kind of microscope. He also makes the polarizing eoye pieces of Iceland spar. Reccommends for the use of the microscope two of them one to be placed below the object to polarize the light, the other above to analyze it and thus show all the effects of minute crystals when in the act of forming under the eye.

The apparatus can be easily attached to a common microscope but does not show as well as with an achromatic glass.

From this place we went to another artist Mr Robison[4] who constructs magnetic instruments. He showed us two dipping needles one 6 inches in diameter the other 5. These are to be used with Mr Loyds[5] needles for determining the intensity by means of a small weight[6] attached to the needle

---

[4] Thomas Charles Robinson (fl. 1821–1837) had a shop on Devonshire Street in London. He first came to the notice of the scientific community in 1821 when he wrote the Board of Longitude describing an improved form of the quadrant. A versatile craftsman, Robinson made balances, prisms, and barometers in addition to magnetic instruments. E. G. R. Taylor, *The Mathematical Practitioners of Hanoverian England, 1714–1840* (Cambridge, England, 1966), pp. 433–434.

Henry purchased a transit instrument from Robinson. See below, Henry to Harriet Henry, May 9, 1837.

[5] Humphrey Lloyd.

[6] Lloyd's method, presented in two papers read in 1833 and 1835, enabled the observer to determine accurately both the dip and the intensity without the need to reverse the poles. "An Attempt to Facilitate Observations of Terrestrial Magnetism," *Transactions of the Royal Irish Academy*, 1837, *17*:159–169; "Further Development of a Method of Observing the Dip and the Magnetic Intensity at the Same Time, and with the Same Instrument," *Transactions of the Royal Irish Academy*, 1837, *17*:449–459.

One of the most enthusiastic supporters of Lloyd's method of making magnetic observations was Edward Sabine. Henry recorded Sabine's views in his diary entry of April 24, 1837, printed below.

which draws it from the point of equilibrium. The dip is first determined without and then with and by means of a simple formula the relative intensity is determined.

Mr Barlow had a method somewhat similar for determining the dip by having a needle loaded perminently with a weight the effect of which is estimated by noting the dip of the loaded needle at a place where the true dip has been determined from many observations.

The needles in this apparatus was of the following form ⊂———•———⊃ with a thin axis. The needles were not accutely pointed on account of presenting near the end a broader surface to produce a greater directive force.

The circle is placed in the magnetic meredian by means of a long needle placed in the centre of the instrument temporarlary on a movable point fixed on an axis ⊥ thus. Beneath this axis which rests on the *Y*s is a weight *a* to keep the point perpendicular.[7]

The price of the larger dipping needle is 15£s of the smaller one 11£s.

Returned to my Lodgings much fatigued with my long walk and while warming myself at the fire in rather a listless mood was aroused by the servent with a package from Mr Vaughan. The writing I immediately recognized to be Stephens,[8] broke it open most eagerly and read with pleasure that all at home were well.

[7] Because few accounts of magnetic observations go into detail concerning the setting of the dip circle in the magnetic meridian, we are uncertain when the needle shown Henry was first introduced or how popular it was. We suspect, however, that it was a fairly recent invention. At least, we have been unable to uncover any mention of this method prior to Henry's diary entry, while there is evidence of widespread knowledge of it in the late 1830s and early 1840s. By 1850 the use of a horizontal needle to set a dip circle was considered one of the two major methods available. James Duncan Graham, "Observations of the Magnetic Dip, Made at Several Positions, Chiefly on the South-western and North-eastern Frontiers of the United States, and of the Magnetic Declination at Two Positions on the River Sabine; in 1840," *Transactions of the American Philosophical Society*, 1846, n.s. *9*:328–329, 345–346; W. Snow Harris, *Rudimentary Magnetism*, 2 vols. (London, 1850–1852), *1*:142.

[8] This letter has not been located.

HENRY'S EUROPEAN DIARY
Henry Papers, Smithsonian Archives

April 18ᵗʰ [1837] Breakfasted this morning by appointment with Mr Faraday, was introduced to his Brotherinlaw Mr Buchanan[1] of Edinburgh, an

[1] George Buchanan (1790?–1852) constructed harbor works and bridges and was an authority on salmon-fishing rights. *DNB*. Buchanan and Faraday were married to sisters.

engineer a very intelligent plesant man who was anxious to learn something of the rail road system in our country. I am to call on this gentleman when I visit the north. Was also introduced to Mrs Faradays[2] Brother a landscape painter a Mr. Barnard.[3]

After breakfast I remained with Mrs F and the two gentlemen until near eleven O'clock. Mrs. F shewed me an interesting book of pictures containing portraits of most of the Philosophers of Europe with letters from them. Also a large volume of the original papers of Sir H Davey which were kept by Mr F after being copied by him for the press.[4] These interesting reliquies of departed greatness could not but inspire me with admiration. I was also shewn an original sketch by the same intended for the artist to copy for one of his lectures. It did not exhibit much talent in the drawing line.

Mrs F is quite an intelligent and good harted lady. She has promised to accompany me on my visit to Mrs Sumerville.

Mr F showed me the room in which the great battery of Davey was kept and also the calorimotor with which the first rotation of electro-magnetism was produced.[5] It is a very large article consisting of plates at least 2 feet by 18 inches; there are however but few of these. The room in which the great battery was kept is directly under the Theater. The wires were passed up through the cealing.

This battery or a part of it is now kept in the museum. I was shewn a number of articles in the way of electricity of much interest and of which the following is a notice.

1   A large copper ball 2½ inches in diameter on one leg of a wire and a small brass ball on the other. This being placed near a prime conductor so that both ball are at the same distance. The spark will fly to the one sooner than to the other.

2   Syphon barometer formed of two tubes of glass or rather one tube with two legs filled with mercury. Sparkes were passed through the cups and the vacum gives the beautiful appearance of electricity in vacum.

---

[2] Sarah Barnard Faraday.

[3] George Barnard (1807–1890), a prolific artist and professor of drawing, was close to the Faradays and helpful to Michael Faraday when he grew old. L. Pearce Williams, *Michael Faraday* (New York, 1965), pp. 492–493.

[4] Faraday had gotten his start in science as Davy's laboratory assistant at the Royal Institution.

[5] See *Henry Papers*, 2:246n–247n. The calorimotor used was Robert Hare's instrument. See Thomas Martin, ed., *Faraday's Diary*, 8 vols. (London, 1932–1936), 1:49.

3 An apparatus by Mr Richie[6] for shewing a wave action and consisting of a number of needles made of watch spring with glass cups and supported 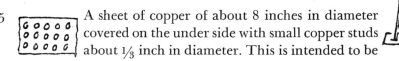 on a board by large needles. The needles (magnetic) were confined in the motion by sturdy pins and their motion rendered more obvious by balls of pith placed on the north end. A magnet was also placed at the further end so as to cause the needles to return to the primary place after an impulse. When a magnet was brought with an adverse pole near one end of the series a wave motion was passed along the whole line illustrating most beautifully the operation of a wave impulse.

3 Wheatstones apparatus for the illumination of the card in motion.[7] A metalic mirror of brass silvered, of a parabolic form and two small balls placed so as to give a spark in the focus. Apparatus about 5 inches in diameter at the mouth and about the same thickness. (Probably the revolving card was placed before this and illuminated by transmitted light?)

4 *Condenser* of two plates of copper nearly a foot in diameter. One of the glass supports is movable.

5 A sheet of copper of about 8 inches in diameter covered on the under side with small copper studs about $1/3$ inch in diameter. This is intended to be placed on a pece of red paper moistened with common salt. One pole of the battery is then placed in contact with this while the other is connected with the paper. Chlorine is evolved and the paper bleached in the spots which touch like a sailors handkerchief. Another form of the apparatus is a device like a flower with a face of platina to prevent the solution of the metal.

6 Two globes of India rubber each 5 or 6 inches in diameter gilt by gold leaf and size and thus forming excellent electrometers.

7 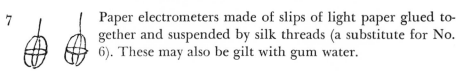 Paper electrometers made of slips of light paper glued together and suspended by silk threads (a substitute for No. 6). These may also be gilt with gum water.

[6] William Ritchie taught at the Royal Institution from 1829. *DNB*.

[7] Henry misnumbered here.

Perhaps Wheatstone's apparatus for testing the duration of a spark. See *Henry Papers*, 2: 125n.

8　Circular glass plate 5 inches diameter with two uprights *a b* and three brass feet to shew the decomposition by common electricity.

9　A pece of zinc about one foot long and 2 inches wide bent four times at right angles and two discs of platinum or silver connected by a movable wire of the same metal to shew the decomposition of the Iodide potassa without metalic contact. Two pieces of paper are placed one under each disc and one of these moistened with acid the other with the iodid, decomposition takes place in the latter when the two discs are united by the movable wire.[8]

10　Large tube 2 feet long which will hold ½ doz eggs to be used instead of the old egg stand.[9]

11　Piece of polished copper with small lump of zinc soldered to it to prevent action of the water &c or to illustrate Daveys protection.[10]

12　Jar with two slips of platinum immersed in strong acid and terminating in wires and discs between which peces of paper moistened with iodide of potassa is placed to illustrate the same principle as that shewn in exp 9.

13　Brass ball on top of larger ivory ball to shew the illumination of the latter by the electric spark. Brass ball 1 inch in diameter, ivory ball 1½ or 2 inches.

---

[8] A primitive decomposition apparatus in which electricity is generated at the acid-moistened disc. "Without metalic contact" meant the separation of the platinum (or silver) and zinc metals by the disc of potassium iodide. See Alfred Niaudet, *Elementary Treatise on Electric Batteries*, trans. L. M. Fishback, 2d ed. (New York, 1882), p. 4.

[9] The stacked eggs were made part of the circuit between the conductors of an electrostatic machine or a battery. The eggs were illuminated and "the contents of the eggs appear to be exposed to the eye, as if divested of their shelly covering." Robert Hare, *Brief Exposition of Mechanical Electricity* (Philadelphia, 1840), p. 43.

[10] Prevention of corrosion. See *Henry Papers*, *1*:393.

14  Straws for Henleys electrometer,[11] the axis pierced by a small hole through which the straw is passed and thus fastened to the axis.

15 The small electrical apparatus used by Sir H Davy[12] consisting of a jar about 9 inches high open at bottom to be placed on a pump plate with small machine with in the cylinder of which is about $3\frac{1}{2}$ or 4 inches in diameter. On the outside of the jar a electrometer is attached by a hole in the side of the glass to the electrical points. The outer jar I should have stated is about 5 inches in diameter.

16 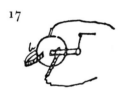 Light copper disc[13] about 7 inches diameter supported on slits in brass arm by small axle so as to vibrate when undisturbed about 40 times before coming to rest. When magnet put in place the vibrations are not more than 5 or 6 before stopping.

17  Wheel of thick copper with cylindrical axis about $\frac{1}{2}$ inch diameter with pece of notched lead pressed against it and also a pice of lead held on the surcumference a magnet being placed at *b* a stream of electricity is set through the wires.

18 Brass globe about 8 inches in diameter[14] made to revolve with great velocity to shew deviation of needle which is suspended in glass jar by silk fibre. Two needles are used. Needles pretty large.

19 Pretty arrangement for shewing the luminous figure *a* plate glass on which tinfoil is paisted about 15 inches high.

---

[11] The slender straw served as an index for electrostatic measurements. See P. M. Roget, *Treatises on Electricity, Galvanism, Magnetism, and Electro-Magnetism* (London, 1832), "Electricity," p. 19.

[12] To show electrical effects in vacua and in different gases. See *Henry Papers*, 2:238n–239n.

[13] François Arago's wheel seemed to show that a nonmagnetic substance could be made magnetic by rotation; it created a great sensation when first discovered. Faraday's attempt to explain the phenomenon was a crucial step toward his discovery of electromagnetic induction. Williams, *Faraday*, pp. 170–173.

[14] Barlow's revolving ball. Henry's figure is unclear; it may be 6 inches. *Henry Papers*, 2: 105.

20 Simple illustration of the compensation ballance[15] suspended by long piece of <*gut*> suspender wire.

21 Mr F in his lectures uses struck plates[16] for printing <*words and*> letters and figures. This can be purchased 145 Fleet street London.

Mr F spent some time with me this morning[17] in showing the arrangements of the great battery of Sir H Davey. Also exhibited to me a book in which many of the original papers of Sir H. were bowned. They were blotted some of them written in pencil and all interlined and in parts eraced.

Mr Faraday having acted as clerk to Sir H retained these papers instead of destroying them as most inconsiderate *lads* would have done.

Mrs Faraday showed me a large portfolio containing portraites of the most eminent men of science in Europe accompanied by their letters to her husband. The same collection contained the likeness of one Lady Mrs Sumerville a duplicate copy of which I was presented with. Mr F has a very active assistant named Anderson[18] formerly a soldier who has been about 8 years in the employment of the Institution.

This person prepares his lectures from the program given by Mr F also makes the tables required for the lectures.

I was surprised in examining the apparatus to see how small the pneumatic system is that is used in the Royal Institution. It is like a small table about[19]

Attended in the evening the Institution of civil engineeres.[20] Did not readily find the place came late and in the midst of a lecture from Mr Brunell[21] on the progress and past history of the Tames tunnel.

---

[15] We are unable to verify the name of the instrument, but it appears to be a modification of a device to show the air currents accompanying electric discharge (emitted from the points). See Roget, *Treatises*, "Electricity," p. 26. Cf. "electric wind" in Henry's first notebook entry of March 1836 above.

[16] Perhaps Faraday's "tin marking plate" mentioned above in Henry's diary for April 8, 1837 (first entry).

[17] Henry repeats himself here, perhaps because the text from this point on was added after the previous portion.

[18] Charles Anderson, see above, Henry's first diary entry for April 8, 1837, footnote 3.

[19] This portion of the entry breaks off here. Again, a possible indication that this entry

was written at more than one sitting.

[20] Founded in 1818, the Institution of Civil Engineers received a Royal Charter in 1828. Initially, the Institution was a forum for conversations and discussions of technical questions, but eventually it assumed a training function as well. No proceedings were published on a regular basis until 1837. At the time of Henry's visit, the organization had 252 members and met at 1 Cannon Row, Westminster. The meeting Henry describes below was reported in volume 1 of the *Proceedings*. J. H. Tudsbery, *Institution of Civil Engineers, Commemoration of the Founding of the Institution . . .* (London, 1918).

[21] Marc Isambard Brunel (1769–1849), one of the great civil engineers. Born in Normandy,

Mr Brunel speaks with a foreign accent is a short man of about 60 years old of very mild and plesant manners ready to answer any question put to him. It appears that he commenced the subject the evening previous.[22] Exhibited several drawing[s] to explain the construction of the chield[23] and the strata of earth above and below the work. The river broke in, was pumped out the leak stopped by bags of sand filled with clay and sticks across. Broke in again when the work was stoped for a long time. When commenced a new chield was required and this was put in the place of the old one by a very dangerous process. The work has since progressed very slowly only 127 feet since the last beginning. Now in a very precarious state, the excavation required to be made slowly and with great caution. The variation of the hydrostatic pressure caused by the great height of the tide 18 feet and more produc[e]s an unfavourable condition for the stability of the work while under operation.

Mr Brunel gave me an invitation to inspect the works.[24] I had a long talk with him about America. He was there in 1794 lived in Orrange Street Albany took the level from Lansingburgh to Stillwater. Went to Oswego as the agent of a French company who had purchased a lot of land on Lake Ontario,[25] was employed by Chancellor Livingston[26] to assist in the con-

---

he left France in 1793 because of Royalist sympathies and sailed to America, where he got his start as a civil engineer and was eventually appointed chief engineer of New York. In 1799 he left for England in an attempt to have the British government accept his plans for machinery to manufacture ships' blocks on a large scale. Brunel's greatest and most famous achievement was the Thames Tunnel, the world's first sub-aqueous tunnel. Begun in 1825, it ran from Rotherhithe to Wapping. Due to numerous irruptions in the tunnel the project was not completed until 1842. Brunel was knighted in 1841, was made vice-president of the Royal Society in 1842, and was very active in the Institution of Civil Engineers. His lectures to the Institution on the Thames Tunnel were famous. *DNB*. Brunel's lecture was excerpted in *The Athenaeum*, May 6, 1837, p. 328. Although a notable feat of engineering, the Tunnel never proved very useful and remained more of a tourist attraction, according to the *Encyclopaedia Britannica*, 8th ed., s.v. "London," pp. 676–677.

[22] Actually Brunel began the week before.

[23] Brunel patented the shield in 1818. The apparatus enabled him to bore the immense tunnel at its full dimensions all at once. It covered the entire area of excavation and con-

sisted of several separate frames and thirty-six cells in which the workers bored independently. The whole structure moved forward by screw power. *DNB*. Brunel's shield technique was extremely important as a precursor of all subsequent tunnel technology. Information from Robert Vogel, Museum of History and Technology, Smithsonian Institution.

[24] See below, "Notes on a Visit to the Thames Tunnel," September 28, 1837.

[25] Lacking an adequate supply of civil engineers in a period of rapid internal development, America initially relied heavily on European talent. See Daniel H. Calhoun, *The American Civil Engineer, Origins and Conflict* (Cambridge, Massachusetts, 1960). The survey of the land near Lake Ontario was Brunel's first major employment as a civil engineer. His next undertaking was a survey for a canal between the Hudson River and Lake Champlain, for the Northern Inland Lock Navigation Company, incorporated in 1792. The company received state loans and donations. Although some of the work was completed, the corporation was soon dissolved without having achieved significant progress. See "Tacitus" [De Witt Clinton], *The Canal Policy of the State of New York* (Albany, 1821), pp. 16–17. As chief engineer of New York,

struction of a steamboat. Found no workmen in the city of New York at that time to do the iron forging required. Left the country for England. I was surprised at the distinctness of his knowledge of things about Albany Schenectady & Rome, Wood creek, Three river points & Oswego.

At the same meeting met with a Mr Hawkins[27] who published a number of years since a paper in the Franklin journal on the method of finding the hydraulic lines.[28]

He resided several years in America and married his wife at Rocky hill near Princeton N.J. I was also introduced to Mr Brama the son of the celebrated inventor of the water press which bears his name.[29]

I forgot to mention that at 3 oclock I attended in the theatre of the Royal Institution a lecture on English poetry by Wordworth the Poet author of Satan and many other poems.[30] His lecture was highly interesting, and although the voice of the speaker was feeble he was distinctly heard. M[r] W appears about 50 or 55. His head is somewhat bald and quite white. He is tall and thin. He gave a definition of poetry, although this was his second lecture, said that it was intended to embalm noble thoughts in imperishable words. The ideas not the only thing to make poetry the method of expres-

---

Brunel was employed to build an arsenal and cannon foundry and to plan defenses in the channel between Staten Island and Long Island. *DNB.*

[26] Robert R. Livingston, *Henry Papers, 1:*7n.

[27] John Isaac Hawkins (1772–1855) left England at an early age to study medicine in the United States, but changed to the study of mechanical pursuits. He returned to England where he worked as an inventor, patent agent, and consulting engineer. He invented the pentagraph, a copying device. He returned to the United States in 1848 seeking more favorable financial conditions for his inventing. He had joined the Institution of Civil Engineers in 1824. *Minutes of the Institution of Civil Engineers,* 25:512–514.

[28] "On an Effectual Method of Cutting Off the Communication between the Damp Foundation of a Wall Built upon a Moist Subsoil, and the Part of the Wall above the Ground; and on a Mode of Securing the Inside of a Wall from Damp Forced through the Brickwork by Driving Rains," *Journal of the Franklin Institute,* 1835, 15:429–430.

[29] Joseph Bramah (1748–1814) took out eighteen patents, including an improved water closet (1778), a hydraulic press (1795) and an ever-pointed pencil. *DNB.*

His son, Francis Bramah (d. 1840), was also a civil engineer. S. P. Bell, comp., *A Biographi-*cal Index of British Engineers in the 19th Century (New York and London, 1975), p. 28.

[30] For some reason Henry appears to think the poet and speaker is William Wordsworth. Indeed the artistic philosophy Henry describes below is similar to that espoused by Wordsworth and the romantics. This passage even led *Coulson* (p. 289) to strengthen his assertions about Henry's "nature worship" and his "fondness for the poets of the Romantic Revival." Wordsworth, however, was traveling on the Continent at the time of the lecture (Edith J. Morley, ed., *Correspondence of Henry Crabb Robinson with the Wordsworth Circle* [Oxford, 1927], *1:*343–346; and Philip Wayne, ed., *Letters of Wordsworth* [London, 1954], p. 225). In fact, the scheduled speaker for April 18 was James Montgomery (1771–1854), who on this date was to deliver the second of six lectures on the Principal British Poets. His lecture on Wordsworth was not scheduled until May 16, but he may have rambled forward a bit in his April 18 segment. (Information from Archives of the Royal Institution.) There is one further complication in Henry's account. The author of the religious poem "Satan" was not the speaker James but the poetaster *Robert* Montgomery (1807–1855). Sir Paul Harvey, ed., *The Oxford Companion to English Literature,* 4th ed. (New York, 1969), p. 555.

sion highly important. Although the ideas were retained, if the method of expressing them were lost all was gone which constituted poetry.

Stated that if one man could transfuse himself into an other man think his thoughts become possessed of his secrets and feelings then perhaps he could describe the peculiar character of the individuals. Poets have the power of transfering them selves into the general characters, &c. I must not attempt to go farther for I find I have no very definite idea of the subject although I was pleased and apparently instructed at the time. His reading from Chaucer was highly interesting although I was somewhat disturbed by the gentleman who sat next to me and consequently could not pay that attention to the discourse which I wished to do.

I forgot to state before that I visited one of the gass establishments of London a few days since.[31] The meters were explained to us by the ade of a glass model which exhibited the interior arrangement of this ingenious instrument with great clearness.

We were also shewn a clock metre attached to the great gasometer[32] for determining the flow of gas per hour. It consisted externally of a large clock face with a smaller face on the lower half against which a pencil is pressed. This face turns with the flow of gas and the pencil is made to move up and down one in every [. . .] by the simple contrivance of connecting the brass stem which carries it with the [?principal] arbour of the clock a little out of the centre thus *a* the arbour *b* the stem fixed excentric to the arbor which consequentally causes the pencil to move in a vertical direction at each revolution. These movements form the ordinates of a curve and

---

[31] Sometime after April 7. Bache and Henry had an appointment with the engineer Lowe to go to the gasworks on April 7 according to Bache's diary entry of that date (printed above), but were unable to keep it. Gasworks were of special interest to Bache, since the Philadelphia gaslight system was being installed at this time with strong support from Bache and other members of the Franklin Institute. See Bruce Sinclair, *Philadelphia's Philosopher Mechanics* (Baltimore and London, 1974), p. 254. This may also account in part for Henry's detailed interest in gas-producing and measuring apparatus. Below, Henry also suggests the applicability of the self-recording feature of gas apparatus to meteorology which, in fact, became an important aspect of that field's instrumentation. Self-registering instruments and graphic recording apparatus had a long history in science and technology, undergoing especially rapid development in the 1830s and 1840s. See H. E. Hoff and L. A. Geddes, "Graphic Registration Before Ludwig; The Antecedents of the Kymograph," *Isis*, 1959, 50:5–21.

[32] Being an important technology of the first half of the nineteenth century, gas instrumentation received detailed treatment in the technical literature. See Samuel Hughes, *A Treatise on Gas-Works* (London, 1853), p. 250, which details the gasometer. William Matthews, *A Compendium of Gas-Lighting* (London, 1827). Samuel Clegg, *A Practical Treatise on the Manufacture and Distribution of Coal-Gas* (London, 1859). As usual, the eighth edition of the *Britannica* (s.v. "Gas-Light") has a superb technical discussion.

the rotatory motion of the smaller face the abcissa. A series of curves are thus formed on the disc and by the form of these the quantity of gas is determined which flows in per hour. Thus a & b being the two consecutiv vertices of two curves the distance of these apart measured by divisions on the circumference of the disc gives the quantity required.

The gas holders excited my astonishment by their immense size. They are made of wrought iron plates rivited together and supported by a large chain passing over a pulley. I was shewn a kind of gasholder called the telescope holder on account of its drawing out like that instrument.

This will be understood by the figure in which a represents the upper and b the lower vessel. The former of these has a flange turned up so as to form a circular trough around the lower rim of the whole vessel. The under or outter tank has a flange some what similar on its upper edge but turning downwards and inwards so as to catch into the grove of the other one and be with it drawn up after the upper one has attained the proper elevation.

This is a very ingenious contrivance to save room but would scarcely answer in our country on account of the difficulty in preventing the water from freezing in the grove for it is filled with this fluid in order to form a water joint.

The gas of this establishment and indeed of all in London is formed of the bituminous coal. It is made in long retorts the section of which at right angles to the axis is in the for[m] of a D thus ⌓ and hence this retort is called the D retort. They are formed of cast iron solid at the farther end and open at the front by a full orrifice which is closed after the charge is put in by a plate and gallows screw of this form. The charge is given to the retort by a long shovel or scop in the form of a trough or rather box augre. This is filled with coal raised to the mouth of the retort by three men two at the end next the retort and one at the handle. The scoop is then shoved in so that its end touches the back of the retort then turned bottom up and immediatly withdrew.

To deliver the gas in proper quantities through the city the pressure must be varied according to the distance the ascent or decent and also at different times of the 24 hours. These pressures are regulated by experience and observation. And to determine with accuracy the amount of pressure and to vary it at will there is a revolving cylender with a paper around it against which a pencil is pressed. The cylender revolves by the clock shewing the hours in perpendicular lines and the pencil is attached to a tube which is connected with the interior of the gasometer and indicates the variation of pressure by rising and falling.

The pressure is then regulated by the attendant who opens or shuts the pipe of discharge by a valv cock.

The several articles in this establishment for registering the several operations are really beautiful and some of them might with success be introduced into the Science of Meteorology.

We afterwards visited the manufactory of these articles and were shewn the different processes of making the meters & other registers. In this establishment much use is made of a water joint for uniting the pipes of a gas burner which require often to be seperated. The joint is thus constructed an outter tube *a* filled with water and surrounding the gas pipe *d* which rises with in to nearly the top of the outer tube. On this a medium tube is placed with its mouth downwards and its upper end terminating in the other part of the gas tube. This of course can only be used with gases of small pressure. The tube however may be made two feet high and if formed of glass and filled with quick silver instead of water might in some phil. exp be useful.

We were shewn at this place a new but not an improved form of the rain gage. It consisted of a funnel *a* under which a hydraulic balance was placed and this connected with a train of wheels similar to those of the gas metre. The sand falling into the funnel and through that into the ballance below causes it to oscillate and the number of these are registered by the wheel indices. The form of the balance is well known   a trough with a partition *a* in the middle. When one half of the   vessel is filled the one end desends, the water then is thrown out the other side fills and it desends and so on.

286

FROM CHARLES BABBAGE
Henry Papers, Smithsonian Archives

[April 19, 1837]

HENRY'S EUROPEAN DIARY
Henry Papers, Smithsonian Archives

April 19th [1837] Visited with Prof Bache and Mr Solly the second largest brewing[1] establishment in London the celebrated Whitbreads[2] being the

---

[1] By the late eighteenth century, brewing was viewed as a prime example of the application of scientific techniques and apparatus to industrial purposes. Increased accuracy in measurement had led to the establishment of standards and the ability to predict, within limits, the quality of the product. One observer in 1838 went so far as to call the brewery a "chemical laboratory."

The English brewery differed from its counterpart in the United States in a number of ways. One was size. The production of a major English brewery was about ten time that of the largest American breweries of the day. As a result of their great size, the English breweries were highly mechanized, having adopted steam power during the period 1784–1800. Since it was not until 1850 that the production of American breweries regularly surpassed the 20,000 barrel mark—the point where it was economically practical to turn to steam power —steam engines did not appear in American breweries, with few exceptions, until after that year. In general, the American brewing indus-

fourth. It belongs to the firm Truman Hanbury Buxton[3] &c. Some idea of its extent may be formed when it is mentioned that 300000 barrels of ail[4] are brewed yearly that 300 men are kept constantly employed also 120 of the large horse only seen at London.

The establishment contains 100 vats each on an average of the capacity of 1000 barrels. During the season on an average nearly 3000 barrels are brewed daily. Besides the man and horse power above mentioned there are also two steam engines one of these a beautiful machin of 50 horse power on the low pressure principle. The coppers of this Brew house are constructed with a pan on the top so as to heat water by the escaping steam.

 Thus in the figure a is the boiler or copper as it is called the vessel above the pan and e a tube with a cover at top passing through the pan and opening into the atmosphere. d d are two tubes bent downwards from the upright tube so that their mouths will be below the water in the pan and when the mouth of the large tube is closed the steam which rises from the copper below will pass into the water above and thus raise it to the boiling heat by the vapour which would otherwise escape.

---

try was a half century behind the English throughout the first half of the nineteenth century.

Peter Mathias, *The Brewing Industry in England, 1700–1830* (Cambridge, England, 1959), pp. 63–65, 78–96; Stanley Wade Baron, *Brewed in America: A History of Beer and Ale in the United States* (New York, 1972), pp. 160–161.

[2] Samuel Whitbread, Sr. (d. 1796) took over a small brewery in 1742. During the last third of the eighteenth century Whitbread's became one of the leading producers of porter in London. The brewery became celebrated when George III acknowledged Whitbread's preeminence by honoring the brewer with a royal visit in 1787. Not only did the King come, but accompanying him were the Queen and three princesses. Figures for 1830 show that this brewery was responsible for about 9 percent of all the strong beer produced in England that year. Mathias, *Brewing Industry in England*, pp. 11, 26, 277.

[3] Joseph Truman, Sr. (d. 1721) had begun brewing in London as early as 1683. Sampson Hanbury became a partner in 1790, while Hanbury's nephew, Thomas F. Buxton (1786–1854, *DNB*), a leading figure in the antislavery movement, joined the firm in 1811. In 1830

the firm produced approximately 10 percent of England's strong beer. Unlike Whitbread's, which went into a relative decline during the first half of the nineteenth century, Truman, Hanbury & Co. improved its position. By 1853 Whitbread's had fallen to fifth place among London breweries; Truman, Hanbury & Co. was number one. Mathias, *Brewing Industry in England*, pp. 26, 263, 294–298; *Encyclopaedia Britannica*, 8th ed., s.v. "Brewing."

[4] The brewery Henry was visiting did not produce ale. Porter, the thick, black brew popular in London, was the output of large London breweries such as Whitbread's and Truman, Hanbury & Co. Ale, a clearer and lighter drink found primarily outside London, was brewed by the smaller breweries, especially the provincial ones. Since Henry did not drink, he may not have been aware of the difference.

In the United States porter had never become very popular. Americans preferred ale, at least until they were introduced to German lager beer in the 1840s. By the coming of the Civil War German lager had become America's favorite brew.

Mathias, *Brewing Industry in England*, pp. xvii, 25–26; Baron, *Brewed in America*, pp. 58–59, 149–150.

To determ the quantity of water or fluid in the copper a float of stone[5] is counterpoised over a pulley as the float rises or falls an index points out the quantity.

The boilers are furnished with safty and also colapsing valves.[6] The latter being quite as necssary as the former.

The thermometer is lowered into the vat or the copper by means of an implement called by the workmen a lumb.[7] It consists of a tube of copper with a valve in the bottom opening upwards which of course fills with the hot fluid as the vessel is immersed and is drawn up thus filled. The valve is opened by a wire down besid the thermometer.

I observed a very simple contrivance for preventing accidents which I do not reccollect to have noticed in America. The trap door through which the malt is hoisted into the upper story is covered with two valves of thin boards which when shut cover the opening except a small hole through which the rope passes. As the sack or large bag is drawn up it lifts these doors or valves. The bag passes through & the valves fall shut by their own weight. The valves are fastened to the sides of the opening by broad hinges of soal leather. By this contrivance the trap is never open but at the instant of the passages of the sack. The roap used with this trap is formed of raw hide which last an indefinite time.

The water to supply this establishment is pumped by the steam engine and besides the quantity raised to fill the vats &c a large reservoyer is kept constantly full on the top of the house to serve as a head to supp[l]y the engin boilers which therefore have no supply pump and also to wash the tuns vats &c which is done by a hose. The head of water gives momentum sufficient to perform the washing without the aid of a scrub.

This is a great convenience since every part must be kept as sweat and clean as possible to prevent the commencement of the acet[o]us fermentation. Should this commence in the smallest part of a large quantity of the materials it would be propigated through the whole. Does this fact not

---

[5] Most likely a whinstone, a general term for various very hard, dark rocks. Whinstones were frequently used as floats. *Oxford English Dictionary*.

[6] When a steam engine was stopped and the fire put out, steam condensing within the boiler could create a partial vacuum; at such times atmospheric pressure might cave-in the sides of the boiler. To prevent such a collapse, a safety valve was often installed on boilers to allow air to flow in upon the creation of a vacuum, equalizing the pressure. This valve

was in addition to the more common safety valve which released excess steam pressure. Dionysius Lardner, *The Steam Engine Familiarly Explained and Illustrated*, 3d American ed. (Philadelphia, 1838), pp. 124–125.

[7] A very uncertain reading. Searches in contemporary brewers' manuals and technical accounts of brewing, as well as in histories of brewing, have failed to uncover any term which is spelled similarly. We suspect this was a local craft term.

appear as if the molecules of matter were in a very unstable state of equilibrium and that the smallest action commenced at any point of a large mass is sufficient to throw the whole into a new arrangement.[8]

We were much pleased with the stables every part of which is formed of cast iron the floors stalls mangers and all. Each horse has his name painted above his stall and soon learns to know his stable and stall. The Brew horses[9] of England are the largest animals of the hors kind I ever saw and probably the largest in the world. They have immense legs with long hair at the fet lock. Four five and sometimes six of these are fastened to one dray but you often see in the streets one of these immense hor[s]es drawing a little truck just large enough to hold ½ a barrel[10] of beer.

Attached to the stables is the horse hospital where large rooms are provided for the sick with regular vetinary attendance by a person kept constantly imployed for the purpose. These horses are all fed on cut stuff and are never given any soft food. A small steam engine is constantly employed in preparing the fodder. When the horse becomes so old as not to be ablle to do his duty in the dray he is then kept in the yard to hall barrels or to do other light work.

Adjoining the stables we were shown the carpenters shop a long room in which a number of men are constantly employed in making signes. These are painted and lettered in an other place and furnished to the *"Publicans"* who sell the ale of the House. We were informed that not only does the signes thus belong to the Firm but also most of the Public Houses in which ale is sold. The larger the brewing establishment the greater the number of houses it ownes. These houses or stands are let out to persons who can advance a certain sum as a security; the firm then advances the remainder and the Publican is retained as long as he conducts himself properly.[11] Some

---

[8] Others had noted how rapidly fermentation would spread once started and had come to similar conclusions about the unstable state of organic molecules. Justus Liebig, for example, argued that the complex nature of organic molecules left them vulnerable to chemical change. The mutual attraction of the elements of the molecule was very weak; Liebig characterized the resulting equilibrium as passive or static. In contrast, inorganic molecules showed an active resistance to change because of the powerful mutual attraction of their elements. Justus Liebig, *Organic Chemistry in its Applications to Agriculture and Physiology*, 1st American ed. (Cambridge, Massachusetts, 1841), pp. 261–266.

[9] The giant dray-horse was one of the enduring symbols of the large London breweries. Bred from the English black or Shire horse, the brewery dray was considered the finest working horse in London. It was renowned for its size and strength. Mathias, *Brewing Industry in England*, pp. 78–79; Richard Lydekker, ed., *The Royal Natural History*, 6 vols. (London, 1893–1896), 2:501–503.

[10] Breweries made small deliveries, such as half a barrel, with four-wheeled carts called caravans. However, the giant dray-horse was more commonly used to pull a two-wheeled cart which carried three butts (a butt contained three barrels or 108 gallons). Mathias, *Brewing Industry in England*, p. 78.

[11] Establishing a public house in London during the first third of the nineteenth century was a venture requiring considerable capital. Licenses were rare and expensive. In-

ide[a] of the wealth necssary to carry on this business may thus be acquired. The floors of this Brewhouse are all made of cast iron which is cheaper than wood.[12] In some parts of the establishment the floor is reticulated with nobs and in others groved to prevent slipping.

Cast iron is much more used in this country to supply the place of wood than with us.[13] The trusses of the roofs of large houses are all of this material. I forgot to mention in its proper place that roofs are sometimes made of thick sheet iron without rafters. The curve of the roof prevents its sagging being firmly supported by the walls first however rivited to a beam of cast iron which forms the wall plates. Additional strength is als[o] given by

---

coming tenants were required to make a "goodwill" payment in order to secure a lease. Equipment and furnishings had to be purchased. Under these circumstances many prospective publicans turned to the breweries for assistance. In exchange for the promise of all the publican's trade, the brewer either loaned him the capital needed to get started or subleased a public house to him. Although figures are incomplete, by 1830 something around one-half to two-thirds of all publicans were controlled by breweries through either loans or leases.

The signboard with the name of both the public house and the brewer supplying the house dates back to the late eighteenth century. By 1820 the providing of a sign was assumed to be one of the services the brewer supplied to the public houses he controlled. Mathias, *Brewing Industry in England*, pp. 117–138.

[12] Two innovations had lowered the costs of cast iron. The initial breakthrough came in 1709 when Abraham Darby developed a process of smelting iron using coke rather than charcoal as fuel. This freed the iron smelting industry from dependency upon the decreasing wood supply. The second development came in 1828 when J. B. Nielsen demonstrated the efficiency of a hot air blast furnace. With Nielsen's method fuel consumption was cut by over one-third.

It was not only lower cost, however, that made cast iron popular. During the last quarter of the eighteenth century English architects realized that the risk of fire could be lowered and construction made easier if cast iron was substituted for wood. At first the iron was used to replace the wood in a few places where it would not be visible—floor supports and the substructures of roofs. Later, the en-

tire interior skeleton of a building was made of iron. At the apex of the iron age in English architecture—around 1850—cast iron was being used for prefabricated cottages, lighthouses, and churches. Perhaps the supreme example of the use of iron was the Crystal Palace of the Great Exhibition of 1851.

Alan Birch, *The Economic History of the British Iron and Steel Industry, 1784–1879* (New York, 1968), pp. 214–216; Norman Davey, *A History of Building Materials* (London, 1961), p. 214; John Gloag and Derek Bridgewater, *A History of Cast Iron in Architecture* (London, 1948), p. 162; Henry-Russell Hitchcock, *Architecture: Nineteenth and Twentieth Centuries* (Hermondsworth, Middlesex, 1968), pp. 115–129.

[13] Henry was quite correct. Although the first iron-framed construction in the United States occurred in 1820, it took another three decades for the technique to become popular. Militating against the widespread use of iron was the lack of an economic motive—wood remained relatively cheap—and a high failure rate among early American buildings constructed with iron. These failures were caused by American ignorance of the theoretical and practical knowledge of iron construction which had been developed in Europe. When the United States finally did turn to iron in the late 1840s and early 1850s, it was due to a need for more fireproof construction. Devastating fires in New York City in 1835 (for Henry's comments on this fire see *Henry Papers*, 2:490) and again a decade later drove New Yorkers to seek an alternative to wood-framed warehouses. New York became the center of a boom in iron construction. Carl W. Condit, *American Building: Materials and Techniques from the First Colonial Settlements to the Present* (Chicago and London, 1968), pp. 78–86.

corrugating the roof in the direction of the slope. The expansion on account of temperature produces only a slight increase of the height of the roof and also a slight increase of the corrugations or in other words the temperatu[re] is compensated for by the rise of the roof in one direction and the corrugation in the other.

In the brew house above mentioned I observed a contr[i]van[ce] which although simple deserves a notic. It was a kind of a candle stick strapped to the hat so as to give light while the hands are both free to be used. A candlestick with a long wooden handle is also used.

We had an engagement to visit Mrs Sommerville the same afternoon and therefore could not stop more than an houre and a half in the Brew house consequently the establishment was seen but very cursoraly. The vats for fermentation rival those in which King George the 3rd onc dined.[14] They are three in number and when first finished held each 80 persons at circular tables to dine.[15]

In the after noon of the same day visited Mrs Sommerville with Mrs Faraday. She lives at Chelsea Hospital where her husband is a Physician.

Mrs S appears about 45 is a very unassuming and interesting person. She is much carressed by the nobility and gentry. While we were there several persons of these classes came to pay their respects. The room into which we were shewn was hung around with Pictures of various masters and amoung the number some very beautiful landscapes in oil which we were surprized to learn were the production of this most talented individual. She is also well skilled in Music and performs admirably it is said on several instruments.

She has one son[16] by a former Husband[17] a young clergyman the author

[14] If this is a reference to the King's visit to Whitbread's, and we suspect it is, then Henry has garbled the story. The Royal family did dine at the brewery, but not in a vat. They only entered the vat to look around. Edward Holt, *The Public and Domestic Life of . . . George the Third*, 2 vols. (London, 1820), *1*: 299–300.

[15] To have the largest vat in London—and therefore, the world—was a mark of great prestige for a brewery. The size of a vat was measured in terms of its capacity to hold both beer and diners. Richard Meux won the prize in 1790 by erecting a vat which held 10,000 barrels or 200 diners. Five years later Meux topped himself with a 20,000-barrel-capacity vat. The brewers, however, soon learned that construction technology was not on a par with their ambitions. In 1814 a vat at the Horse Shoe Brewery gave way. Perhaps as much as 7,600 barrels of porter were released, destroying the brewery and flooding the surrounding neighborhood. Eight people died as a result of the porter flood. This disaster curbed the competition for great vats. The risk of human and financial loss (the Horse Shoe Brewery lost £23,000 because of the collapse of the vat) was too great. Mathias, *Brewing Industry in England*, pp. 61–62.

[16] Woronzow Greig was educated at Trinity College, Cambridge, then became a barrister of some note. He served as a conduit between the English scientific community and his mother when the Somervilles made Italy their home in the 1840s. Elizabeth C. Patterson, "Mary Somerville," *British Journal for the History of Science*, 1969, *4*:314, 327.

[17] Samuel Greig (d. 1807) was a Russian

of some literary productions. Her present[18] husband has children by an other wife. To one of these, a young lady[19] we were introduced.

Mrs Faraday who accompanied us to Mrs Sommerville's is a plesant unassuming person well read of not much personal pretentions yet with an agreable countenance.

She gave us some anectdotes of her Husband. Said he 45 years old very fond of novels; not desposed to go into company but associates principally with a few persons; denies himself to every person three days in each week; never dines out except when commanded by the Duke of Sussex[20] at the Aniversary of the Royal Institution. Mrs F seldom goes out and see[s] but few persons. She says that she is a good nurse and that Mr. F. puts himself implicitly under her directions. She precribed for my cold &c.

---

naval captain on a training mission in Britain when he met his cousin, Mary Fairfax. On their marriage in 1804 he was appointed Russian consul in London. He was completely unsympathetic with her desire to study science. Martha Somerville, ed., *Personal Recollections, From Early Life to Old Age, of Mary Somerville* (reprint of 1876 ed.; New York, 1975), pp. 73-75.

[18] For William Somerville, see *Henry Papers,* 2:186.

[19] William and Mary Somerville had two daughters: Martha and Mary. Patterson, "Somerville," p. 338. He had had no previous wife.

[20] In a letter to Sir John Rennie, dated February 26, 1835, Faraday rejected an invitation with words which confirm the truth of Mrs. Faraday's remark to Henry: "I never dine out except with our Presidents—the Duke of Sussex or the Duke of Somerset whose invitations I consider as commands." L. Pearce Williams, ed., *The Selected Correspondence of Michael Faraday,* 2 vols. (Cambridge, England, 1971), *1*:290.

HENRY'S EUROPEAN DIARY

Henry Papers, Smithsonian Archives

April 20th [1837] Visited by invitation the celebrated Blue coat school or as it is sometimes called Christ church Hospital.[1]

This Institution was founded in 1553 by the young King Edward the 6th who died before the age of 16. It now contains 720 boys from the age of 7 to 18. These are designed for the Army the navey, the church. They are

---

[1] From Bache's diary account of this visit, we know that Henry and Bache were accompanied by William Vaughan, a governor of the institution. Bache's longer and more colorful version is in the Rhees Collection, Huntington Library (RH 809); a copy, not in Bache's handwriting, is in the Bache Papers, Smithsonian Archives. For Bache, this visit was part of his survey of European educational institutions. He published an account of the school in his *Report on Education in Europe to the Trustees of the Girard College for Orphans* (Philadelphia, 1839), pp. 65-82. For more information, see *The Christ's Hospital Book* (London, 1953).

drawn from among the lower classes principally by the patrons or governors of the establishment of whom there are about 500.

The pupils are found in every necssary and are permitted to visit their parents only occasionally. They ware a most grotesque costume the same as that used at the founding of the Institution nearly 300 years ago. It consi[s]ts of a long blue gown or coat strapped around the waist with a red belt. Under this is a yellow petticoat or kilt which reaches below the knee and under this again short bretches with yellow stockings and shoes; but the most singular part of the costume is the cap which is about the size of a tea saucer placed on the top of the head when worn but most generally carried in the pocket.

The whole costume partakes of the dress of the monks of the middle ages. The boys are under the care of the matrons one of whom has the charge of a ward containing from 20 to 30 boys.

We were present at dinner, a very interesting spectacle more than 700 boys of nearly the same age all dressed exactly alike in a long Hall. At the noise of a blow on a table they all came to order with their faces in one direction. At an other signal a larger boy commenced reading a portion of scripture from a pulpit. They next sang all in concert and at an other stroke of the hammer they all as with one impulse fell on the knees and with crossed hands said a prayer. After this the meat and soup were served.

We were conducted over every part of the Institution, shewn the kitchen the sick wards the dormitories &c.

The kitchen is filled up with bakers on the plan of count Rumford made of wrought iron of the same form as the old ones at Princeton college except that the iron is much thicker being plates nearly $\frac{1}{8}$ thick. There is a hole in the front to admit the air and another at the back to produce a draft across the meat since it is found that the air is necessary to give meat a good flavour in the process of roasting.

In this kitchen there is a strange mixture of good and bad arrangements, old plan mixed with new; the old however predominating. The sick boys are seperated from the others and placed in what are called the sick ward where they receve constant attendence from Matrons each of whom have charge of a certain number. Every part of this necssary appendage to the establi[sh]ment is kept in most excellent condition as regards cleanliness warmth and ventillation. The boys are in general under better treatment when sick here than if with the parents. The sleeping rooms contain small beds placed in rows very near to each other. The bead steads are of iron with wooden bottoms. At the foot of each is a small chest for any article the individual may possess not of the cloat[h]ing kind.

Near the sleeping rooms are the washing appartments. They are furnished with troughs extending 30 or 40 feet into which by two cocks at the upper end hot and cold water is admitted, the temperature being thus regulated according to the state of the weather. There are no wash bowls but each pupil has a fasset which he lets run while washing. The water falling on his han[d]s is thus always clean and is found better than using a bowl. In some of the rooms each boy has a small wash cloath made of flannel with a loop to hang it to a nail. The Privey has a constant stream of watter running through it by which the whole is kept clean. A long trough passes the whole distance of a long range of seats and by this simple contrivance produces an important result.

The remainder of this day was spent until 11 o'clock at the meeting of the Royal society. The Earl of Burlington was in the chair. This person is quite a young man a collateral descendant of the celebrate[d] Cavendish who was his grand uncle; he is spoken off as the next president of the Royal Society.[2]

I should have mentioned that we took a seat in the Antiquarian Society which meets in the same house previous to going to the Royal Society. The Earl of Aberdeen was in the chair and presided with much dignity. A paper was read on some points of English history.[3]

In the Royal Society a paper from Capt now Major Sabine was read on the character and labours of David Douglass the bottanist who died in an attempt to explore the country around the Columbia river.

This communication was quite interesting. It stated that Mr Douglass qualified himself to observe Astronomical and Magnetic phenomena by a

---

[2] William Cavendish (1808–1891), later founder of the Cavendish Laboratory, had become the second Earl of Burlington upon the death of his grandfather in 1834. His great-grandfather was a cousin of Henry Cavendish (1731–1810, *DSB*). Having graduated from Trinity College, Cambridge, as second wrangler in 1829, Cavendish served various constituencies in the House of Commons and took an active interest in politics until the death of his grandfather entitled him to a seat in the House of Lords. Cavendish turned from politics to concern himself with railways, the iron and steel industries, and agriculture. He was also involved in education, serving as Chancellor of the University of London from 1836 to 1856 and of Cambridge University from 1861 until his death. In 1858 he became sixth Duke of Devonshire.

At this time Cavendish was a Vice-President of the Royal Society, having been elected a Fellow in 1829. He never served as President; the next President, succeeding the Duke of Sussex in 1838, was Spencer Joshua Alwyne Compton, Marquis of Northampton.

DNB. Proceedings of the Royal Society, 1892, *51*:38–41.

[3] George Hamilton-Gordon (1784–1860, *DNB*), fourth Earl of Aberdeen, served as President of the Society of Antiquaries from 1812 to 1846. Bache's diary (Bache Papers, Smithsonian Archives) identified the paper read at this meeting as a manuscript account of Perkin Warbeck (*DNB*), a fifteenth-century pretender who proclaimed himself Richard IV and was subsequently hanged.

laborious application to the study of practical mathematics under Capt Sabine himself for three months previous to his departure.[4]

After the meeting I was introduced to Capt Sabine and have promised to Breakfast with him on Monday at 10 o'clok.[5]

I had some conversation with an Irish Gentleman who informed me that he had been engaged in some experiments on the vegetation of the crypto-

[4] Sabine's report on Douglas was prefixed to a paper on Douglas's explorations entitled "Observations Taken on the Western Coast of North America." The presentation by Charles Grant (1778–1866, *DNB*), Baron Glenelg, continued into the next meeting on April 27. An abstract is printed in *Proceedings of the Royal Society, 1830–1837, 3:471–472*. Sabine's manuscript is in the Royal Society.

David Douglas (1798–1834, *DNB*), discoverer of the Douglas fir, explored extensively in North America on several trips under the auspices of the Horticultural Society of London. His first trip in 1823 was to the east coast. In 1824 he left for the northwest where he explored around the Columbia River before crossing the Rockies and returning to England via Hudson's Bay in 1827. It was before leaving on his third trip in 1829 that Douglas was instructed by Sabine in making geographical, meteorological, astronomical, and terrestrial magnetism observations. On this trip Douglas returned to the Columbia River area but also spent a year and a half in California and several months in the Sandwich Islands. On his second trip to Hawaii in the summer of 1834, on the way to England, he was gored to death by a wild bull. A biography of Douglas by A. G. Harvey, *Douglas of the Fir* (Cambridge, Massachusetts, 1947), describes his explorations in detail.

Although many of Douglas's collections and papers were lost in a canoe accident, Sabine had received the surviving volumes of observations including those on astronomy, terrestrial magnetism, meteorology, and geography.

[5] Henry had long been aware of Edward Sabine from his own work in terrestrial magnetism (see *Henry Papers, 1:*290, 291, 336, 338). Sabine (1788–1883) was active in the British scientific community for over fifty years. He was an army officer and an explorer, a physicist specializing in terrestrial magnetism, an administrator of the British Association and the Royal Society, and a prolific author of government reports as well as other publications.

Born in Dublin, educated at Marlow and Woolwich, Sabine was commissioned an officer in the Royal Artillery in 1803 and remained in the Army, with regular promotions, until his retirement in 1877. He was able to pursue a scientific career at the same time by being granted, in 1827, a leave of absence provided he was not needed for military service. He had served as astronomer on the Ross and Parry Arctic expeditions of 1818 and 1819–1820. In 1821–1823, on two separate journeys, he conducted experiments to determine the variation of pendulum vibrations in different latitudes, first in areas including Sierra Leone and the West Indies and later in the North Atlantic, including New York and Greenland. In 1825 he had joined John Herschel in determining by rocket signals the difference in longitude between Paris and Greenwich.

For the first half of the 1830s Sabine was on military duty in Ireland. Even during this period he participated in a magnetic survey of the British islands which was soon extended to Scotland and England. In 1836, he and Humphrey Lloyd and others on the Royal Society's committee on physics worked out the details of a network for terrestrial magnetism observations, specifically in response to a stimulus from Humboldt but generally as part of a previously launched, well-coordinated movement. See Henry's diary for April 21, 1837, footnote 22, printed below.

Sabine served as General Secretary of the British Association (1839–1859, except 1852 when he was President), as Foreign Secretary of the Royal Society (1846–1850), as Treasurer (1850–1861), and as President from 1861–1871.

Sabine's wife from 1826 was Elizabeth Juliana Leeves (1807–1879). She not only aided him in his scientific work but translated several scientific works including Humboldt's *Cosmos* (4 vols., London, 1849–1858).

DNB. The *DSB* account by Nathan Reingold, based largely on manuscript sources, discloses the politics of Sabine's many activities and associations. The surviving correspondence between Henry and Sabine dates almost entirely from Henry's Smithsonian period.

gamia excluded from the air. These plants were put under an air pump glass which was puttied to a board and suffered to remain thus cut off from the ambient atmosphere. They grow beautifully and present many interesting appearances.[6]

[6] We do not know the identity of the Irish gentleman. There was a great deal of interest among British botanists at this time in a plan for growing plants under glass. Nathaniel Bagshaw Ward (1791–1868, *DNB*), discouraged in his attempts to grow healthy plants in a smoky environment, stumbled on the process in 1829 and found he could grow healthy plants under glass for long periods of time without water. The technique was especially useful for transportation of plants on long voyages through great extremes of temperature. In 1836 the British Association named a committee to investigate Ward's plan and in 1837 the results appeared in "Reports on the Subject of the Growth of Plants in Closed Glass Vessels," *BAAS Report, 1837* (1838), pp. 501–508.

ALEXANDER DALLAS BACHE'S EUROPEAN DIARY

Copy, Bache Papers, Smithsonian Archives

Friday April 21st [1837]. This morning Henry & I set off at nine for Woolwich. The little steam boat carried us down by the help of the tide, but against the wind in an hour & 20 minutes, stopping several times for passengers who were brought off in small boats. Our boat was probably 80 ft. long & about 12 broad. The wheels placed over the guard,[1] two cylinders & cranks at right angles: the crank 30 in. diameter, pressure of steam _____ paddles[2] _____. A shilling carries you to Woolwich, 8 miles in the best cabin, & 6^d on deck. A harper & his boy amused us in passing down & collected pence for *his* passage. The Thames wherry is a beautiful boat, so sharp at both bow & stern & sitting so lightly upon the water, one man propels it with ease. The luggers are peculiar—no bowsprit—a spritsail—a little sail aft upon close to the rudder. Flat with keel boards. Looking somewhat thus in full rig.[3] Black with smoke, & red with vermillion a favorite colour. Strangely shaped vessels of foreign build are to be seen at some of the wharfs, or lying in the stream, & this with the docks, the red cross fl[4] presents the most foreign picture which I have seen. On this trip the bridges are seen to great advantage. Of all I like the Waterloo with its elliptical arches best: the London with its large arc of a circle next, & the Southwark of cast iron & small portion of an arc of long radius, least of all. The columns

[1] The copyist may have originally written "gunnels."

[2] The spaces after "steam" and "paddles" may have been left for figures.

[3] Here the copyist left a space for the drawing but did not copy the drawing.

[4] This word is not complete in the copy.

on the sides of the piers of black friars bridge & the Waterloo, are very ornamental. In passing under London Bridge the pipes of the steamer has to be slightly lowered which is accomplished by a joint in the upper part[5] on a hinge, acted upon by a lever or sort of yoke which came down on each side of the chimney & was firmly chained below so as to prevent any disturbance by the action of the wind.[6] The captain stands on the wheel guard, & word is passed to the Engineer below by a boy standing at the gangway: "stop her," "Easy," "back her," & all is done. On reaching Woolwich I found it quite new & uncomfortable to trust to Henry's "locality" which is small, but by dint of asking we got upon the common & to Mr Christie's which is one of a row of houses skirting it to the East. He had gone to town, but we were fortunate enough to meet Dr Gregory who was most kind & communicative. Henry had already made a favourable impression on both the D^r & his wife, whom we saw in due course.

[5] This copyist left a small space here, perhaps for a sketch.

[6] A space for a drawing was left after this word.

HENRY'S EUROPEAN DIARY
Henry Papers, Smithsonian Archives

April 21st [1837] Went with Prof B to woolwich[1] to meet Mr Christie; did not find the gentleman at home. Called on Dr Gregory; was very kindly received. Was shewn the parts of the establishment open to Foreigners. If however we get a letter from our Embasidor we can get in without difficulty. We wer shewn the lecture room occupied by Mr Faraday and Dr Gregory. The apparatus was not visible except some few articles which had been constructed by the celebrated Simpson:[2] one of these an instrument for illustrating the doctrine of projectiles by spouting fluid; the other a machine for showing the direction of a cannon ball the ordinates of which wer peces of brass wire suspended from a ruller.[3] The several wires being once cut to the form of a parabola retained that shape at every movement of the brass ruller which indicates the direction of the piece of ordinance.

[1] For Henry's previous trip to Woolwich, see his diary entry of March 24, 1837, printed above.

[2] Thomas Simpson (1710–1761; *DSB* and *DNB*), British mathematician, was appointed Professor of Mathematics at Woolwich in 1743. Though Simpson was interested in the application of mathematics to problems in mechanics, we have found no specific references to the apparatus described here by Henry.

[3] We assume that Henry means "ruler."

Dr G informed us that the now common experment of the whirling ring taking a horizontal position was a discovery of the Reve Mr Cartwright and was communicated by him to Dr Garnet who afterwards went to America and resided at New Brunswick.[4] Dr Gregory shewed us several very interesting autographs, among the number one from Dr Hutton,[5] the autograph of Sir Isaac Newton which was an order for a [?sum] on the West India [?dock] called the bubble.[6]

Dr G gave us some interesting anecdotes relative to his coadjuters. Stated that he had reccommend Prof Barlow to his present situation. That he had taken an active interest in the exp on the attraction of soft iron and the deviation of the compass on ship board. That Dr Young was opposed to Mr Barlow for some aristocratical or other motives and wished to keep the merits of the discovery in the background.

Dr G managed to get the ear of Davies Gilbert and succeeded in getting Mr Barlow into favour with the board of admiralty.[7]

---

[4] While we have been unable to identify the precise nature of this experiment, we suspect that it was a variant of the demonstration in *Henry Papers*, *1*:274. The Reverend Cartwright indicated as the discoverer of the experiment may have been Edmund Cartwright (1743–1823: *DNB*), the reputed inventor of the power loom, and an ordained minister. Cartwright's activities embraced a wide variety of experiments and inventions, although we have no evidence of work in this particular area.

John Garnett (ca. 1748–1820) emigrated to America from England shortly before 1800 and settled in New Brunswick, New Jersey. He was active in mathematics, natural philosophy, and especially astronomy, and was a member of the American Philosophical Society. We have been unable, however, to discover anything linking Garnett to either Edmund Cartwright or the whirling ring. Clark A. Elliott, *The American Scientist, 1800–1863; His Origins, Career, and Interests* (Ph.D. dissertation, Case Western Reserve University, 1970), p. 305. New Jersey Historical Society, *Proceedings*, 1921, n.s. 6:18–20.

[5] Charles Hutton (1737–1823; *DSB* and *DNB*) was Professor of Mathematics at Woolwich from 1773 until 1807. *Henry Papers*, *1*: 247.

[6] We have been unable to make sense of this passage, which contains several doubtful readings. The West India Docks, the first of the large nineteenth-century dockyards constructed on the Thames to accommodate London's expanding commerce, were not opened until 1802, but Henry is perhaps using the term generically to indicate the location of the West India trade in Newton's day.

[7] Peter Barlow's study of compass deviation on shipboard, published in 1820, won him considerable fame. His correcting plate, which was ultimately adopted by the Admiralty as the best solution to the problem, is described in considerable detail by Henry later in this document. Henry had been familiar with the correcting plate at least since his teaching days at the Albany Academy, when it appeared as a lecture topic in the notes for his course on natural philosophy. *Henry Papers*, *1*:467.

The British natural philosopher, physician, and Egyptologist Thomas Young (1773–1829; *DSB* and *DNB*) was Secretary of the Board of Longitude, the body responsible for directing inquiry and advising the Admiralty on all scientific questions concerning navigation, from 1818 until 1828, and would therefore have had a key role in any decision regarding an issue as important as compass correction. Young's personality seems vulnerable to Gregory's charge of "aristocratical" behavior. According to the *DSB*, Young, though brilliant, lacked "sensitivity, in his professional relations, to other people's emotions or differing perspectives. In his professional life he seems to have been formal almost to coldness and self-assured almost to be cocksure." Specifically, during his tenure as superintendent of the *Nautical Almanac*, an office which he held concurrently with his post at the Board of

Barlow has more genius but less patience than Mr Christie; rather too hastey in jumping at conclusions. After taking dinner with this kind and interesting old man and his amiable lady we called on Mr Barlow.

He said that he had just been reading Mr Bonycastles letter of introduction for me[8] and had expressed his surprise to his daughter that I had not again visited Woolwich.

He is now engaged by the government on the surveys of rail roads in Ireland.[9] Showed us his globe around which the spiral wires are wound to show the probable electrical origin of the magetism of the earth. The globe is one of about 13 inches in diameter and the wires covered with the paper. Mr Sturgeon's method is an improvement of Mr B.s.[10]

He also showed us his correcting plate. It consits of two plates of sheet iron about 1/10 of an inch in thickness and 16 inch in diameter. These are screwed together with a disc of wood between and a brass collar in the axes by which it is fastened in its proper position behind the compass.

All the plates used by the admiralty are passed through his hands and their action on the needle determined.

Miss Barlow a plesant intelligent lady assists her Father in all his investigations and makes all the tables for the corrections by means of the

---

Longitude, Young antagonized much of the astronomical community (and particularly Francis Baily) by his insistence that the *Almanac* remain primarily nautical, rather than astronomical, in orientation.

On the specific issue of Barlow's correcting plate, however, we have found nothing to support Gregory's contention that Young attempted to block its acceptance by the Admiralty. Indeed, in 1821 Young wrote to Sir John Barrow, Secretary of the Admiralty, recommending the award of £500 to Barlow "in consideration of the practical utility of his invention of a plate of iron to be so placed as to compensate for the magnetic attraction of the ship" (Wood and Oldham, p. 307). Whether this was genuine enthusiasm on Young's part, or merely graceful resignation to a *fait accompli*, is impossible to say, however. Alexander Wood and Frank Oldham, *Thomas Young, Natural Philosopher, 1773–1829* (Cambridge, England, 1954), pp. 303–316. George Peacock, *Life of Thomas Young* (London, 1855), pp. 356–366.

Davies Gilbert (1767–1839) was born Davies Giddy but adopted his wife's name in 1817. A member of the House of Commons from 1804 until 1832, and a participant on numerous boards and commissions, Gilbert used his considerable wealth and influence to become a leading promoter of the cause of science and art in Britain. From 1827 until 1830 he served as President of the Royal Society, in which capacity he nominated the writers of the eight Bridgewater Treatises. As a member of the Board of Longitude, and through his connections in Parliament and the Royal Society, Gilbert would have been in a position to exert considerable influence on Barlow's behalf. *DNB.*

[8] Charles Bonnycastle had written several letters of introduction for Henry to take with him to England. Although we have been unable to locate the letter to Barlow, one from Bonnycastle to John Knowles (February 1837) is printed above.

[9] See above, Henry's European Diary, March 24, 1837, footnote 6.

[10] Barlow's detailed discussion of this experiment is contained in "On the Probable Electric Origin of All the Phenomena of Terrestrial Magnetism; with an Illustrative Experiment," *Phil. Trans.*, 1831, pp. 99–108. For Sturgeon's variation of Barlow's globe, see the next document.

plate. A table accompanies each plate with its action on the needle at different distances below and from the centre of the needle.

The plate is fixed behind the needl when it points du north. The deviation caused, with the distances of the centre of the plate from the centre of the compass, noted and registered. A different distance is then chosen for the same cardinal point and this again registered. The needl is caused to point to some other part of the compass card, when the plate is removed, by turning around the card. The plate is again put in its place, the deviation noted, and the effect again observed for different distances. The table thus constructed is sent with the plate and when the article is to be applyed on ship board the vessel is made to turn on its centre so that it points successively to every part of the horizon. The variation of the compass is noted for each position and when the ship has made a complete rotation the eye is cast over the table thus formed and also the one accompaning the plate. The set of variations of the latter will be found to agree very nearly with the former and the distances corresponding to this gives the position of the plate behind the compass and below it proper for the correction.

Mr B. gave me a copy of one of his printed directions for using the plate.[11] I should have mentioned that Dr Gregory gave each of us a copy of a chart of the curves of ascent and descent of balls fired at different elevations and with different charges of powder. He also showed us a drawing of his balistic Pendulum, the same one figured in the work of Dupan.[12] The same pendulum has lately been repaired and the Dr intends to make some experiments with it as soon as the weather and his health will permit. The amplitude of the arc made by the pendulum after the ball strikes it is noted by a point of steel which just grases an arch on which a coating of tallow and wax is placed so as to leave a trace. Some of the officers have asserted that they could see a faint light along the track of the ball. Dr G. never saw this but as I have before stated could fire powder at the lead face where the ball entred the pendulum.[13]

Our visit to Woolwhich in reference to the persons seen was quite plesant but in regard to the weather was very disagreable. It commenced raining soon after we landed from the steamboat and continued thus until we returned home.

I made some observations on the steam boat which carried us to Wool-

---

[11] A pamphlet bearing the title *Directions for Finding the Local Attraction of Vessels, and for Fixing Barlow's Correcting Plate* is in the Henry Library.

[12] Pierre-Charles-François Dupin, for whom see above, Henry's European Diary, March 24, 1837, footnotes 16 and 19.

[13] For the ballistic pendulum, see above, Henry's European Diary, March 24, 1837, footnote 18.

wich which howe[ve]r are not of much importance. The vessel is quite a small one, has two engines which according to the English method are placed beneath the deck.[14]

The cylenders have each 2½ feet stroke, carry 6 inches of steam, make 35 strokes (double) in a minute. The speed is quite moderate: we were nearly 1½ hours in going the 8 miles, or moved at the rate of about 6 miles per hour.[15]

In the evening of the same day dined by appointment with Mr Baily the president of the Astronomical society.[16]

The party of several persons; among the number was Mr D Morgan,[17]

[14] This was in contrast to the general American practice of placing the engines at least partially above deck. In the United States, where steamboats were employed mostly in river navigation, ship design was dictated by the need for a shallow draught, partly for greater maneuverability but primarily because only the larger eastern waterways were sufficiently deep to accommodate vessels with traditional hulls. This meant that there was simply not room below deck for either cargo or engines and accounts for the familiar multi-tiered superstructures of American riverboats, as designers sought to compensate above the water line for the lost hull space. Furthermore, with the engines above deck the stroke of the piston could be lengthened so as to obtain substantially greater speeds, a crucial consideration for distance-conscious Americans. In England, however, where steamboats were intended primarily for use on the open sea, speed was secondary to the need for seaworthiness, which demanded a deep draught and a large keel. This both allowed space for and made desirable the placement of the engines below deck, since a low center of gravity was generally considered essential to stability. Louis C. Hunter, *Steamboats on the Western Rivers: An Economic and Technological History* (New York, 1969), pp. 65–79, 89–94. Dionysius Lardner (edited by James Renwick), *The Steam Engine Familiarly Explained and Illustrated*, 3d American ed. (Philadelphia, 1838), pp. 242–243. James Renwick, "On the Steam Boats of the United States of America," in Thomas Tredgold, *The Steam Engine . . . ,* 2 vols. (London, 1838), *1*:Appendix VI, pp. 109, 111.

[15] By American standards, this was indeed quite modest. Steamboats on the Hudson River, with which Henry was most familiar, routinely averaged speeds of nearly fifteen miles per hour. James Renwick, *Treatise on the Steam Engine,* 2d ed. (New York, 1839), p. 270. The question of the relative capabilities of American and British steamboats was the source of a confrontation between Henry and Dionysius Lardner at the 1837 meeting of the British Association, for which see below, Henry to Bache, October 1, 1837, especially footnote 14. Ironically, the American edition of Lardner's own work on steam engines contained a note by the American editor, James Renwick, upholding Henry's position in the dispute. Lardner, *The Steam Engine . . . ,* p. 265.

[16] Francis Baily (1774–1844), British astronomer. After a youthful ambition to become an explorer proved fruitless, Baily embarked on a commercial career. Success as a stockbroker enabled him to retire at the age of fifty-one to devote himself full time to astronomy. Baily's work on standards, the ellipticity and density of the earth, solar eclipses, and his many star catalogues is documented in footnotes accompanying Henry's description of his visit to Baily's workship in his diary entry of April 28, 1837, printed below. Baily was active in the Royal Society, the British Association for the Advancement of Science, the Geological Society, and was one of the founders and four-time President of the Royal Astronomical Society. *DSB.* Though not exceptionally proficient in mathematics, his dedication and range of activities made him one of the leading astronomers of his generation. According to the *DNB,* Baily "presents an almost unique example of laborious usefulness to science. More than to any single individual, the rapid general advance of practical astronomy in the British islands was due to him."

[17] Augustus De Morgan (1806–1871) was Professor of Mathematics at University College, London, from 1828 until 1866, except for a

Mr Christie,[18] and a Mr Denison who had spent some years in Canada in the English corps of Engineeres in the construction [of the] Readeau canal.[19]

Mr Baily informed us that he had visited America about 35 years ago and that he had travelled through the woods from Philadelphia to Pittsburgh. Had been with Mr Elicot while making his public survays not as an assistant but fellow traveller.[20] Gave me some account of the experments in vacuo with the ocillations of the pendulum. Promised to devote a morning to exhibiting the apparatus &c.[21]

Had some conversation with Mr Christie on the subject of establishing magnetic observatores to cooperate with those established by Humboldt. The committe of the Royal society will recommend that similar apparatus be forwarded to all the stations. The probable cost will be about 30£s consisting of a barometer, thermometer and variation needle. Many observations are not though[t] advisable to be made at once. Several stations will be formed in Canada and about 3 are wished in the United states.[22]

---

brief interval between 1831 and 1836. In 1865, he became the first President of the Mathematical Society. At the time of Henry's visit, De Morgan was serving as Secretary of the Astronomical Society. *DSB. DNB.*

[18] Samuel Hunter Christie was the only one of Henry's dinner companions who was not at this time a Fellow of the Astronomical Society. He was soon to become one, however, and would later serve as its Vice-President. Royal Astronomical Society, *Memoirs,* 1846, *15*:458, and 1858, *26*:213.

[19] Sir William Thomas Denison (1804–1871), British soldier and colonial governor. Educated at Woolwich, Denison was at the time of Henry's visit employed in making astronomical observations at Greenwich, and in 1838 served on the Council of the Royal Astronomical Society. In late 1837, Denison was placed in charge of the works at Woolwich dockyard by the Admiralty, in whose employ he remained for nine years, first at Woolwich and then at Portsmouth. In 1846, he embarked on a long and distinguished career as a colonial governor in Australia and India. Throughout his life, he maintained a lively interest in scientific matters. *DNB.* Royal Astronomical Society, *Memoirs,* 1838, *10*:446.

As a young man, from 1827 to 1831, Denison served in Canada with the Royal Engineers in the construction of the Rideau Canal. The canal, which opened in 1832, ran from Ottawa on the Ottawa River to Kingston on Lake Ontario, and was intended to provide a water route between Montreal and Lake Ontario

which bypassed the treacherous St. Lawrence River. Robert Legget, *Rideau Waterway* (Toronto, 1955).

[20] Baily sailed for America in October 1795 and spent the next two and a half years in adventurous travels throughout the Ohio and Mississippi Valleys. His account of his journey is contained in *Journal of a Tour in Unsettled Parts of North America in 1796 and 1797* (London, 1856), edited by Augustus De Morgan.

The American surveyor Andrew Ellicott (1754–1820) was at the time of Baily's visit engaged in plotting a road through the Pennsylvania wilderness from Reading to the newly established town of Presqu'Isle (now Erie). Ellicott, who conducted state boundary surveys up and down the east coast, was best known for his work in western New York, and for his role in the mapping of what was to become the District of Columbia. In 1813, he was appointed Professor of Mathematics at West Point, where he remained until his death. *DAB.*

[21] The exhibition took place during Henry's visit to Baily's workshop on April 28, 1837. The pendulum in vacuo is discussed in footnote 5 to Henry's diary entry of that date.

[22] Christie had been active in the support of geomagnetic research for some time. It was his paper on the subject to the meeting of the British Association in 1833, in which he charged that Britain was "the only country in Europe in which [magnetic] observations are not regularly carried out in a national labora-

tory," that helped bring about the magnetic survey of England. S. Hunter Christie, "Report on the State of Our Knowledge Respecting the Magnetism of the Earth," *British Association Report, 1833* (1834), p. 130.

But British activity on the international front awaited a push from abroad. In 1836, at the suggestion of British geophysicist Edward Sabine, Alexander von Humboldt wrote to the President of the Royal Society urging British participation in the proposed worldwide network of magnetic observatories, designed to augment the *Magnetische Verein* which had already been organized by Gauss and Weber in 1834. Christie and Sir George Biddell Airy, the Astronomer Royal, were appointed to co-author the Society's response to Humboldt's proposal, and their report, presented later that year, recommended enthusiastic support. Nevertheless, it was not until 1838 that the Royal Society and the British Association, marshalled by Sabine, John Herschel and Humphrey Lloyd and appealing to patriotic pride as well as the cause of science, succeeded in winning government support for their program of geomagnetic research throughout the Empire. The "magnetic crusade" thus launched represented one of the most significant scientific undertakings of the early nineteenth century, and opened a new era in international scientific collaboration.

In 1838, Sabine and Lloyd met with Humboldt and Gauss in Berlin and Göttingen to coordinate an international program of observations. With British participation, the number of magnetic observatories worldwide grew from approximately twenty in 1835, confined to northern Europe and Russia, to about fifty by mid-century, spread throughout Europe, Asia, Africa, North America, and the South Seas. Using Lloyd's recently constructed observatory at Dublin as a model, British colonial magnetic observatories were established at Toronto, Cape Town, St. Helena, and Hobart Town. With the cooperation of the East India Company, stations were also instituted at Singapore, Madras, and Bombay, and at Simla in the Himalayas. In England, Airy's magnetic observatory at Greenwich was supplemented in 1842 by the foundation of Sabine's facility at Kew under the auspices of the British Association. Meanwhile, in the United States magnetic observatories were established at Cambridge, Philadelphia, and Washington.

At the same time, the British government dispatched Captain James Clark Ross on a four-year expedition of geophysical discovery to the Antarctic, the largest enterprise of its kind yet attempted.

Royal Society *Proceedings*, 1830–1837, *3*: 418–428. *DSB*, s.v. "Sabine," "Lloyd," "Ross," "Humboldt." *Encyclopaedia Britannica*, 8th ed., s.v. "Magnetism," p. 18. John Cawood, "Terrestrial Magnetism and the Development of International Collaboration in the Early Nineteenth Century," *Annals of Science*, 1977, *34*:552, 584–587. S. Chapman and J. Bartels, *Geomagnetism*, 2 vols. (Oxford, 1940), 2:931–935.

HENRY'S EUROPEAN DIARY
Henry Papers, Smithsonian Archives

April 22nd [1837] Agreeably to appointment went to Kings college to make experiments with Prof Wheatstone on the production of a spark from *thermo* electricity.[1]

---

[1] Knowing that electric currents generated heat as they passed through conductors, scientists were anxious to find the reciprocal thermoelectric effect: the induction of electric currents by heat. The discovery was made in 1822 by Thomas Seebeck of Berlin, who joined semicircular pieces of bismuth and copper and applied heat to one of the bismuth-copper junctions. A magnetic needle placed next to the metal ring indicated the flow of current, although Seebeck himself believed a magnetic, not an electric, current was excited. *DSB*, s.v. "Seebeck." Henry carried out occasional experiments on thermoelectricity, both for re-

When I first came to London Mr. Daniell gave me the liberty of using his laboratory and his apparatus for any experiments I might wish to make during my stay. He also informed me that he had been constructing a coil of copper ribbon acording to my plan as described in Sillimans Journal[2] but that the article would not opperate according to the description. I had looked at this coil and supposed that I had detected the cause of failure and as this article was necessary to be used in our attempts to get the spark from the thermo electric pile my first operation was to take it appart and readjust it after working however nearly two hours with the assistance of an operator on trying the coil it was found much to my mortification not to answer better than before. This placed me in rather an aquard position before strangers since the failure would almost lead them to doubt the veracity of my printed statments.

I therefore determined to persevere until I discovered the causes of failure and this I reduced to two namely either the coil was too thin or the insulation not sufficiently perfect. I guarded against both of these in my next attempt by doubling the ribbon and wrapping it with silk and paper with great care.

The length of the coil was however now rather to[o] small and the double strands made somewhat bungling work. I had therefore still some doubts of success and almost regretted that I had attempted to experiment in a strange Laboratory and amoung those to whom I had always looked up as masters in Science.

After finishing the article the 2nd time to my great releave it performed tolerably and although not equal to those I have at Princeton yet sufficiently well to call fourth the admiration of all present. This sucess inspired [me] in taking the lead with the exp on the spark from the thermopile.

The thermoelectric pile produces elect in great quantity but of exceedingly low tension. Many attemps have been made to produce a spark from

search purposes and for lecture-demonstrations. See *Henry Papers*, 2:408, as well as forthcoming volumes of this series. His (undated) lecture notes on thermoelectricity can be found in Box 19 of the Henry Papers, Smithsonian Archives, folder 11 A: "Notes for lectures on Magnetism; on Galvanism, and on Electricity." Henry's lectures incorporated some of the results of the thermoelectric experiments described in this diary entry. Henry noted that the electrical and heat currents flowed oppositely and, on at least one other occasion, he speculated about the causes of thermoelectricity:

It is probable that the action of heat in the development of thermoelectricity is in a measure an accidental effect due possibly to the changes of temperature. The electricity may be produced by the contact of the different metals but the electro motive force being the same at each end no current can take place—by heating however one of the junctures a circulation may be effected.

Notebook [23919], Henry Papers, Smithsonian Archives, p. 204.

[2] "Facts in Reference to the Spark, &c. from a Long Conductor Uniting the Poles of a Galvanic Battery," *Silliman's Journal*, 1835, *28*: 327–331 (abstract of "Contributions II: Spiral Conductor").

it but without sucess.[3] I had attempted it at Princeton and from my previous views and experiments was confident that it could be obtained. I had however no proper apparatus for the attempt as it requires a pile of 30 or 40 elements.[4]

Mr Lukens promised to make one for me and I furnished him with the metal for the purpose but he has never finished the article. When I came to London and was shewn a number of these instruments I immediatly resolved the first leisure moment to repeat the attempt. Mr Wheatstone however informed me a few evenings since that he had seen in an Italian Journal an acount that the spark had been obtained from thermoelectricity by means of a spiral.[5] Dr Daniell thought it would be impossible to obtain it with the means at command. I however prepared the apparatus,[6] made the attempt by holding a hot poker to one side of the pile and ice to the other; the pile, the coil and a small movable piece of wire forming the circuit which could be broken by drawing out the end of the movable wire from the mercury cup. The heat and cold was managed by Prof Wheatstone; the parts of the apparatus was held by Prof Daniell; I managed the wires. All ready. No effect. Again—no effect and again the same result. The other gentlemen now withdrew to another room to inspect some letters. I made a new arrangement of the apparatus, adjusted every part more carefully, called the others, again got all prepared. Prof Wheatstone as before applying the ice and Prof Daniell the poker. 1st attempt no effect perceived. The second a small spark each time I broke the connection. This was seen by all in succession. Bache had arrived just before our first attempt & had gone into another room to inspect the letters above alluded to. He re-

[3] Highly stable but of feeble intensity, thermoelectric currents were capable of exciting the galvanometer and the muscles of a frog, but, in early experiments, failed to produce the common intensity effects of other forms of electricity, such as chemical decomposition, ignition of metals, and sparks. Electrical researchers hoped eventually to achieve all of these effects in order to show that thermoelectricity was not fundamentally distinct from other electricities. For the state of thermoelectric science as of 1832, see P. M. Roget, *Treatises on Electricity, Galvanism, Magnetism, and Electro-Magnetism* (London, 1832), "Electro-Magnetism," pp. 92–97.

[4] See *Henry Papers*, 2:408.

[5] Wheatstone, a leading disseminator of foreign scientific literature, communicated the Italian researches in his article "On the Thermo-electric Spark, &c.," *Phil. Mag.*, 1837,

3d ser. *10*:414–417. Wheatstone reported that Vincenzio Antinori of Florence elicited a spark from a thermoelectric pile with the aid of an electrodynamic helix and magnet. The Florentine physicist reported his results to Santi-Linari of Siena, who reproduced the thermoelectric experiments and published those results along with additional observations in an article for *L'Indicatore Sanese*, 1836, no. 50, the article cited by Wheatstone.

At Bache's urging, the Franklin Institute *Journal* quickly reprinted the Wheatstone piece in its June 1837 number, n.s. *19*:465–467. Bache to Franklin Institute Journal, April 28, 1837, Outgoing Correspondence, Bache Papers, Smithsonian Archives.

[6] A Melloni thermopile was used for the following experiments. The apparatus is fully described below in Henry's Diary of April 26 (first entry), and June 29, 1837.

quested to be called if the experiment succeded. The noise we made on the occasion call[ed] him fourth. He afterwards made much sport with our enthusiasm. Prof Daniell flourishing the poker Wheatstone with the ice and I jumping as he said in extacy. The experiment is however an interesting one and not the less so that we are the first mortals who have witnessed it in England. I was however somewhat vexed at not having the apparatus for making the same experiment two years before in Princeton. The experiment however depends on a principle discovered by me in 1832 published in Sillimans Journal and afterwards in the Transactions of the Amer. Phil. Society. (The influence of a spiral conductor).[7]

Although much fatigued I went with Prof B and Mr Roberton assistant secretary of the Royal Society to a lecture by Mr Sturgeon. We saw nothing very new but were interested in some of his experiments the rotation of zinc by zinc, cast zinc acting as copper rooled as zinc. Amalgamated zinc is the zinc to cast zinc which acts as copper.[8]

Mr S. exhibited a pleasing variation of Mr Barlows exp with the globe

surrounded with wires.[9] The electricity was sent into the coil through the axis. A dipping needle was placed on the top and a small [. . .][10] on each side of this. When the globe was slowly turned round the needles were affected and took a position corresponding with the position of the electro-magnetic poles. The globe was about 12 inches in diameter and covered with copper wire around the temperate zone. A galvanometer was exhibited composed of several [s]trands of copper wire proposed to be used as an instrument of research.

Mr. Sturgeon is a very good experimenter but an indifferent lecturer. He does not use good language and is very obscure in his theoretical notions.[11]

---

[7] "On the Production of Currents and Sparks of Electricity from Magnetism," *Silliman's Journal*, 1832, 22:408; "Contributions II: Spiral Conductor." The principle was that of self-induction. Wheatstone reported the successful outcome of these experiments in "On the Thermo-electric Spark," p. 416, noting that ". . . it supplies a link that was wanting in the chain of the experimental evidence which tends to prove that electricity, from sources however varied, is similar in its nature and effects. . . ." Wheatstone and Henry differed on the extent of the latter's contribution to the successful result. While Henry wrote that he had "prepared the apparatus," "taken the lead" in the experiment, and even found in the results confirmation of his principles of self-induction, Wheatstone merely noted that Daniell, Bache, and Henry had "assisted" in the experiment.

[8] See *Henry Papers*, 2:440n, for Sturgeon's research comparing the galvanic behavior of different forms of zinc. Presumably the rotation was induced in a set of Ampère's cylinders (*Henry Papers*, 1:317n). In *Recent Experimental Researches in Electro-Magnetism and Galvanism* (London, 1830), p. 41, Sturgeon observed that when amalgamated and sheet zinc were in galvanic combination the "amalgamated piece will operate as zinc, and of course the other piece as copper. . . ."

[9] See Henry's entry for the preceding day, above.

[10] One missing word.

[11] Although noted chiefly for his genius at divising scientific and technological instruments, William Sturgeon took a serious interest in uncovering the basic physical causes of

He is however a very industrious person and if he would give his labours to the world free of all speculation he would do well.

He mentioned that a current of elect could be generated in a continuous wire by applying heate to the various parts in succession.[12] From the lecture we returned to the Kings college to see an exhibition of the lime microscope. Got there a little before the close. The apparatus was constructed by Mr Carey[13]—is without a reflector which he sais answers well with the low powers.

Saw an exhibition of the larva of some insects which on the screen were 2 feet long. Imagined them to be microscopic animals was surprised to find they were animals at least an inch in length when viewed by the naked eye.

Larva of insects do not propigate. Their organs not sufficiently developed & in some states of animals of this kind the mail impregnates several generations of suceding females. A fact analogous to that which takes place with a femall of the quadruped which is impregnated by one mail and then by another. The ofspring of the 2nd connection often partakes of character of the first mail.[14]

Returned to Prof. Bache's with Prof Wheatstone. Was shewn an experiment with a feather of some importance to those who stuff birds &c. A common goos quill; the feather of a hen would shew better. Was rumpled so

---

electrical phenomena and did not hesitate to put his speculations into print. Henry's reservations about Sturgeon's theoretical inclinations were shared by others. According to the *DNB,*

> It has been urged against Sturgeon that his work did not result in the discovery of any great generalizations in electrical science. His phraseology, in accordance with ideas current in his day, was from the modern point of view faulty. He spoke of "magnetic effluvium," of "caloric" particle, electrical fluid, and electrical matter.

A comment by Humphry Davy on Sturgeon's scientific style is noted above in Henry's first diary entry of April [8], 1837.

[12] William Sturgeon was a notable contributor to the science of thermoelectricity, especially with regard to homogeneous bodies. Sturgeon's biographer in the *DNB* ranks him as the preeminent authority in thermoelectricity after Seebeck.

[13] See above, Henry's Diary, March 23, 1837 (second entry).

[14] Henry's remarks about inheritance reflected widespread attitudes of the period.

Many practical animal breeders as well as biologists believed in the possibility of "double paternity:" the ability of more than one male to contribute to the offspring of a single female. It was during this period, in fact, that the question of double paternity was being decided, mainly on evidence from plant hybridization. In 1837 and, more definitively, in 1849, the German botanist Carl Friedrich von Gaertner concluded that when a flower is fertilized by a mixture of its own and foreign pollen, no blending of traits occurs in the offspring. The idea that pollen grains operated independently contradicted assumptions of experimenters such as J. G. Kölreuter and T. A. Knight. In the 1840s Nathaniel Pringsheim delivered another blow to double paternity when he denounced the widely held view that more than one antherozoon or spermatozoon is necessary to fertilize a single egg. Robert C. Olby, *Origins of Mendelism* (London, 1966), pp. 44, 52–53. Hans Stubbe, *History of Genetics*, trans. T. R. W. Waters (Cambridge, Massachusetts, 1972), p. 118. We are grateful for the assistance of Frederick B. Churchill of Indiana University, Bloomington, Indiana.

as to be broken in various places and the plumage almost apparently destroyed.

This was then thrown into water near boiling and afterwards dried and thus in a few minutes it was restored to its pristine appearance.

The effect was very striking, and is one I must exhibit to Prof. Jager.[15] Descovered at Manchester accidentally by a bird stuffer.

Prof W also described a number of experiments he had made with a top —a common humming top. If one of these be spun rapidly it will give a sound which will decrease in intensity, afterward increase making an interval of almost perfect silence. This phenomenon he explains by the vibrations within the top interfering with the sound produced by the percussion of the side of the orrifice on the external air. The effect may be varied by making a number of groves on the outside of the top and also by causing a large top of the kind to revolve in a lathe.

In speaking of the lecture on paper making[16] I neglected to mention an experiment to determine the strength of common writing paper. A sheet of this was pasted at its two ends together, a rooler placed then at top and another at bottom. To the lower rooler a cord was attached and this to a large weight (a 56). The same paper had lifted a full sized man.

Among the apparatus at the Royal institution is a small kite which Mr F suspends near the high cealing of the theatre and when the machine has been worked for some time this becomes electrical and a spark may be drawn from any part of the copper wire which comes down to the table.[17]

One room at the Royal Institution contains specimens of minerals &c. Another the mechanical apparatus which was used by Dr Young, and among the articles I reccognized many described in his book. The apparatus for shewing the vibrations with a glass is formed of a common looking glass about 20 inches wide 3 feet long the frame puttied to the glass to prevent leakage. I need scarcely mention that the silvering is removed.[18]

In using the lime microscope common street gas may be substituted for hydrogen but not with quite the same effect.

---

[15] Henry's Princeton colleague, the entomologist Benedict Jaeger (*Henry Papers*, 2: 55n–56n).

[16] See above, Henry's diary entry of April 11, 1837.

[17] Presumably the kite had acquired a static charge by induction from the electrical machine.

[18] We assume that Henry refers to Thomas Young and his *Course of Lectures on Natural Philosophy and the Mechanical Arts*, 2 vols.

(London, 1807), a work Henry cited on several occasions in his scientific notes. Unfortunately, we are unable to find a piece of apparatus in Young's book corresponding closely to Henry's vague description. The mention of vibrations would suggest fluid motion or perhaps optical wave effects. One possibility for the former is a thin plate equipped with an orifice to demonstrate the behavior of a jet of fluid, described in *Young*, *1*: Fig. 255, p. 777.

Cannot the alcohol lamp be applied when gas cannot be procured to the same purpose.

I purchased of Mr Clark[19] a pice of glass on which fine lines are drawn so as to produce a beautiful effect when the cand[l]e is viewed through it— the interference[20]

I was informed by a gentleman at Mr Baileys of a circumstance in reference to the climate of London somewhat singular namely that several animals cannot live in smoke of the metropolis.[21] Swallows beas wasps and other insects. Roes[es] cannot be cultivated. The smoke also destroys the astronomical apparatus exposed to the air.[22]

I have been invited several evenings to Mr Babbages. His house contains many interesting objects among these a very pretty cheap and good lamp. It consisted of a plaster figure of hercules carrying on his sho[ul]der not a globe but a large glass basin filled with water on which a number of floating lamps were placed.

In the room with his machine is placed a portfolio of drawings preserved in a case which when opened forms a support for the paper.

Also a figure of a lady which by wheel work when wound up is made to turn on its foot to nod to the company while a bird on her finger is made to flutter. The motion continues for half an hour. It is a toy constructed by an Italian artist and attracted Mr Babbages attention when he was a lad. Travelling in Italy a few years since he found in some obscure place the same article but much out of repair. He purchased it and set about puting it in order, no very difficult task for the inventor of the calculating machine.

I was also shewn a simple philosophical toy which brought little *Willie* to my mind very forcibly. It consists of a wheel turned by sand falling from a funnel into the buckets; on the out side of the box, containing the wheel, is the figure of a tumble[r] made of past board which turns with the wheel and thus produces a very plesant article with simple means. Cannot the same contrivance be applied to regulate the motion of the lime in using the oxy hydrogen microscope.[23]

Since Mr Babbage's publication of the decline of science[24] he has not much visited the Royal Society. He is now ingaged in writing a work on

---

[19] E. M. Clarke.

[20] The sentence breaks off at this point. Henry bought a diffraction grating. Early studies of the interference spectra produced by diffraction gratings were done by Thomas Young and David Rittenhouse. In the early 1820s, Fraunhofer made the first sophisticated quantitative studies of the phenomena. *DSB*, s.v. "Fraunhofer," "Rittenhouse."

[21] Cf. Henry to Harriet, April 10, 1837, foot-note 3.

[22] Especially susceptible to such deterioration were the metal mirrors commonly used in reflecting telescopes.

[23] On methods of feeding lime to the flame, see Henry's above entry of April 11, 1837.

[24] *Reflections on the Decline of Science in England* (London, 1830) is discussed in *Henry Papers*, *1*:342n–343n.

natural Theology to prove mathematically the posibility of miricles. He has been led to this by the study of the principles of his calculating machine which renders it possible that an exception to a general rule may take place only once and that for ever afterwards the calculation shall proceed as if no such deviation had taken place. The subject is interesting and cannot but be productive of curious results in the mind of such a person as Mr Babbage.[25]

I was informed by Capt Sabine that the government had advanced towards the construction of the machine the sum of 9000£, that 7000 of this sum was expended in the constuction of tools which were invented by Mr Babbage, that a difficulty having arisen between Mr B and his chief workman the latter left the service and on the ground of an old custom of the city of London claimed and got all the tools. The machine cannot therefore go on without a great expendature of money while Mr B will not of course give from his own property.[26] I will probably get some more facts in reference to this machine and note them down.

[25] A work grandly conceived but only partially completed, Babbage's *Ninth Bridgewater Treatise* (London, 1837) was an attempt to bring mathematics to the service of religion. Babbage argued—contrary to Hume—that miracles were not violations of a continuous natural order but rather interruptions in natural events foreseen and entirely foreordained by the Creator. As such, miracles are simply manifestations of a more fundamental, divinely instituted natural order. Babbage attempted to illustrate this truth by making an analogy with certain potential capabilities of his calculating engines. Exceptions to general mathematical rules could be built into a calculating machine such that a machine would operate according to a given rule for, say, one hundred million calculations, generate a single deviation, then return to the original rule for all subsequent operations. Such deviations were not miraculous violations of mathematical law, Babbage asserted, but aspects of a more fundamental law encompassing both the given mathematical rule and the deviation. See especially chapters 2, 8, and 11 of Babbage's *Bridgewater Treatise*. For Bache's impressions of this same work, see below, Bache to Henry, June 7, 1837.

The Babbage treatise reflected a general revival of concern with the problem of miracles in natural theology in the 1830s. The concern was chiefly a reaction to certain problems in natural history and geology, especially the Uniformitarian-Catastrophist debates of the period. The *Bridgewater Treatises* were a central forum for this controversy, whose notable participants included Whewell and Buckland. Cannon contends that Babbage's treatise, a "strictly unofficial contribution to the Bridgewater series" (p. 23), satisfied neither Uniformitarians nor Catastrophists in its attempts to reconcile miraculous discontinuities with the natural order. Walter Cannon, "The Problem of Miracles in the 1830's," *Victorian Studies*, 1960, *4*:5–32.

[26] In 1828 Babbage received renewed support from the Royal Treasury for construction of his calculating machine. Soon after, he and his chief engineer Clement had a disagreement which reached a final impasse when Babbage refused to compensate Clement for having to move his tools and business to government-provided fireproof buildings near Babbage's residence. In retaliation Clement "withdrew his men, carried off (as he was legally entitled to do) the valuable tools made at the expense of his employers, and thus brought about a complete deadlock in the construction of the machine." (*DNB*, s.v. "Babbage," p. 777.) While this project came to a standstill, Babbage's thought began to take a different direction, away from the "difference engine" to a more sophisticated calculator, the "analytical engine." See Henry's diary entry of April 3, 1837, above.

HENRY'S EUROPEAN DIARY
Henry Papers, Smithsonian Archives

Monday April 24th [1837] This morning according to appointment met Capt now Major Sabine at Breakfast[1] at Professor Baches had much conversation on the subject of america magnetism &&.

The Major was in Canada during the war of 1813 & 14. He was at the sortie of Fort Erie and constructed one of the works taken by the americans at that gallant action on the part of our troops.

He was again in america and through the united states in 1821 when he made the pendulum experiments there.

On the subject of magnetism Major S. informed me that a needl might have its axces of magnetism disturbed by placing it on a keeper a little obliquely, but that the proper direction will again return by time.

Prof Bache stated that he had found that the bottom of the vacuum apparatus should be of wood; brass reduces rapidly the arch of vibration. This is in accordance with the experment shewn by Mr Faraday with the vibrating plate.[2]

Major S. reccomends a needle by Gambie[3] of Paris. The cost however is an objection for the artist since his name is up charges 50£s instead of less than ½ that sum which was given for the needle at West Point[4] from the same maker.

On the subject of the dip said that it should be taken at the very spot where the intensity by the vibration of the needle is noted. Local attraction will sometimes make a great deviation in stations only a few yards distant from each other. For the state of New York he strongly reccommended the

---

[1] This appointment was made on April 20, 1837. See Henry's European Diary entry of that date, printed above.

[2] We have been unable to locate such an experiment among Faraday's published papers or in his diary, although we have seen mention made of Faraday's theory of electromagnetic induction as an explanation for the damping of a needle. On the other hand, knowledge that brass could become magnetic under some circumstances and adversely affect a needle predates Bache and Faraday by at least two decades. Peter Barlow, *An Essay on Magnetic Attractions, and on the Laws of Terrestrial and Electro Magnetism*, 2d ed. (London, 1824), pp. 17–18; Tiberius Cavallo, *The Elements of Natural or Experimental Philosophy*, 2d American ed., 2 vols. (Philadel-

phia, 1819), 2:270; John Cawood, "Terrestrial Magnetism and the Development of International Collaboration in the Early Nineteenth Century," *Annals of Science*, 1977, *34*:580–581. For mention of an intentional damping of a needle, see Henry's diary entry of June 29, 1837, below.

[3] Henri Prudence Gambey (1787–1847) was a Parisian precision instrument maker. From 1819 until his death he was recognized as one of the outstanding practitioners of his craft in Europe. *DSB*. Henry and Gambey would later meet during Henry's visit to Paris. See below, Henry's European Diary, June 28, 1837.

[4] Henry probably used this needle in 1833 while making observations of the magnetic dip. *Henry Papers*, 2:60–62.

apparatus of Professor Loyd as being more easily used and in high latitudes more correct[5] giving results comparable with each other. In the method of the horizontal needle[6] a small variation of the dip gives a great change in the number denoting the intensity.

In reference to the variation of the needle no better method could be adopted than that of tracing as correctly as possible a meridian [line] by means of a small transit instrument and then to put the apparatus for the variation on this. To avoid local action the bearing of a distant object should be taken on different parts of the meridian prolonged and also on lateral points a reduction being made for the parallax. If the same result is given then we may presume that there is no local action at that place. It would be important to determine with accuracy the variation at a few places and for this purpose to draw more than one meridian line in the same line and test all the needles by these.

Major S has been engaged in determining the lines of magnetic intensity through Ireland. While on the subject of magnetism I may note that I ought to repeat the experiments of Becquerrell or Quettellet on the weakening influence of a change of polarity on the maximum or saturating power of the magnet. This I could readily doe by means of a coil with a standard battery or one of Prof Daniell's retaining apparatus.[7]

2[nd] visit to the apparatus of the Royal Institution.[8] There are two rooms in which lectures are given one almost a c[e]llar b[e]low the surface of the

[5] For a description of Lloyd's method see above, Henry's European Diary, April 17, 1837. Lloyd showed that for the latitude of Ireland the error in terrestrial magnetic observations with his method was about 0.1 percent. This was an improvement of nearly threefold over previous methods. Humphrey Lloyd, "An Attempt to Facilitate Observations of Terrestrial Magnetism," *Transactions of the Royal Irish Academy*, 1837, *17*:169.

[6] Charles Coulomb devised a method of determining the dip from the ratio of the moment of the weight necessary to bring a needle into the horizontal position to the number of oscillations of that horizontal needle; the tangent of the dip was equal to this ratio. Biot had declared that this method was the most accurate manner of determining the dip. In this he was contradicted by Lloyd who, although impressed by Coulomb's method, raised a number of objections. Lloyd viewed his own method as an improvement upon Coulomb's technique. Lloyd, "An Attempt to Facilitate Observations of Terrestrial Magnetism," pp. 160–161.

[7] Quetelet had discovered that when the polarity of a magnetized needle or bar was reversed, the maximum magnetic force which the needle could acquire was less than when the needle was initially magnetized. Moreover, the maximum magnetic force grew proportionally smaller as the number of reversals increased, although the force eventually converged at a lower limit. Adolphe Quetelet, "Recherches sur les degrés successifs de force magnétique qu'une aiguille d'acier reçoit pendant les frictions multiples qui servent à l'aimanter," *Annales de chimie et de physique*, 1833, *53*:248–284. Becquerel reported Quetelet's work in his *Traité expérimental de l'électricité et du magnétisme. . .* , 7 vols. (Paris, 1834–1840), *1*:377–380.

From Henry's remarks it appears he planned a variation on the Quetelet experiments. The Belgian had magnetized his needles through friction, while Henry is considering using electricity.

[8] Henry had already been shown around by Faraday. See above, Henry's European Diary, April 18, 1837.

street. This is the work Laboratory discribed in Prof Brands chemistry 1st Edition.[9] The furnace given in the plate of that work occupies the middle directlly behind the lecture table. It is on the top about 5 feet long and 3 feet wide covered on the top with an iron plate and contains two sand baths one circular the other oblong 2¼ feet long by about one foot wide. The circular one is of the diameter of the width of the other.

River sand is used to fill the baths which is much cleanner than common sand, the latter produces dust which gets into the precipitate.

The other Laboratory is the one called the theatre and is used for the crack lectures on Friday evening and Saturday afternoon when it is filled with ladies *ie* on saturday after noon. A few females also attend on friday but these are not admitted into the reading room because anatomical specimens are sometimes exhibited and matter discussed improper for a mixed audience.

But to go on with the peculiarities of the lower laboratory which is by far 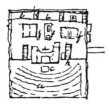 the most interesting since from it have proceeded some of the most important discoveries of the present century. The annexed is a sketch of the laboratory lecture room of the Institution: *a* the part for the audience *d* the lecture table, *e* the furnace figured in Brand's chemistry, *h* furnace under a recess draft downwards, *p* recess for articles, *f* tables.

The table is about 6 feet long 4 or 5 wide with a hollow part for the station of the observer. At the end is a draw board on which gasses for the tests are placed. There are shelves under this table for holding articles. The pneumatic apparatus is the same as that described in Brand but I was surprised at its diminutive size. It is about 3 feet or less long and 18 inches wide with a deep pan at one end. The whole is lined with copper and made by Newman. The tables in the Laboratory have a gutter around the edge for catching the quicksilver. The seats of all the lecture rooms are quite steep and generally covered with green or red cloth. In Kings college the seats have backs the tops of which serve as writing boards for those behind.

The square blocks are used for illustration of the atomic weights in the Royal Institution of about the same size as those used in America by Dr Torrey, ie about 2 inches square. There is however one point of difference —namely the blocks have a thickness such as to represent the combining volumn. This is an improvement.

[9] William Thomas Brande, *A Manual of Chemistry*, 1st American ed. (New York, 1821), pp. vii–viii. Plate I is a floor plan of the laboratory; plate III illustrates some of the apparatus, including the furnaces.

Mr Faraday has finished his course of lectures and his place is now filled by Mr Brand. I had a letter [for] this gentleman from Professor Hare. Was received by him with much kindness. Invited to visit the mint[10] which however is now not in operation. I will therefore defer my visit until I return.[11]

Mr Brand is quite a plesant lecturer; his style is however intirely different from Mr Faraday. He is not as good an experimentor and requires more assistance than Mr F. His language although not as delivered with as much animation is perhaps some what more chaste than Dr F's.

His face is a singular one and could be easily carachtured. There is a dent in the bridge of his nose which appears to have been produced by some accident. He lectured the morning I attended on the approximate principle of vegetable substances[12] and illustrated his subject by some large drawings.

[10] In 1823 William Brande had been selected to conduct an investigation to select the best material for coin dies. His success, although limited, was sufficient to lead to an appointment in 1825 as superintendent of machinery at the London Mint. One of the conditions of his employment was permission to keep his salaried professorship at the Royal Institution.

Brande's relationship with the Mint was modified in 1852 in the wake of the reorganization of the Mint. From 1823 until 1850 the mastership of the Mint had been a political office; masters came and went as governments changed. But in the latter year the position was taken away from the politicians. John Herschel, the first of the nonpolitical masters, initiated a number of reforms, including the prohibition of private work by Mint employees. Brande was appointed first superintendent of the operative department at a raise in salary. In return, however, he was pressured to resign his paying position at the Royal Institution, although he was allowed to remain affiliated through the post of Honorary Professor. John Craig, *The Mint: A History of the London Mint from A.D. 287 to 1948* (Cambridge, England, 1953), pp. 293, 300–301, 317–320, 326–327.

[11] We have no record of Henry ever taking up Brande's invitation to visit the Mint.

[12] Proximate principles were the complex compounds obtained through the chemical analysis of an organism. In turn, the proximate principles could be broken down into the ultimate principles—elements and some simple compounds. There were at least fifteen well-identified categories of proximate principles of vegetables known to the chemists of Henry's day. These include sugar, starch, coloring matter, and wax. Brande, *Manual of Chemistry*, pp. 459–463.

HENRY'S EUROPEAN DIARY
Henry Papers, Smithsonian Archives

April 26[1] [1837] In the evening of monday 24th I called by appointment at the room of Professor Daniell to meet Prf Wheatstone for the purpose of

[1] Unclearly emended by Henry, this dating could be either the 25th or 26th of April. In any case, the content of the entry indicates that it was written retrospectively. It appears that at least two separate occasions are described, an experiment of April 24 and a second one at some unspecified later time, probably at the end of April or early May.

repeating before Dr Faraday the experiment on the spark from thermo electricity.[2]

Two new piles were procured. The thermopile of Meloni was the one used on the other occasion. The two were united together so as to form a single article of larger plates. The spark was readily produced by the ribbon coil[3] but *not by the wire one of Dr Faraday* which consists of large wire ⅛ or more in diameter 72 feet long and coiled round a core of soft iron about 18 inches in diameter. The coil of Dr F gave with the galvanic battery a brighter spark than that constructed by me but not quite so large. I attempted to explain the difference of the action of the two coils in reference to thermo electricity by stating that the thermo current could not produce magnetism and therefore the long coil had no assistance from the iron. To this Mr F objected and said that there was magnetism developed in the iron and that he had often magnetized needles in a small thermo pile.[4] I said that I must certainly doubt the correctness of the experiment, that I had tried it myself.[5] Mr F remarked that he did not know that it was new but that he certainly had magnetized needles at his lectures by means of a single pile. But to put the matter to the test the pile was put in connection with the wires of the large coil containing the core of soft iron. A needle was placed so as to indicate the magnetism of the bar. The heat being applied the needle moved. When the other solder was heated the reverse effect was produced. I was surprised at the result and at the time saw no objection to the experiment but Mr F a few days after[6] when an account of the exps. were about to be published by Mr Wheatstone[7] attempted to magnetize needles by means of a single thermo element and then it struck me that

[2] i.e., the experiments of April 22, printed above.

Michael Faraday's interest in thermoelectricity arose from his concern with the problem of establishing the identity of the various electricities, a major aspect of his experimental program in the 1830s. Chiefly because of their low intensities, thermoelectrical currents presented difficult anomalies. Faraday listed a number of these in his 1833 Third Series of *Experimental Researches in Electricity,* "Identity of Electricities Derived from Different Sources; Relation by Measure of Common and Voltaic Electricity," paragraphs 349, 350, 360. Noting that as of 1833 no spark had yet been obtained from thermoelectricity, Faraday asserted that the lack of a producible spark was not attributable to fundamental differences in kind but to the meager intensities of thermoelectric currents (paragraph 350).

[3] Preserved among the scientific apparatus of Charles Wheatstone at King's College, London, are two ribbon coils attributed to Joseph Henry. It is alleged that these were the coils used in the present experiment. Rollo Appleyard, *Pioneers of Electrical Communication* (London, 1930), p. 104.

[4] Faraday had long believed thermoelectricity capable of producing the usual magnetic effects. In his Third Series, paragraph 349, he wrote that thermoelectricity "was discovered, and is best recognized, by its magnetic powers." In fact, Seebeck believed that thermoelectricity was essentially a magnetic, not an electrical, phenomenon. *DSB,* s.v. "Seebeck."

[5] Records are lacking of any such experiment.

[6] The precise date is unknown.

[7] The publication is discussed in Henry's diary entry of April 22, 1837, footnote 5, above.

there was some doubt as to the correctness of the result since the action of a coil itself would tend to deflect a needle and although there might be a greater action when a core of soft iron was inserted yet this might perhaps be due to the action of the iron in its natural state on the needle. Mr F did not succeed in communicating magnetism to a needle by a simple element whatever he may have accomplished by a pile of a greater number of elements and so far was he convinced of the justness of my chritisism on his experiments at the time that he struck the paragraph out which related to the magnetization of the soft iron although the article for the philosophical magazine was already in type.[8]

---

[8] Although Henry seems to take his vindication somewhat casually, Faraday's retraction must have been rather gratifying in light of past rivalries. We can only guess that Henry was the source of the following news item in the November 6, 1837, issue of the *Newark Daily Advertiser*: "Professor Henry, of Princeton it is stated, attracted much attention in England by performing some electro-magnetic experiments in public, which Mr. Faraday had attempted in vain." In fact, this became part of the heroic mythology of Joseph Henry. Like all mythologies, the story was embellished in ways which enhanced Henry's image as well as the image of American science. Bache, who had apparently witnessed the April 24th encounter, referred to the incident several years later in a speech to the National Institute. Although clearly inaccurate on several points, Bache's version is worth quoting at length for what it reveals of the patriotic sensibilities of at least some leading American scientists:

If the American cultivator of science were less of a patriot and more wrapped up in self he would find his readiest avenue to scientific distinction, by sending his papers abroad, for publication. With the Royal Society stamp or that of the London and Edinburgh journal of science they would return with a currency which neither the American Academy, nor the American Journal of Science could give them. Is this a meet return for days and nights of study and toil and struggle amidst discouragements little to be estimated by the world in general, not to be understood by European men of science who from their position can never feel them. But let me say that this is unjust—it is considering the unknown as the magnificent. If we are apt to underate men whom we are familiar with, so we overrate those who are known only by their fame. In

one case at least I have the best reason for knowing that an American philosopher was able to engage in a keen encounter on his own subject with the most admired of British philosophers and to come off the victor. I witnessed the encounter with mixed emotions; the philosopher was not only a countryman, but a cherished friend. More talent than that evening was collected in the laboratory of King's College does not often come together: there were Daniell, and Wheatstone, and Forbes and Graham, and first among equals Faraday. They came to see the spark from the Thermo-electric battery which was then a new result. Faraday and Henry differed about a result in electro-magnetism, as such men differ, mildly but firmly. Faraday was surely right, and proposed an experiment to prove his correctness: it was tried and succeeded: while trying, Henry pondered and gave his reasons why it was inconclusive. Faraday saw their force, proposed another experiment which with characteristic quickness he put in train, it was again set aside and thus the final examination was adjourned to the morrow, and to the laboratory of the Royal Institution, when, not to detain you longer, Faraday found and admitted that he was wrong.

Manuscript of "The Wants of Science in the United States," delivered at the April 1844 meeting of the National Institute, Bache Papers, Smithsonian Archives. The incident became officially linked with the Henry memory when, in 1880, the physicist A. M. Mayer memorialized Henry with a dramatized version of the events, supposedly deriving from Henry:

. . . Henry loved to dwell on the hours that he and Bache had spent in Faraday's society. I shall never forget Henry's account

I was happy on these two occasions to have an opportunity of seeing **Mr F.** experiment in private and was much pleased with his method. It is however altogether of the tentitive or emperical kind. He attemps many experiments and collects facts with great rapidity. These he afterwards arranges but does not deduce many experiments appriori from known principles.[9]

---

of his visit to King's College, London, where Faraday, Wheatstone, Daniell and he had met to try and evolve the electric spark from the thermopile. Each in turn attempted it and failed. Then came Henry's turn. He succeeded: calling in the aid of his discovery of the effect of a long interpolar wire wrapped around a piece of soft iron. Faraday became as wild as a boy, and, jumping up, shouted: "Hurrah for the Yankee experiment."

"Henry as a Discoverer," in *A Memorial of Joseph Henry* (Washington, 1880), p. 506. Silvanus Thompson picked up Mayer's account of the incident in order to convey Faraday's élan for experiment in *Michael Faraday: His Life and Work* (London, 1901), p. 241. Coulson repeated it in his Henry biography, p. 119. The anecdote served to introduce Henry into Mitchell Wilson's pantheon of heroic inventors and scientists in *American Science and Invention* (New York, 1954), p. 108.

[9] Since Henry advocated the judicious use of working hypotheses in experimental inquiry, there may be some implied criticism in his remarks that Faraday's experiments were altogether of the "emperical kind." Yet, Henry notes that, after collecting his facts, Faraday "arranges" them, presumably to find general correlations and laws. Henry may simply have meant to characterize Faraday as an inductive scientist, not a disapproving label if seen in the context of John Herschel's inductivism, a philosophy that apparently appealed to Henry (see below, Henry's "Visit to Melrose Abbey to Dr Brewster," August 19–21, 1837, footnote 15). Proper inductive method, according to Herschel, began with the collection of instances, which are then compared and arranged so as to reveal common characteristics. From these are derived general descriptions and abstract laws. Henry would certainly have agreed with Herschel's definition of the perfect observer as one who approaches the phenomena with a philosophically prepared mind, that is, a mind well-informed in current theories. In actual practice, Herschel allowed

that a natural division of labor had occurred between purely practical observers and abstract theorists, both crucial to the inductive process. *Preliminary Discourse on the Study of Natural Philosophy* (London, 1831), pp. 102, 131–133, published as a Natural Philosophy volume of Dionysius Lardner's Cabinet Cyclopaedia. The Faraday depicted by Henry would seem to fall somewhere between Herschel's categories.

At the extreme, Henry may have believed Faraday bereft of guiding theories. It was true that Henry seemed unaware of those electromagnetic theories of Faraday that appeared in print. He hardly reacted to the British electrician's notion of the electrotonic state, for example, or to the theory of the field. Henry's contrary theoretical views may have led him to overlook them.

Henry's ambiguous comments reflect longstanding divisions of opinion about the role of theory in Faraday's physics. Contemporary biographers often felt moved to correct popular impressions that Faraday was a mere empiricist. John Tyndall put it this way:

> Faraday has been called a purely inductive philosopher. A great deal of nonsense is, I fear, uttered in England about induction and deduction. Some profess to befriend the one, some the other, while the real vocation of an investigator, like Faraday, consists in the incessant marriage of both. He was at this time full of the theory of Ampère, and it cannot be doubted that numbers of his experiments were executed merely to test his deductions from that theory.

Faraday as a Discoverer (London, 1868), p. 23. In fact, if anything, Tyndall believed Faraday a bit too speculative, too heterodox in his views (pp. 69, 72). To the same effect, another biographer, Silvanus P. Thompson, wrote that his "dogged tenacity for exact fact was accompanied by a perfect fearlessness of speculation," a boldness that even led some to deem him "vague and loose in thought." *Michael Faraday: His Life and Work* (London, 1901), p. 241. Faraday's most recent biographer, L.

The principal peculiarity in his carachter is his rapid and happy invention of expedients for the production of a result. Articles of the most common kind are used with success to produce the most wonderfull results. Wishing to test the decomposing power of the thermo pile and having no platina poles at hand two gold sovereigns were put in requisition. To make an extemporaneous thermo pile a piece of copper wire was twisted around each end of a piece of platinum wire of about the same diameter.

Mr F appears to be deeply imbued with the true spirit of philosophy. I remarked that our only object in investigation should be the determination of truth; his answer was yes but this is the most difficult to learn.[10]

I forgot to mention in its proper place that on monday after leaving Maj. Sabine Prof Bache and myself called at the Museum[11] according to appointment to meet Mr Fox Talbot to see some of his experiments on the colours of different salts by polarized light. An account of these has been published in the Philosophical magazine.[12]

They are made by placing a calc spar polarizing eye piece under the object and another above so that the light would be polarized before it reached the object and analysed before it reached the eye. Or the whole arrangement is the same as that for producing coloured images by mica or quarts between two glasses which polarize and analyse the ray. The experiments are excedingly beautiful and are susceptable of great variation. The object is simply some saline substance placed on a slip of glass and then crystalized by the flame of a spirit lamp. Sometimes the field is entirely dark except the crystal in the middle, at other times the crystal is dark while

---

Pearce Williams, reconciles Faraday's contrary reputations by distinguishing the public from the private scientist. Extremely wary of publicly revealing his underlying scientific assumptions, Faraday often gave the impression of eschewing a theoretical framework for his experiments. In fact, Williams argues, basic theoretical constructs—such as Boscovichean point-atoms and interlinking forces—were the secret lifeblood of Faraday's physics. *Michael Faraday* (New York, 1965), pp. 77–78.

[10] Silvanus Thompson quotes the following from a manuscript found after Faraday's death:

Do not many [natural philosophers] fail because they look rather to the renown to be acquired than to the pure acquisition of knowledge, and the delight which the contented mind has in acquiring it for its own sake?

Michael Faraday: His Life and Work, p. 243.

Thompson also celebrated the "True Philosopher" in Faraday with the comment that Faraday declined to patent his discoveries, that he sought principles, not processes, that he wanted scientific facts, not marketable inventions, being convinced that others would develop his ideas for the marketplace. In fact, Thompson asserted that when Faraday's discoveries were on the verge of acquiring commercial value, he deliberately turned away from them (p. 248). Any of these descriptions could, of course, be ascribed with equal force to Henry, a fact not overlooked by A. M. Mayer who, in comparing Henry to Faraday, wrote that "each loved science more than money . . . ." "Henry as a Discoverer," p. 506.

[11] The British Museum.

[12] "Experiments on Light," *Phil. Mag.*, 1834, 3d ser. 5:321–334. Further (undated) jottings by Henry on Fox Talbot's experiments can be found in Henry Pocket Notebook [13269].

the field is bright. The experiment succeeds best with an achromatic object glass, but may be shewn by a common glass.

May not these experiments lead to some interesting results when the crystal is touched by the wires of a galvanic battery weakly charged particularly when the crystalization of substances has been effected by this agent.[13]

JH

---

[13] Compare this suggestion with Henry's earlier speculation on the effect of magnetism on crystallization, documented in *Henry Papers*, 2:319–320.

HENRY'S EUROPEAN DIARY

Henry Papers, Smithsonian Archives

April 26th [1837] Tuesday[1] According to appointment went with Mr Wheatston to breakfast with Mr Cross the insect maker[2] at the house of a friend of Mr C. Mr Faraday was also invited but as he has made a rule never to dine or breakfast out he did not come until after the meal was over.[3] There wer several persons at the table interested in science namely Mr Conebear the geologist the writer of a work on that science well known in America.[4] Also an old gentleman the Brotherinlaw of Davies Gilbert who has been in America and was once through Princeton College.[5] I was much amused

---

[1] April 26, 1837, was a Wednesday, not a Tuesday. While the meeting could possibly have occurred on Tuesday, April 25, 1837, the position of this entry in Henry's diary suggests the later date.

[2] Andrew Crosse (1784–1855), British country gentleman and amateur scientist. A dabbler in electricity, chemistry, and mineralogy, Crosse was at the time of Henry's visit enjoying brief notoriety as a result of his claim to have generated insects of the genus *Acarus* while conducting experiments in electrocrystallization. *DNB*. For an account of his insect observations as well as the experiment in electrocrystallization which Henry describes below, see Andrew Crosse, "Description of Some Experiments Made with the Voltaic Battery, for the Purpose of Producing Crystals; in the Process of Which Experiments Certain Insects Constantly Appeared," *Annals of Electricity, Magnetism, and Chemistry . . .* , 1838, 2:246–257. See also Cornelia (Mrs. Andrew) Crosse, *Memorials, Scientific and Literary, of Andrew Crosse, the Electrician* (London, 1857).

[3] For more on Faraday's dining policy, see above, Henry's European Diary, April 19, 1837, footnote 20.

[4] William Daniel Conybeare (1787–1857, *DSB*), British clergyman and geologist. *Henry Papers*, *1*:125. While we cannot be certain of the work to which Henry refers, Conybeare's most important single contribution was his *Outlines of the Geology of England and Wales* (London, 1822), written in collaboration with William Phillips (1775–1828, *DNB*). The Henry Library contains an earlier version of this work, written by Phillips alone. Henry had been familiar with Conybeare's work at least since his canal tour of May–June 1826, on which it was used as a standard reference (see e.g. *Henry Papers*, *1*:137, 142).

[5] Henry must be mistaken about the relationship of this man to Davies Gilbert. Both Gilbert and his wife were only-children, and there could therefore have been no brother-in-law. *DNB*. Mark Antony Lower, *The Worthies of Sussex* (Lewes, 1865), pp. 212–215.

with the appearance of Conebear. He is quite tall very awkward and absent. He appeared much interested in the experiments of Mr Ross[6] but appeared almost intirely ignorant of all the principals connected with them.

When Mr F arrived the articles of curiosity which Mr C had brought to town with him were exhibited and his explanation given. The object which had excited most interest was a small but very distinctly formed crystal of quartz about $\frac{1}{8}$th of an inch long and 1/20th in diameter.

This was formed according to Mr Cross by putting two platina wires into a piece of soft porous brick called Bridgewater brick and this immersed into a basin of a solution of the silicate of Potash. When the whole had been subjected to the action of a galvanic battery for about two months with a charge of water[7] and a great number of plates the crystal was found at the bottom of the bricke *a* and at first appeared soft. No attempt was made to produce the same crystal without the battery and thus no definitive results were obtained. The brick contains a notable quantity of lime which by decomposing the fluoric acid and thus give freedom to the silica which would probably crystalize without the aid of the battery.[8] Thus when all the wonders came to be sifted the[y] vanished. Mr Cross appears a very amiable person but almost cracked with the attention he has received. Wishes to do something in the way of science. Would be honest but cannot bear to contradict the statements which his friends have so injudiciously made in reference to his experiments. Mr F gave Mr Conebear something of a rebuke in reference to what had been published about Cross at the meeting of the association.[9] This was on our return from the meeting with Mr Cross. The

---

[6] A slip of the pen; Henry's subject remains Andrew Crosse.

[7] Crosse's electrocrystallization experiments required the application of a steady current over a long period of time. For this purpose, the customary acid battery was unsuitable, because of the rapid corrosion of the plates which occurred under the influence of the acid. Crosse slowed down the corrosive process by filling his cells with water instead of acid, and then compensated for the reduced current by greatly increasing the number of plates involved. By this method, he was able to extend the life of his batteries to several months.

[8] In the published account of his experiments, Crosse dismissed this objection in a fashion which suggests the reasons for Henry's skepticism about his methods. Crosse argued that a repetition of the experiment without the use of the battery would prove nothing, because while this would remove the influence

of "artificial electricity" it would not eliminate the electricity which he believed to be always present in nature. Crosse, "Description of some Experiments made with the Voltaic Battery . . . ,"*Annals of Electricity, Magnetism, and Chemistry* . . . , 1838, 2:254–255.

[9] Crosse had labored in comparative obscurity until his appearance before the annual meeting of the British Association for the Advancement of Science in Bristol in August 1836. He was invited to address both the chemical and the geological sections, where he was warmly received, and returned home from the meeting with his reputation considerably enhanced. *DNB*. For a description of Crosse's reception by the geological section, see Sir Richard Phillips, "A Brief Account of a Visit to Andrew Crosse, Esq. of Broomfield, on the Quantock Hills, Somersetshire, in September, 1836," *Annals of Electricity, Magnetism, and Chemistry* . . . , 1837, *1*:135–136. Crosse's re-

Rev gentleman did not appear to take it in very good feeling but was appearently somewhat nettled at the remarkes. The only emmotion produced by the interview with Cross was that of Pity for the man. He has been raised to an altitude which he cannot sustain and will ultimately find his level and sink much below it. Injudicious publications of the kind will have an effect to weaken the confidence of foreigners in the character of English science.[10] Men of reputation in one department of science should be careful in lending their name to the puffing or condemning labours in another department.[11] Nothing was said at the meeting with Mr Cross about his insects. He has probably before this time discovered that they are not connected in their generation with galvanism and would be produced by a little warmth equally well.[12]

He has a very large galvanic battery consisting of 12 hundred pair of plates excited only by water and these he keeps in action for many months at a time.

He has also several thousand feet of wire insulated with which he can charge a jar and a large battery by immediate contact. The large glass battery can be charged instantaneously by contact with the galvanic battery and it will then strike through a small distance producing deflagrating and other effects. Is there not a great inductive action in a pile of so great a length?

---

port to the chemical section was printed in the published proceedings of the meeting. *British Association Report, 1836* (1837), part 2, pp. 47–48.

While Faraday shared Henry's sympathetic view of Crosse as a man, he too had a low opinion of Crosse's work, and was presumably irritated that the British Association should have conferred upon him an undeserved stature. In Faraday's case, there was a personal as well as a professional motivation for his touchiness on this subject. In newspaper accounts of Crosse's work, it had been erroneously asserted that Faraday had verified Crosse's findings, forcing Faraday to publish a public denial. L. Pearce Williams, *Michael Faraday* (New York, 1965), p. 356. The *Times*, March 4, 1837.

Conybeare was a natural target for Faraday's criticism, since he was not only a vice-president of the British Association and a leading participant in the geological section, but had recently published a laudatory account of Crosse's work in the London *Mining Journal*

(reprinted as "Crosse's Galvanic Apparatus," *Silliman's Journal*, 1837, 32:372–374).

[10] Henry was continually concerned about the effect of amateurs and charlatans on the reputation of science. Later, at the Smithsonian, he saw to it that high professional standards were observed in the research and publications activities of the Institution. For Henry's concern over the injury done to the reputation of American science by the publication of shoddy work, see above, "Record of Experiments," May 9, 1836, footnote 3.

[11] In the case of Crosse, much of the praise for his work in electricity had come from geologists, including Conybeare and Adam Sedgwick (1785–1873, *DSB*).

[12] Crosse's insects would not die quite so easily, however. In 1838, in a letter to be printed in Volume 4 of the *Henry Papers*, Henry felt compelled to write to the editor of an American publication refuting an account of Crosse's observations which had appeared in its pages.

FAREWELL DINNER FOR JOSEPH SAXTON[1]

Saxton Papers, Smithsonian Archives

1837. April 26th

Piazza Coffee House[2]

present

Stedman Whitwell[3] Chairman	H. P. Le Drew[8] (Surgeon).
Edw Cowper	Richard. Rippon.[9]
Charles Wheatstone	Francis Watkins
Petty Vaughan	Charles: M: Willich[10]
John Isaac Hawkins	Davies Jnº Oldham Jr..[11]
Alexander Gordon[4]	John Jones.[12]
W. Maugham.[5]	W. Gettings[13]
James Gardner.[6]	Thomas Cock[14]
Willm P. Lardner[7]	Joseph Henry
Ed. J. Dent	John Macneill,[15] vice President

[1] On May 1, 1837, Joseph Saxton left London to become curator of measuring and weighing apparatus at the United States Mint. The week before his departure a group of his friends gave a farewell dinner "as a token of the high estimation in which they hold him as a Mechanician of the first rank, and a Man of Science generally." At the dinner a copy of M. Camus, *A Treatise on the Teeth of Wheels, Demonstrating the Best Forms Which Can Be Given to Them for the Purposes of Machinery*, ed. John Isaac Hawkins (London, 1837) was presented to Saxton. On one side of the front flyleaf is an inscription written by Hawkins from which the above quotation is taken.

Henry mentions the dinner in his eulogy of Saxton (National Academy of Sciences, *Biographical Memoirs*, 1877, *1*:305–306), and quotes Hawkins's inscription.

On the other side of the flyleaf is this list of the men present at the dinner. Henry termed them "some of the most prominent engineers and savants of the city."

[2] Located in Covent Garden and much frequented by those associated with the theater. John Timbs, *Curiosities of London* (1867; reprint ed., Detroit, 1968), p. 268.

[3] See above, Bache's European Diary, April 8, 1837, footnote 4.

[4] Alexander Gordon (1802–1868) was born in New York, but raised and educated in Scot-

land. Although interested in a variety of engineering problems, including bridge design and construction, the management of gasworks, and locomotion, his chief concern was the construction of lighthouses in the colonial possessions of England. He was only twenty-four when elected an Associate of the Institution of Civil Engineers. In 1835 he became a member of that organization. *Minutes of the Proceedings of the Institution of Civil Engineers*, 1870, *30*:435–436.

[5] William Maugham was the lecturer on chemistry at the Adelaide Gallery. *British Association Report, 1838* (1839), part 2, pp. 72–73.

[6] James Gardner (fl. 1790–1838) worked for the Trigonometrical Survey as a draftsman and surveyor from about 1790 until about 1822. Around 1827 he set up a map and chart shop in London, having been appointed an official agent of the Board of Ordnance, and therefore entitled to sell the maps produced by the Survey. He was still selling maps in the late 1830s. E. G. R. Taylor, *The Mathematical Practitioners of Hanoverian England, 1714–1840* (Cambridge, England, 1966), p. 363; Charles Close, *The Early Years of the Ordnance Survey* (Chatham, 1926), pp. 77–79.

[7] A conjectural reading; not identified.

[8] A very close friend of Charles Wheatstone. Brian Bowers, *Sir Charles Wheatstone* (Lon-

don, 1975), p. 155.

⁹ Unidentified.

¹⁰ Henry's Address Book identifies Charles M. Willich of Regents Park, London, as a friend of Saxton's. Willich's major scientific interest seems to have been mathematics, although not on a very sophisticated level. Charles Willich, "On a Simple Geometrical Construction, Giving a Very Approximate Quadrature of the Circle," *Proceedings of the Royal Society of London*, 1854–1855, 7:379.

¹¹ There are a number of Oldhams whose interests and careers would have brought them into contact with Saxton. Unfortunately, none of them have names corresponding to the signature on the flyleaf.

¹² Perhaps John Edward Jones (1806–1862), who was trained as a civil engineer, but instead chose a career as a sculptor. He studied and eventually settled in London. Highly successful, he exhibited at the Royal Academy from 1844 until his death. *DNB*.

¹³ A friend named Gettings appears frequently in Saxton's London notebooks, Saxton Papers, Smithsonian Archives. Perhaps this is the William Gettings who was an annual subscriber to the British Association in 1837.

¹⁴ Possibly Thomas Astley Cock (1811–1885), who received his B.A. from Trinity College, Cambridge, in 1834. He went on to become mathematics tutor at King's College, London, and then professor of mathematics at Queen's College, London. Frederic Boase, *Modern English Biography*, 6 vols. (1892–1921; reprint ed., London, 1965), *1*:661.

¹⁵ John Benjamin Macneill (1793?–1880) obtained his engineering skills while employed as an assistant to Thomas Telford and soon became an expert in bridge and road construction. After Telford's death in 1834 Macneill became a consulting engineer, working on railroads and problems in canal-boat traction. His system of laying out railway plans was adopted for England by order of the House of Commons, while his system of nomenclature for slopes was widely accepted by English civil engineers. *DNB*. His and Henry's signatures are on the right side of the original, perpendicular to the other names.

HENRY'S EUROPEAN DIARY

Henry Papers, Smithsonian Archives

April 27ᵗʰ [1837] Attended Mr Brands[1] lecture in the morning. Prof Richees[2] in the afternoon.

Met Prof Graham[3] of Glasgo the person who repeated the experiments of

[1] William Thomas Brande.

[2] William Ritchie. Both men were lecturing at the Royal Institution.

[3] Thomas Graham (1805–1869) graduated the University of Glasgow in 1826 with the M.A., then went on to study chemistry at the laboratory of Thomas Charles Hope at the University of Edinburgh. He became Professor of Chemistry at Anderson's College (later the Royal College of Science and Technology) in 1830. Seven years later he obtained the Chair of Chemistry at the University College, London. He was among the founders of the Chemical Society and its first president. In 1854 he left the academic world to become Master of the Mint, succeeding John Herschel.

Graham was a well-known figure in chemistry circles when Henry met him in England. He had already published a significant paper clarifying the relationship between the various phosphates and phosphoric acids (1833) and the paper which stated Graham's law for the diffusion of gases (see below, footnote 5). He had been elected a Fellow of the Royal Society in 1836. *DSB*.

Two of Graham's writings survive in the Henry Library. One is the American edition of Graham's *Elements of Chemistry*, ed. Robert Bridges (Philadelphia, 1843); the other is a collection of Graham's papers, *Chemical and Physical Researches*, ed. R. Angus Smith (Edinburgh, 1875).

Mitchel[4] and detected the law of the permeability of the gasses.[5] He is apparently quite a young man not more than 27 or 8 very ordinary in appearance and speaks with quite a scotch accent. He is now on a visit to London relative to the chair of chemistry in the London University. There are several applicants for this post among the number Mr. Reed[6] of Edinburgh, Philips[7] of London and Johnson[8] of Durham. I have been introduced severally to these persons and treated by all with much attention. Johnson is quite a plesant person and much better looking than Graham but by many is thought not to be quite as prominent a candidate.[9]

[4] The American physician John Kearsley Mitchell (1793–1858) was educated at the University of Edinburgh and the University of Pennsylvania (M.D. 1819) and practiced medicine in Philadelphia. From 1833 through 1838 he was a lecturer on chemistry at the Franklin Institute. In 1841 he became Professor of the Theory and Practice of Medicine at Jefferson Medical College. *DAB.*

In addition to his experimental work in chemistry, of which one aspect will be discussed below (footnote 5), Mitchell published extensively on the causes and cures of disease. A presentation copy of his *On the Cryptogamous Origin of Malarious and Epidemic Fevers* (Philadelphia, 1849) is in the Henry Library.

[5] Although Mitchell and Graham conducted somewhat similar experiments during the years 1829–1833 on the diffusion of gases through membranes, the two men differed greatly in their approach to the experiments. Mitchell was a physician interested in chemistry, stealing moments from his medical practice to conduct experiments. As he himself admitted, his procedures were sometimes not conducive to accurate results. His primary interest was in the penetration of fluids through organic membranes. Graham, in contrast, was an experimental chemist, aware of but not primarily concerned with the physiological implications of his work. Graham's gas experiments were far more precise than Mitchell's. Graham gave no indication that he was aware of Mitchell's work, giving credit to Johann Wolfgang Döbereiner (1780–1849, *DSB*) for inspiration, although the reprinting of one of Mitchell's papers by an English journal made it unlikely that Graham was entirely ignorant of the American. In contrast, Mitchell, aware of Graham's growing reputation among the chemical community, felt obligated to respond in print to the work of the Scot.

The law mentioned by Henry is now known as Graham's law of diffusion. Announced explicitly in 1831, the law stated that the mutual diffusion of two gases in contact is inversely proportional to the square root of the density of each gas.

Thomas Graham, "On the Law of the Diffusion of Gases," *Phil. Mag.*, 1833, 3d ser. 2: 175–190, 269–276, 351–358; J. K. Mitchell, "On the Penetrativeness of Fluids," *Journal of the Royal Institution of Great Britain*, 1831, 2: 101–118, 307–321; J. K. Mitchell, "On the Penetration of Gases," *American Journal of the Medical Sciences*, 1833, *13*:100–112; Annette Ruckstuhl, "Thomas Graham's Study of the Diffusion of Gases," *Journal of Chemical Education*, 1951, *28*:594–596; E. A. Mason and Barbara Kronstadt, "Graham's Laws of Diffusion and Effusion," *Journal of Chemical Education*, 1967, *44*:740–744.

[6] David Boswell Reid.

[7] Richard Phillips.

[8] James Finlay Weir Johnston (1796–1855) was the reader in chemistry at Durham University from 1833 until his death. *DNB*. Presentation copies of a number of his publications exist in the Henry Library.

[9] The death of Edward Turner (1796–1837) left vacant the Chair of Chemistry at University College, London. There were five candidates for the position. Four are mentioned by Henry in this entry of his diary. The fifth was James Apjohn (1796–1886), then Professor of Chemistry at the College of Surgeons' School, Dublin. R. A. Smith, *The Life and Works of Thomas Graham* (Glasgow, 1884), p. 40; *Proceedings of the Royal Society of London*, 1887, *41*:i–ii.

Henry wrote a letter of recommendation for one of the candidates for the post. We have

But to return to Prof Richee['s] lecture; it was on electro magnetism and magneto electricity. He exhibited to the class his revolving magnet[10] which surprised me with the rapidity and force of its motion. It consists of a piec of hollow gun barrell curved like a lifter, wrapped with wire and supported on a spindle of iron resting on or in a glass tube. See Phil transactions.[11]

By the same instrument he was ablle also to shew magneto electrical action by twerling between his finger and thumb the upright wire *a*. The apparatus was connected to a galvanometer by copper wires.

His apparatus for producing the spark in a mixture of oxygen and hydrogen is also very simple and efficient.[12] It consists of a tube open at the lower end. The gas was forced in from a bladder a cork stoping the lower end. While the spark was made an explosion of considerable intensity was produced.

The cylinders around which his wires were coiled are hollow and the wheel which turns these are placed on one side of the magnet not connected with the article but by the string which turns the pinion or pulley.

---

been able to locate only an undated draft of the letter (Bache Papers, Smithsonian Archives). It reads:

> In reference to your being a candidate for the chair of chemestry in <Kings> The London University <I beg leave> it gives me pleasure to state that you[r] name as a successfull cultivator of the science of chemestry is familiarly known and your labours highly appreciated in the United States of America.

Since Henry seems to have been more familiar with the chemical work of Graham, who eventually was selected for the professorship, than any of the other candidates, it seems likely that this letter was written on his behalf. In that case the letter was probably written sometime between this meeting with Graham and May 5, the day the recommendations and other documents supporting the candidacies of the five men were filed.

That Henry was asked for a recommendation is an interesting commentary on his status within the English scientific community. Someone must have felt that Henry's support would be of some significance. Unfortunately, we have no evidence whether Henry's endorsement was decisive, or even sent, since there is no mention of it in the reports on testimonials

which we have located.

Another interesting aspect of this recommendation is that the draft was written on the back of a copy of a letter from Bache to his mother. We speculate that this occurred because Henry consulted with Bache while writing the recommendation. Perhaps Henry wanted Bache's opinion on the wording of the letter, or perhaps he wanted Bache's concurrence on the choice, so that the Americans might show a united front.

[10] A detailed discussion of Ritchie's rotating electromagnetic motor, including some remarks upon Henry's feeling that Ritchie might be guilty of plagiarism, is in *Henry Papers*, 2: 162–163.

[11] Ritchie's rotating electromagnetic motor is described in "Experimental Researches in Electro-Magnetism and Magneto-Electricity," *Phil. Trans.*, 1833, pp. 319–320.

[12] Probably the apparatus described in Ritchie's "Experimental and Physical Researches in Electricity and Magnetism," *Phil. Mag.*, 1836, 3d ser. 8:455–456. This apparatus superseded the one he described in "On a Mode of Detonating a Mixture of Oxygen and Hydrogen by a Spark Induced by a Small Horse-Shoe Magnet," *Phil. Mag.*, 1834, 3d ser. 4:104–106.

By this arrangement the magnet is readily taken from its place and used for other purposes.[13]

From Mr Richees lecture I was led to conclude that the spark of the common magneto electric machine was produced principally by the inductive action of the long wire on its own electricity. Thus if the smallest current possible be formed and the contact broken a spark will be produced and this is principally on account of the induction. It would be well under this vew of the subject to make experiments relative to the proper position of the point which leaves the mercury whether it produces a brighter spark when placed at right angles to the plane of the middle of the two legs or in the same plane.[14]

Professor R also explained the rotation of the magnet around its own axces and in so doing gave me some new ideas which like the one relative to the inductive action of the coil appeared not very clear in his own mind. To explain the action suppose a copper wire soldered to the side of the magnet bent at its upper end so as to dip into mercury and also at its lower, then the wire would attempt to turn around the magnet and would carry the latter with it. This explanation is the one given in the books but did not satisfy me when I came to reflect more on it since there is no force exterior according to this vew to act on the bar. The motion must be caused by the radient lines or something exterior to the bar.[15] On the same principle I do not clearly see why a wheel not notched

---

[13] To meet the demands of public lectures Ritchie had constructed his apparatus so that the same magnet and lifter could be used for a number of different demonstrations. This would reduce the number of pieces of apparatus necessary. Ritchie, "Experimental and Physical Researches," p. 455.

[14] Henry later conducted a series of experiments on the inductive action of the magneto-electric machine (these experiments, in the "Record of Experiments" entry of May 14, 1840, will be published in the next volume of the *Henry Papers*) in which he confirmed some of his suppositions of 1837. For these experiments he chose Saxton's configuration of the machine, in which the keeper and the contact with the mercury are in the same plane as the legs of the magnet.

[15] In little more than a decade, the application of the phenomena of a wire rotating about a magnet and a magnet about a wire evolved from philosophical toys to primitive electric motors. But this advance did not provide a completely satisfactory explanation of

rotary motion, especially when dealing with a magnet moving about its own axis. Henry's own unease is reflected in his reaction to Ritchie's lecture.

Henry's usual frugality with words and the lack of essential punctuation have combined to make this an extremely difficult passage to interpret. One major difficulty is deciding where Henry's description of Ritchie's theory ends and his own thoughts begin. Another is selecting from among the variant readings of the book view and new ideas.

The lecture presented what appears to be a thought experiment, in which a current is sent through a wire which has been soldered to the ends of a bar magnet. The explanation of the resulting rotation which Henry attributed to "the books" is analogous to, although not identical with, that given in P. M. Roget, *Treatises on Electricity, Galvanism, Magnetism, and Electro-Magnetism* (London, 1832), "Electro-Magnetism," pp. 25–27, 81–86, which in turn depended upon the acceptance of Ampère's electrodynamic theory. Roget had

on its edge should revolve in mercury[16] since the metal is a conductor. The line of electricity would be thrown out and move as there is nothing to prevent it without giving motion to the wheel.

Also on the same principle there appears some difficulty in giving the rational[i]ty of the revolution of mercury[17] sinc this metal is a good conductor and would thus admit the current to revolve without moving the ponderable mass of liqu[i]d metal.

Prof R showed me a prism of his own construction the largest and clearest I have ever seen. It exhibits of itself and without any other apparatus the lines of the spectrum and still more plainly the lines in nitrous gass.[18] The light used was a slit in a window shutter in a dark room with only the light of the sky. The room was not much darkened.

The method of forming this kind of glass has not yet been made public but is now under examination by a board of the Longitude commissioners.[19] Prof. R sais that it will greatly reduce the price of achromatic tellescopes.

I should have remarked that Mr Faraday said when on the subject of papers that he made no account of any descriptions of a general kind such as a great deal very strong &c but always required definite quantities to be stated.

---

argued that if we assume that the current through a magnet passes near or on the surface (the net effect in Ampère's theory), then it is the surface of the magnet which is set in rotation by the difference in polarity between the surface and the core of the magnet. If one substitutes the wire attached to the magnet for the actual surface of the magnet, then we have Henry's book explanation. Henry finds this explanation lacking.

He seems to believe that an external physical force was necessary for the rotation, perhaps in the form of "radient lines" acting on the magnet. We assume he had in mind something analogous to the radiant currents evident in the electrochemical motion of mercury (for Henry's previous investigation of this phenomenon, see above, "Record of Experiments," March 16, 1836). There is, however, no evidence that Henry was any closer to a personally satisfactory explanation of rotary motion. It remained a problem which nagged him in subsequent years.

[16] Peter Barlow had placed a small cistern of mercury between the poles of a horseshoe magnet, then suspended a spur so that the ends of the spur were in contact with the mercury. When a current was transmitted through the spur, it would begin to rotate.

Sturgeon discovered that under certain conditions, a continuous disc could be substituted for the spur. Roget, *Treatises*, "Electro-Magnetism," pp. 30–31.

[17] If a current was transmitted through a shallow basin by immersing the endpoints of two wires in the basin, and a magnet then held above or below the basin, the mercury would revolve about the endpoints of the wires. Roget, *Treatises*, "Electro-Magnetism," p. 32. In both this case and that discussed in footnote 16, Roget saw no difficulty in fitting the phenomenon into Ampère's general scheme. Henry had conducted similar experiments, using his large inductive coils instead of permanent magnets, without any evidence of special theoretical interest. See *Henry Papers*, 2:246–247.

[18] An optical effect studied by David Brewster. See below, Henry's notes on his visit to Brewster of August 19–21, 1837, especially footnote 41.

[19] The commission authorized George Dollond to construct an eight-inch telescope using Ritchie's glass, but the performance of the telescope was not impressive enough to persuade the commission to allow additional public expenditures for the project. *DNB*.

April 27, 1837

On the same day I visited Kings college to see the result of an experiment of Prof Daniell with a battery[20] of his construction. It consisted of a globe of brass about 6 or 8 inches in diameter filled with a solution of sul copper and a bullet suspended by a thick copper wire in the middle, the bullet and wire being seperated from the brass globe by a piec of bladder. The globe was formed of brass inorder to indicate more clearly the deposition of copper which might take place on its surface.

It was formed of two hemispheres and kept in action for 7 or 8 hours when at the end of that time the bullet was desolved off from the copper wire and fell to the bottom of the globe.

When the globe was taken apart the under part was found bright but the upper covered with copper and this concreted in a most beautiful manner into rings or zones evidently connected with the phenominon of Nobiles rings.[21]

The under half of the batter[y][22] had no deposition of copper on account of its being insulated from the upper by a collar of leather.

Prof Daniell thinks some interesting result will be obtained by this process and concludes that the larger the copper the greater the effect with a given quantity of zinc. The ball of zinc in this experiment was about ¾ of an inch in diameter.

Prof Daniell's retaining battery is a very beautifull contrivance and produces effects that may hereafter be applyed to useful and economical purposes. Several attempts however have been made to detract from the meriet of the invention or to rob him of the credit.

A Mr Mullens member of parliament has made a claim to it[23] but it after-

[20] From theoretical considerations, Daniell concluded that the most perfect and simple battery would consist of a solid generating metal sphere surrounded by a hollow conducting metal sphere. The two spheres would be separated by a liquid electrolyte. He decided to build such a battery and use it to trace the activity of the electrochemical force by the distribution of the reduced copper. The apparatus described by Henry was the resulting battery.
Daniell described the experiments conducted with this battery in his "Fourth Letter on Voltaic Combinations with Reference to the Mutual Relations of the Generating and Conducting Surfaces," *Phil. Trans.*, 1838, pp. 41–56. His conclusion, arrived at after reading Faraday's "Experimental Researches in Electricity—Eleventh Series," *Phil. Trans.*, 1838,

pp. 1–40, was that his experiments supported Faraday's thesis of the nature of the electrical force. In particular, his results could be explained in terms of curved lines of force.
At the time of Henry's visit, however, Daniell was just beginning his work. The experiment described by Henry corresponds to what Daniell described as the first experiment using this apparatus. The recognition of a similarity between these experiments and Faraday's work was still some eight months in the future.

[21] Henry was familiar with these rings, having conducted a series of experiments duplicating Nobili's work. See above, "Record of Experiments," March 16, 1836.

[22] Another possible reading of this word is balloon.

[23] Frederick William Beaufort De Moleyns

wars was discovered that Clark the optician sold[24] Mullens the invention for 5 £s.

(1804–1854), a member of Parliament from Kerry from 1831 through 1837, changed his last name from Mullins in 1841. De Moleyns, who always felt his contributions were never appreciated, lived most of his life involved in some sort of controversy. Indeed, he died in prison while charged with forging a power of attorney. Even after death controversy surrounded him. He had left his estate to University College, London to endow a chair in electrical science. The college chose instead, after some delay, to use the money to buy electrical apparatus. Gerrit P. Judd, *Members of Parliament, 1734–1832* (New Haven, 1955), pp. 172, 284; Frederic Boase, *Modern English Biography*, 6 vols. (1892–1921; reprint ed., London, 1965), 5:69.

De Moleyns's position in his conflict with Daniell, a conflict which continued for a number of years, was that Daniell had invented a "constant battery" (which is described in detail, above, Henry's European Diary, March 23, 1837 [first entry], footnote 22), while De Moleyns had invented a "sustaining battery." The differences, according to De Moleyns, were numerous: the dimensions of the battery; Daniell's use of an acidic solution, in contrast to De Moleyns's use of an alkaline solution; Daniell's diaphragm was to prevent the mixing of the liquids on the two sides of the cell, while De Moleyns's purpose was to allow limited mixing; the use of amalgamated versus non-amalgamated zinc and cast versus rolled metal. Contemporary observers and later writers agree that the voltaic battery devised by De Moleyns was different in some ways from Daniell's invention, but that overall it was simply a different version of the same principle. F. W. Mullins, "On the Voltaic Sustaining Battery," *The Annals of Electricity, Magnetism, & Chemistry*, 1837, *1*:205–211; F. W. Mullins, "On the Sustaining Voltaic Battery: in Reference to some Observations of Professor Daniell, in the April Number of the 'Philosophical Magazine,'" *The Annals of Electricity, Magnetism, & Chemistry*, 1842, *8*:465–469; *Encyclopaedia Britannica*, 8th edition, s.v. "Voltaic Electricity;" P. J. McLaughlin, "Some Irish Contemporaries of Faraday and Henry," *Proceedings of the Royal Irish Academy*, 1964, *64*:24.

[24] At least one contemporary account disagrees with Daniell's opinion. According to William Sturgeon, E. M. Clarke merely manufactured the battery for De Moleyns. The idea, however, was De Moleyns's. "Description of a Voltaic Battery, Invented by Frederic W. Mullins, Esq.," *The Annals of Electricity, Magnetism, & Chemistry*, 1837, *1*:107–108.

HENRY'S EUROPEAN DIARY
Henry Papers, Smithsonian Archives

April 28th [1837] Went this morning with Prof Bache to visit Mr Fransis Baily,[1] was recd by him very kindly; he spent several hours in showing to us the various interesting articles of apparatus with which he has inriched the science of astronomy for several years past. Mr Baily is about 55 years old stout and apparently of excellent constitution. In his younger days he visited America made a voyage from Phil^a to Pittsburgh and thence down the ohio and the missippee to New Orleans. In this tour he met with Ellicott and was with him several days.

---

[1] See above, Henry diary entry of April 21, 1837, footnote 16. The meeting took place at Baily's home, the site of his workshop and private observatory.

Mr Baily first introduced us to his work shop in which his dividing apparatus is placed and also his instruments for the experiments on the vibration of the pendulum in a vacuum. He first explained to us the method of compairing standard measures of length, showed us the standard which belongs to the Royal Astronomical society and a copy of it which belongs to himself.[2] These are almost precisely alike. They are hollow tubes made of a number of concentric cylenders of Brass drawn together to prevent warping. In the older standard ie the one belonging to the society the thermometers belonging [to] the instrument are placed on the out side with the bulbe turned in while those on the standard of Mr Baily are put into the hollow tube and thus are not liable to be broken. These standards rest on a stout wooden frame and are supported at about a quarter of the distance from each end by a small rooler, it having been found that the standard did not keep its perfectly straight form when on a flat surface which did not expand equally with it—a tension took place which caused a slight curvature. The divisions were read by means of powerful microscopes with cross hairs in the focus; while these remain fixed at a given distance another bar is placed in the position of the first and the distance which has been taken from the one is transferred to the other. I was much pleased with the whole process and particularly so with the simple process of dividing a space, the yard as an instance, into 3 equal parts. This was done by the method of stepping as it were with a pair of compasses. The microscopes are seperated to the distance approximately and then this stepped off by moving the bar instead of the compasses as in the ordinary method. The mark in the focus of the microscope was that of the intersection of two cross hairs at an acute angle.

Mr B next showed to us his pendulum apparatus first the invariable and *convertable pendulum*,[3] explained his method of rendering the two ends synchronous by filing off a part from the end or by adjusting it with a small piece of lead between two screws.

He prefers this method to that of Katre[4] on account of the stability of the

---

[2] Baily's inquiry into the British unit of length was a direct outgrowth of his observations on the seconds pendulum (see footnote 5), a natural standard of length. In 1833, the Royal Astronomical Society commissioned Baily to construct a standard scale for the Society, which Baily accomplished by making careful comparisons with the Imperial Standard Yard at the House of Commons. Baily's improved scale was sixty-three inches long and consisted of three concentric brass tubes resting on two rollers. The results of his research

appeared in "Report on the Standard Scale of the Royal Astronomical Society," *Astronomical Society Memoirs*, 1836, 9:35–184. Included in the article is a history of standard measures in Britain. Baily was later asked to reconstruct the Imperial Yard, which had been burned in the Houses of Parliament fire in 1834. Baily died in the middle of that effort. *DNB*. John L. E. Dreyer and H. H. Turner, eds., *History of the Royal Astronomical Society, 1820–1920* (London, 1923), p. 69.

[3] Baily had been experimenting on the form

whole and the guaranty against all risk from slipping of weights and the giving of screws. The same pendulum also answers for an invariable pendulum and by means of the several knife edges enables the observer to make several sets of observations with the same bar as if they were different bar[s] by inverting the apparatus.

The apparatus for getting the time of the ocillations of the pendulum consisted of a clock fixed to the angle of a room (or rather let into the masonry) with a mercurial pendulum. On the bottom of this were wings for observing the coincidences of the two pendulums namely of the clock and the invariable or convertable apparatus. All the part under the clock was painted black and in the first experiments and those I believe described by Mr Baily in the astro. transactions there was a disc of about 3 inches in diameter attached to the lower part of the pendulum thus on which were marked with gilt paper four small markes for noting the disappearance of the pendulum of the clock behind the experimental pendulum. But in the later experiments this disc has been replaced by two wings with litle holes in them through which a part of a sheet of guilt paper can be seen. There are two wings attached to the pendulum by two wires inorder that they may be bent into proper adjustment. The coincidence of the two pendulums are noted by that of the edge or edges with a diaphram like a pair of parallel rulers.

---

and material of pendulums for many years, producing a number of publications, including: "On the Material Compensation Pendulum," *Astronomical Society Memoirs*, 1822, *1*: 381–420; "Short Account of Two Invariable Pendulums, the One of Iron and the Other of Copper," *Astronomical Society Monthly Notices*, 1827–1830, *1*:78–80; "On the Discordances in the Results of the Methods for Determining the Length of the Simple Pendulum," *Phil. Mag.*, 1829, 2d ser. 5:97–104. (For another publication see footnote 5.)

In 1828, Baily designed a simplified convertible pendulum for the use of Commander Henry Foster on his expedition to recalculate the ellipticity of the earth. When Foster died in mid-project, the Admiralty, who had dispatched Foster, enlisted Baily to reduce his data and to complete the observations by swinging the pendulums in London. Baily's results appeared as "Report on the Pendulum Experiments Made by the Late Captain Henry Foster, R.N., in his Scientific Voyage in the Years 1828–1831, With a View to Determine the Figure of the Earth," *Astronomical Society Memoirs*, 1834, 7:1–378. The figure for ellipticity derived by Baily accorded very well with previous measurements by Sabine. A further application of the pendulum, following directly from the experiments on the figure of the earth, was Baily's attempt to repeat Cavendish's experiment on the density of the earth. The project was suggested by the Astronomical Society in 1835 and successfully completed by Baily in 1843, an effort that won him the gold medal of the Society. *DNB*; Dreyer and Turner, *Royal Astronomical Society*, pp. 68, 69–70.

[4] The British geodesist Henry Kater (1777–1835). Like Baily, Kater refined and improved geodetic instruments and (as a member of a Royal Society committee established at the request of the government) contributed to the standardization of weights and measures. In 1817, he won the Royal Society's Copley Medal for his pendulum experiments. Kater is remembered for the invention of a reversible pendulum, known as "Kater's pendulum," based on a principle of Huygens that the centers of suspension and oscillation are interchangeable. By adjusting knife edges at the centers, Kater made accurate estimates for the length of the seconds pendulum under various conditions. *DSB. DNB.*

These are placed at such a distance as to [?leave] the opening a little greater than the width of the pendulum. The coincidence is then noted by the side of the pendulum on the out side of the diaphram at *a* then at the inside *b* again at *c* and lastly on the out side at *a'*. The mean of these four observations are taken as the true one. The amplitude of the arc is noted by a diagonal scale. A slit in a pece of paist board forms the opening through which the whole is noted.

We were shewn one of the sets [of] observations and were much pleased with the beauty of the effect and the ease and precission with which the time of coincidence can be obtained by these observations. The tellescope for the observation was about one foot in focal length and placed at the distance of about 12 feet from the clock. It was furnished with a prismatic diagonal eye piece and mounted on a stool.

The contrivance for raising the knife edges from the planes of the aggates is simple and effectiv. It consists of a stage lifted up gradually by sliding under it an inclined plane thus The motion of the plane was given by a rack work and crank. By this arrangement the motion is slow and gentle, the knife never comes on the agate with any percussion. *a* is the notch for receiving the end of the knife.

The apparatus for the pendulum in vacuo[5] consisted principally of a large tube about 6 inches or perhaps a little more in diameter made of the brass tube of an old telescope s[h]ut at the lower end permanently and closed at the upper by a movable brass plate on the top of which a tall glass receiver was placed. Thus. The object of the receiver was to exclude the air from the upper part of the pendulum and afford a movable part by which the suspension could be adjusted. The exaustion was made by attaching a tube to the side of the large tube with an air pump. The amount of the vacuum was then indicated by a short gage placed within the glass receiver. This amount varied from ½ an inch to one inch.

It was found very difficult to [?pressure] the apparatus perfectly tight

---

[5] Baily had constructed this apparatus for use in an elaborate series of experiments to determine the length of the seconds pendulum. In 1828, Bessel pointed out a neglected element of air resistance in the standard "correction for buoyancy." To determine the necessary additional correction for this element, Baily constructed a vacuum apparatus in his home workshop and, in 1831–1832, conducted experiments on eighty-six pendulums of various types. Baily found that the new correction, taking into account the additional allowance, was sometimes twice the old. He published his results in "On the Correction of a Pendulum for the Reduction to a Vacuum; Together with Remarks on Some Anomalies Observed in Pendulum Experiments," *Phil. Trans.*, 1832, pp. 399–492. While Agnes Clerke, in her *DNB* account, assesses these experiments as "distinguished," Dreyer, supplying no particulars, comments that "his pendulum work contains serious oversights." Dreyer and Turner, *Royal Astronomical Society*, p. 87. *DNB.*

particularly around the windows through which the coincidences were observed and there are two of these one on each side of the tube so that the clock pendulum could be seen directly through. On the front of the tube there was an aditional window for observing the amplitude of the arc. These windows were at first attempted to be made tight by putty but without success. The only thing found to answer was a layer of oiled blotting paper. Perhaps a stratum of cork would have answered very well. There was also a pretty contrivance for letting the pendulum into its place without the risk of injuring the tube or the agate plates by its falling and this was a weight or counter poise over a pully to let the pendulum easily down. To give room for the article to be drawn out intirely of the long tube a circular tube was placed in the cealing at the top of which the pulley was placed. This arrangement was necssary on account of the low cealing of the room. The clock as I before stated was placed in the corner of the room and the support for the pendulum and also for the vacum tube was a stout brace of mahogany placed transverse on which the tube was hung by a notch. To detect any shake in this a litle instrument called a noddy was placed on it. The noddy is formed of a glass tube containing a pendulum worked by a spring which vibrates in unison with the clock and can be put in motion by the smallest jar. It can be regulated to the beat of the clock by screwing up or down the bob at the top.

It should have been mentioned that when the pendulum is set in motion in the air it will continue to move about 5 hours when in a vacumm about 12 hours.

The noddy is not necssary to shew the tremor of a structure. In the case of a waggon passing this will be exhibited by a basin of mercury.

I must not forget to mention the use of gilt paper for reflectors used by Mr Bailly in several experiments. This was paisted on pieces of wood and used to throw the light upwards to illuminate the under surface of a scale &c.

We were next shewn Mr Bailys observatory.[6] It consists of a circular or rather octagonal hole cut in the roof of his house and this surmounted by a

[6] Baily conducted few notable astronomical observations. Although credited with the discovery of what became known as Baily's beads, drops of light seen on the solar crescent during an annular eclipse (an effect due to the gaps between the mountains of the moon), the observation was apparently first made by the American Samuel Williams. Brooke Hindle, *The Pursuit of Science in Revolutionary America, 1735–1789* (New York, 1974), pp. 335–336. Rather, Baily was most important for "imparting a higher value to the observations of others, both by connecting them with the past and by assuring them for the future." (*DNB*, p. 900). His star catalog revisions were considered a major astronomical contribution.

Henry begins with a description of the dome housing Baily's transit instrument, then describes the dome covering the telescope.

an octagonal cupola with windows on all sides. The covering was larger than the opening in the roof so as to form a shelf interely around of about 15 inches in width on which the transit instrument was placed. The diameter of the opening *a* was about 5 feet and the observer is placed in it so that the shelf is about brest high and supported on a stand of wood with steps at one side. The shelf or ring on which the instruments are placed is supported independantly of the roof or the cupola above by two cross beams which are fastened at the ends into the walls of the house. These beams are two and are of the form shewn in the figure. The thick supports support two cross pieces on which rest with the two principle beams the shelf. a represents a^7 X section and *b* a plan of

the structure. On *d* the circular shelf (or rather octagonal) is placed the cupola being supported by the roof or ceiling *c*.

The transit was one of about 30 inches focus and cost about 30 guineas. The clock was one with a mercurial pendulum and placed in the room or rather on the garet floor and fastened to the wall. To regulate this clock Mr B takes a pece of wire of a certain length places it on the pendulum and then determins the loss of time by this additional weight. He afterwards cuts this wire into lengths corresponding to seconds or some adequate part [of] a second and then places these on the pendulum one after another until the proper rate is obtained. This is a cheap and sufficiently exact observatory for ordinary purposes.

We were next shewn into the tellescope observatory very similar to the other. It also consists of a hole in the roof of the house covered with a hood of boards which revolves easily by means of three balls of wood each 3½ or 4 inches in diameter. They are confined in a grove or rather a square trough in the upper part the circular cil being perfectly flat. Being once placed at equal distances and of the same size they always keep the same relative position and enable the dome to be turned with the force of a single finger. This opening was about 5 feet in diameter and in the centre was placed the stand of a telescope of about 5 feet in diameter and this was mounted by a very simple contrivance so as to have an equatorial motion by means of a block of mahogany screwed to the stand and cut so as to form an angle with the horary equal to that which the equator at London makes with

[7] Henry mistakenly underlined this "a" instead of the preceding one.

the same plane. Thus ———◣ the triangular block is screwed down to the table or shelf ———◆——— mentioned before in the other observatory or to the top of the stand. The telescope is again attached to the block by a screw collar. This simple mounting enables the observer to follow a star with great ease and precission. One side of the dormer opens so as to turn the telescope up to the zenith. This was shut when not used by a small door on hinges. A pan[e] of glass in the dome served to give light when the door was shut. The dome was fastened in its place during an observation by a small wedge stuck into the space where the balls are placed.

The trap door at top had a quadrant screw to keep it at any elevation. I should have mentioned that the door for the telescope consisted of two doors one for low and the other for hight observations, both or one could be opened as circumstances may require. The stands are made of very thick timber and surmounted by a triangular board with a small ledge on it.

▽ Mr Baily reccommends for a private observatory a small transit instrument with a meridian mark at a distance or near at hand with a lense to transmit the rays parallel, a good clock with a mercurial pendulum. When a temporary observatory is to be erected a barrel of sand or earth may be used as a stand for the transit instrument.

On the method of placing this instrument in the meridian see Mr Bailys paper in the Astronomical transactions.[8] Also for an account of his experiments on the pend[ulum] and the standard of the society see the same.

I gave Mr B one of Mr S Alexander's papers on the eclipse of Feby 1831.[9] He was apparently much pleased with the article and said that had he seen it a short time before he would have noticed it in his paper to the astronomical society. He has promised a copy of his paper to Mr Alexander & myself.[10]

On the evening of the same day visited the Royal Institution and attended a lecture of Mr Faraday on the peculiar state of iron when plunged into nitric acid. A notice of the facts of this lecture is given in the Philosophical magazine.[11]

---

[8] "On a Method of Fixing a Transit Instrument Exactly in the Meridian," *Astronomical Society Memoirs*, 1822, *1*:59–67.

[9] "Elements of the Solar Eclipse of February 12th, 1831 . . . ," *Albany Institute Transactions*, 1830, *1*:243–250.

[10] The article, which would appear in 1838, announced the discovery of what became known as Baily's Beads: "On a Remarkable Phenomenon that Occurs in Total and Annular Eclipses of the Sun," *Astronomical Society Memoirs*, 1838, *10*:1–42.

[11] "On the Causes of the Neutrality of Iron in Nitric Acid," *Phil. Mag.*, 1837, 3d ser. *10*: 175–176.

TO T. ROMEYN BECK

Retained Copy,[1] Henry Papers, Smithsonian Archives

[May 9, 1837][2]

My Dear Sir

Permit me to introduce to your acquaintance Dr Malcolmson[3] of Madrass who is now on a visit to England. He is a young Scotchman and was introduced to me by Dr Daniell of Kings College. He appears to be much esteemed in London and may perhaps become an interesting correspondent of yours. He informs me that he became acquainted with your work on medical Jurisprudence[4] in India and that he had designed to write you on the subject of Prison discipline in the United States &c—but felt some hesitation in commencing a correspondence.

I have forwarded by the packet President a copy of his work on some diseases of India and also a pamphlet.[5]

I start to day for Paris after a stay of 8 weeks nearly in London. Mr Kirk[6] of Albany I am informed is in the city. I will try to see him before my departure but do not know that I shall succeed. I see in the windows of the

---

[1] Henry's two-page letter introducing John G. Malcolmson to Beck begins on the same page as the last line and closing of a letter from Malcolmson. The lines, presumably in Malcolmson's handwriting, read:

Strand, London and will be thankfully received.

John G. Malcolmson

East India Company's Med! Establishment and late Secretary to the Madras Medical Board

Henry's letter is folded and addressed to Beck in Albany but bears no postmark. Near the address, in Henry's handwriting, are two notes: "Method of determining the meridian" and "Boston journal No for Jan & Feby 1836." Henry apparently retained this copy and sent another to Beck.

[2] We are assuming that Henry wrote his letter during his last day in London before leaving for Paris early in the morning of May 10.

[3] John Grant Malcolmson (1802–1844) was a surgeon with the East India Company's Medical Establishment in Madras from 1823 to 1838. In addition to several monographs (see footnote 5, below), he published nine articles on geology and paleontology. Malcolmson belonged to learned societies in India and in Britain; he was a member of the Asiatic Society of Bombay, the Royal Society of London (elected 1840), the Geological Society of

London, and the Royal Asiatic Society of Great Britain and Ireland. D. G. Crawford, *Roll of the Indian Medical Service, 1615–1930* (London, 1930), p. 313.

[4] Beck's *Elements of Medical Jurisprudence* was first published in Albany in 1823. The *DAB* terms it "the first authoritative book on medical jurisprudence published in the United States." By the date of this letter it had gone through five editions.

[5] The Albany Institute library catalog of 1855 lists Malcolmson's *Essay on the History and Treatment of Beriberi* (Madras, 1835) as a gift from the author. (*Transactions of the Albany Institute*, 1855, 3:219.) The pamphlet may have been Malcolmson's *Letter to the Right Hon. Sir Henry Hardinge, . . . on the Effects of Solitary Confinement, on the Health of Soldiers, in Warm Climates* (London, 1837), a copy of which is in the Henry Library. Another possibility is *Observations on Some Forms of Rheumatism Prevailing in India* (Madras, 1835).

[6] Edward Norris Kirk, the New York evangelist (*Henry Papers*, 2:14n), was traveling and lecturing in Europe at this time. Kirk returned to the United States in late 1839 to become Secretary of the Foreign Evangelical Society and continue promoting religious revivals in cities on the East coast. *DAB*.

London booksellers the 5th edition of your work exposed for sale. In great haste

Yours &
Jos Henry

P.S.

I have forwarded through O Riche to the Albany Institute two packages one from the Royal Society and the other from Dr Fitton containing a copy of his work on geology.[7]

I have met James D Forbes of Edinburgh in London. He informed me that he had sent a paper to me a few weeks before and also some copies of the same for the Institute.

London is at present thronged with men of science from every part of the United Kingdom. The chair of chemistry is now vacant in the London University and there are said to be more than 20 applicants. Amoung the number are Johnson, Graham & Reid of Scotland and I know not how many of Ireland.

[7] The Albany Institute library catalog, p. 134, lists William Henry Fitton's *Observations on Some of the Strata Between the Chalk and Oxford Oolite, in the South-East of England* (London, 1836) as a gift from the author. Fitton (1780–1861, *DNB*) was a well-known geologist.

TO HARRIET HENRY

Family Correspondence, Henry Papers, Smithsonian Archives

London May 9th 1837

My Dear Harriet

I start tomorrow morning at 4 oclock in the steam Packet the Magnet for Bologne on my way to Paris. All my affairs are on board and I am now at ½ past 10 o'clock in a snug little room at No 70 Fenchurch street with old William Vaughan where I am to remain until about 12 or one o'clock and then to go on board. The vessel starts at this unreasonable hour on account of the tide in the Port of Bologne and as I lodged in the far end of the city I concluded to spend the evening with my very kind old friend. If this letter should not be quite as connected as it might be you must attribute it to the fact that while I am writing this I am carrying on a conversation with Mr Vaughan. I have been nearly 8 weeks in this place and have not yet exhausted the wonders of science and arts which it contains. I have however spent as much time in it as my stay in Europe will allow and have ob-

338

tained as much information as will I hope repay for the time and money expended. I however must not take into this account the pain my absence has cost my Dear little wife or the feelings of gloom and homesickness I have experienced when the fatigue of the evening sometimes follows the excitement and labour of the day. Were you with me My Dear Dear Harriet I would enjoy this visit very much but I now feel that any thing that I do in the way of mere pleasure is not proper and that I must confine my attention to the main object of my visit. Your last letter made me quite melancholy although I was as you well supposed well pleased to receive it and thankfull to learn that you were all well. I regret that any disturbances have occurred in college and think the managers of the Institution will do well to adopt a more strict and consistent aim of policy. Stephen must be hurt at the course in reference to the affair he mentions relative to the assault on him by one of the student.[1] I may however administer some words of comfort by assuring him that he may be of quite as much importance in other places as at Princeton. I happen to have with me a few copies of his paper on the eclipse of 1832 and gave one of them to Mr Baily the President of the Astronomical Society. He stated to me a few days afterwards that he regretted not having seen the paper a few weeks sooner as he had just published a paper in the Transactions of the Astronomical Society on a similar phenominon witnessed in the eclipse of 1836 and that he would have referred to Stephens paper. He stated that he would send a copy of his paper to Stephen through me when I return from France. Mr Baily was very attentive to me and you may inform Stephen that he gave me a particular description of every part of his small observatory and reccommended instruments proper for one of a similar kind which may be fitted up at small expense at Princeton.[2] I have made notes and sketches of the several parts and if my life be spared intend the trustees to the contrary notwithstanding immediatly on my return. I have purchased a very pretty portable transit instrument[3] which will answer well for getting time and will also serve in tracing meridian lines for determining the variation of the needle in different parts of the State of New York should the magnetic Survey be agreed

---

[1] We do not know precisely which altercation at Princeton in 1837 involved Stephen Alexander. The most likely incident seems to have been the one recorded in the Faculty Minutes of April 4, 1837, in which a Hilliard M. Judge, a senior from Winnsboro, South Carolina, was dismissed from the College for attempting to fire a loaded pistol at a College officer. Faculty Minutes of April 4, 1837, Princeton University Archives.

[2] Henry's diary entry of April 28, 1837,

printed above, includes both an account of the discussion with Baily concerning Stephen Alexander's paper on the eclipse of 1831 (not 1832) and a description of Baily's observatory.

[3] A receipt dated May 2, 1837, indicates that Henry bought a transit instrument from Thomas Charles Robinson for eight pounds. (Folder of Accounts with Various Instrument- and Apparatus-dealers, Joseph Henry for the College of New Jersey, 1837, Princeton University Archives.)

on.[4] Henry James informed me when I left N.Y. that he had some idea of coming to Europe this summer to visit his relatives in Ireland. I wish I knew his final determination since I have purchased a lot of books for him which I am now at a loss how to dispose of.[5] You are now I hope snugly situated at James' and I hope amid the circle of our warm friend almost recconciled to the temporary absence of your truant husband. Nancy, James, Mother, Aunt, Stephen, Louiza and Caroline not to forget our dear dear little ones are all well I hope. I never pass a toy shop without thinking of something that would please one of them: a beautiful doll for Mary a machine for William and this evening I was on the point of purchasing an ivory [?gumb] ring for the litle one. I however reccollected that she would scarcely need the article by the time I re[t]urn. I hope you have receved all my letters and also the package which I sent to the care of the Albany Institute. This is my fourth letter but I would have written some days ago but was very much engaged in preparing an analysis of the experiments and reports of the Franklin Institute of Phila[a] on the bursting of steam boilers to be published in one of the scientific Journals of the city. It is now finished and in the hands of the printer. It cost me several days assiduous labour but was at length completed to my satisfaction.[6] I will write again as soon as I am

[4] Henry was still hoping that terrestrial magnetism would be made part of the New York Natural History Survey.

[5] Unknown to Henry, Henry James had already made the trip, landing in Plymouth the same day Henry wrote this letter (see his letter of May 13, below, announcing his arrival). Disaffected with the strict Calvinism of his upbringing and of the Princeton Theological Seminary, Henry James decided to take a six-month leave of absence—a separation that turned out to be permanent.

Although his considerable contributions to American intellectual life have been well documented, biographical details are, as one scholar has noted, "as meagre and as undramatic as the intellectual life is rich and rewarding." In fact, what we do know of James's travels in Great Britain comes from his correspondence with Henry, his former teacher in Albany and good friend (see *Henry Papers*, *1*: 19n, 2:35n). Frederic Harold Young, *The Philosophy of Henry James, Sr.* (New York, 1951), p. 3; Giles Gunn, *Henry James, Senior: A Selection of His Writings* (Chicago, 1974), p. 16.

[6] Bache's calendar of activities (Bache Papers, Library of Congress) mentions that he and Henry worked on this manuscript all day

on May 6 and again on May 8. This is Henry's first mention of an article he wrote for the *Magazine of Popular Science and Useful Knowledge* published in London. In this article Henry injected himself into a major scientific controversy involving Anglo-American cultural rivalries. This dispute began in 1836 when the magazine published an analysis of the report by Bache's subcommittee on steam boiler explosions ("Prevention of Explosion in Steam-Boilers," 1836, 2:114–124). The piece included a number of sarcastic comments on the timidity of the American experimenters and on the report's conclusions. The Franklin Institute received the article just as it was going over the proofs of the next installment of the *Report* and issued a rebuttal.

When Henry was in London, J. W. Parker, the editor of the *Magazine of Popular Science*, asked him to comment on the Institute's *General Report*. Though Bache warned Henry about Parker's attitudes toward American science, Henry agreed to offer his analysis provided that Parker promise to publish his remarks as written or not to publish them at all. Instead Parker published a badly mutilated version of Henry's account ("Prevention of Explosion in Steam-Boilers. II.," 1837, 3:321–332), prefaced by comments which offended

settled in Paris and give you an account of what may strike as peculiarly strange or interesting. I feel somewhat unplesant in parting from my very kind friends in this place namely the two Messrs Vaughan and Bache and his good little wife. I am much indebted to the last named person and always restorted to her society when I found my self gloomy in reference to home wife and children and was permitted to converse on these subjects so near my heart and found in her sympathy a kind response. Bache went this morning to Cambridge and we parted probably not again to meet until on the american side of the water.

There are a great number of americans in London just at this time. Among the number is the Rev Mr Kirk of albany with a son of Mr Delavan who accompanies him.[7] I attempted to see the Rev. Gentlemen this morning and spent several hours in the persuit but did not succeed. I only accidentally herd of his being in the city yesterday and hoped that he might bring me some intelligence from Albany. I addressed a note to him requesting that any communications for me might be left with Prof Bache. I also learned that the Rev Mr Bethune[8] and his Lady sailed for New York yesterday. I was at the vessel when she sailed but Mr B. and his Lady did not arrive at the warf in time to get on board. I however learned that they met the ship at another warf. I waited more than an hour to see them and regret that we did not meet. Prof Proudfit[9] of the New York university as well as Abbot the author of the corner stone[10] are in London but in this wilderness of persons we have not come in contact. I called this morning to bid fare

---

American cultural sensibilities. A complete account of this quarrel may be found in Bruce Sinclair, *Philadelphia's Philosopher Mechanics: A History of the Franklin Institute, 1824–1865* (Baltimore, 1974), pp. 186–188.

Bache wrote to Henry in Paris about the alterations, requesting Henry's permission to submit the article in its original form to another journal. See his letter to Henry of June 7, printed below.

[7] Despite the prominence of Edward Cornelius Delavan (1793–1871, *DAB*) in New York affairs, we have not been able to identify his son. The elder Delavan was a noted New York publisher and temperance reformer.

[8] George Washington Bethune (1805–1862) was a Presbyterian minister in Philadelphia. Born in New York City of Scotch and Huguenot antecedents, Bethune was educated at Columbia and Dickinson College and studied theology at Princeton Theological Seminary before taking up a Dutch Reformed pastorate in Rhinebeck, New York. He and his wife,

Mary Williams, moved to Philadelphia in 1834 and remained there until 1849. An extensive traveler, Bethune and his invalid wife made several trips to Europe. *DAB*.

[9] John Williams Proudfit (1803–1870) was professor of Latin and Greek at New York University from 1834 to 1841. Proudfit was born in Salem, New York, graduated from Union College in 1821 and attended Princeton Theological Seminary from 1823 to 1824. Ordained in 1825, Proudfit served as pastor of the Federal Street Church in Newburyport, Massachusetts, before joining the faculty of New York University. He later taught Greek and Greek literature at Rutgers from 1841 to 1860 and served as a chaplain in the Union Army during the Civil War. *Roberts*, p. 34.

[10] Jacob Abbott (1803–1871) was the author of *The Corner-Stone*, a popular work on theology originally published in 1834. Abbott enjoyed a varied career as a Congregational clergyman, a teacher and an immensely successful writer of children's stories. *DAB*.

well to our minister Mr Stevenson and found him much engaged in the affairs of the nation highly dissatisfied with the arduous and responsible duties of an ambasador. A very important question being at this time to be adjusted between our government and that of Great Britain relative to the liberation of a vessel of slaves which accidentally was driven by distress of weather into one of the West India islands and were there immediately set free by an order of the Judge of the Supreme Court. This happened several years since and the owners of the slaves ask of the government remuneration for their property. The English government refuse to make any payment. The american minister is ordered by the cabinet at home to insist on the payment so that the affair looks at this time rather squally. Mr Stevenson says that he would by far rather be a laborer in virginia than a minister at the Court of St. James.[11] Mr Vaughan has been talking to me all the time I have engaged with this letter. He tells me not to stop on his account and not to forget to send his complments and this he has repeated several times. He has just been giving me an account of an interview he once had with the Sister of the celebrated Baron Trench.[12]

It is now ¼ past mid night. The younger Mr Vaughan has just come in and proposes to accompany me at this late hour to the boat. I am to have a

[11] Henry is relating an incident in one of the major controversies that erupted in Anglo-American diplomatic relations between 1815 and the Civil War. During his tenure as Ambassador, Stevenson was called upon by the American government to secure an indemnity for slaves of American owners who had been liberated by British colonial authorities in the Bahamas.

The claims centered around the slaves from three ships: the *Comet*, *Encomium*, and *Enterprise*. In 1831 the *Comet*, carrying 165 slaves from Alexandria, D. C., to New Orleans, ran aground in the Bahamas. The colonial governor ordered the slaves freed. Similarly in 1834 the *Encomium* with 45 slaves out of Charleston was stranded in the Bahamas and its cargo of slaves released. A year later another brig, the *Enterprise*, out of Alexandria with 78 slaves, was driven by a storm into Hamilton, the Bahamas, and its slaves ordered freed by the Chief Justice of Bermuda.

Under pressure from the proprietors of the slaves, the American government instructed Stevenson, himself a slave owner sympathetic to his aggrieved compatriots, to petition Foreign Secretary Lord Palmerston for compensation. The demands created some controversy in Great Britain since the Parliament had recently abolished slavery in the colonies and was mounting an international crusade to stamp out the slave trade, some of which was surreptitiously carried on by Spanish, Portuguese, and Brazilian slavers under the American flag. It was not until January 1837, five months after Stevenson made his request, that Palmerston agreed to work out a formula for compensation for the slaves of the *Comet* and *Encomium*; no indemnification was offered for slaves from the *Enterprise* since the ship was seized after the British Emancipation Act went into effect on August 1, 1834. After three more years of negotiation over details, the British government finally agreed to pay the slave owners $115,630 or about $479 per slave. Francis Fry Wayland, *Andrew Stevenson: Democrat and Diplomat, 1785–1875* (Philadelphia, 1949), pp. 112–118.

[12] It is difficult to determine here whom Henry is referring to. Baron Richard LePoer Trench (*DNB*), the second Earl of Clancarty, had three sisters—Florinda, Harriet, and Frances. *Burke's Peerage*, 102d ed. (1954), p. 464. Henry, or Vaughan, may have mistaken Melesina Trench, a distant relative to Baron Trench by marriage, for one of his sisters. Melesina Trench (1768–1827) was the author of a number of popular ballads and poems of a historical nature. *DNB*.

settee until morning but do not expect to sleep much. Adieu my Dear Dear wife and be assured that although I have as yet found no cause to regret my visit yet I shall never again leave my family should providence spare my life. Adieu again Dear Harriet and believe me as ever only yours. J H

Mr Petty Vaughan sent me a ticket this afternoon for a Lecture on the art of embossing paper but I could not attend. Mr Vaughan sends you with his compliments a specimen of the art which was made at the Lecture. It is a head of Sir Walter Scott. I hope it will reach you safely. Mr V is putting in a bundle of blotting paper. Good night and may heaven protect you and ours.

FROM THE DUKE OF SUSSEX[1]
Henry Papers, Smithsonian Archives

[May 13, 1837]

His Royal Highness The President of the Royal Society requests the favor of ____ Mr. Henry's ____ Company at the Soirée, at Kensington Palace on Saturday May 13 and June 10th 9 o'clock

[1] Henry was not in London for either soirée, a type of entertainment which had been offered by previous Presidents of the Royal Society, notably Joseph Banks. The receptions allowed the Fellows to mingle with distinguished foreign guests but the expenses, borne by the President, could be considerable. A motion, citing these expenses, was made in the House of Commons in July 1838 to increase the Duke's allowance, but the government opposed the measure and it failed. The Duke resigned the Presidency in August 1838. *Record of the Royal Society of London*, 4th ed. (London, 1940), p. 62. The *Literary Gazette* (London, 1837), pp. 323, 387, reported on both parties.

May 13, 1837

FROM HENRY JAMES
Henry Papers, Smithsonian Archives

Portsmouth. May 13, 1837.

My dear friend:

Much to your surprise no doubt, this letter will inform you of my arrival in England. I landed at Plymouth on Tuesday last, after 18 days sail from New York in the London Packet *Westminster*. I unaccountably slipped your family between Princeton & Albany. I left them well on going home to make my preparations, & promised to return to Princeton before I sailed & take whatever they might furnish me with for you. I saw Mrs Alexander[1] frequently in A[lbany] who told me that her husband wished to send a Regents Report &c (which by the way I procured for you myself) and that I would be able to see him in Princeton. The difficulty of procuring money in New York detained me there later than I had designed, and it was as well as I can conjecture owing to this forced delay that I missed yr family, for on my visit to P[rinceton] they had all left. Mr Chilton gave me a letter for you and $200. in American gold which I have.[2] I go in a few moments to the Isle of Wight, to stay for the Sabbath & Monday probably. Shall be in London, God willing, on Tuesday or Wednesday. If you are now there, you will find my direction at the North & South American Coffee House, as soon as possible after I arrive. If this finds you in Edinburgh or elsewhere, write to me Care of George Wildes & Co, 19. Colman St. detailing your locum in quo, your plans &c, & what I shall do to see you. I shall find it difficult to leave London before hearing from home, perhaps a month. Meanwhile in great haste.

Yrs Ever affectionatly
H. James

[1] Louisa Alexander, Stephen's wife.

[2] The letter from James R. Chilton has not been found. He apparently wanted Henry to purchase chemicals and apparatus for him. We have found two bills from French firms listing articles purchased by Henry for Chilton. One is from Robiquet for approximately $259 and the other is from Pixii for $170. Both are in the folder "Accounts, 1837–1838," Box 31, Henry Papers, Smithsonian Archives.

TO HENRY JAMES
Draft,[1] Henry Papers, Smithsonian Archives

Paris May 23ʳᵈ 1837

My Dear Friend

I received through my Friend Mr Vaughan of London your letter[2] which gave me the interesting intelligence of your arrival in Europe. I was not intirely unprepared for the news since my wife informed me that you intended to sail on the 17ᵗʰ of april.[3] I waited some time in London longer than I intended in part with the hope of seeing you before my departure for this city and with the intention of indeavoring to prevail on you to accompany me. Cannot you now make it compatible with your plans to come to Paris before going to Ireland and then make a short excursion with me through Belgium perhaps Switzerland and then return to England visiting Ireland when the weather is more settled and warmer. You will scarcely return to America now that you have crossed the atlantic without seeing Paris. I regret that I did not get your letter sooner. It had lain several days at my Bankers before I called yesterday to leave my address. I have written to my very kind Friend Mr Vaughan[4] and requested him to introduce you to Professor Bache. I will also write to Bache[5] in reference to your being in London and should you conclude to come to Paris as I think you will perhaps you will so arrange matters as to accompany my Friend Bache and his good Lady. I hope to see them here in a few weeks. I have taken Lodgings near Dr Hun of Albany at No 3 (bis) *Place du Pantheon*[6] a situation somewhat retired but convenient for attending the lectures at the Garden of Plants[7] and the several colleges of Paris. Angelo Ames[8] has just (yester-

---

[1] Henry's file note reads "My letter to H. James—written over." We have not found the outgoing letter.

[2] Immediately above.

[3] Harriet Henry's letter informing her husband of James's European trip has not survived.

[4] The letter has not been located.

[5] See below, Henry to Bache, May 28, 1837.

[6] The Place du Panthéon is in the Latin Quarter.

[7] Founded in 1635 as a medical garden and a school of pharmacy and medicine, the Jardin des Plantes (Jardin du Roi) had been converted into a center for botanical study by Charles-François Dufay (1698–1739, *DSB*), director during the last seven years of his life.

Dufay's successor, the Comte de Buffon (1707–1788, *DSB*) directed the Jardin from 1739 until his death. Buffon doubled the area of garden and enlarged its collections. He also greatly strengthened the place of zoology at the Jardin. During the Revolution the Jardin was reorganized, renamed the Muséum d'Histoire Naturelle, and given responsibility for the animals which had previously resided in the menagerie at Versailles.

The policy of the Muséum d'Histoire Naturelle has been to diffuse knowledge as widely as possible. All of its collections and facilities were available to those individuals who expressed interest in them, while certain collections and facilities were open to the public at large. Public lectures were given by the

day) returned from Rome. He left Paris on the first of March and since then has made a tour through Italy.

I was very kindly received in England and am much indebted to Mr Vaughan his Uncle and most of the Scientific gentlemen of the city for their polite attentions. I am in the way of picking up a good deal of knowledge in this place but as yet have not delivered but one of my letters of introduction. I have purchased in London a complete set of the Edinburgh review and also one of the Quarterly.[9] As I did not know where you were to be found I deferred sending them to America until I would hear further from you. They are now in London and perhaps had better be sent with the other articles I may purchase and thus escape the duty. In reference to the $200 forwarded by Chilton please keep this and pass the sum to my credit. On my arrival in London I found in examining the paper that you had given me instead of a letter of credit[10] a bill of exchange to the amount of 250£ and that according to the usages in mercantile transactions of the kind it was necessary for me to send the bill to Ireland to have it accepted. Otherwise in case of a bankruptcy of the party the money would be lost.[11] It was not my original intention to draw on this money except in case of need

---

staff of the Muséum.

Henry's contemporaries held the Muséum in the highest esteem. Both the British Museum and the London Zoo modeled themselves after aspects of it.

Joseph P. F. Deleuze, *History and Description of the Royal Museum of Natural History* (Paris, 1823); Albert E. Gunther, *A Century of Zoology at the British Museum Through the Lives of Two Keepers, 1815–1914* (Kent, 1975), pp. 78–81; Philip Street, *The London Zoo* (London, 1956), p. 13.

[8] Ames and Henry had been friends in Albany. *Henry Papers*, 2:151.

[9] Both the *Edinburgh Review* and the *Quarterly Review* were widely read literary journals. Their contributors were often leaders in their fields. To give but one example—the physical sciences—two frequent reviewers were David Brewster and John Herschel. Historians have found these reviews to be very useful in discussions of the epistemological and methodological positions of scientists. See, for example, Richard Olson, *Scottish Philosophy and British Physics, 1750–1880: A Study in the Foundations of the Victorian Scientific Style* (Princeton, 1975), pp. 169–193.

Henry's purchase of a complete set of each

journal meant that he had acquired a mini-library for James. The two journals combined ran to over 110 volumes by this date.

[10] A letter of credit is a document addressed by a banker to his correspondents, requesting that they make payments to the party named in the letter, providing certain stated conditions are fulfilled. It was a common way for individuals traveling abroad to obtain funds. *The Business Encyclopaedia and Legal Advisor*, 1st ed., s.v. "Letter of Credit."

[11] A bill of exchange, an early form of bank draft or check, is a written order to one person, known as the drawee, to pay another person named on the bill a specified amount on a certain date. In this case James ordered an Irish firm or bank to pay Henry £250. Henry's problem was that if he wanted to cash the bill with anyone but the drawee, he would have to endorse it. This would make him personally liable for the bill if the drawee was unable to honor the bill. The depressed financial conditions of 1837 made such an occurrence not unlikely. *Encyclopaedia Britannica*, 8th ed., s.v. "Credit," "Exchange," "Money." James's assistance was substantial. It amounted to over $1200.

or for the purchase of some articles of apparatus should the college fail to make me a remittance according to promise. I have received as yet no communication from the College and will make a few purchases on my own account in addition to a small sum I received from Mr Maclean before my departure from Princeton. I have now given up the idea [of] being able to purchase an apparatus for the Institution and have come to the determination of procuring on my own account the instruments most essentially necessary for my own use in the way of original research and on my return (should it be the will of Providence for me to do so) to devote myself to the main object of my life the extension of science.

I regret that the managers of affairs at Princeton should be so blind to the best interests of the College as not to exert themselves to send me the money since it must be evident to every one that after securing a good Faculty the Institution should be well furnished with all the necessary implements of instruction[12] and now that I am on the spot with some experience in such matters I could purchase for $5000[13] as many articles as would serve our present purpose and which if procured through a less interested agent would cost nearly double that sum.

[12] Henry is expressing the commonly accepted wisdom of his day. Most American colleges made extensive purchases of natural philosophy apparatus during the second quarter of the nineteenth century. Whereas the average college had approximately $100 worth of apparatus in 1820, it had at least $2000 invested in apparatus in 1850. Princeton's outlay of funds during Henry's tenure, either directly or through the later reimbursement of Henry for personal monies spent, was comparable to that of such institutions as Wesleyan and Columbia. Stanley M. Guralnick, *Science and the Ante-Bellum American College* (Philadelphia, 1975), pp. 72–73.

[13] This was the original sum Henry had been promised by the Alumni Association to purchase apparatus. On February 17, 1837, Henry received $500 from John Maclean on behalf of the Alumni Association (receipt, Maclean Papers, Princeton University Archives). Maclean intended to transmit an additional $500 to Henry in Europe. The money was raised but Maclean was advised against sending it because of unfavorable exchange rates. Henry did not receive any additional money from Princeton while he was in Europe. He spent, however $1410, with the difference coming from his personal resources. Princeton reimbursed Henry with $100 in April 1839. The remaining $810, plus other monies owed Henry, plus simple interest, was not paid until 1865. By that time the debt Princeton owed Henry had reached $3390. Allen G. Shenstone, "Joseph Henry's Bills: 1832–1837–1844–1865," *The Princeton University Library Chronicle*, 1967, 28:150–155; "The New Jersey College D͞r to Joseph Henry for Philosophical Apparatus Purchased in Europe," Folder of Accounts with Various European Instrument- and Apparatus-Dealers, Joseph Henry for the College of New Jersey, 1837, Princeton University Archives. *Maclean*, 2:362, 363.

TO HARRIET HENRY[1]

Family Correspondence, Henry Papers, Smithsonian Archives

Paris [May 26–June 16], 1837
½ past 12 oclock at night

My Dear Little Wife

I have just returned to my Hotel after spending the evening to a very late hour with my kind and attentive friend Dr. Hun. My last words with him on seperating were relative to you and our children and you may judge of my surprise and pleasure when I entred the gate to have presented to me by the old woman of the Lodge a letter which I instantly recognised to be from you. The Porteress seeing the avidity with which I opened it said in French *"that letter must be from your very dear friend."* It is, it is was the reply. It comes from my Dear Dear Wife.[2] I am much rejoiced to learn that you have safely arrived in Albany and also to find from the whole tone of your letter that you are in much better spirits than when you last wrote. Your detail of the incidents relative to the children is highly interesting and the letter in every respect gives me much pleasure. Indeed I could not refrain from devoting a few minutes in answer although it is now past the middle of the night and I am engaged to meet M Gay-Lussac at ½ past 7 in the morning.

I am writing this in a snug little room nearly as large as the one we occupied *together* at Princeton. It is very neatly furnished in the French style with a Bureau, a secretary, & French bed in a recess and a sofa, besides an arm chair 3 other ones, a book case and an article of furniture very convenient but not known in america called a *Table de nuit*. This room is situated on the 3rd floor of the house or as it is called Hotel No 3 (bis) *Place du Pantheon* on the south side of the river and near the Garden of Plants, the College of France and the other principal literary Institutions. In front of the window is an open area called the Place du Pantheon and on one side of this is the celebrated structure which gives it the name and which was erected as a monument to the most distinguished of the sons of France either in the arts of war or Peace. The ground floor of our Hotel as is common with houses of the kind in Paris—an open paved court the entrance of which is a gate sufficiently large to admit a coach; this entrance is

---

[1] A fragmentary Mary Henry Copy of a letter to Harriet of May 17, 1837, survives in the Henry Papers. The text relates, in less detail, the crossing of the Channel and arrival in France. This long letter is a tourist's warm response to France, tinctured with a number of realistic observations.

[2] Not found.

attended by a middle aged woman who has a room or lodge at the side where all the keys of the several chambers are left and w[h]ere the candle is lighted when we ascend to our apartments. A broad stair-way leads as a public high way to the apartments of the numerous inhabitants of the hotel. De Witt occupies a chamber contiguous to mine and I have communicated to him through the boards of a shut door the intelligence of the reception of your letter. The news has rather served to irritate him in reference to his relatives. He has not received a single line since he left home while I have had the good fortune, thanks to the Love of those I left behind, to have no fewer than four. I stated in my last letter that De Witt had left London a few days before to go to Paris to procure Lodgings. I found him when I arrived at a Hotel waiting for me to come before choosing a place of residence. My last letter which I hope you will receive was written as I stated on the eve of my departure for Paris and from the parlor of Mr William Vaughan; I should perhaps state that it is also the parlor of Petty Vaughan for the Uncle and Nephew live together; the one a Bachelor of 45 and the other of 85. I was escorted to the Steamboat by the Younger Vaughan at about ½ past 12 at night and on leaving my kind conductor descended to the cabin to endeavour to get a little sleep previous to the mornings sail. In this however I was disappointed for I found the settees chairs and floor occupied in every part with sleeping snowering passengers—men women and children promiscously mingled. The Stewardess had promised, when I engaged my passage in the afternoon, to give me a mattress but I came so late that all were engaged. I was compelled to put up with a bed quilt, a sitting place in a corner and to resign myself not to sleep but to rather gloomy reflections about home, leaving London, and the kind Friends I had there met with; The hours however soon passed and at 4 o'clock the vessel was put in motion; the Passengers roused and preperations made for an early breakfast. The day proved clear although cold; the sea was perfect tranquil and after a more than usually quick passage of just 10 hours we landed at *Boulogne* in France. In our passage down the Thames we passed several interesting and celebrated Places. *Tillbury* fort *Scheerness Margate* &c. In passing out into the channel we had a view of Shakespere cliff among the albion cliffs of Dover. In landing at Boulogne we had immediate evidence that we were in a Foreign land; and it was a matter of no little surprise to An American who in his own country can travel thousands of miles and meet with little to attract his attention in the way of novelty of manners and customs; to find himself in a few hours transported to an intercourse with beings as dissimilar to himself in Language and general habits as the inhabitants almost of an other planet. The strange language, the singular appearance of the houses, the throng of women with large wooden shoes and baskets straped to their backs for carrying fish or the trunks of the Passengers. Women in Boulogne are the only porters and stout ones they are. You may be convinced wen I inform you that one of them took my large trunk placed another of goodly dimentions on it and then the two on her basket trotted off to the hotel with the speed of a cart horse at least. Before being permitted to pass the centinel on the warf we were obliged to go into a little office and be searched to prevent the smugling of articles subject to duty. We were also obliged to show our pasports. When I came to exhibit mine the official motioned me to pass on without being personally inspected. My trunk was also passed without being scarcely at all disturbed although it contained a number of packages intrusted to me by Persons in London for friends in Paris. I was however somewhat indebted for this easy passage of the custom house, to the representations of a person called a comissary who is attached to each Public House in the ports of France, speaks english and for a few franks manages all the affairs of the traveller, gets his place in the dilligences, has his pasport countersigned &c &c and in short is quite a factotum to a man in a strange land where that most important member, the toung is next to useless.

As we landed at Boulogne quite early in the afternoon after dinner I took a strowl through the city. It is a very old place contains the remains of a Roman fortification, is divided into two towns; the upper a walled city, and the lower which is situated on the waters edge. The streets are without side walks, very narrow and paved with large flat stones. Although the weather was not very warm yet all the operations of the domestic and culinary kind were going on at the door in the street. Boulogne is a great fishing town and supplies the market of Paris with most of its dainties in the fish line.

I strowled into a burrying ground in the suburbs of the Place and was surprised and amused with the singular appearance. It seemed at a first view like a forest of crosses. Each grave had one of these emblems at the head generally painted black with white streaks but sometimes intirely white. I here for the first time saw the graves decorated with flowers; with pictures and the favourite articles in some cases of the deceased. The garlands are like those of *Pere la Chase* formed of a kind of ever green or rather ever yellow flowers. The graves are attended with great care visited and decorated with flowers as soon as the opening of the Spring will permit. There is a fixed day in the Autumn I believe when the garlands are renewed on all the graves in France which contain the remains of those that were loved or respected by the living.

I was much struck at first sight with the beauty and simplicity of one grave and on closer inspection was still more highly pleased. It contained the remains of a beloved child, was surrounded with a slight grating of wood cleanly weaded and decorated with wild roses. At the head was placed a slender marble column of perfect whiteness, & exquisite workmanship but alas! the simetry of the structure was mared; as a simily of the fate it was designed to commemorate, it shaft was broken and its capital reposed in the dust. On the pedestal one rose was sculptured with its stem broken and the flower falling to the ground. But that the gathering darkness warned me to hasten back to my Inn I would have attempted a sketch of this monument for you.

We started after an excellent nights rest much refreshed at about 9 o'clock in the dilligence for Paris. You have often read and heard of the dilligence but unless you have been more fortunate in your conceptions of this vehicle than I was you have but little idea of it. It is a four wheeled carriage resembling very much in appearance and size the rail way carriages first used; which consisted of three apartments forming a whole resembling three carriages joined together. The front apartment is called the *Coupé* the middle *Interior* and the rear one the *Rotund*. Besides these there is a place on the top with a cover like a gig top called the *Banquet*. As all the other seats were taken I was obliged to take up my quarters in the latter place and a situation of honor it was, according to the sailors considerations for I was seated immediately beside the most important person in the whole company as far as the success of the voyage was concerned namely the *Conductor* of the dilligence or the *Captain du vesseau*.

This person has the full command during the whole Passage; he is armed on the one side with a small copper trumpet which he manages to sound with much noise when the dilligence is about entering or leaving a village. On the other side by a huge leather purse well filled with silver and copper coin and with these in accordance with the old adage short accounts [...][3] he pays while on the way the several drivers in succession. There is now a great opposition between London and Paris and the fare is consequently very cheap. I gave only 4 shillings about one dollar for my passage from London to Boulogne and 28 franks the remainder of the distance.

The speed of the dilligence is also much increased on the same account and we made a more rapid passage than had ever before been accomplished with the same conveyance. My situation on the top was quite plesant. During the day it afforded a delightful view of the country and gave me an opportunity of making a beginning with attempting to make myself under-

---

[3] The last word of the "adage" is illegible.

stood in speaking french. My seat on the top was quite plesant during the day but very cold in the night. I suffered much until I found on the top a large sheep-skin in which I wrapped my feet. The *conductor* I found a very plesant fellow who took much pains to inform me of the names of the different places through which we passed and to give me my first lesson in the spoken language of his country. The cenerry in many places reminded me of America but the appearance of the villages and cities are intirely different. They have an air of antiquity which carries you back in imagination to the infancy of the arts. The houses in the country are generally in clusters, built of mud or straw, plastered and covered with huge thatched roofs and far less comfortable in appearance than the log houses in the new settlements of our own country. The implements of agriculture are of the most simple and imperfect kind. The carriages consist generally of carts with a long narrow body which some person has properly compared to a large hen coop placed between two large and clumsy wheels. The harness appears in every case as if made some hundred years ago and there is an appendeage to the collar which gives the horse a grotesque and unnatural appearance. It consists of a large board on each side forming as it were two wings intended it is said to defend the body of the horse from concussion in passing carriages. It appears however to me that it only defends the body at the expense of the neck. These wings are always painted and in some cases adorned with guilding which makes a singular and gaudy contrast with the other parts of the harness composed of unblackened leather fastened together with pieces of rope. The dilligence is drawn by 5 horses, two behind and 3 before, one of the wheel horse is road by the driver or Postillion who makes a constant cracking of his whip [and] keeps all parts of his body in continual motion. His legs are incased in boots such as even yanky invention could never conceive. They are nondescripts of a shape something similar to the sketch. Made of wood and sole leather and weigh certainly not less than 20 lbs a pair. They are intended to prevent the leg of the rider from receiving injury from collision with passing carriages. How much better is this effected and the poor horse relieved from the weight of the man as well as his boots by placing the driver on the box of the carriage. There are no fences seen on the road we travelled either along the public high way or between the lots of different proprietors. Cattle therefore require the constant attention of the Person who makes so much figure in all Pastoral poetry namely the shepherd. We passed several of these during the day, all old men with long beards each accompanied with two dogs and armed with a long pole terminated at the upper extremity by the Shepherds hook which we have often seen in pictures but of which I never before understood the use. It is intended to cach any member of the flock which may be required. For this purpose the shepherd passes the hook by means of its long handle gently around the leg of the animal, then slips it up over the hip joint and thus secures his object. Of how litle value is human labour and how little the expansion of intellect where a man is required to spend years of his existance in the fields with scarcely no employment for mind or body and no companions but his dogs and sheep. What a monotinous life?

At intervals along the road crosses may be seen erected for the use of Pious travellers and in some cases perhaps to commemorate or point the location of a scene of accident or crime. It appears very remarkable that in a country like France where science litterature and the arts are more advanced than in any other in the world except england that the common country people are scarcely more inlightened or advanced in the arts of life than they were hundreds of years ago. It is this which forms the most striking differences between the several nations of Europe and our own country. With us all is new and a general spirit of improvements prevade the Tillers of the ground as well as the highest officers of government. Here while the few are deeply learned the cortiers and the wealthy inhabitants of the city highly refined, the Agriculturalists are sunk in ignorance little better than pure barbarism and in such poverty that as I am informed of the 36 millions of inhabitants of France not more than $\frac{1}{4}$ of the number taste meat more than once a week.[4] The same is also the case with a great porportion of the inhabitants of great Britain and particularly of Ireland. How much more favourable is the general condition of the multitude in the united states? In this respect we are as much in advance of Europe as we are behind it in what we sometimes attempt to ape the splendor and pomp of Royalty.

You can scarcely imagine the contrast between Paris and the country arround. It appears as if all the intellect the riches and comforts of the nation had been draned from every other part to enrich *la Belle city*. We entred Paris through the *barrierr* St. Dennie and the arch of *Ludovicus Magn[u]s*. At the gate of the city our dilligence was searched by a soldier to prevent clandestinately the introduction within the bounds of any article subjected to a duty. Wine in particular is required to pay a duty which renders the prices very different at places within a few yards of each other situated on different sides of the barrier. I was struck with the height of the houses, the high and sharp roofs, the lamps suspended by wires across the streets, the multitudes of women and men engaged in occupations in the

---

[4] Georges Dupeux, *La Société Française, 1789–1960* (Paris, 1964), discussing industrial workers in this period, states that three quarters of their incomes went for food, mostly bread. He cites a contemporary observer to the effect that urban laborers ate meat and drank wine only on pay day or the day after—i.e. two times a month.

streets which with us and in England are generally performed within doors. It had rained during the night and most of the streets through which we passed were filthy and wet. After passing through a number of narrow streets we at length stopped in the Court of the grand Depot of the dilligences from various parts of France. Here our trunks were again examined to prevent smugling from the country into the city. Our pasports were also inspected, names registered &c. Several persons thronged around the passengers with cards of the different Hotels each extolling the particular advantages of his own establishment. After some hesitation I suffered my self to be led by a fellow to the Hotel de Normandie Rue St Honore, a third rate establishment where however I found two americans just arrived from New York in the Haver Packet. My first business in Paris after getting breakfast was to find the residence of Dr Hun and for this purpose I procured a cab and ordered the driver to take me to the Banking hous of Messrs Wills &c there I received the address required and immediatly drove to the place. I was at first somewhat startled with the name of the street which the Dr had chosen for his residence—Rue L'Enfer or in other words *Infernal Street*. And indeed the appearance of the street itself was not much more prepossessing. Like most of the old streets rather passages of the city it is narrow, dirty, without sidewalks and quite steep near the residence of the Dr. This street however runs quite near one of the most delightful parts of Paris the garden of the Luxemburg and in entering the large gate which opens into the Hotel in which the Dr's apartments are situated you are immediatly introduced as it were into another part of the world. The Dr has thus a delightful dwelling and lives in as much comfort and almost even luxury as is compatible with a state of single blessedness. The Dr was not at home when I called. His howse keeper made me under stand partly by signes and partly by words that he woul[d] soon return. On the table I found the address of De Witt who had only called on the Dr the day previous although he had been in the city more than a week and had defered procuring lodgins until I should arrive. I was received very cordially by the Dr who detained me the whole day until night and then accompanied me to my Hotel. Since then I have seen him every day and am indebted to his kindness for a sight of most of the Lions of the city. I regret to have trespassed so much on his time but a person in Paris who cannot speak this language is in a worse condition than one born deaf and dumb since he has not the advantage of an intimate knowledge of the language of signes. I found De Witt the next morning after my arrival at a tavern. He had managed to pick up a little French during the week although at first was much perplexed. As one means of making myself familiar with the spoken language of France I commenced immediatly to attend the Lectures at the garden of Plants. At first I could not even make out the subject of discourse but now with the assistance of an old Frenchman who does not speak a single word of English I am able to understand without missing almost a single idea a lecture on any scientific subject. My teacher[5] spends with me two hours a day three times a week and occupies the time principally in conversation.

I would have made more progress in the language but would have been much less plesantly situated had I not been thrown intirely on my own resources and met with assistance from my Friend the Dr. The French we learn in America at first is scarcely of any use and all those I have spoken with on the subject inform me that they could not make out a single word of the rapid parlance of the common people. The ear however soon becomes accustomed to sounds heard every moment in the day and where a person can read the language he soon begins to understand it in conversation. My intercourse with men of science was at first much retarded on account of the language but lately I find little difficulty in keeping up a conversation. Most of them understand English or at least can read it with facility and in one interview I had with M Becquerelle[6] a considerable part of our conversa-

---

[5] In Henry's Address Book the name "Delavaux" appears with the notation, "my teacher." The address given is 22 Rue du Four, St. Germain, Paris. This is François-Urbain Delavaux (1775–?) one of the very little men of science thrown up by the revolutionary period in France. Born in Port-Louis and a "student of Christian doctrines" before the Revolution, Delavaux served as a pharmacist with the army in 1793. After teaching in various institutions in Paris, he was on the faculty at the Lycée in Nîmes in the second decade of the nineteenth century. His later career is not known to us. In the year Nine, Delavaux became Professor of Natural History at the École Centrale de Saintes and at other posts taught mathematics. There is some evidence that botany was his specialty. A plant found originally near Arles is attributed to him. In 1838 Torrey was interested in obtaining Delavaux's herbarium. But the only work of his in the Royal Society *Catalogue* is on meteorites. A few letters of Delavaux are in the Musée Calvet, Avignon. Most of our knowledge comes from information furnished by the Archives Départementales de Gard and Morbihan and the Bibliothèque Séguier, Nîmes. Torrey to L. R. Gibbes, April 17, 1838, Torrey Papers, New York Botanical Garden Library. *Bullétin de L'Académie Internationale de Géographie Botanique, 19*:253. His article on meteorites is in the *Comptes Rendus,* 1841, *12*:1190. It was reprinted in *Sturgeon's Annals,* 1841, 7:221–223.

[6] Antoine-César Becquerel (1788–1878), the first of a long line of a distinguished family of French scientists. A graduate of the École Polytechnique, Becquerel served as an army engineer to 1815 and then devoted himself to science. He became a member of the Academy in 1829; in 1838 he obtained the chair in physics in the Muséum d'Histoire Naturelle. His original interest in mineralogy led to studies of the effects on minerals of pressure, heat, and electricity. Becquerel was an early investigator of the piezoelectric effect. In his research on the voltaic cell, he was an adherent of the chemical theory. He used the cell to study the formation of crystals.

This is the only account surviving of Henry's meeting with Becquerel. In November 1835 Henry acquired the first three volumes of the French scientist's *Traité expérimental de L'Électricité et du Magnétisme . . .* which had started appearing just the year before. The entire work (7 vols. plus an atlas of plates) survives in Henry's Library, with some annotations, as do other works such as the two-volume *Traité de physique* of 1842–1844. Henry had Becquerel's address in his address book and sent him copies of "Contributions I–III." Accompanying "Contributions III" is an important letter of June 19, 1839, which will appear in volume four. No evidence survives to our knowledge of other direct contacts between the two men.

tion was carried on by means of a slate. When we were at a loss he wrote French and I English. My residence in Paris will therefore add something to my knowledge of French and could I remain here a few months I would probably be able to speeck with some ease.

But to return to Paris. Had I come to the city before visiting London all the curiosities of the Latter would have appeared common placed, not that the objects of interest in London are in themselves less worthy of admiration and study but they are of a kind more familiar and in some respects known to us from our earliest lessons in reading. Every thing in Paris on the contrary has a strange aspect. The style of building is different and the public structures in general more imposing than those of London. Ever[y] thing here is not as in the latter city covered with smoke and the more modern structures have a beautiful whiteness which has revived my taste for architecture which was almost stifled with the smoke and fogs of London. The old streets as I before stated are dusty and narrow without side walks, a single gutter in the middle along which in many cases a stream of water is continually flowing. The houses on each side are very high 5 and 6 stories so that the passage resembles a deep irregular chasam in a rock of gray stone. The modern streets are however much wider and furnished with side walks of a composition which resembles stone and which forms a beautiful and plesant surface. The most perfect contrasts to the narrow streets of Paris are those called the Boulevards where the old wall of the city formerly stood. The name is said to be derived from the circumstance of this part of the city having been used for ball playing on the grass.[7] You will find them on the map[8] which I intend to send with this letter.* They occupy about the middle of the northern part of the city on the north side of the river and resemble a wide street the different parts of which are known by different names such as Boul. de Madelaine, *Bul. des capuchines Bul. des Italians* &c. The bulevards are in fact nothing but a long wide street with side walks paved with the artificial stone before mentioned and in which every article of Luxury or convenience may be purchased that the most fertile imagination has ever conceived or the most ingenious workman executed. The Boulevards in some respects resemble Broadway but the

---

* I have cut off the margin of the map so as to diminish its size as much as possible without taking off any essential parts. I hope you will find some amusement in comparing my letter with the map. I know you will be interested in Paris now that I am here.

[7] An incorrect etymology. From the German, bollwerk, a bulwark. "The French word originally meant the horizontal portion of a rampart; hence the promenade laid out on a demolished fortification." *Oxford English Dictionary.*

[8] Not surviving in the Henry Papers.

street is wider and the side walks next the road occupied the whole length with stands on which articles of all descriptions are offered at very low prices. You see on each side of the street, stores filled with immense Looking glasses, others with mantle clocks, others devoted to shalls, and one which I noted as peculiarly singular exposed only female articles of mourning. This street, several miles long appears like an immense museum from one end to the other & I have never passed through it without being strongly tempted to empty my pockets with purchasing some of the many articles which arrest the attention on all sides. But by far the most interesting features of this city are the beautiful gardens and *places* found in almost every part. To begin with these you will see on the middle of the map enclosed by buildings nearly on all sides and forming a parallogram the *Place du Carousel*. This is merely the court of the palace of the Tuilleries and the Palais of the *Louvre*. The Palace of the Tuilleries or the residence of the King is that block of buildings represented on the map by a wide black spot which forms the Western boundary or side of the parallelogram of the *Place du Carusel*. The side of the same parallelogram along the river is the long gallery of the museum of the Louvre in which are placed the great collection of Pictures and curiosities &c the wonder and pride of Paris. On the east side of the parallogram (top of map being the north) is the *Palace* of the Luver. The whole of the area called the Place du carousal was intended originally to be enclosed with buildings but the part on the north as you will see by the map is unfinished and has thus remained for perhaps more than 100 years.

From the *Place du Carousal* there is a Public passage during ordinary days through a Triumphant arch[9] (marked by a small black spot on the map) and also through a vaulted passage in the middle of the Kings Palace into the most beautiful place to be found perhaps in the world *the garden of the Tuilleries* or as it may be called the garden * of the Palace of the King. The larger part of this area as you will see by the map is occupied with groves of trees principally of horse chestnut. The trees are all trimed underneath so as to present the appearance of perfectly horizontal plane of green about 8 feet from the ground. Under this not a blade of grass is suffered to grow and the whole is kept as clean as a newly swept floor. The part of the garden

---

* I have made a small dot of ink directly in front of my lodgins. You will find the Pantheon on the map and in front of this you will see the Number 97. The tail of the figure 7 is almost directly opposite my lodging. I have also made a dot of ink on right hand side of the garden of the Luxemburg to designate Dr Huns appartment.

[9] Erected in 1806 by Napoleon in imitation of the arch of Septimius Severus in Rome. This is at the other end of the "triumphal way" from the Arch of Triumph which Henry mentions below.

next the Palace is occuped with grass plots and flower beds with a great numbers of orrang trees in large boxes. You will perceive on the map two circles. These represent ponds of water or large basins with marble rims in the centre of which a [j]et of water in plesant weather is almost constantly playing. In each of these there is also a pair of beautiful white swans. Each side of this garden is occupied with raised terraces. Towards the close of the day this place is thronged with the beauty and Fashion of the city. It is furnished with thousands of chairs the use of which can be procured for an evening for the sum of 2 sous a little less than 2 cents. The company here is somewhat select since the gates are all guarded and no person permitted to entre carring a bundle or who is without a coat, wears a cap instead of a hat or has on a [hostler's] or a hunter's frock. Also I believe females without an attendant is not admitted. I should have stated that every part of the garden is ornamented with marble statues in many instances perfectly naked and which are thus at first rather revolting to an american taste but which are beautiful specimens of modern art. One part of this garden the north west corner appears to be consecrated to children under 7 or 8 years old. Hundreds of these boys and girls with their *bons* or nurses are seen engaged in various sports among which trundelling the hoop and jumping the rope appears most fashionable and in which both sexes are indiscriminately engaged. This is as you may suppose a very beautiful sight. The French children are mostly lively and very pretty. They however appear to loose their good looks as they grow up and the same features which may have been beautiful in child hood by a slight contortion or a want of propper development become insipid and disagreable in more mature life. This garden is closed as well as the other gardens at nine o'clock at the sound of a score of drums. The people are requested to withdraw and as soon as the whole is clear the gates are shut. A person is surprised at the perfect order and want of disturbance in the public places in this city but his surprise will cease when he reccollets that there are 30,000 soldiers distributed in different parts of the city and that they are posted at all the principal avenues to prevent disturbances by their presence and to instantly to quell any which may arrise. In standing in front and in opposite the middle of the Palace of the Tuilleries directly before you is a long avenew which offords from the window of the Palace some of the most beautiful scenes immaginable. This avenew is terminated at the farther extremity and at the distance of two miles by the triumphal arch commenced by Napoleon and now just finished called the *arch de Triumphe*. You will find it in a circle almost at the N W corner of the map. The avenew above mentioned after passing through the Garden of the Tuilleries also passes through the *Place de la Concord* or as it is sometimes called the *Place du Louis XVI*. This is the spot on which the gullitine was placed during the Revolution. The very place where the Father of the present King was beheaded is thus visible from the window of the Royal Palace. In the centre of this place you will see on the map a mark which represents the position of the Egyptian obelisk lately erected. Its place was occupied for some years by a wooden model that the public might judge of the effect that would be produced by the real object. The obelisk is a highly interesting specimen of ancient art and in most perfect preservation. The hierogliphics are as distinct in all parts as if they had been made but yesterday. A curious circumstance is mentioned in reference to the preservation of animal life connected with the obelisk. It was brought from Africa in a vessel and encased in wood. When the whole was raised to its pedestal and the wooden casing removed a great number of the large Egyptian venomous spiders called the Tarantula were discovered and became quite active when exposed to the light. The Parisians were in great dread lest some of these should escape and thus introduce this venomous animal into France.[10] The *Place du Concord* opens to the right and left into two avenews or rather one avenew passes through it at right angles to the grand avenew before mentioned. This is terminated in the distance on the south and over the river by the Palace of the Bourbons now occupied as the chamber of Deputies and on the other side also in the distance by the beautiful church of the *madelane*. Next to the place *de carousel* is the Champs Elysees or Elezean fields. These are something like the garden of the Tuilleries but are devoted to the sports of the lower orders and are crowded every evening with multitudes formed into groupes in the centre of which is some kind of amusement, a jugler, a tumbler, or a person making faces, punch and judy, or in some cases a quack Doctor lecturing on the potancy of some new and before unheard of nostrum. In different parts of this place machines are erected which give motion to flying horses "*up and down's*" artificial ships and like contrivances. This place is not closed at any hour and is a general rendevous for all those whose costume exclud them from the other garden.

Another very interesting spot and a favourite place of resort for all classes is the garden of the Palis Royal. You will see this on the map near the Place du Carousal. It also is in the form of a parallelogram the sides of which is formed by the suit of buildings which constitute the *Palis Royal*. This is a beautiful little garden adorned with trees statues and a basin of water. This building formerly belonged to the Father of the Present King and its several appartements were first rented by him to various shop keepers where every article of luxury is now exhibited in great profusion. This structure was

[10] We are unable to verify this story or refute it.

erected by Cardinal Richelieu for his own residence. It now I believe belongs to the King and yields him a great income from the rent of these shops. A little to the West of the Palis Royal is the Place Vendome in the centre of which is a high column of bronze made from the cannon taken at the several battles of Napoleon and surmounted by a statue of the Emperor. On the south side of the River is the garden of the Louxemberg which is not far from my residence and which I have before mentioned as the place on which Dr Hun's chambers look out. It is not quite as aristocratical as the Garden of the Tuilleries and is much more quiet and retired. You will see on the map a broad alley leading to the south from this garden which is terminated by the Royal observatory. All the alleys or avenews of the city are thus terminated by some large structure which produces a very pleasing effect. In the avenew leading to the observatory the spot is shewn where the brave marescal Ney was shot.[11] Every spot about and in Paris abounds with associations connected with the history of this country and indeed with that of the human race—since the French Revolution was one of those moral convulsions which have at different times affected the whole condition of the human race.

To wards the south east part of the map you will see an other garden called the Garden of Plants or the *Jardin du Roy* as it is sometimes called. This is also a delightful spot but its interest is of another kind. This place is consecrated to science and is supported by the government. Lectures free to all are given on various subjects of natural history including geology and chemistry. It appeared at first quite strange that I should find myself in the very presence of those whose names are associated with my earliest reccollections of Science and who have always before appeared almost to belong to another age. But I must reserve for another occasion a description of the garden of plants and now only mention a place which you will find on the right side of the map caled the Champ de Mars. This is only a very large parade ground and is directly in front of the Politechnic School. I have visited the chateau of St Cloud and the Palace of Versailes and never before had a conception of Regal Splendor but I must tell you of this in Person and will endeavour to illustrate the descriptions with drawings of the several places which may be obtained at a reasonable rate. You have probably seen by the papers that [the] Duke of Orleans the oldest son of the King has just married the Princess Helena of Mecklenburgh. The bride arrived in Paris about 10 days since. On this occasion a series of feets have * been given

* June 15th 1837

[11] Michel Ney (1769–1815).

and are now in Progress. The first were those at Marsales which consisted of fire works, a grand review and the playing of the great water jets. Yesterday the feets of Paris commenced. For several weeks past a great number of workmen have been busily engaged in erecting a large castle or fort of wood covered with canvass painted in imitation of stone. The papers stated that this was to be demolished in a sham fight between 10 thousand men. Last evening however it was used as a stage for setting off a grand set of fire works which lasted for two hours. The fort however was not demolished and may perhaps be reserved for another occasion.

The amusements of the French are of a very singular kind and even those furnished by the government partake largely of the burlesque. Yesterday in the Champs Elissee two emmense canvass theatres were erected at public expense opposite each other and about 100 yards apart. In these pantomimes were acted alternately during the day. In the middle space between these a tall mast 60 or 70 feet high was erected on the top of which was placed a garland of flowers and entwined with the flowers were several articles of some little value such as a silver cup one or two silver watches. You cannot possible immagine the object of this. I must therefore tell you that the mast was first covered from top to bottom with soft soap and then about 20 poor wretches set to clime the slippery pole for the sake of the treasures above. The several competitors for the honor were arranged in order around the post and each took a trial in succession as his number was gravely called by one of the Gen d'armes who superintended the amusement.

Each man climed a little higher than the last carring in his pockets a quantity of saw dust which he threw on the soap and in descending wiped off a portion of slipery unction. In this way after nearly a day's labour some one more lucky or more active than the rest succeeded in gaining the summit and carring off the prise. In the evening there was a great display of fire works on the opposite side of the river nearly in front of the Palace of the King. The gardens were also illuminated and that which produced the most astonishing effect of all, was the illumination of the intire length of the long avenew in front of the Kings Palace which I have before described. The termination, that is the Arc of Triumph, was allso illuminated the whole producing an effect which cannot be described.

Another grand feet was to be given this evening but on some account it has been posponed—the cause is not generally known. It is whispered by some that the King of England is dead and by others that there is sickness in the family of Louis Philip. The papers most probably of the morning will give the news.

June 15ᵗʰ 1837

I[12] believe that I have not yet stated that I have received [two letters] from Henry James one informing me that he landed in Portsm[outh] after a voyage of 18 days, another a few days latter from London.[13] He arriv[ed] in England about the same time that I left London. I wrote him in answer advising him to come to Paris before going to Ireland. I have not yet again heard from him but learn by a letter from Mr Vaughan who called on Mr James that probably he will come with Prof. Bache and his Lady.

I have devoted my Dear Little Wife nearly the whole of this day to you. The first part of this letter was written to be sent by the Packet of the 8th but I was so much interrupted that I did not finish it in time. The next Packet will probably sail the day after tomorrow & I hope not again to miss the opportunity. I have given you something of an epistle and only regret that I could not have sent it in seperate vessels that you might oftener receive letters even if they be not quite so long.

Your letter of the 10th of may came to hand to day[14] through my kind friend Mr Vaughan. It gives me much pleasure to learn that you have enjoyed yourself in Albany and that you are all enjoying the blessings of health. You cannot be too minute in your account of our Dear Dear little ones. It now appears that I could not possibly enjoy a greater earthly pleasure than to have with me this evening in this little room mammie, Bub, Mary and Little Helen. I find here much to amuse as well as to instruct but nothing to make one forget the pleasures of home or to value less the love of those from whom I am widely seperated by space but with whom I am if possible more closely united in feeling. While engaged most actively in the principal object of my mission the slightest association such as the sight of a child sends my thoughts across the broad atlantic and all else for the time disappears. Angelo Ames has just returned from Rome where he has been since april. He rooms near me and we see each other almost every[day. P]rofessor Stanley[15] lately elected to the chair of mathematics of [Yale] college is Lodging at the same house. We have also in the [sa]me neighbourhood Mr Loomis[16] of Yale college lately appointed [to] the chair of mathematics

---

[12] The second to last sheet of the letter, which begins here, is torn at one corner and along one side.

[13] Of which only the May 13 letter, above, survives.

[14] Not found.

[15] In 1836 Arthur Drummond Stanley (1810–1853) became Professor of Mathematics at Yale, retaining that post until his death. A Yale graduate (1830), Stanley wrote a textbook and prepared a compilation of seven-place *Tables* of *Logarithms of Numbers and of Logarithmic Sines* (1841). He was not a contributor to mathematical research. S. M. Guralnick, *Science and the Ante-Bellum American College* (Philadelphia, 1975), p. 214.

[16] Elias Loomis (1811–1889), an important ante-bellum scientist who will reappear in subsequent volumes of the *Henry Papers*. A Yale graduate (1830), Loomis was spending the first year of his service at Western Reserve abroad, a practice of various institutions of

in the western reserve college. Also a son of Robert Boyd[17] of albany was in Paris a few days since and perhaps is here still. He lives on the opposite side of the river, at a great distance from me and I have therefore not seen him often. Besids these the two Miss Bridgens[18] of albany are now in Paris and intend to leave for albany next month. They have been several years from home. There have been a great many persons from America travelling in Europe the last winter but many of these have returned home on account of the great commercial difficulties. Many persons now travelling in Europe are almost in a destitute condition. Their Bankers have failed in America and they have now no credit abroad. Almost all the American houses have stopped payment both in London and Paris and every person from America is in a state of some anxiety relative to his money affairs. I see by the papers that the house in New York from whom my bills of credit or rather of exchange were obtained have stoped payment and had I not taken the precaution to have the bills immediately accepted on arriving in London I would have lost the ammount. My only danger now is that my Banker in London may not be safe. Of this however I have little fear since he has given me a letter of credit of 1000 dollars on the great Banker Rothchild of Paris which has been accepted and the amount draw[n] to purchase apparatus &c.

De Witt received his first letter from home yesterday and was much disappointed to learn the bad state of things in America. His banker in London has stopped payment. I do not think however the money deposited (about 500 dollars) will be lost. If it should De Witt will not have sufficient funds left to bear his expenses home. I can however very easily procure him a passage from London or Liverpool in an extremity of the kind. It would be of great service to De Witt if all expectation of fortune were banished

---

higher learning in the United States, a form of graduate or postgraduate education. From 1844 to 1860 Loomis was at New York University except for a brief period (1848) when he was Henry's successor at Princeton. In 1860 he returned to Yale. On his death he bequeathed a considerable sum to his alma mater, the funds presumably deriving from his success as a textbook writer. Best known today as a meteorologist, Loomis had many geophysical interests in common with Joseph Henry. Many of Loomis's writings survive in Henry's Library, including *The Recent Progress of Astronomy; especially in the United States* (1850), an important work in the efforts of the leading U.S. scientists to convince fellow citizens and overseas scientists alike of the value of the research contributions from this country. *DAB, DSB.*

While overseas, Loomis's letters home appeared between July 1836 and November 1837 in the *Ohio Observer* (later, the *Cleveland Observer*).

[17] Perhaps the brewer of that name who appears in the Albany City Directory of 1837. The son is unknown to us.

[18] We know little about the ladies in question. Anna M. Bridgen died in 1857 at age 69. Munsell notes she was "recollected as a person of extraordinary intellectual faculties." Munsell, *Ann. Alb.*, 9:339.

from his mind. He would then excite the [. . .] he possesses and become of some value in life. [The] news from America has had a good effect on him and will tend to make his visit to Europe more valuable.

My[19] love to all Nancy, James and family, Aunt, Mother, Stephen & *family*, Mrs Meads family, Mrs Bullons family, all our friends in Schenectade, Mr and Mrs Van Slyck. Perhaps the latter will be interested with the manner of harnessing horses in France. Kiss the children for me. Tell Bub and Mary that Papa says they must be good [children] and that he will love them & when he returns will bring them something [prett]y from Europe

My Dear Dear little Wife

My Dear Wife I have given you in the within a long letter but much regret that I did not succeed in sending a part of it with the Packet of the 8ᵗʰ. I am glad to learn that James has commenced business and has notwithstanding the pressure of the times a prospect of success. I regret that Shankland will not be able to keep his place. I suppose there will be a great change in the Politics of the country and I do not envy Mr Van Buren in his situation exalted as it is. I do not think however and it is the general opinion also in London that the government of the United States have caused the present distress. It has been produced by the wide spred spirit of speculation and I may say gambling which has pervaded every class. [For] a few years past all the ordinary means of making riches by patient industry have been disregarded and nothing but an immense fortune made in a day would answer. The whole difficulty commenced in London just before our arrival. The bank of England became alarmed at the speculations going on in America and refused to give further credit to the American Merchants living in England. This produced a call on the United states and as soon as the news went over all was in confusion.[20]

June 16ᵗʰ 1837

I am as ever your
Hubby

---

[19] From here to the end of the letter Joseph Henry is writing (hastily we presume) on the sheet which will enclose the rest of the letter. The hand is different; the sheet is torn or frayed at the edges; holes appear in the page at the intersection of creases.

[20] Henry's contention that the depression of 1837 began in England and was aggravated in the United States by widespread speculation is a view that has become accepted by most students of the Jacksonian economy. Peter Temin, *The Jacksonian Economy* (New York, 1969), pp. 102–106, 172–175.

TO ALEXANDER DALLAS BACHE

Bache Papers, Smithsonian Archives

Paris May 28th 1837

My Dear Friend

I arrived safely in Paris on Friday morning at about 8 o'clock after a plesant voyage to Boulogne of 10 hours and a passage of about 24 from there to this place.

I found my Friend Dr Hun who has been living in Paris the last three years and through him procured Lodgins at No 3 (bis) Place du Pantheon a retired situation but plesant and near the garden of Plants the Sorbonne the College of France &c. I found my Friend De Witt at a Hotel waiting my arrival. The weather was plesant during my journey but until yesterday has been cold wet and disagreable almost beyond endurance.

I have as yet made but little advance with the men of science of the Place and have devoted most of the time thus far to the Lions of the city.

I have attended one meeting of the Institute[1] and was introduced to Pouillet,[2] Arago,[3] Magendie,[4] and Gay Lussac. They were polite invited me to call &c. I have attended all the Lectures of Pouillet and have commenced with those of Gay Lussac. Both these gentlemen are very polite to me and give free access to their cabinets but they have at each meeting been so much ingaged with there classes that I have had only a half hour at a time with them.

I am in the way of picking up much valuable information relative to Science and although from my imperfect knowledge of the Language and the manners perhaps of the French Savants I do not expect to become as

---

[1] For a description of Henry's first visit to the Institut de France, see his second diary entry of May 1837, printed below.

[2] Claude-Servais-Mathias Pouillet (1790–1868) was a professor of physics at the Sorbonne. He was especially interested in electrical and thermal phenomena. He experimented on the expansion and compressibility of gases and sought improved methods of measuring high temperatures and atmospheric absorption. At the time of Henry's visit, Pouillet was refining the technique for measuring weak currents, a technique which enabled him in 1839 to verify Ohm's law of resistance. *DSB.*

No doubt because of the language barrier, Henry's relationship with Pouillet, as with most of the French scientists, was superficial. The fourth edition (1844) of Pouillet's book,

Éléments de physique expérimentale et de météorologie (first published in 1827) is in the Henry Library.

[3] See *Henry Papers*, 2:257n.

[4] François Magendie (1783–1855) held the chair of medicine at the Collège de France and directed the women's ward at the Hôtel-Dieu. Born in Bordeaux, Magendie was raised and given a medical education in Paris. Noted for his scorn for all theoretical speculation, he exerted his greatest influence in orienting physiology toward experimental investigation. After his appointment to the faculty of the Collège de France in 1831, he delivered a famous series of lectures in which he sought as far as possible to provide a purely physical explanation of vital phenomena. *DSB.*

intimate with any person here as in London yet I think that much of interest can be obtained.

I already find but little difficulty in following the lecturers but can make no progress with the jabber of the common parlance of the multitude. I am disposed to be much better pleased with Paris than London as a place. Every thing is here freer and the expence of living about $\frac{1}{4}$ of that in London. All my expences thus far deducting purchases have not exceeded one dollar per day. My Lodgins are very good and cost 45 franks a month including servants wadges &c. De Witt's room adjoining only costs 28 franks. My Breakfast 15/20 th of a Frank and a dinner as good as your 9/— one[5] costs 2 franks. These necessaries therefore amount to $4\frac{1}{4}$ franks a day or about 82 cents.[6] I have not been in a cab since the first day of my arrival. The omnibus costs 6 sous[7] or about 6 cents for a ride from one end of the city to the other. They do not stop like those of London or proceed until filled at a snail's pace.

You may reccollect that I was obliged to start from London at 4 o'clock in the morning. Should you come by the same route do not forget to choose a day when the boat leaves about from 6 to 8 as this time will be convenient for leaving London and will make your arrival in Boulogne at a plesant hour in the afternoon.

I would advise Mrs Bache to put off purchasing articles of a smal kind or I should say fancy articles until she comes to Paris. The whole city appears to me to be an immense toy shop, where every thing may be had for money and at a very reasonable rate. This is only an apology for a letter and if you do not soon arrive I will inflict a very long scrawl on your patience.

Tell my friend your good Lady that I received a long letter from Mrs H. She is now with her friends in Albany and apparently in good spirits. My Friend Henry James of Albany has arrived in London and intends to join me in Paris. I would be pleased could he accompany you and Mrs B. He is a person to whom I am indebted for very special marks of Friendship and would be pleased to serve while in Europe. I think it probable I will accompany him to the North. I mean to Edinburgh and Dublin.[8]

He has had the misfortune to loose one of his legs and on this account

---

[5] This was not a normal dinner but something Bache referred to as a "nine shilling experience." Bache's European Diary, April 7, 1837, printed above.

[6] At the contemporary official exchange rate one franc would have equaled about nineteen American cents, and one shilling twenty-four cents. Thus by Henry's reckoning, a meal costing $2.16 in London would have come to only 38 cents in Paris. At this time the official exchange rates recognized by most nations, including France and the United States, were set by the British Parliament, the last one having been designated in 1816 at five shillings per ounce of silver. *Encyclopaedia Britannica*, 8th ed., s.v. "Money," pp. 438, 441.

[7] The sou equaled five French centimes and was equivalent to one American cent.

[8] Henry did not go to Dublin.

will be somewhat unplesantly situated among strangers.[9] He is the son of the late Mr James of Albany. I spoke to you of him while in London. His project of a visit to Europe was formed since I left America.

In haste as ever   Your Friend

My respects to Mrs Bache and the Little Lady your sister.[10] I hope to meet you all in Paris before I start. You must come here as soon as possible for the sake if nothing else of making money by living cheap.

Mr Vaughan has kindly forwarded my letters.

[9] At the age of thirteen, Henry James lost his leg above the knee while attempting to stamp out a stable fire and was confined to a bed for the next two years. Frederic Harold

Young, *The Philosophy of Henry James, Sr.* (New York, 1951), pp. 3–4.

[10] Bache's sister-in-law, Maria Fowler.

FROM WILLIAM C. REDFIELD

Henry Papers,[1] Smithsonian Archives

New York May 31 1837

Dear Sir,

I forward to you by the ship Mediator, Capt Champlin,[2] a copy of Halls statistics of the West,[3] which I have at length succeeded in procuring from Cincinnati, but which I apprehend will not quite meet your expectations.

I also forward to you a few more copies of my reply to Mr Espy,[4] together with several copies of some short sketches in Meteorology,[5] an abstract of my former observations on storms[6] &c with a short article on currents,[7] in

[1] A copy of this letter by Charles B. Redfield in Redfield letterbooks, volume 1, Beinecke Library, Yale University, is printed in Nathan Reingold, ed., *Science in Nineteenth-Century America* (New York, 1964), pp. 94–96.

[2] Henry L. Champlin, a veteran of the London packet service, was Captain of the *Mediator* from 1837 to 1840. R. G. Albion, *Square-Riggers on Schedule* (Princeton, 1938), p. 333.

[3] James Hall (1793–1868), *Statistics of the West, at the Close of the Year 1836* (Cincinnati, 1836). Henry probably wanted to use the book in preparing his communication to the British Association on canals and railways in the United States. Henry's Library contains a copy of a later work by Hall, *The West: Its Soil, Surface, and Productions* (Cincinnati, 1848).

[4] "Mr. Redfield in Reply to Mr. Espy, on the

Whirlwind Character of Certain Storms," *Journal of the Franklin Institute*, February 1837, *19*:112–127. A copy is in the Henry Library.

[5] "Cursory Remarks and Suggestions on Various Topics in Meteorology, by an Amateur Observer," *Blunt's American Coast Pilot*, 13th ed., June 1837, pp. 689–696. This article appeared later in *Silliman's Journal* and the *Naval Magazine* as "Meteorological Sketches, by an Observer."

[6] "Observations on the Hurricanes and Storms of the West Indies and the Coast of the United States," *Blunt's American Coast Pilot*, 13th ed., June 1837, pp. 697–705.

[7] "Remarks . . . on the General Character of the North Atlantic Currents," *Blunt's American Coast Pilot*, 13th ed., June 1837, pp. 666–668.

the form in which they appear in the forthcoming edition of the American Coast Pilot. A proof copy of the sketches I believe was also forwarded to you with my letter[8] by the first of May Packet. I have marked in your copy of the sketches some emendations, in view of the possibility of a reprint in England;[9] in reference to which and to my views thereof I beg leave to refer you to a copy of a letter which I have addressed to the Editor of the Nautical Magazine[10] which you will find inclosed with the pamphlets. If you can interest yourself in this matter so far as to learn what course it takes I shall esteem it a favor, and if nothing of this sort will be attempted, as is most probable, I suggest the propriety of offering the pamphlet as copy for reprint in the London Atheneum, Literary Gazette or some other of their *sub-scientific* newspapers. Capt Beaufort,[11] hydrographer to the Admiralty (who probably own the plate of my chart which was prepared for the "Nautical")[12] will probably lend the plate for a republication, or the Editor of the Nautical, in case it belongs to that Periodical. A stereotype cut for the figure on the page I will enclose you with the pamphlets, and if their map is reprinted I should like to have the whirlwind figures which are found on the American map (on Tracks I, V, & VII.) transferred to the English map to correspond with the text. I am a little apprehensive however that too much *Jonathanism*[13] will be discovered in this proposition to allow of its acceptance on that side of the water; but these mis-givings may perhaps prove to be unfounded. Appropos of this matter, I wish you to notice the article on Professor Olmsteads shooting stars which appears in the Saturday Magazine for the last of December 1836[14] and which is published by a committee appointed by the Society for promoting *Christian Knowledge*.[15]

[8] Not found.

[9] No English reprint is listed in the Redfield bibliography in *Silliman's Journal*, 1857, 2d ser. 24:370–373.

[10] Alexander Bridport Becher (1796–1876) edited the *Nautical Magazine* from 1832 to 1870. A captain and later admiral in the Royal Navy, Becher was an assistant in the hydrographic office of the Admiralty from 1823 to 1865. He authored several books on navigation. In his farewell as editor of the *Nautical Magazine*, Becher mentioned the hurricane theory of Redfield among things he had especially advocated as editor. *Nautical Magazine*, 1870, 39:699.

Frederick Boase, comp., *Modern English Biography*, 6 vols. (1892–1921; reprint ed., London, 1965), *1*:214–215.

[11] Francis Beaufort (1774–1857, *DNB*).

[12] The chart accompanied "On the Gales and Hurricanes of the Western Atlantic," *Nautical*

Magazine, April 1836, 5:199–211.

[13] Derived from Brother Jonathan, the predecessor of Uncle Sam as a symbol of the United States.

[14] The article, based on Denison Olmsted's description of the November 1833 meteor showers, includes the following anti-American slight:

> The well-known American proneness to exaggeration, would, perhaps, have prevented these descriptions of so remarkable and novel a wonder from attracting much attention from scientific men in Europe, if other collateral testimony had not, in some measure, confirmed the circumstance of an unusually-numerous appearance of shooting stars at that season of the year.

"Shooting Stars and Meteors," *The Saturday Magazine*, December 1836, 9:259–260.

[15] Redfield had originally written that the

Having recently been called to make a journey to Washington I availed myself of the opportunity to spend a few hours in Philadelphia, which were passed very pleasantly. I saw Dr Mease,[16] Dr Hare, Prof. Patterson, Prof. Dugglisson,[17] Prof Parke,[18] Dr. Pickering,[19] Mr Vaughn, Dr Emerson,[20] Mr Sears C. Walker[21] &c and am much indebted to several of these gentlemen for their politeness. Prof. Parke called with me at Mr Espy's, but we did not find him at home, and I afterwards learned that he was then lecturing before the American Lyceum.[22] A good deal of interest appears to be awakened in Philadelphia in the subject of Meteorology, at least in the circle into which I happened to fall.[23] Since I saw you an additional article of Mr

---

Saturday Magazine was published by "the Useful Knowledge Society headed by Lord Brougham," but then corrected himself.

[16] James Mease (1771–1846, *DAB*), Philadelphia physician and author. See *Henry Papers*, *1*:290n.

[17] Robley Dunglison (1798–1869, *DSB*, *DAB*), born in England, came to the United States in 1825 and taught medicine at the Universities of Virginia and Maryland before joining Jefferson Medical College in 1836, where he remained until 1868. Dunglison was an effective lecturer and author and greatly influenced medical education in the United States.

[18] Roswell Park, Professor of Chemistry at the University of Pennsylvania. See above, Patterson to Henry, August 23, 1836, footnote 2.

[19] Charles Pickering. See above, Torrey to Henry, September 26, 1836, footnote 5.

[20] Gouverneur Emerson (1795–1874, *DAB*) was a successful Philadelphia physician. He was an active member of the American Philosophical Society with interests in agriculture, mineralogy, botany, geology, and physics.

[21] Sears Cook Walker (1805–1853, *DAB*), a graduate of Harvard (B.A. 1825), taught school in Boston and Philadelphia before becoming an actuary for a Philadelphia insurance company. Walker used his spare time for astronomy and was soon contributing articles to and active in the Franklin Institute and the American Philosophical Society, of which he became a member in October 1837. Walker was also a member of "the club" (*Henry Papers*, 2:291n). In the late 1830s and early 1840s, Walker directed (unofficially) the new observatory at Philadelphia's Central High School. Having made himself familiar, through his knowledge of German, with the latest German astronomical technology and methods, Walker equipped the observatory with superb instruments imported from Germany and taught German techniques to his assistants. Leaving Philadelphia, Walker worked at the U.S. Naval Observatory for a little more than a year before joining the Coast Survey in 1847, where he was responsible for longitude determinations.

Walker was an innovator in the techniques of astronomical observation, particularly in the use of the telegraph for longitude determinations and for observing transits. He also worked on a system of automatic time-registering for observers. But his most extensive work was on Neptune, for which he worked out the orbit and calculated an ephemeris.

The demands of Walker's Coast Survey work and his own research led to mental problems. He spent part of his last year in an asylum. For a discussion of Walker's contributions to astronomy in America, see Marc Rothenberg, "The Educational and Intellectual Background of American Astronomers, 1825–1875" (Ph.D. dissertation, Bryn Mawr College, 1974), pp. 81–88.

[22] Espy lectured on meteorology at the annual meeting of the American Lyceum, which was held in Philadelphia in May 1837. The convention passed a resolution requesting that individual lyceums keep meteorological records and forward them to Espy and drafted a statement to Congress requesting an appropriation for simultaneous weather observations throughout the United States. Cecil B. Hayes, *The American Lyceum*, U.S. Office of Education Bulletin No. 12 (Washington, 1932), pp. 64–65, 67.

[23] Within a few years James P. Espy had made Philadelphia the center of meteorological activity in the United States. In 1834 Espy had recommended that the Franklin Institute set up an organized system for meteorological observations. When Bache indicated the will-

Espy's has appeared in the January No. of the Franklin Journal in which our friend attempts to press two or three more storms into his service; but on refering to the facts in these cases as I find them on record in numerous instances, from unbiased sources, I find, that like Salmagundi's ship, these storms obstinately refuse to be blown up into the sky, by a concentrating wind from every point of the compass.[24] It is not my present intention to reply publicly to these specifications, as I am quite willing that Mr Espy's exertions should earn him any degree of encouragement to which he may be thought entitled. He has been lecturing before our legislature at Albany this spring, with a view to procure legislative aid and assistance in his inquiries.[25]

---

ingness of the American Philosophical Society to participate, a joint committee was formed. Besides Espy as chairman and Bache as a representative of both groups, the members were Gouverneur Emerson and Charles Nicoll Bancker for the APS, and H. D. Rogers, S. C. Walker, and P. B. Goddard for the Franklin Institute. The committee solicited observations and in 1834, 1835, and 1836 made reports which were then published in the Franklin Institute *Journal* (1835, n.s. *16*: 4–6; 1836, n.s. *17*:386–391; 1837, n.s. *19*:17–21). Espy used these reports not only to argue for a federally supported national network but also to support his own meteorological theories, particularly against those of Redfield.

Early in 1837, the Pennsylvania Legislature appropriated $4,000 to be used by the Franklin Institute to set up a state meteorological network. With this money, the joint committee bought instruments for distribution, made up forms, and published a handbook for observers. Sometime around June 1838, when the joint committee found themselves "at a loss to determine to which body they were accountable," the APS part of the committee was discharged (Franklin Institute *Journal*, 1839, *23*:93). The successor to the joint committee was a Franklin Institute committee on meteorology with Robley Dunglison as chairman and Bache, Bancker, J. K. Kane, H. D. Rogers, S. C. Walker, R. M. Patterson, John C. Cresson, Emerson, and Espy as members. Espy was now also Meteorologist of the Franklin Institute.

The APS participation in the joint effort was never equal to that of the Franklin Institute and was limited to the efforts of the individual members on the joint committee. Walter E. Gross assesses the APS failure to rise to the challenge in "The American Philo-

sophical Society and the Growth of Meteorology in the United States: 1835–1850," *Annals of Science*, December 1972, *29*:321–338.

The Franklin Institute committee continued to distribute instruments and publish meteorological results for Pennsylvania but their efforts became increasingly local after Espy left for Washington to try to set up a federally supported national network there. The focus of meteorological activity shifted from Philadelphia to Washington. In 1842 Espy became Meteorologist to the War Department and set up another network of observers which was eventually absorbed by the Smithsonian's national meteorological system.

Bruce Sinclair, *Philadelphia's Philosopher Mechanics: A History of the Franklin Institute, 1824–1865* (Baltimore, 1974), pp. 152–158, 209, 242–244. Armand N. Spitz, "Meteorology in the Franklin Institute," *Journal of the Franklin Institute*, 1944, *237*:271–287, 331–357. The joint committee's reports and circulars are also printed in James P. Espy, *The Philosophy of Storms* (Boston, 1841), pp. 77–172.

[24] The Espy article Redfield refers to is actually the third report of the joint committee (Franklin Institute *Journal*, January 1837, *19*: 17–21). Espy undoubtedly authored the report. He used data from three recent storms to support an earlier conclusion "that the air moves inwards towards the centre of great rains, and consequently upward in the region of the cloud" (p. 20).

[25] New York had the earliest (1825) and most successful state meteorological network. See Franklin B. Hough, *Historical and Statistical Record of the University of the State of New York* (Albany, 1885), pp. 766–774. We were unable to locate any account of Espy's lobbying activities in the spring of 1837.

You will doubtless have an interesting time at the Liverpool meeting of the British Association in August. In case the "Sketches" should not be previously published in England perhaps you may think it best to bring the substance of them to the notice of the section on Meteorology; but of the propriety of this you can best judge.[26]

I have had the pleasure of seeing one of your fellow passengers in the Wellington, but was sorry to hear that you suffered much from sea sickness. Wishing you a *full freight* of European knowledge and improvements and a safe return to your country and friends, I remain your friend and obedient servant

Wm C. Redfield

---

[26] We have found no evidence that this was done.

HENRY'S EUROPEAN DIARY

Henry Papers, Smithsonian Archives

[May 1837][1]

Just returned from a lecture by Gay Lussac[2] on carbonic acid in which the most interesting of all late experiments was exhibited namely the solidification of carbonic acid.[3] The following is the principles of the experiment

---

[1] This entry was probably made in late May or very early June. Henry wrote Stephen Alexander (July 28, 1837, below) that he had attended this demonstration "soon after my arrival," which was May 12, and he was attending the lectures of Gay-Lussac by May 28 (see Henry's letter of that date to Bache, printed above).

[2] Gay-Lussac was lecturing at both the École Polytechnique and the Muséum d'Histoire Naturelle. We are uncertain where Henry saw the demonstration.

[3] Early nineteenth-century chemists divided gases into two classes: the permanent gases, which had resisted all previous attempts to be liquified through either pressure or cold, and the condensible vapors. But during the first quarter of the century a number of these so-called permanent gases, including carbonic acid (carbon dioxide), were liquified. Although solidification of permanent gases was not achieved for over a decade, from 1823 on it was assumed that given the proper conditions,

matter could exist in all three states. Confirmation came in 1835 when Charles Saint-Ange Thilorier announced the solidification of carbonic acid ("Solidification de l'acide carbonique," *Comptes Rendus*, 1835, *1*:194–196).

Thilorier's paper generated widespread interest. French, German, English, and American journals reported his success or reprinted the paper. It was a sensation in England and impressed some of America's leading physical scientists, such as Henry, Bache, and John Locke (see below, Locke to Henry, August 25–27, 1837, and Henry to Coquerel, October 1, 1837). Among those who took notice of Thilorier's success was Michael Faraday, the leading figure in the liquification of permanent gases. Faraday asked Henry to gather information on Thilorier's work while in Paris (see below, Henry to Stephen Alexander, July 28, 1837, below). This Henry did, eventually obtaining an invitation from Thilorier to watch him reproduce his experiment (see Thilorier to Henry, June 30, 1837, below). In response

Just returned from a lecture by Gay
Lussac on carbonic acid in which
the most interesting of all late experiments
was exhibited namely the solidefecation
of carbonic acid   The following is the
principles of the experiment as far as I can
make them out from my imperfect under
standing of the language .

The process was invented by Chiolier
No 21 Place Vandom the manufacturer
of hydrostatic lamps which bears his
name .   The process is as follows –

A quantity of carb
onate of soda is put
into a strong iron vessel a and on this is poured
a quantity of sulphuric acid probably
not directly poured in but placed in an
upper box so that the apparatus may
all be arranged before the desengagement
of the gas takes place . The sulphuric acid is
thrown on the carbonate by shaking the appara
=tus or by turning the whole bottom upwards

First page of Henry's diary entry describing the solidification of carbonic acid (May 1837).

as far as I can make them out from my imperfect understanding of the language.

The process was invented by Chiolier[4] No 21 Place Vandom the manufactorer of hydrostatic lamps[5] which bears his name. The process is as  follows—A quantity of carbonate of soda is put into a strong iron vessel *a* and on this is poured a quantity of sulphuric acid probably not directly poured on but placed in an upper box so that the apparatus may all be arranged before the disengagement of the gas takes place. The sulphuric acid is thrown on the carbonate by shaking the apparatus or by turning the whole bottom upwards after the connection with the other iron box is formed. This second box may be called the receiver and is the only vessel which was exhibited at the lecture. It is in the form of a cylender about 20 inches long and 6 in diameter, judging by the eyes, strengthened by flanges or wings on all sides. There is also a large screw at each end for colosing the interior. Perhaps the article was formed of a solid piece of cast iron bowered out and then the caliber stoped at each end with the large screw before mentioned. The screw however was not sufficiently large to admit the truth of this supposition. The receiver at the commencement of the exhibition contained <*just*> a gallon of Liquid gas. I should have mentioned that the condensation is aided by keeping the receiver cool during the process.

---

to Henry's visit, Thilorier wrote Faraday (Thilorier to Faraday, July 10, 1837, Faraday Papers, The Royal Institution), explaining his work.

Faraday continued to be impressed by Thilorier's experiment. On May 17, 1838, he used a copy of the apparatus, obtained from Thomas Graham, to cool metals. Six years later Faraday conducted his own experiments on the solidification of permanent gases, including carbonic acid. In his published account of this work, Faraday was very careful to give Thilorier proper credit and praise for "one of the most beautiful experimental results of modern times."

Duane H. D. Roller, "Thilorier and the First Solidification of a 'Permanent' Gas (1835)," *Isis*, 1952, *43*:109–113; L. Pearce Williams, *Michael Faraday* (New York, 1965), pp. 127–131, 381–382; Thomas Martin, ed., *Faraday's Diary*, 8 vols. (London, 1932–1936), *3*: 280, *4*:190; Michael Faraday, "On the Liquefaction and Solidification of Bodies Generally Existing as Gases," *Phil. Trans.*, 1845, p. 165.

[4] Henry must have misheard the name. Charles Saint-Ange Thilorier (b. 1797) seems to have been a mechanician rather than a

chemist, although he did show considerable interest in the properties of liquid carbonic acid. It was during an attempt to determine the physical and chemical properties of liquid carbonic acid that Thilorier—quite accidentally, he later admitted to Faraday (see his letter to Faraday, cited in footnote 3)—solidified the substance. J. Pelseneer, "Thilorier," *Isis*, 1953, *44*:96–97; Roller, "Thilorier," *Isis*, *43*:111.

[5] Thilorier's lamp, which we assume was similar to the one he presented to the Académie des Sciences in 1839 (*Comptes Rendus*, 1839, *8*:638), was just one of a number of lamps applying the principles of hydrostatics to the problem of raising the oil to the wick. His was based on the example of Hero's Fountain, in which Hero of Alexandria (fl. 62 A.D., *DSB*) used water and air pressure to raise a column of water from a reservoir well below the spout. The application of this principle to a lamp was not new. Jacob Bigelow described two different forms of this type of hydrostatic lamp in his *Elements of Technology* (Boston, 1829), p. 179, a work Henry had been familiar with since at least 1830 (*Henry Papers, 1*:309).

The other part of the apparatus for producing the acid in a solid state consits of a circular box which opens in a section at right angles to its axes and around each external axis a hollow tube is placed. These serve for handles and permit the part of the gas to escape. In the side of the circular box is a tube t placed obliquely. This is con[nected] with the receiver by a tube and cock of peculiar construction and when the connection is opened the gas rushes in to the box, strikes against a pice of metal plate *d* which deflects it and causes it to revolve in the centre of the box; a part escapes through the hollow handles and this so cools the rest or remainder that it becomes solid by the reduction of temperature. When the stop cock of the receiver is opened the gass issues in the form of vapour and dilates as it comes out and is thus dicipated but in the arrangement described prevents this dicipation and enables the gas which escapes to condense the remainder by its absorption of heat.

HENRY'S EUROPEAN DIARY
Henry Papers, Smithsonian Archives

[May 1837][1]

Atended a meeting of the Institute which is held in a large building which bears the name of the Institute although it is sometimes known as the Palais des Beaux Arts. The building is very old although in perfect preservation. It was built in 1662 by the order of the cardinal Mazarine and was originally intended for the free instruction of 60 young nobles from the provinces.[2]

This building is directly opposite the Louvre and was erected at the same time with that building. Its grown plan is given on the map and it will be seen that it has the form of a horse shoe terminated at each extremity by large square structures.

[1] This entry, too, lacks a date. But the visit described below must have occurred before May 28 when Henry mentioned having made it in his letter to Bache, printed above.

[2] Suppressed by the Revolutionary Convention in 1793, the former Royal Academy of Sciences was reorganized in 1795 as the First Class of the National Institute of France, known as the Institut. The other two Classes replaced defunct nonscientific academies of the Old Regime. Originally housed in the Louvre, the Academy was moved in 1801 by Napoleonic decree to more commodious quarters in the neighboring Palais des Beaux Arts, where, following renovations, the first meetings were held in 1806. This building, formerly known as the Palais des Quatre-Nations, was initiated by Mazarin in 1662 to receive students of the provincial nobility. "Institut" appeared in gilded letters above the entrance to the Academy of Sciences in the right wing of the Palais. Ernest Maindron, *L'Académie des sciences* (Paris, 1888), pp. 71–78, which contains ground plans of the Academy. Pierre Couperie, *Paris Through the Ages, an Illustrated Historical Atlas of Urbanism and Architecture* (New York, 1971), unpaginated, section b, 1.

The Institute first held its meetings in this place in 1806. The galery for the meetings is a long parallelogram with tables around for the members also arranged as a parallelogram. The president occupies one side of the parallelogram formed of the tables at *a*. Tables also are placed within transversely except opposite or directly before the chair of the president where a single table is placed for the person who makes a communication. I should have mentioned that the members are placed on the outside of the parallagram. Strangers of distinction[3] occupy places within.

The meetings are public that is to persons introduced by a member and the spectators occupy seats around the walls.[4] The room is generally so much crowded that a seat cannot be obtained unless at an early hour. Punctual attendance is secured on the part of the members by stopping a part of their pay unless in case of sickness.[5] The meetings commence at ½ past two or 3 oclock and continue until 5. The members are from time to time called to order but they in general do not appear very attentive to the paper which may be in progress of reading.[6] The National Institute of France was

---

[3] Henry is referring to the *associés étrangers*, a select group of nonresident academicians associated with both the pre- and post-Revolutionary Academy. Much later Henry was several times nominated, but apparently never elected, to another, far more numerous class of nonresident academicians, known as the *correspondants*. Roger Hahn, *The Anatomy of a Scientific Institution: The Paris Academy of Sciences, 1666–1803* (Berkeley, 1971), pp. 77–78. The lists of *correspondants* showing Henry as a nominee appear in the *Comptes rendus hebdomadaires des séances de l'Académie des Sciences, Paris*, January 26, 1852, May 11, 1857, June 6, 1864, December 27, 1869, January 3, 1870, January 17, 1870, May 23, 1870.

[4] From the founding of the Paris Institut, the meetings of the Academy of Sciences were open, resulting in crowding and distraction. Several attempts were made to limit public access, for example, by allowing academicians only a single guest. (Henry does not mention a sponsor for his own visit.) In 1809 and 1849 the Academy attempted to restrict its audience to those of scientific accomplishment or affiliation with specified institutions. Such regulations soon fell into disuse, however, and the meetings again became public. Despite the public presence, Maindron noted in 1888, "l'Académie des sciences poursuit ses travaux avec le calme convenant à la nature de la mission qu'elle est appelée à remplir...." *L'Académie des sciences*, pp. 85–87.

[5] Especially at the height of its prestige under the Old Regime, the Paris Academy embodied professionalism in science. In return for a government stipend and privileges, the core group of working academicians were expected to attend all meetings, to work actively in assigned committees, and, in general, to be involved in Academy business. The system of salaries was initially swept away by the Revolution, but was reinstituted by the Directory. Hahn, *Anatomy of a Scientific Institution*, pp. 78–79, 293, 303. For an analysis of the Paris Academy's salary structure and a detailed reconsideration of the meaning of professionalism for the academicians, see Roger Hahn, "Scientific Research as an Occupation in Eighteenth-Century Paris," *Minerva*, 1975, *13*:501–513.

[6] Its members might not have been noticeably engrossed in the proceedings, but the post-Revolutionary Academy carried a full schedule of meetings and activities, much as it had in its eighteenth-century heyday. Scientific papers continued to be read, elections held, and government commissions carried out. While many of the Academy's bureaucratic structures were superficially intact, its real power and significance as a research institution had fallen off drastically in the nineteenth century. There were both political and intellectual reasons for the decline. Napoleon had shaped the Institut into a cultural symbol of considerable prestige but at the same time

formed in 1795 from the union of several societies. It was again reorganized in the 11ᵗʰ year of the republic (1803) and divided into 4 Academies.[7] It was also increased by the Present King in 11 [8]

---

carefully curbed the independence of the academicians in order to secure their allegiance to the state. Even without Napoleon's actions, growth in scientific activity and pressures toward scientific specialization made the Academy increasingly superfluous. Although participating in the Institut, the academicians performed and communicated their creative researches elsewhere: at the Observatory, the École Polytechnique, the Bureau des Longitudes, and, less formally, at the Society of Arcueil. Hahn argues that the Academy functioned more and more as an honorific body and a storehouse of knowledge, less as a bearer of new knowledge. These trends were not limited to France. Elsewhere on the Continent and in England specialized forums had begun to eclipse the academies of science, although in London attempts were being made to shore up the sinking reputation of the Royal Society. Similar trends were overtaking the general academies of science and learning in American centers like Boston, Philadelphia, and New York. Hahn, *Anatomy of a Scientific Institution*, pp. 287–288, 304, 305, 307, 310–311.

[7] The reorganization into four Classes was imposed from above by Napoleon, apparently to cover his suppression of the Second Class of Moral and Political Sciences where ideological opposition to him was centered. The four Classes, corresponding to pre-Revolutionary Royal academies, were now the physical and mathematical sciences, French language and literature, ancient history and literature, and the fine arts. Hahn, *Anatomy of a Scientific Institution*, p. 312. *Encyclopaedia Britannica*, 8th ed., s.v. "Institute."

[8] We doubt that Henry meant 1811 but suspect that he abruptly left off writing the entry in the midst of putting down some other date or period. In 1832, Louis Philippe reinstated the suppressed Class of Moral and Political Sciences. *Encyclopaedia Britannica*, 8th ed., s.v. "Institute."

FROM ALEXANDER DALLAS BACHE

Henry Papers, Smithsonian Archives

London June 7. 1837

My dear friend

This is merely a pro forma answer to your kind letter[1] for I have hardly any thing new to say, & it seems so odd to be upon the same ground over which you have passed & that ground a foreign one, that what is really new I think you have seen. Your kind attempt in regard to the explosion report has not succeeded,[2] indeed Parker has behaved most unhandsomely about it. Instead of returning to me your paper according to your direction to him he has published it in a mutilated form, cutting out the pungent part, reflecting in a balderdash way upon brother Johnathan's thin-skinnedness &ᶜ &ᶜ & says his analysis is from an American *savan*. [3] So I am likely to get the

---

[1] May 28, 1837, above.

[2] For background to this episode see above, Henry to Bache, June 4, 1836, footnote 3, and Henry to Harriet Henry, May 9, 1837, footnote 6.

[3] In his copy of this publication ("Prevention of Explosions in Steam-Boilers," *Mazazine of Popular Science*, 1837, *3*:321–332), Henry annotated this passage identifying himself as the American "savan."

credit of reviewing my own works unless you direct him to state in a future number that the analysis was written by one Joseph Henry. It is a dirty thing. He feared the attack thro' another journal & has taken advantage of your absence. Hearing nothing from Mr Parker I got Wheatstone to call upon him & to him he said the article was in type: spoke of his having but one of three courses to take, leaving out the honest & right one, a fifth,[4] to return the article when it would have been published by Mr Holl in the Analyst. If you will authorize me to do so I will still hand Mr Holl your abstract with notes, if he should be inclined to publish. On this point let me hear at once.[5]

We have made a most interesting visit to Cambridge since you left us, & an interesting one to Oxford. Commend me to the Cambridge men for absence of jealousy & backbitings & for sticking to friends. It was well said at a dinner of the Greenwich Obser^y visitors the other day,[6] by a Trinity Coll. Camb. man, that he never would go into a contest without true backers. A more intelligent gentlemanly Society I never met with. With the love of Science they are many of them deeply imbued tho' it is plainly impossible that experimental science should flourish where there is such a dearth of instruments. I looked rather upon the darker sight of Oxford as Mr Powell who befriended me is uneasy in his position, conceiving physical science to be lamentably neglected.[7] Dr Daubeny yet doubts if he will visit America this year.[8]

---

[4] sic.

[5] William Holl (*DNB*) and Neville Wood were editors of *The Analyst; A Quarterly Journal of Science, Literature, Natural History, and the Fine Arts*. Henry's article, perhaps with some reworking by Bache, was handed over to Holl, appearing in volume 6, 1837, pp. 315–328 of the *Analyst*. This version differed significantly from that published by Parker, and included the footnotes that were missing from Parker's version. Bache visited Holl on June 6 and again on June 7 according to his diary for April 15, 1837–October 24, 1837, Bache Papers, Library of Congress.

[6] According to Bache's diary, he visited Cambridge May 9 to May 12 and May 19 to 23. He then visited Oxford May 30 to June 2 and Greenwich on June 3. He attended examinations at both universities.

[7] Bache's comparisons between the states of science at Oxford and Cambridge were accurate reflections of contemporary opinions and realities. Oxford was not a congenial home for science in the 1830s and early 1840s due in great part to the combined influences of the University's classicists, who actively resisted incursions of science into the curriculum throughout the first half of the century, and the leaders of the Tractarian Oxford Movement, especially John Newman, who asserted the primacy of religious over scientific truth. Baden Powell, Professor of Geometry at Oxford, mixed actively in the religious debates, maintaining, contrary to the Tractarians, that science did not threaten religion.

At the same time a counterbalancing intellectual tradition was developing at Cambridge making that university a more favorable home for science. George Peacock, one of the leaders of the informal "Cambridge Network," stood for the modernization of mathematics at Cambridge through the introduction of French analysis. Other members of the alliance were Airy and Whewell. While the love of science was indeed present at Cambridge as Bache notes, laboratory and other scientific facilities were inadequate due to money problems. Susan Faye Cannon, *Science in Culture: The Early Victorian Period* (New York, 1978), chapters 1 and 2. *DSB*, s.v. "Baden Powell."

[8] Charles Daubeny (*Henry Papers*, 2:194n–

Immediately after the receipt of yours to Mr Vaughan I called upon Mr James, but have not seen him except a glimpse (at St Paul's) since.

Wheatstone is excessively busy with his electrical telegraph for which he has taken out a patent.[9] Mr Babbage's 9th. Bridgewater is out containing arguments from his calculating machine to establish a new theory of miracles[10] &^{c} There is more genius in this "fragment" to my notion than in several vols. wh. I could mention put together. It does not seem to meet with favor, perhaps because the author is out of favor himself. It is aimed at Mr Whewell's idea that no good can come out of the Galilee of maths. in regard to Nat. Theology.[11] I saw a brief answer beginning "Dear Babbage" from Mr W. in a gentleman's hand the other day: whether published or not I do not know.[12] Sir John Herschel's theory of volcanoes deduced from the invasion of central heat into more superficial regions, from the effect of deposits, was brought out at the Geolog. Soc. a few weeks since & is in a note to Mr Babbage's 9th.[13] There is an exception in the Greenwich Observ^y rules in favour of men of science. So go when you come back. I found Mr Airy polite, but stiff.

Good-bye.

Two weeks more will close my affairs here I trust. I have been as busy as circumstances would allow in getting my materials into shape, not wishing to return home with a crude mass which will take months to digest.

Mrs Bache & Maria send kind regards to you

Very truly Yours A. D. Bache.

The child has made a sad looking affair of this—but it cannot now be helped—Yrs

---

195n) did go to North America in 1837. See below, Torrey to Henry, November 1, 1837, footnote 5.

[9] See above, Henry's diary for April 1, 1837, footnote 11.

[10] See above, Henry diary, April 22, 1837, footnote 25.

[11] Babbage criticized points in William Whewell's *Astronomy and General Physics Considered with Reference to Natural Theology*, published in 1833 as a Bridgewater Treatise. Babbage felt that Whewell betrayed the purposes of the Bridgewater series by implying that the proofs of religion were outside the domains of science and mathematical logic. See Babbage's *Ninth Bridgewater Treatise*

(London, 1837), pp. x–xiii. Babbage elaborated on these opinions in the second (1838) edition of his work. Whewell was not sympathetic to Galileo's stand against the Church.

[12] A rejoinder was printed in 1837, entitled "Letter to Babbage" (7 pp.).

[13] The first edition of Babbage's treatise contained excerpts from two Herschel letters on central heat and volcanoes, one to Charles Lyell and one to Roderick Murchison. Herschel gave Murchison permission to read his letter to the Geological Society. The second edition of Babbage's book contained parts of a third letter to Lyell, acknowledging that Babbage had made similar suggestions independently.

June 15, 1837

FROM HENRY JAMES
Henry Papers, Smithsonian Archives

London June 15. 1837

My dear friend:

I received yours of the 27[th1] ult. just as I was finishing a letter to you. The information it Contained relative to books &c rendered a great part of mine needless, and I accordingly laid it aside to send another in a day or two instead. Since when I have been engaged so much in various ways as hardly to have time to write to any one.

I am very much obliged to you for the calls you procured me from Dr Bache & Mr Vaughan a couple of weeks since, and for the kind attentions I have received since at the hands of the latter gentleman. I was quite overwhelmed at seeing two such great men enter my door, and in my embarrassment displayed the holes in my old coat, I presume to great advantage. I have dined with Mr Vaughan since, & attended him to a meeting of the Society of Arts, & the Zoological Society.[2]

You did just right with the money. I shall relieve you of all drains upon it in the way of book purchases for me also. Use it without stint, and I trust we shall both have enough to get out of the country with. I have a letter for you from Mr Chilton, which I have hitherto been doubtful whether to keep for you or not. However I have concluded now to send it off by this Evenings mail in company with the one I am writing.

One or two arrivals last week at Liverpool from home, the news by which you have seen of course. My letters represent public feeling in NY. has wrought up to the last pitch of indignation against the President, and predict the establishment of a national Bank as the very first act of next Congress.[3] The distress is inconceivable all over the country, and when & how

[1] Henry's letter is actually dated May 23 (printed above).

[2] The London Zoological Society, an offshoot of the Linnean Society of London, was founded in 1826 by Sir Stamford Raffles and granted a royal charter of incorporation in 1829. While the Linnean Society tended to concentrate on botany, the Zoological Society specialized in collecting zoological specimens, publishing scientific papers, and conducting experiments in animal physiology. At the time of Henry's European visit, the Society had grown to 3,106 members and had 931 animals in its menagerie at Regent's Park. Henry Scherren, *The Zoological Society of London* (London, 1905), p. 10; Philip Street, *The London Zoo* (London,

1956), pp. 11–16.

[3] Henry James was alluding to the tribulations of the Panic of 1837, a severe business depression that lasted until 1843. The depression was so acute, in fact, that in February of 1837 laborers rioted in New York City and by the next spring over 20,000 in the city were unemployed. See Peter Temin, *The Jacksonian Economy* (New York, 1969), pp. 113–120. The causes of the Panic were complex, but a number of factors contributing to the financial collapse were rampant speculation in land, overinvestment in industry and internal improvements by the states and private entrepreneurs, and President Andrew Jackson's hostility toward the Bank of the United States

it will end the Lord only knows. That He may overrule it to our eventual welfare & his own glory in our midst is my prayer.

I have commenced my arrangements for getting a good Cork leg, and hope I shall succeed. It will keep me here for some days yet, and render my return necessary sometime during the summer. I should like very well to go on to Paris with Bache, but fancy I shall be obliged to go into Ireland, and spend a few weeks with an uncles family there. However I shall be careful to meet you at as early a day as possible somewhere.

The only things I care about seeing on the continent—seeing I should have such a short time to spend there—are Venice & Rome, but presume the malaria of those southern regions will keep me from visiting either during the summer.

I feel a little homesick occasionally, but in the main do charmingly. I spend my time pretty much in my room, & am as happy generally as the day is long. Boyd[4] is here now, about returning to America. He was in Paris, but could not find Dr Hunn's[5] lodgings— and was ignorant of your being there. Goodbye & believe me, with all affectionate wishes

Yours faithfully
H. James

(about which, see *Henry Papers*, 2:150n, 173n, 176, 180n, 490n). Despite attempts by congressional supporters of the Bank to revive its charter in 1832, Jackson's veto remained in force, and it went out of existence in 1836. Robert V. Remini, *Andrew Jackson and the Bank War* (New York, 1967).

[4] Probably Andrew Hunter Holmes Boyd, for whom see Henry to Bache, June 4, 1836, footnote 1.

[5] Thomas Hun.

TO ALEXANDER DALLAS BACHE

Mary Henry Copy,[1] *Henry Papers, Smithsonian Archives*

Paris June 19, 1837

My dear Bache . . . Since I last wrote I have been much engaged purchasing books and apparatus, seeing the Lions, attending lectures and taking lessons in French. I have as yet made but little progress with the men of science here but this is owing to myself. I have had interviews with several of the principal savans which were interesting and profitable, and have been of-

---

[1] A longhand and a typed copy survive; this text is based on the more complete longhand copy. Both indicate an omission between the salutation and the opening words of the surviving text.

fered attentions and introductions. Still the French are different from the English and we were spoiled by the kind attention we met in London.[2] I am in the way of picking up much valuable information which may I hope be useful in the way of science in our own country and now that I am gaining confidence in the use of the language I hope to do more.

Say to "your daughter"[3] for me that she will find no lack of children in Paris for thousands assemble in the gardens of the Tuilleries and of the Luxembourg but she must make good progress in her French in order to hold converse with them.

You have heard through the papers of the great fêtes given in honor of the marriage of the King's son and of the melancholy loss of lives by the pressure of the crowd at the gates of the *Champs de Mars.* More than two thousand persons had assembled to witness the fireworks in the champs and as soon as the display was ended there was a general rush to the gates in order to reach the Tuilleries before the exhibition given at that place should be over. I happened to be near the fatal spot and was twice carried by the pressure into the current setting towards the gate; at one time was only ten feet from it; by great exertions I pushed my way backward out of the stream and made my escape through a distant passage.[4]

The commercial pressure in America has produced much anxiety and difficulty among travellers from the United States on the Continent. Everyone in Paris is eager to draw the full amount of his credit from his banker and many are destitute on account of the failures in New York and London. Those in Italy or far in the interior will suffer most since the news of the decline of the American house in Paris will prevent the acceptance of their letters. I was somewhat uneasy about my funds but am informed that they are in no danger. I have turned some little attention to the subject of Political Economy in the course of my life; since my arrival in Paris I have had access to several files of American papers and am much interested in the cause of this great depression. It is absurd to attribute it to the arts of the administration. The distress commenced in England and was produced in our country by the ruinous system of paper money and the consequent spirit of gambling and speculation which for two years has infected everyone. Instead of employing our means in the production of objects of real value we

---

[2] The comments on Henry's reception by the French scientists show an initial uneasiness or unhappiness on his part which changes as the contacts grow. Yet, Joseph Henry never had the same kind of cordial and close relations with the French that existed with British scientists. Comments on science in France will appear in later volumes.

[3] Maria Fowler, Bache's young sister-in-law.

[4] See Catherine I. Gavin, *Louis Philippe, King of the French* (London, 1933), p. 81.

have been entirely engaged in making paper fortunes or rather in inflating a bubble which at length has burst. But you are beginning to laugh; it is however no matter for amusement. A friend of mine in Albany purchased a lot of land for twelve thousand dollars. It arose in value to 70000 and he actually refused to sell at that price. He is now much disgusted, since his fortune depended upon a forced state of things and his land is now worth less than the sum he originally paid for it. The French do little in the way of banks and consequently have no money revulsions of the kind now agitating our country.

Come to Paris as soon as possible. I will stop a week longer than I intended to meet you. Thanks for calling on my friend Mr. James. I have received a letter from him since. My respects to Mrs. Bache, tell her I have received two letters from Mrs. Henry. She is among her friends in Schenectady and is in good spirits.

FROM JEAN-B.-F. SOLEIL[1]
Henry Papers, Smithsonian Archives

Paris le 21 juin [1837][2]

Monsieur

Il ne sera pas possible de voir les phares demain jeudi comme nous en étions convenu parce que desirant vous les montrer completement et sur tout vous en donnér[3] tout les details. J'ai demandé une audience a Monsieur Fresnel[4] qui me l'accorde pour samedi prochain 24 du courant a 8

---

[1] Active in the manufacture of optical instruments from as early as 1823 until 1849, Jean-Baptiste-François Soleil (1798–1878) provided the technological skills necessary for French physicists to carry out their research. One researcher who benefited from Soleil's expertise was Augustin Jean Fresnel (for whom see the next document, footnote 2). It was Soleil who provided the bulk of the apparatus that Fresnel used in his later work demonstrating the wave theory of light. Both the lens and the rotation mechanism in the Fresnel light were constructed under the direction of Soleil. *DSB*.

Henry used his visit to Paris to utilize Soleil's skills. He purchased forty-six items from Soleil, worth 625 francs. See the Appendix.

[2] Although this portion of the date was lost when a corner of the letter was ripped off, there is a file date on the verso.

[3] In this and other questionable readings of the French text, we have followed our general practice of hewing to the original.

[4] For Henry's account of his visit with Léonor Fresnel, see the next document.

Léonor-François Fresnel (1790–1869), brother of the physicist A. J. Fresnel, was educated at the École Polytechnique and the École des Ponts et Chaussées. He served as a civil engineer for the French government from 1814 until his retirement in 1846. In 1825 he became a member of the lighthouse service, and eventually rose to secretary of the lighthouse commission and director of the service. He

heures précise du soir je vous attanderai chez moi et j'aurai l'honneur de vous y conduire.

Je suis charmé que Monsieur Fresnel ai pu nous accorder ce moment sa sera beaucoup plus agréable pour vous. Monsieur Fresnel parle Anglais et il vous donnera toute les explication que vous desirez. Veuillez avoir la bonté de ne pas manquer au rendez-vous parce que Monsieur Fresnel fera allumer le phare a l'heure indiquer. Ainsi je vous attandrai—donc a 8 heures tres precise du soir.

Veuillez Monsieur agrée le respect
de votre tres humble Serviteur
Soleil fils opticien
Rue de l'Odéon N° 35

---

published three different sets of directions for the organization and operation of the lighthouse service. *Encyclopédie des Travaux publics. Notices Biographiques* (Paris, 1884), pp. 186–187.

HENRY'S EUROPEAN DIARY
Henry Papers, Smithsonian Archives

June 24th [1837] Went this [evening] by invitation to see the lights prepared in Paris for the coasts of France under the direction of M Fresnel[1] the Brother of the celebrated Philosopher of the same name who was the inventor of this kind of light.[2]

The principle of this lantern is that of the echellong[3] lense or as it is

[1] Henry encountered Léonor Fresnel a second time in Scotland. See below, Henry to Harriet Henry, August 16, 1837.

[2] Léonor's more famous brother, Augustin Jean Fresnel (1788–1827), was also educated at the École Polytechnique and the École des Ponts et Chaussées. He too was a civil engineer for the French government, and was forced to fit his scientific research around his official responsibilities. However, the assistance of friends in the French scientific establishment enabled him to obtain frequent leave and convenient assignments. Beginning in 1814, working in relative ignorance of the literature in the field, A. J. Fresnel began a systematic attempt to turn the wave hypothesis of light into a comprehensive mathematical theory. His success was crowned in 1823 with his election to the Académie des Sciences. In 1824 Fresnel's career entered a second phase. His responsibilities with the lighthouse commission—improving lenses, designing and locating lighthouses—took up most of his time during the few years he had left to live. *DSB.*

[3] i.e., echelon lens, now known as the Fresnel lens. Before A. J. Fresnel designed a lens to focus the rays from the lighthouse lamp, lighthouses used a system of parabolic mirrors. Of far greater power than reflectors, Fresnel lenses soon supplanted the reflectors in France and Scotland, and eventually in the United States. To minimize spherical aberration and losses to absorption in the lens glass of the great lighthouse lenses, Fresnel built the lens

sometimes called the poligonal lense. I was promised a particular description of the apparatus but M Fresnel could not at that time procure the article. It is published in english and from the pen of the english engineere who has the charge of the northern lighthouses.[4]

I was much pleased with my reception by M Fresnel and with his gentalmanly deportment. He appears to be a man of about 35 years old remarkable intelligent and agreable in countenance.

He has the whole charge of the works which is carried on at great expense by the government. All the parts however are not finished at the place where we were shown the lights. The lenses are ground in one part of the city, the lamps which are of the hydrostatic kind in some instances and worked with pumps another.

We were shewn 4 large lanterns of the first order.[5] They consisted of a cylendercull set of lenses which would throw a bundle or rather a plane of rays of about 30 inches thick at the lamps and slightly diverging [as] it passed from the centre.[6] In order that as much of the light as possible may thus be thrown in nearly a horizontal direction the upper and lower part of the lamp is occupied by mirrors slightly cylindrical which reflect the light horizontally which would otherwise b[e] lost by eradiation upwards or by absorption of the earth downwards.

This ingenius arrangement is due to the elder Fresnel. We were also shown another arrangement entirely of glass for producing the same effect. The middle part of the lantern was the same as the above but the upper and lower instead of the mirrors were furnished with circular prisms from the face of which by total reflection the light is directed parallel to the hori-

---

of separate pieces, consisting of a center lens and concentric circular bands or zones. The elements of curvature were recalculated for each band to bring aberration to a minimum. Soleil constructed Fresnel's prototypes. Finding circular zones difficult to manufacture, Soleil constructed the first lenses so that the zones were polygonal. For a full discussion of these and other aspects of lighthouse optics, see Alan Stevenson's *A Rudimentary Treatise on Lighthouses* (London, 1850), especially Part II: 1–41, and Stevenson's article on "Lighthouses" for the eighth edition of the *Encyclopaedia Britannica*, pp. 471–476.

[4] Probably Alan Stevenson's *Report to the Commissioners of the Northern Lighthouses on the Illumination of Lighthouses* (Edinburgh, 1834). See Henry to Harriet Henry,

August 16, 1837, footnote 5, below.

[5] In France dioptric lights were divided into six orders referring to the power and range of the light. First order lights were the largest, having a focal distance of 92 cm. and a lamp of four concentric wicks. *Rudimentary Treatise*, II:111.

[6] To illuminate all points of the horizon equally, Fresnel broke down the large annular lenses into thin vertical sections connected in the form of a polygon approximating a cylinder. The lamp stood in the center. Eventually Scottish engineers made the lens of a solid cylindrical piece. The arrangements described here were for stationary lamps, where the lamp and the cylindrical lens did not revolve. See Stevenson's encyclopedia article, pp. 472 and 475. *Rudimentary Treatise*, II:45.

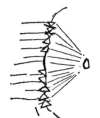

zon. This is also an invention of Fresnel the elder but it was not put in execution before he died.[7] The effect is very brilliant and being produced by a very simple but philosophical arrangement gave me much pleasure. The light presents the appearance of a broad line perpendicular to the horizon of the len[g]th of the apparent height of the cylinder forming the lantern. This apparatus is inclosed in a large frame the sides of which are composed of glass to protect it from the weather. The glass

is set in frames of brass both of the outter frame and the smaller light within. The arrangement just described has not been applied to the large lights the working of the cylendrical prisms would be to difficult. The size of the lantern proper which has been constructed on the plan is about 20 inches high and perhaps a foot in its greatest diameter. When it is intended to illuminate all parts of the horizon the lamp within is introduced by a glass door of the same construction as the other parts of the body of the lantern but when it is intended to remain stationary and to throw its light in one direction as off for instance into the sea then the back of the lantern is occupied by a concave reflector. In order that the light may be recognized at a distance by some property peculiar to it a frame is made to revolve around the out side of the lantern and this carries 4 large lenses which at intervals peculiar to each light transit the line joining the eye of the observer and the centre of the light and by collecting all the rays into a convergg[ing] cone or almost a cylinder the long broad line of light is for an instant changed into a small circular disc or at a great distance becomes a star of great brilliancy. The length of time elapsed between two consecutive appearances of this kind gives the name of the light. Thus in Light *A* the interval is 2 minutes in Light B 3 minutes & so on as there are but a small number of lights which can be mistaken for each when these intervals are known to the sailor there is no danger from want of knowledge of the particular light or I should say of confounding one light with another.[8]

The large lights with the mirrors instead of reflectors are about 6 feet in diameter and perhaps 8 in height. The cylender composed of glasses was not a perfect cylinder but rather a pologon of many sides. It is found much more difficult to construct the lenses perfectly cylindrical.[9]

---

[7] This was designated the "catadioptric light." The prisms gave more perfect reflections than mirrors, whose polished surfaces were also subject to deterioration. Léonor Fresnel put the finishing touches on his brother's invention and the first catadioptric apparatus was installed at Alan Stevenson's Skerryvore Lighthouse. *Encyclopaedia Britannica*, "Lighthouses," p. 475.

[8] The modification of the fixed apparatus to produce flashes was replaced by a revolving apparatus. See below in Henry's text.

[9] See footnote 6.

The revolving part of the apparatus is moved by wheel work and a weight to regulate the motion. I was shewn a very ingenious application of the conical pendulum or governor of Watt. It consisted of two pairs of Fans for preventing the t[o]o great velocity and to render these more censitive and the check on a change of motion more immediate. These fans were attached to a governor which instantly changed the position of them in reference to the motion through the air bringing them nearer or farther from the wind as it is said in the action of the wind mill.

The lamp as I have stated before is of the kind in which the oil is pumped up[10] (*ie* that is in the lamp where the whole horizon is lighted) since the reservoir for the hydrostatic lamp would obscure a part. This lamp however is used where the light is only thrown around part of the horizon. The pump lamp is worked by wheel work to which a weight is attached. The pumps are very short and moved very simply by a number of excentric wheels [which are] geered into each other as the wheels all move together and the shackle bars are connected with pins at different points on the several wheels. The strokes of the pumps are simultaneous and hence the oil flows in a continued streem. As it would be impossible to adjust the quantity of oil to the burner the extra oil is suffered to run over the circle just below the flame and to fall into the reservoyer below from which it is again pumped for use.

I am promised an inspection of the process of forming the lenses at the establishment of the elder Soleale and shall therefore give an account of this at another time[11] but I must here mention that I was much delighted with a very simple but ingenious plan for polishing the concave reflectors shewn me at the manufactory of M Fresnel.

It consisted of a pice of metal convex on the under surface suspended by an iron pyramidal frame from the roof and this was free to move like a pendulum in every direction. The mirror being placed on a table under this was ground in to the proper form of surface, the radius of convexity being the length of the pendulum.

There is another form of the light which I have not mentioned in which the whole lantern revolves, it consists of 8 ? square lenses each at least 30 inches in diameter formed of parts of glass arranged in circles. The revolution of this arrangement produces at intervals as each lense passes before the eye a flash of light of great brilliancy which can be seen at the distance of 17 French leagues of which 23 make a degree. The name of the light in this plan can be determined by the period of flashing as the brilliant

---

[10] The design of the burner and fuel feed for dioptric lamps was also largely due to A. J. Fresnel. *Rudimentary Treatise,* II:92–95.

[11] If Henry ever made such a visit it was not recorded in his diary.

appearance is called.[12] The Drumond light I am informed by M Fresnel is not now in use in Great Britain. The difficulty of keeping it in order prevents its general use.[13]

The lime soon gives was is[14] subject to crack also the management of the gases is difficult. It is impossible to procure men of science to attend a light house.[15]

---

[12] *Rudimentary Treatise*, II:127. For the revolving apparatus, see Stevenson's *Britannica* article, p. 476.

[13] For the Drummond light, see Henry's second European Diary entry of March 23, 1837, footnote 2. Experiments by Fresnel showed the intense Drummond light unfit for use in dioptric systems, which required a large body of flame to produce a sufficiently broad beam. *Encyclopaedia Britannica*, 8th ed., s.v. "Lighthouses," p. 480.

[14] This sentence about the Drummond lamp and lime fuel is garbled.

[15] Of great concern was the reliability and skill of the lighthouse keeper, responsible for maintaining the efficiency and steadiness of the lamps. The dioptric apparatus and the mechanical lamps used with it were thought to be especially demanding. Fresnel, however, believed that the difficulties in finding suitable keepers were greatly exaggerated, that "ordinary mechanics or laborers" capably manned the apparatus in France. *Senate Executive Documents*, 32d Congress, 1st Session, 1851–1853, No. 28, pp. 581–582.

HENRY'S EUROPEAN DIARY
Henry Papers, Smithsonian Archives

[June 28, 1837][1]

Visited M Baben[e]t[2] was kindly received had been introduced by Mr Warden[3] at the Institute.

Was introduced by M Babenet to M Gamby[4] the maker of magnetic instruments. Found him intelligent. He speakes english a little, understand[s]

---

[1] This undated entry actually consists of two visits to Jacques Babinet, perhaps on the morning and afternoon of the same day. Both evidently occurred sometime after June 24th but before the visit to Melloni on the 29th. We have arbitrarily assigned the entry the last possible date for Henry's visit.

[2] Jacques Babinet (1794–1872) was Professor of Physics at the Collège Louis-Le-Grand in Paris. An optical physicist noted for research on diffraction gratings and for the design of optical instrumentation, Babinet was an early supporter of the wave theory of light, as many of the experiments he shows to Henry clearly illustrate. Babinet also did extensive studies of optical effects in meteorology and mineralogy. *DSB*.

[3] David Bailie Warden (1772–1845), diplomat and author. A student of natural philosophy at Glasgow, Warden later immigrated to the United States and obtained his citizenship in 1804. He spent a number of years as an American diplomat in Paris. After being forced to retire in 1814, he remained abroad to serve as an unofficial cultural ambassador to France. Warden published books about the United States and even maintained specimen collections to acquaint the French with American flora and fauna. *DAB*. See Francis C. Haber, *David Bailie Warden, a Biographical Sketch of America's Cultural Ambassador in France, 1804–1845* (Washington, D.C., 1954).

[4] See Henry's diary entry of April 24, 1837, footnote 3, above.

the language when written—is decorated with the red ribbon the badge of the Legon of honor.

Also introduced to M Cockerell[5] who is acquainted with Dr Sprague—is an excellent english schollar and has promised to give me an introduction to Melloni.[6]

M Babenet exhibited several very interesting experiments on light. A plate of thin glass on which or rather between to pices of glass, powder of Lycopodium[7] is strewed. A corona is formed by this when the sun is viewed.[8]

A button with small parallel lines engraved on it produces by reflection beautiful colors arranged as in the sketch. A bright spot of common light in the middle is the reflection from the whole surface. This is an exhibition of one of the phenomena of interference.

Three different kinds of polariscopes or instruments for detecting the smallest quantity of polarized light.[9] One the polariscope of Arago.[10] The other of Babenet and the last of Savart.[11] The first exhibits two coulered circles complementary. The second the lines and curves of unannealed glass and the third formed of a pice of rock cristal and a tourmaline exhibits parallel bands of coulered light by a very small quantity of polarized. These instruments are valuable for researches on the phenomina of light.

Also exhibited the lines in the spectrum with a small prism made for me by Soleal. The only contrivance necessary for this experiment was the window shutter closed and the light of the day vewed through the prism as it entred the crack. The window was opened or shut by an assistant until

---

[5] Charles Augustin Coquerel (1797–1851) was a lay theologian and historian and author of numerous scholarly works. He took an amateur interest in science and wrote astronomical articles for the *Revue britannique,* a journal he helped found. J.-M. Quérard, *La France Littéraire, ou Dictionnaire bibliographique* (Paris, 1828), 2:283. Roman D'Amat, ed., *Dictionnaire de biographie française* (Paris, 1961), 9:575.

[6] Henry and Coquerel visited Melloni on the 29th, described below.

[7] A yellowish flammable powder made of the spores of club moss and used as a dusting powder for the hands and as a component of fireworks.

[8] Babinet's work on different diffraction phenomena resulted in what became known as Babinet's principle: "If parallel rays fall normally on a diffraction system formed from a large number of openings . . . the diffraction phenomena will remain identically the same if the transparent parts become opaque, and reciprocally." Quoted from *DSB.*

[9] For the study of polarization Babinet invented the "compensator" which produced and analyzed light polarized in any direction. *DSB.*

[10] Arago invented his polariscope in 1811, consisting of a mica or rock-crystal polarizer and an Iceland spar analyzer. Arago's polariscope enabled him to determine the degree of polarization of light rays. *DSB,* s.v. "Arago."

[11] Probably the acoustical physicist Félix Savart (1791–1841). The Savart polarization apparatus is described in Delezenne, *Notes sur la Polarisation* (Lille, 1835), pp. 38–41.

the proper width of Light was obtained. Then the principal lines were distinctly seen. They were not however as perceptable as those shown me by Mr Richie in London with a very large prism of his own construction and with which he also showed me the lines in a beam transmitted through nitrus gas a bottle of this merely being held between the light and the prism.[12]

M Babenet make[s] great use of cork for adjusting and fi[tt]ing up his apparatus. The polariscope which he showed me as his own was formed of a tube of paper with a brass ferule at the end next the eye for the tourmaline and a pice of unannealed glass at the other end.

He stated that several of the most interesting experments on polarized light could be exhibited to a class by means of a screen. The rings from the interferences &c.

2nd visit to M Babenet. I am much indebted to the politeness with which this Savant has treated me and for his kindness in exhibiting with much patients the most recondite experiments on light as well as the most more elementary ones of the same subject.

This afternoon he first exhibited to me a series of experiments on the fringes[13] produced by the interferance of rays by means of the *plate* prism. This is a simple method of showing the fundimental experiment of Fresnel invented by himself and consists is using a prism with a very obtuse angle instead of the two mirrors of the first method.[14] ⊏▭ It is not however necssary to have the mirror[15] of that form. It may be made by grinding off one side or end of a plate of glass thus ⊏▭ Inorder to do this in the simplest manner possible a thin pice of glass is cemented to one end of the flat pice thus ▭ *a* The surface is then growned down and when sufficient *b* ▭ quantity is removed from *a* then the glass at *b* is removed.

To exhibit with this apparatus the fringes a slit is formed between two knife blades placed in a frame. These knife edges are kept in place by two bars *a c b d* which are screwed to the frame and thus secure the opening a permanancy during the experiment.

[12] See above, Henry's diary of April 27, 1837.

[13] The following experiments were designed to illustrate the wave, as opposed to particle, properties of light as postulated by A. J. Fresnel.

[14] A. J. Fresnel's initial experiments to prove the interference of light waves were done with diffracting objects—a hair or other thin edge—illuminated by the light beam. Since some of the diffraction experiments might still be given corpuscular interpretation, Fresnel did a further series of interference studies using mirrors. Fresnel placed a light source in front of two slightly angled mirrors. He detected bands of color produced when the rays reflected from the two mirrors intersected and interfered with each other. *DSB,* s.v. "Fresnel."

[15] Henry meant prism, not mirror.

The knife edges and the prism were disposed on a board as shown in the figure, the several parts were stuck together with wax; this substance with cork and pins  form the most important substances for the experiments of M Babenet on this important and recondite departement of Physic.

The lines were observed at the distance of 6 or 7 feet by a glass on a foot stand of about 1½ inch in diameter.[16] The lines were larger as the lense was removed farther from the opening and with the light of the sun could be thrown on a screan and seen by a whole class. The light used in this experiment was a small wax candle. The effect would have been much better if the exp had been made in perfect darkeness. The fringes were perceved without the lense but very small; M Babenet even produced the fringes by making a slit in a card and holding up between the candle and the eye.[17]

I was next shewn a beautiful exhibition of Newtons rings which M B informes me were discovered by Dr Hook as has been proved he says by Arago.[18] The apparatus here mentioned consisted of a circular pice of black plate glass with a black paper pasted on the opposite

[16] The knife-edge slit threw a beam onto the surfaces at the angle of the prism, bending adjacent rays into each other, producing interference.

[17] The prism is apparently eliminated. Interference in this case is caused by simple diffraction at the slit in the card.

[18] Henry is here encountering some of the politics of optical science in the period. Newton's rings referred to the periodic iridescent color phenomena seen in soap bubbles, thin glass plates, and especially between thin plates of glass pressed together. Although Robert Hooke, in his *Micrographia*, is generally credited with the first accurate experiments on the colors of thin plates, Isaac Newton, a few years later in letters communicated to the Royal Society of London, made his famous analysis of the effect in terms of "fits of easy transmission and reflection." Newton came into bitter conflict with Hooke over priorities and relative theoretical contribution toward understanding what came to be known as Newton's rings. The issue continued to be hotly debated and is the subject of modern historical controversy, especially since Hooke cast his argument in terms of an undulatory theory. Although Newton's "fits" are not unambiguously corpuscular, some believe that Newton was responsible for the eclipse of Hooke's "correct" undulatory concepts until the nineteenth century. Like Babinet, François Arago was an opponent of the Newtonian emission theory and a supporter of undulatory optics. Thomas Young's paper of 1801 on the color of thin glass plates was one of the original sources of Arago's optical interests. Arago went on to perform his own experiments on Newton's rings and to marshal the defense for the wave theory. In 1838 Arago, inspired by Wheatstone, suggested a crucial experiment for deciding between the wave and emission theories (see above, Henry to Alexander, April 10, 1837, footnote 21). Understandably, then, Arago and Babinet took up Hooke's cause against Newton. For the extent of Arago's devotion to Hooke, see his "Mémoire sur les couleurs des lames minces," *Mémoires de physique et de chimie de la Société d'Arcueil*, 1817, *3*:323–370, in which Arago asserts Hooke's priority and claims his work was revived by Thomas Young (p. 328). Other comments in the same vein appear in his biography of Fresnel in his *Biographies of Distinguished Scientific Men*, trans. W. H. Smyth, Baden Powell, and Robert Grant (London, 1857), p. 420. See *DSB*, "Arago" and "Hooke." For Hooke's optics see Richard S. Westfall, "Newton and His Critics on the Nature of Colors," *Archives internationales d'histoire des sciences*, 1962, *15*:47–58.

side; it was about 3 inches in diameter and on this was placed a thick lense of 6 feet focus. By a very slight pressure very large and beautiful rings are produced.

The other surface of the lense is more convex having a radius of only about 3 feet. With this the rings are small. These rings vary in number and distinctness when light more homegeneous is used than common light. In monochromatic light the number is indefinite. To make the monochromatic lamp put into a small cup or saucer about 4 inches in diameter a quantity of salt. Make a dent into the middle of the mas and into this pour a quantity of alcohol. This being fired gives a chromatic light of but one colour a lightish yellow. When the rings are viewed by this they appear to cover the whole glass. M Babenet has made great use of this monochromatic lamp and has made the light from it the standard for measuring the index of refraction, the circular polarization &c. It is always the same and is always at hand when experiments are required.

I was next shewn the phenomenon of the rays produced when a pice of garnet which has been cut acrossed the stria and vewed between a candle.[19] An exhibition of the kind sketched is seen except if I recollect aright the garnet gives 6 radii with a circle crossing one of them. M Babenet has found that all crystals of a striated structure produces the same or rather analogous effects. A pice of *mica, berril cats eye,* Tourmaline &c.

I was then shewn a pice of glass rod about 5 inches in diameter cut at right angles at its two ends to the axes, the ends polished so as to be perfectly well see through. When this was looked through at the light a circle was seen around the open end and when the spectrum was received on the one end of this and the eye placed at the other the appearance was beautiful. With the same rod of glass M B informed me that he was able to produce the appearance of 7 spectrums at once. M Soleile showed me something similar with a tube covered with black paper not however for the spectra.

I was also shown a pair of tourmalins which produce very intense polarization but these according to M Babenet are not always the best since they are generally very dark and the rings and images produced not as conspicuous.

The polarscope of M Biot[20] is nothing more than a plate of tourmaline placed before a plate of Iceland spar cut at right angles to the axes. This shows with a very feeble polarization of light the colourd rings and black cross.

---

[19] i.e., the stone was held between the eye of the observer and the candlelight.

[20] Biot is credited with the invention of one of the first polariscopes. *DSB,* "Biot."

The double figure is beautifully shewn by [. . .][21] of lead of which M B has a piece as large as a two frank piece. The double curves are shown when the tourmaline is placed so as to give no light. When turned a little from this position the curves become irregular.

I was next shown some experiments on *circular polarization*[22] a subject on which M B. has done much. A pair of Tourmalines were placed at right angles to each other so as to be nearly dark. A plate of quartz was then inserted and immediatly the whole became light! ! In this experiment the polarized beam which had passed through the first tourmaline was partially twisted round so that it was no longer in its vibrations perpendicular to the axes but oblique to it so that a portion could pass through and thus produce apparent transparency. The effect is most interesting.

But now turn the cristal of tourmaline next the eye either to the right or to the left and a slight appearance of a cross will begin to appear. As you continue to turn the tourmaline the cross changes colour. It is first blue then orrange and pases into red.

If these changes take place in the above order in turning the crystal from the right to the left or in the direction of the sun when the face is to the north then the crystal is said to be a left handed circular polarizing crystal. If in the other direction right handed.

In a left handed crystal a slight turn to the right cause all the images to di[s]appear so that a right or left handed crystal is read[i]ly reccognized.

The succession of colours is caused by the vibrations of the different coulors being differently [t]wisted the blue less than the red.

To produce polarization of the circular kind several circumstances are necssary 1[st] a beam of light must be polarized and this must be passed through the axis of[23]

---

[21] Henry left this blank.

[22] The polarization of light, where a light beam is made to show distinct properties on its different sides, was another phenomenon of great theoretical importance to the debates over wave and particle theories. Circular polarization is discussed below, "Visit to Melrose Abbey to Dr Brewster," August 19–21, 1837, footnote 23.

[23] The text breaks off.

TO HARRIET HENRY

Mary Henry Copy, Family Correspondence,
Henry Papers, Smithsonian Archives

Paris June 28th 1837

The first part of my residence in Paris was not very profitable but I have made up for lost time in the last two weeks. The French Savans of the older class are so much occupied in the business of teaching, also in politics and legislation (they are all members of the Chamber of Deputies) they have no leisure for attention to strangers. I have now however got into a different current and have picked up much valuable knowledge among a younger class.[1] They have been very kind to me and will form valuable acquaintances in the way of correspondents.[2]

Bache writes to me that he hopes to meet me in Paris in a few days. I shall be very glad to see him. He appears to me almost like a relative and his good little wife has been as kind to me as a sister. You will thank her for me some time I hope. De Witt starts on Wednesday for Belgium and intends to make a short excursion up the Rhine.

The principal news of the day is the death of the King of England and the proclamation of the young Queen. She has declared herself in favor of the Whigs or the liberal party. The Tories generally are abusing not the queen but her mother for influences [on] her daughter.[3]

I have been engaged almost every day since I last wrote in visiting dif-

[1] It was typical of the established French scientists to hold multiple salaried posts as teachers and consultants in addition to their duties as members of the Academy of Sciences. Many also served in the legislature. In 1837, for instance, Arago and Gay-Lussac were members of the Chamber of Deputies; Thenard served in the Chamber of Peers. Tudesq (2: 462) notes that in 1840, eight of the sixty-five Academicians served in the Chamber of Peers, three in the Chamber of Deputies. As politicians, scientists could lobby for concerns of importance to the scientific community. Involvement in politics, however, drew the following criticism from Liebig, quoted by Crosland (p. 473):

The era has passed when Berthollet was able to gather about him at Arcueil a circle of eminent young talent. These men have now grown old and have attained high office in the State and that has perforce robbed them of the leisure and the inclination for scientific work.

Teaching responsibilities were time-consuming under a system known as "*le cumul*" where one man held several posts. Crosland (p. 231) cites the example of Charles Dupin, "sometimes called the prince of *cumulards* on account of the dozen salaried posts which he held simultaneously." While the system en-

abled the older scientists to make a nice living, it inevitably cut into the time available for research. Henry's comment about the accessibility of the younger scientists reflects their relative exclusion from the system of multiple posts.

For a description of this system and its implications, see Maurice Crosland, *The Society of Arcueil* (Cambridge, Massachusetts, 1967), especially pp. 223–231, 471–473. André-Jean Tudesq, *Les Grands Notables en France (1840–1849)*, 2 vols. (Paris, 1964), 2:457–463, analyzes Academicians as of 1840 in regard to age, social background, wealth, political affiliation, teaching and other responsibilities.

[2] Despite Henry's wish here, he subsequently had little correspondence with the scientists he met in Paris.

[3] In the month preceding William IV's death on June 20, Tory fears were focused on Victoria's domineering and hated mother, the Duchess of Kent. The *Times* (June 19) warned of "an intriguing, sordid, female, foreign tyranny" and advised the eighteen-year-old Victoria to "cut her leading-strings." Immediately following Victoria's accession, the Whig Prime Minister Melbourne replaced the Duchess as the main influence on Victoria and as the target of Tory charges of manipulation. Although Victoria's declaration to the Privy Council on June 20 is a seemingly innocuous statement

ferent men of science and in studying their modes of instruction and experimenting.

I have also purchased a lot of apparatus for the college having received for that purpose the large sum of 500 instead of the 5000 which was promised. It was promised that an additional sum should be sent over to me but I have heard nothing of it and from the bad times in America do not expect to receive anything in the money line. I have therefore concluded to lay out the $500 to the best advantage for the college and to purchase a few articles on my account which are most necessary for my researches.[4]

We are too far removed[5]

---

with no explicit espousal of the Whigs, the *Times* (June 21) considered it a Whig document authored by Melbourne and designed to promote his own selfish interests by misrepresenting the dead King's desires to a politically naive young Queen.

[4] See above, Henry to Henry James, May 23, 1837, footnote 13.

[5] The copy ends here.

HENRY'S EUROPEAN DIARY
Henry Papers, Smithsonian Archives

June 29 [1837] Visited to day M Melloni[1] the celebrated Italian Professor

[1] Macedonio Melloni (1798–1854). Born and educated in Parma, Melloni went to Paris in 1819 to further his education. In 1824 he returned to Parma to teach physics at the university. In 1831, his association with liberal politics forced him to flee following an abortive uprising against the government which was headed by Napoleon's second wife, Marie Louise, the Duchess of Parma. Seeking refuge in France, his attempts to establish himself there are described in the autobiographical introduction to *La Thermochrôse* (Naples, 1850). Unable to support himself in Paris, he accepted a college professorship in Dôle, a provincial town which he soon realized lacked the facilities for research. Melloni moved on to Geneva where, with a warm welcome and assistance from De La Rive and Pierre Prevost, he was able to prepare his first memoir on radiant heat. Returning to Paris to present his memoir to the Academy of Sciences, Melloni met resistance from the commission charged with reviewing his work. Acceptance came only after the Royal Society of London, on Faraday's advice, awarded him the Rumford Medal. Melloni became a corresponding member of the Academy of Sciences and worked productively in Paris until 1839 when, upon a successful application by Arago and von Humboldt to Metternich, he was allowed to return to Italy. Promising not to indulge in politics, he was appointed head of the Naples Conservatory of Arts and Crafts and later of the meteorological observatory at Vesuvius. Accused in 1849 of involvement in liberal politics, he was forced to leave his posts. During his retirement in Portici, he continued his investigations on radiant heat, studied electric induction, and published *La Thermochrôse*. An unpublished continuation of the book was discovered after his sudden death from cholera.

E. Scott Barr, "The Infrared Pioneers—II. Macedonio Melloni," *Infrared Physics*, 1962, 2: 67–73; for biographical details Barr relied on a Melloni memorial issue of the supplement

now in Paris, exild by the wife of Bonepart from Parma. He has been in Paris about 5 years, was made a member of the Institute after his celebrated descovories on the permibility and other properties of heat. He has a very intelligent countenance, appears to be about 35 years old, has a family, lives very retired in the 5th story of a French house where he has a suit of appartements on[e] of which serves for his study and work shop.

This room in which the most important results are deduced is not more than 12 feet one way by 8 the other. M Melloni was banished from Italy with almost all the literary men of Parm[a] on account of a revolution which was commenced in 1830 immediatly after the revolution of France. It was expected in Italy and in Poland that the revolutions of these countries which were started immediately after the celeebrated 3 days of France would be supported by the armies of the new government but Louis Philip was too cunning to embroil himself in foreign quarrels and secured his recognition in other countries by promising to keep peace at home or to restrain the French and do all in his power to check the spirit of the Revolution. Poland and Italy were therefore abandoned to their fate, the men of influence in both obliged to fly or suffer death.

But to return to the subject of Melloni I was accompanied to his house by Mr Cockerell who speaks English remarkably well. Melloni reads and understands the language but does not speak much. He was extremely kind, had waited two hours for us to Breakfast with him and made preparations to exhibit to me his most interesting results.

A description of his apparatus is given in Becquerels work on electricity but the description or rather the account of the experiments are not very correct.[2]

---

to *Nuovo Cimento*, 1955, 10th ser. 2, no. 3. Barr closes with a translation of most of Melloni's autobiographical introduction to *La Thermochrôse*. The *DSB* account sketches Melloni's scientific work but cites no biographical sources and no Melloni articles past 1840.

Melloni's work in physics centered on investigations of the properties of radiant heat, particularly in relation to light. His thermomultiplier (see the next footnote) enabled him to detect minute quantities of heat and thus to study thermal radiation effects in a way not previously possible. Melloni's work was widely known and was influential in the acceptance of the wave theory of heat (see footnote 4, below). He reported his results in numerous and very detailed articles. Four of his papers on radiant heat, all reprints from the *Annales de chimie*

et de physique, are in Henry's Library; two are presentation copies.

[2] The reference is to Antoine-César Becquerel, *Traité expérimental de l'électricité et du magnétisme*, 7 vols. (Paris, 1834–1840),*3*: 424–443.

Melloni's thermomultiplier, designed to detect small quantities of heat, consisted of two major parts: a thermoelectric pile which would generate a current when a source of heat was present, and a galvanometer to indicate the intensity of the heat. In an 1830 article on his thermomultiplier, Leopoldo Nobili reported that his original pile was composed of six elements of bismuth and antimony. Nobili states that Melloni, after seeing his apparatus, made several improvements, the most critical being an increase in the num-

The principal parts of the apparatus are the Thermeolectric pile used for a thermometer and the galvanic multiplyer to indicate the degree of heat. The pile is composed of 32 elements or 32 couples very short not more than ¾ or ⅞ of an inch long. The whole is not more than ¾ of an inch in diameter. The multiplyer is of the most delicate construction, not placed on a table or a support liable to be shaken but supported on a strong shelf nailed against the wall forming a bracket. The pile in most experiments is

enclosed in a screen made of sheet zinc of the form of a pentagonal prism longer in one direction perpendicular to the axis namely 15 inches by about 11. This cuts off all eradiation from surrounding objects and the instrument is not affected by the heat of the body of the operator. To transmit

---

ber of elements. With Melloni's modifications, the thermomultiplier could detect the heat of a human body at eighteen to twenty feet. Leopoldo Nobili, "Description d'un thermomultiplicateur ou thermoscope électrique," *Bibliothèque universelle*, 1830, *44*:225–234. A joint article described further improvements. The instrument could now detect the heat of a human body twenty-five to thirty feet away. The authors emphasized the advantages gained by increasing the number of elements while diminishing the size of each bar. "Recherches sur plusieurs phénomènes calorifiques entreprises au moyen du thermo-multiplicateur," *Annales de chimie et de physique*, 1831, 2d ser. *48*:198–218.

Melloni's contributions to the thermomultiplier were sometimes slighted in later accounts. In response to the attribution by Despretz of the entire apparatus to Nobili, Melloni reviewed the history of heat measurement by thermoelectricity, beginning with Becquerel and ending with his own considerable improvements to Nobili's original device which resulted in a substantially different instrument sensitive enough to measure minute quantities of radiant heat. Melloni, "Mémoire sur la Polarisation de la Chaleur," *Annales de chimie et de physique*, 1837, *65*:43–45 (translated in Taylor's *Scientific Memoirs*, 1841, 2: 167–168).

Henry had used a Melloni thermoelectric pile in his attempt with Wheatstone and others at King's College to obtain a spark from a thermoelectric current (see the diary entry of April 22, above). Although here he is obviously fascinated with the apparatus and the experiments on radiant heat that could be performed with it, he did not attempt to acquire a set for himself until 1841 (Henry to Melloni, November 29, 1841, Henry Papers, Smithsonian Archives). When Henry received the apparatus, he used it for experiments on polarization of heat, diathermancy of substances, and on possible increases in heat from magnetization of soft iron bars ("Record of Experiments," April 27, 1843, May 1, 1843, Henry Papers, Smithsonian Archives). He then began using the apparatus for meteorological observations, proposing several modifications to adapt it specifically for this purpose, and for measuring the heat of the sun and the moon ("Record," May 1, 1843, May 12, 1843, October 3, 1843, January 11, 1845, Henry Papers, Smithsonian Archives). Henry's published articles on these observations include "On the Application of the Thermo-Galvanometer to Meteorology, Etc.," APS *Proceedings*, 1843–1847, *4*:22; "Observations on the Relative Radiation of the Solar Spots," ibid., pp. 173–176, and "On Heat, and on a Thermal Telescope," *Silliman's Journal*, January 1848, 2d ser. *5*: 113–114.

the heat to the pile there is a window in one side of the prism of zinc filled with different sized sliders one within the other thus In the middle of one is a small hole about ¾ of an inch in diameter or about the size of the end of the pile. When the pile is used with the screen for all of the experiments that were shewn to day except the exebition of the sensibility of the instrument the pile was furnished at each end with a tube polished within and furnished at the ends with covers. The farther end was closed and the heat entered the tube at the other.

When the instrument was used without the screen to show its sensibility it was furnished at each end with a conical reflector which consentrates the rays and increases the action on the pile. This sketch of the cone is rather too large but gives the general appearance. To show the sensibility of the instrument the trumpet shaped reflector at one end was turned towards the wall of the room while the cover on the other end was closed. The needle marked 50 d[e]grees of cold. The trumpet was then turned to the other end of the little room and when a persons face was placed before the reflector and at the greatest distance which could be obtained the deviation was more than 20 d[e]grees. In an open space or rather a large room the needle will indicate the heat of a person at the distance of 50 feet.

In these experiments three sources of heat are used, one from a small brass lamp with oil giving a constant *luminous* heat, the next from a spiral of platina suspended over a lamp of alcohol, this he calls radient heat. The other sourse is from a plate of brass smoked on one side and heated at the other by a lamp of spirits of wine. The flame of the lamp is behind and in contact with the back of the plate which is concave in front and smoked with a candle.

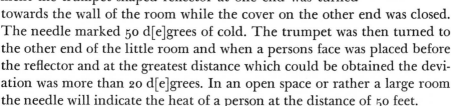

M Melloni operates generally with a standard temperature and this he obtains with different sources of heat by moving the source to and from the pile until the needle stands at 35 degrees. In most experiments on the transmission of heat the source is placed at the distance of fo[u]r or 4½ feet from the pile. This prevents the possibility of the plate or article experimented on becoming warm on the one side and transmitting its heat to the other and thus vitiating the results as has been thought. To prove that the heat radiating from the near side of the substance does not affect the results obtained from transmission &c the pile and the substance is a little turned to the right or left so as not to be precisely in the same straight line with the heat. Then the needle instantly falls to the position it had without the plate.

The plate is at the same distance from the heat in the last position as at first and receives very nearly the same quantity of heat. If it affected the pile by the heat from the near side the diminution shoul[d] be little as shown by the needle. There may possibly be a small quantity of heat given off from the near surface but it is from this experiment shown to be to[o] small while the other effects are so large that it may be entirely neglected.

All the resu[l]ts described by Mellonie are so striking and the results so well marked that there can be no doubt in the mind of a person who views them of the truth of the circumstance.

Mellonie does not much esteem the addition made to the apparatus by M Forbes. He says with justice that the errors are as much magnified as the true results and that he puts little reliance on indications which are only given by parts of a degree of the needle.[3]

The first experiments shown were those on the different diathermity of glass, salt and alum.

Three plates of these about one inch or perhaps a litle more in diameter were placed end wise on a slip of cork fastened by wax. In this form they were I believe stuck into a crease in the cork and perhaps there fastened with wax. This article was placed on a little brass table of which there were two belonging to the apparatus and this table was placed with the plates before the hole in the screen opposite the end of the pile. The nedle however was first brought to the standard temperature by moving the lamp which in this experiment was of oil (and the source of heat of course luminous) a litle nearer to or farther from the pile.

The figures in the squares indicate the d[e]grees as shown by the needle. It must however be reccollected that these d[e]grees show increasing quantities of heat which would be express[ed] nearly by the tangen[t]s of these

---

[3] By viewing the galvanometer needle through a telescope, Forbes got readings to a tenth of a degree. "On the Refraction and Polarization of Heat," *Phil. Mag.*, 1835, 3d ser. 6:134–142. Refinements of the technique appeared in "Researches on Heat," *Phil. Mag.*, 1838, 3d ser. *12*:545–559.
Encountering difficulties in his own work on radiant heat, Forbes had visited Melloni in Paris in 1833 and ordered a set of his apparatus (*DSB*). Although his experimental work and results were very close to Melloni's, Melloni criticized many of Forbes's techniques in his "Mémoire sur la polarisation de la chaleur," *Annales de chimie et de physique*, 1837, 65:5–68. The translation published in Taylor's *Scientific Memoirs*, 1841, 2:141–183, drew a rebuttal from Forbes in the form of a letter to the editor (at the end of part 6).

degrees. The first is 35 *ie* that is without a screen; the nex is 33 showing that when the salt was interposed scarcely an[y] heat was stopped. The next 20 shows the diminution caused by glass and the 3rd 6 shows a still greater [?diminution], more than 3/4 of the whole being stopped. The quantities may be found by taking the tangent of the angles 35 and 6 (approximately).

These three glasses are equally permeable to light and appear to the eye equally transparent. The heat however from a luminous flame as we see by this experiment passes through them very differently.

The source of heat was next changed and for a lamp of oil one of spirits was substituted with a coil of platina enveloping the wick which becoming red hot gives off rays as from an incandesent body. The effect of the screnes in stopping the heat was now very different.

The source of heat in this case gave off rays of less penetrating power, the quantity for air being the same that is the thermometer being again brought to the standard temperature of 35° by moving the source to and from the pile until the point was obtained.

The quantity transmitted by salt was the same as in the first exp. namely 33 but in glass much less (10) and through the alum no rays passed from this source.

The source was again changed and a black heat substituted and this was produced by a plate of brass smoked on one side and placed in contact with the flame of a spirit lamp on the other. The effect of transmission was now also very different.

In this experiment glass and alum stop all the rays while salt transmits the same quantity as before. The exp. was made as before with the standard temperature of 35°.

From these experiments it appears that transparent bodies oppose very different resistance to the free transmission of heat and that bodies perfectly transparent to light are not in the same state for heat. From this and many other experiments M Melloni concludes that light and heat are different although they may be both produced by the vibrations of the same etherial medium.[4]

---

[4] In his conclusion to an 1835 article Melloni had stated: "Light and heat, therefore, proceed from two distinct causes." He continued in a footnote:

These two causes themselves are, perhaps, but different effects of a single cause. The conclusion which appears to me to follow so clearly from my experiments is therefore by no means opposed to the general theory of undulations, according to which light and radiant heat arise from the motions communicated to the aether by the molecular vibrations of luminous bodies and bodies possessing heat. It will only be necessary to admit that the luminous and the calorific

June 29, 1837

Sinc[e] rock salt is the most perfect dia thermal substance known it is the most proper for the construction of lenses for the concentration of heat.[5] M Melloni has several of these of different thickness mounted in cork. *a* the lense, the largest 3 inches in diam. *b* the plate of cork through the bottom of which was thrust a piece of thick sheet lead to serve as a foot. To show the effect of a lens of this kind in concentrating the rays of light the apparatus was first arranged so that the heat through a lens of glass of about 4 inches in diameter and a focus of 6 or 8 inches gave no effect. The lens of rock salt was then substituted which had the same length of focus and the needle instantly showed 40 or 50 d[e]grees of the scale. I should mention that M Mellony has a very ingenious method of saving time in these experiments otherwise lost in the long vibrations of the needle. He has constructed a table by observation which gives him from an inspection of the first impulsive effect what the needle will settle at. This table being once constructed from direct observation answers ever afterwards for all other experiments.[6]

---

rays are two essentially distinct modifications which the aethereal fluid suffers in its mode of existence.

Taylor's *Scientific Memoirs*, 1837, *1*:392 (from "Observations et expériences relatives à la théorie de l'identité des agents qui produisent la lumière et la chaleur rayonnante," *Annales de chimie et de physique*, 1835, *60*:426).

By this time the undulatory or wave theory of heat had largely displaced the caloric theory. Melloni's well-publicized researches showing that radiant heat shared all the properties of light, which was already being explained according to wave theory, played a major role in the change. But Melloni was more interested in investigating the behavior of radiant heat than in endorsing any particular theory. In an 1836 article he wrote "I chose the language of the undulatory system, but I might as well have employed that of the system of emanation" (Taylor's *Scientific Memoirs*, 1837, *1*:346; *Annales de chimie et de physique*, 1836, *61*:410). Melloni also resisted the idea of the identity of heat and light. Results such as different transmission through transparent bodies and the phenomenon of brilliant light without heat (see footnote 8, below) seemed to argue against identity. In the 1840s Melloni finally accepted the idea that light and heat proceeded from one system of undulations in one ether, different effects resulting only from waves of different length and speed.

See Stephen G. Brush, "The Wave Theory of Heat: A Forgotten Stage in the Transition from the Caloric Theory to Thermodynamics," *The British Journal for the History of Science*, 1970, *5*:145–167. See also Weiner, "Joseph Henry's Lectures," chapters 4, 5, 6, and 9, which discusses Henry's advocacy of the wave theory.

[5] Melloni emphasized this property of rock salt, which he termed the *"true glass"* of radiant heat, in "Nouvelles recherches sur la transmission immédiate de la chaleur rayonnante par différens corps solides et liquides," *Annales de chimie et de physique*, 1833, *55*:337–397:

> It is easy to conceive . . . with what serious disadvantages those persons have had to contend who have undertaken to investigate the composition of solar heat with common prisms of flint or crown glass, water, alcohol, or some other diaphanous body. It was exactly the same as if they pretended to be able to analyse solar light with a prism formed of coloured glass.

Taylor, *Scientific Memoirs*, 1837, *1*:56–57.

[6] In addition to simply saving time, Melloni felt using the tables to shorten the time between two comparative experiments gave more accurate results since the temperature of the heat source could vary slightly over time. His explanation of the construction and use of the tables is in "Mémoire sur la transmission libre

400

Besides this inorder to render the oscillations of the needle as few as possible the bottom of the galvanometer is made of thick heavy brass which by its action on the needle soon brings it into a state of rest according to a well known principle.[7]

Since rock salt possesses the power of transmitting all the rays it may be used in a variety of ways for consentrating radiant heat. Also glass and more particularly alum may be employed to abstract the heat from sun light. Water also possesses the same property in a less degree than alum so that M Melloni has been able to procure a brilliant light absolutely without heat. For this purpose he passed the rays through water and a kind of green glass coloured by the oxide of copper. The light which immerged from the arrangement contained much yellow with a tint of greenish blue. When concentrated by the burning glass so as to produc[e] a spot as brilliant as the light from the sun it gave no indications of heat even to the thermoelectric pile. The phenominon of *Brilliant* light without heat.[8]

(Would it not be well to examine the chemical rays of the spectrum with lenses of salt.)[9]

To show that bodies may be almost perfectly diathermal and not transparent a large pece of smoky quartz was placed before the screen.[10]

---

de la chaleur rayonnante par différens corps solides et liquides," *Annales de chimie et de physique*, 1833, *53*:23–30 (translation in Taylor's *Scientific Memoirs*, *1*:10–15), and "Mémoire sur la polarisation de la chaleur," *Annales de chimie et de physique*, 1836, *61*:382–385 (Taylor's *Scientific Memoirs*, *1*:329–331).

[7] Another time-saving technique. Melloni attributed the neutralizing action of a copper (not brass) disc to a discovery of Arago. "Mémoire sur la polarisation de la chaleur," *Annales de chimie et de physique*, 1836, *61*: 378 (Taylor's *Scientific Memoirs*, 1837, *1*:327).

[8] Melloni reported the complete separation of light and heat in "Observations et expériences relatives à la théorie de l'identité des agents qui produisent la lumière et la chaleur rayonnante," *Annales de chimie et de physique*, 1835, *60*:426 (Taylor's *Scientific Memoirs*, 1837, *1*:392). He concluded from this that waves of light were different from waves of heat. He later repudiated the experiment, blaming carelessness in separating the more refrangible from the less refrangible rays and

the use of a thermoscope that was too large. Joseph Lovering, "Melloni's Researches in Radiant Heat," *American Almanac and Repository of Useful Knowledge, for the Year 1850* (Boston, 1849), pp. 64–81, especially pp. 80–81.

[9] By "chemical rays of the spectrum" Henry means ultraviolet rays, the existence of which was first detected by the chemical effects they produced. See J. F. W. Herschel, "Light," *Encyclopaedia Metropolitana* (London, 1845), *4*: 581–582. In investigating the transmission of the chemical rays through different substances, Mary Somerville found that rock salt was very permeable to these rays. *On the Connexion of Physical Sciences*, 5th ed. (London, 1840), p. 248.

[10] The diary entry ends here. Following a page and a half of blank space, there are several undated observations by Henry concerning the motion of amalgamated zinc, Savary's alternations with the magnetization of needles, and the polarization of light.

FROM CHARLES SAINT-ANGE THILORIER

Henry Papers, Smithsonian Archives

Paris le 30 juin 1837
rue de bouloy N⁰ 4.[1]

A Thilorier[2] se fera un plaisir et un honneur de recevoir demain *à Midi* Monsieur Henry et de repete devant lui quelques expériences sur l'acide Carbonique Solide. Il profitera de cette occasion pour lui faire voir ses appareils.

[1] This appears at the end in the original.

[2] For Thilorier and his experiments, see the first diary entry of [May 1837], above. According to a Bache letter to C. Dearne of August 21, 1837 (Bache Papers, Smithsonian Archives), Henry visited Thilorier twice. This invitation is presumably for the first encounter.

TO HARRIET HENRY

Mary Henry Copy,[1] Family Correspondence,
Henry Papers, Smithsonian Archives

Paris July 5. 1837

My dear dear little Wife I commence this letter very much fatigued in body, having been much engaged the whole day in making arrangements for my departure and fear I will not give you a very interesting communication, but if not interesting in itself I may certainly think you will still read it with pleasure. I have been engaged for several days past in arranging my affairs relative to the transportation to America of the articles I have purchased and in executing the commissions entrusted to me. I regret every time I go into a shop that I do not know what articles within the means of my purse would be interesting and useful to you. I have made a few purchases at random. . . .

I have now been nearly two months in Paris, much longer than I intended but time passes rapidly where there are so many objects to attract and distract attention. The distance from one part of the city to another, the things I wished to purchase in a philosophical line, the different men I have seen, the acquaintances made, the lectures and societies attended have stolen my hours and days imperceptibly. The time indeed seems long since I left London, but in its passage it has flown most rapidly and the impres-

[1] Mary Henry also produced a second, less complete typewritten copy.

sions the several objects have left on my mind are not of the most vivid kind. Of those which related purely to Science I have managed to make rough notes generally on the spot and at leisure to transfer them to my journal. The journal is only a note book of merely scientific articles which I hope will be of great use to me although scarcely of interest to others. I believe however I could furnish more material for sketches in the line of English and French science than anyone who has of late years visited Europe since I have been usually fortunate in gaining admission to intimacy with most of the men actually engaged in science in London and Paris. The latter part of my stay has been much more profitably passed than the first. I neglected to bring letters with me from England I could have had, and on this account lost time in forming acquaintances.

There has been about two hours interruption in my writing since the last lines. I had just ordered tea and was about to help myself to a cup when Ames[2] and Prof _____[3] of New Haven entered to give me a visit. They refused to partake with me of the exhilerating beverage but permitted me to continue the occupation while the news political philosophical &c were pleasantly discussed. I mentioned that I was in the act of making tea when they entered. I may as well inform you I have become quite skilled in the management of the tea-pot, having had considerable experience now in the practical <*management of the*> philosophy of the article as well as having given it some attention in the way of investigation.[4] You will permit me to occupy a few lines with the subject particularly since I am under the reviving influence of a few cups from the alembic which distills the exhilerating but not intoxicating liquid. 1st In making tea the kettle must be so heated that the water boils at least for two minutes. It must not be a simmering but a real boiling and this may be determined when there is a difficulty in getting at the cover of the kettle by placing the end of the poker against the kettle and the other at the ear. The sound conveyed by the iron will give with great precision the state of affairs within the vessel. 2nd The

---

[2] Angelo Ames.

[3] A. D. Stanley. Mary Henry's copyist had a question mark after the blank.

[4] European tea-drinking rituals were a source of both fascination and anxiety to visiting Americans, especially to those of a philosophical bent. Touring in 1825, the inventor Zachariah Allen made comments similar to Henry's in his *Sketches . . . in Great-Britain, France and Holland*, 2 vols. (Boston, 1833), *1*:35–37. Allen noted that self-conscious Americans unfamiliar with the art of tea preparation usually avoided embarrassment by opting for coffee, always a ready-made beverage. If Henry cared to seek them out, there were practical guides available such as that by a "Tea Dealer" [Smith], *Teiology: A Discourse on Tea* (London, 1827). Smith gives not a "receipt" for brewing tea but rather the "principles,' believing that "it is by the application of philosophical principles to the ordinary and even trivial concerns of life that science diffuses her benefits. . . ." (pp. 82–83). Smith explains the reasons for the rules of preparation Henry outlines below.

sides of vessel should be well polished to retain the heat and the bottom black to absorb it from the fire. 3rd It was some time before I learned the proper quantity of tea to be added to a given quantity of water but after some experiments it was determined that one half teaspoon to each cup produced a very pleasant strength of decoction at least for my palate and also that the hot water should be poured on the tea and not the tea thrown into the water. 4th A little hot water should be thrown into the cup to take off the chill. 4th[5] In order to give the tea a peculiar delicacy of taste, the suger should be first put in the cup,[6] the <*milk or*> cream next added and after about half a minute the hot tea. Some chemical action probably takes place between the sugar and cream before the addition of the tea. 5th China tea-cups of the kind we used in London were very highly polished, the saucers were smooth on the bottom and consequently the cup could be kept in its place without slipping only by particular care: a principle of science not often applied thus to the conveniences of life obviates this difficulty namely a few spoon-fulls of the tea thrown into the saucer produces by the attraction of cohesion between the liquid and the two solids such an adhesion that the cup will require considerable force to push it from its position, a fact of some importance.[7] I have made a few observations on the subject of coffee but will not occupy time with giving you an account of them. I may however state that Mr. Babinet instructed me in the way of making excellent coffee by a philosophical arrangement of a very simple kind. I will show you the experiment when I return. When tea is called for both in London and Paris the materials are always furnished and the duty of mixing left to the partaker. De Witt when we first landed in England was extremely anxious not to be recognised as an American. He was however betrayed by his ignorange of the philosophy of tea-making. When the article was placed upon the table with the hot water, much to the amusement of the waiter and to his own mortification my friend put the tea in his cup and made the mixture with his spoon. But enough of this subject.

I believe I informed you that the fêtes on the occasion of the marriage of the Duke of Orleans[8] were postponed after the death of the King of England. The Gallery of the Louvre has been closed all the time I have been in Paris for the purpose of making some arrangements in it for a grand dinner to be given by the King to the chief citizens of Paris. I fear it will not

[5] Either Henry or the copyist misnumbered.

[6] The Dutch, according to Smith, carried this refinement to an extraordinary degree. They refused to mix sugar directly with the tea, believing it injured the flavor and preferring to suck a piece of sugar candy which they removed when they sipped the tea (p. 88).

[7] Smith notes that polished surfaces "retain heat (or caloric) better than rough ones" (p. 83). We wonder if a cultivated Frenchman or Englishman would have approved of Henry's philosophical innovation.

[8] See above, Henry to Harriet, May 26–June 16, 1837.

be open while I remain. I have visited several times the Gallery of the Luxembourg....

I have been so long in Paris that I have become accustomed to the peculiarities of the place. There are many curious customs such as eating in the street, <*men and*> women sitting on the sidewalk in groups sewing and talking as freely as if they were in a house, men harnessed to carts, drawing stone or other articles about the street, the general employment of women as clerks and shop-keepers, women engaged in many occupations followed only by men in America, such as watch-making street-cleaning and even shoe-making.[9] One is struck both in London and Paris with the number engaged in unproductive labor earning a scanty subsistence by exhibiting feats of strength or by passing through the streets picking up rags bits of paper and other discarded articles. Some are thus engaged in the night and may be seen with a large basket on the back and a lantern

---

[9] A notable feature of French society, as far back as the seventeenth century, was the employment of women in what may be considered typically "male" occupations. In urban areas, women worked as shopkeepers and in the trades. Women ran and in many cases owned salt shops, pawn shops, stationery stores, tobacco shops, and lottery ticket booths. They were vendors of all kinds of foodstuffs, conducting their business in small stores or in the streets and marketplaces. Women also worked in the trades, as plumbers, butchers, bakers, and bread carriers. Women usually entered these occupations in a way different from the men. They often began as their husbands' assistants or business partners, with varying degrees of responsibility and independence; on the death of the husbands, widows frequently took over the shop or trade. By entering occupations in this unorthodox fashion, women frequently were able to circumvent normal competency tests and apprenticeship training (and, thus, restrictive guild regulations that might otherwise have excluded them). In the nineteenth century the industrial revolution in France doubtless affected occupational patterns for females, not driving them out of the trades and small businesses but opening up other possibilities, in the factory system and in large mercantile establishments, chiefly as sales clerks. See Edmund Charles-Roux et al., *Les Femmes et le travail du Moyen-Age à nos jours* (Paris, 1975), pp. 95–105, 155. Precise comparisons with women in American urban life are difficult to make. A recent study of female occupations in Baltimore at the end of the eighteenth cen-

tury discovered no economic or social bars against women working outside the home to support themselves and their dependents. Many women assisted their husbands in business or trade and poor laws encouraged widows or women with ill husbands to work toward their own support. Their occupations seemed fully as diverse as those pursued by their Parisian counterparts. If there were not differences in kind, there were perhaps differences in degree since only a very small percentage of Baltimore women in this period actually pursued occupations outside of the household. Kathryn Allamong Jacob, "The Woman's Lot in Baltimore Town: 1729–97," *Maryland Historical Magazine*, 1976, 71:290–293. While Henry was reacting to what were real differences between France and the United States, his observations were also conditioned by a provincial background (even Philadelphia, for example, was only one-fourth the size of Paris), class assumptions, and his experience as head of a rather traditional American household.

The working women of Paris made an impression on other American travelers. Visiting Europe at the same time as Henry, Elias Loomis considered these differences between French and American society fundamental. In America women were considered delicate beings to be spared severe labor. In Paris, by contrast, women were conspicuous contributors to every "department of commerce, of industry, of manual labor, . . . of buffoonery . . . ." "Letters from Europe," *Cleveland Observer*, October 12, 1837, p. 1.

in the hand inspecting every pile of rubbish in their road. But the inspection of the refuse of the streets does not end here. It is taken up in carts and carried to an extensive reservoir without the city and thrown into large vats for manure and here hundreds of persons of both sexes are constantly engaged in searching for articles which may have been accidentally dropped. I should dislike much the military system. A Colonel happens to lodge in one of the lower apartments of our Hotel and we constantly have a guard at our door and almost every morning a parade before the windows of one or two companies with a band of music. Last Sunday for this is the review day there was a grand display in the same place of one thousand men. Besides the troops of the line of which there are three thousand in Paris there are every day on duty the National Guards. These are composed of all the able-bodied citizens from eighteen to sixty years old, who are required to be properly armed and equipped to appear as often as once a month, spending the whole day on guard, at any point to which they may be directed. Very few are exempt. The professors of the colleges as well as the lowest citizens are obliged thus to mount guard perhaps at the Tuilleries.[10] I met a gentleman at breakfast this morning who postponed his engagement with [me] of yesterday because he was to be ordered on duty. There is another class of men attached to the police, who appear everywhere in citizens dress but are secretly armed. They mingle among the crowd when any of the Royal Family are driving out and give signals from one to the other if the royal carriage is approaching and are on the alert to repel any attack. The necessity of means of this kind must be a sad draw-back to the pleasures of royal station. The King is seldom seen in public; it is his policy as Napoleons not to make himself too cheap. On the day however of the entrance of the newly married pair into Paris, His Majesty appeared on a balcony of the palace fronting the Garden of the Tuilleries and presented his new daughter to the people. On this occasion he was called out by the cries of the multitude much as an actor is made to appear in front of the curtain at the theater. The applause however was not very great. A royal actor is far from being popular. I had a good opportunity of seeing the Royal family a few days since in the Garden of the Luxembourg. They came to inspect the gallery of pictures[11] and while an immense crowd were waiting outside of the palace expecting

[10] Organized in 1789 as a citizens' militia, the French National Guard was a most visible police presence and upholder of the state under the July Monarchy. What Henry says about the role and composition of the Guard is essentially accurate. See Louis Girard, *La Garde Nationale, 1814–1871* (Paris, 1964).

[11] In 1817 the lower galleries of the Luxembourg Palace were devoted to exhibiting the works of living artists. *Paris Guide* (Paris, 1867), pp. 574–583.

their appearance, the party passed through a passage in the rear into the garden, and as this was nearly deserted, those who as myself happened to be there had a good opportunity of seeing them. The whole company about ten in number formed a very ordinary collection of individuals. The ladies with the grand duchess were absolutely plain and were chosen as maids of honor perhaps on that account, it would not do for an attendant to be better looking than her mistress. The Duchess is not unpleasing in appearance, but is far from beautiful; she is tall, well dressed and has the air of a well educated woman. The Duke is a tolerably good-looking young man of about twenty-five. The great in circumstances are not always the favorites of Nature either in mind or body.

Bache appeared in Paris about four days ago and we have been together nearly all the time since.[12] His wife as himself appeared very glad to see me again. They propose remaining in Paris about six weeks. Mrs. Bache is not as well pleased thus far as with London. She is surrounded by strangers speaking an unknown tongue and cannot ask for an article or give an order to a servant. De Witt has gone to Geneva for a short excursion. . . . I believe that I have forgotten to mention that I reside near Dr. Cabell,[13] the brother in law of James Alexander[14] who is a most excellent young man and has been very kind to me. I am generally too much engaged to be homesick but often at night and after the fatigues of the day I feel lonely and send my thoughts across the broad waters to those who do not forget me and whose existence is a part of my own. I look forward with pleasure to the moment when I shall leave these shores and commence my homeward journey although I reflect with much emotion that all I see here and all with whom I have formed acquaintance, will never be seen again, that I leave this and the city of London with all its kind inhabitants forever. But I have an engagement <*at ten o'clock*> and my watch indicates that I will be late. Adieu my dear dear little wife. Believe that "where e'er I roam, what ever place I see, my heart untravels still returns to thee."[15] God bless you my wife.   J.H

---

[12] According to Bache's diary (Bache Papers, Library of Congress) Henry visited Bache after dinner on July 3 and on July 5 (the date of this letter) Bache and Henry spent the day looking for instruments.

[13] James Lawrence Cabell (1813–1889, *DAB*), physician and educator. Graduating from the University of Virginia and receiving an M.D. from the University of Maryland in 1834, Ca-

bell went to Paris in 1836 for further instruction. He became Professor of Anatomy, Surgery and Physiology at the University of Virginia and one of the leaders of the public health movement.

[14] James Waddel Alexander, Sr.

[15] Where'er I roam, whatever realms to see,
    My heart untravell'd fondly turns to thee.
Oliver Goldsmith, *The Traveller*.

TO HARRIET HENRY

Mary Henry Copy, Family Correspondence,
Henry Papers, Smithsonian Archives

[July 5, 1837][1]

I have been engaged laboriously for two days past in preparing a memoir at the request of M. Melloni for the French Institute, on some of my unpublished experiments,[2] but the article is longer than I supposed it would be and there is difficulty in getting it properly translated into French. The person I engaged to make the translation I find does not understand the subject and I do not therefore like to trust the article in his hands. I will see M. Melloni tomorrow and confer with him about it. Melloni is celebrated for his discoveries relative to heat particularly in its connection with light. I was surprised to find that he is one of the youngest men of the Institute in appearance although he must be thirty-five. He is an Italian refugee residing in Paris and has been very kind to me.

I believe I informed you I had great pleasure in making the acquaintance of M. De La Rive of Geneva and also of his Lady.[3] He has gone to England and I am to meet him at the British Association.

This letter starts in a few moments and I have only time to assure you that I am as ever your own own

J.H.

[1] Although undated, this fragment may possibly have been attached to the preceding letter, also a copy by Mary Henry.

[2] On the lateral discharge (see below, Henry to Coquerel, October 1, 1837). There is no evidence, however, that Henry actually presented the paper to the Institut, perhaps because of the problems mentioned further in the paragraph. Henry eventually read the paper to a section of the British Association.

[3] We have found no other mention of their meeting in Paris. Henry later saw him in London.

ALEXANDER DALLAS BACHE TO BASIL HALL[1]

Gratz Collection, Historical Society of Pennsylvania

Paris July 16. 1837

My dear Sir.

Your kindness to me while in Edinburgh induces me to wish for my friend Professor Henry, of Princeton College N.J., the advantage of your acquaintance. Professor Henry stands first with us among the zealous pour-suivants of physical science and I trust that in the absence of M.ʳ Forbes[2] from Edinburgh you will introduce him into the interesting scientific circle which is there.

With my best wishes for your health
I remain Very truly Yours
A. D. Bache

[1] Basil Hall (1788–1844), a retired Royal Navy captain and author, was prominent in Edinburgh and London scientific circles. During his tour of duty in the Navy, he published a number of popular accounts of his voyages to the Orient and the western coasts of the North and South American continents and contributed articles to the *Philosophical Transactions* of the Royal Society to which he was elected a member in 1816. After his retirement in 1823 he spent his time in private travel, including a trip to the United States in 1827–1828, and in scientific and literary pursuits in Edinburgh and London. *DNB.*

From Captain Hall's visit to the United States came one of the ubiquitous books of travel popular before transportation and communication improvements made that genre less meaningful. Written a few years before DeTocqueville's famous *Democracy in America* (1835), Hall's work, *Travels in North America in the Years 1827 and 1828*, 3 vols. (Edinburgh, 1829) contains a number of comments on issues relevant to the rise of the American scientific community. On visiting West Point, for example, Hall noted the high level of mathematics and the teaching of astronomy even in the absence of an observatory to use this knowledge. He described the purpose of the Academy as not so much to prepare for actual military service but to disseminate throughout the United States knowledge of the sciences and the taste for literary and scientific pursuits. Because of American dependence on British intellectual development, Hall doubted the success of this purpose.

On visiting Harvard and Yale, Hall made complimentary observations but, as in the case of West Point, found reasons to doubt the growth of an autonomous high culture in the United States. Acknowledging the diffusion of basic knowledge to all classes, he was critical of the neglect of the classics, an essential element of learning. Characteristic American restlessness and independence due to the geographic and political situation, as well as an indifference to abstract learning because of its impracticality, limited incursions into classical knowledge, let alone "into the regions of any abstract science." Despite abundant capacity and desire to learn, the rewards were inadequate. The great men of science and literature in the United States were few, a disproportionally small number for the size of the population.

But Philadelphia drew Hall's praise as a center of culture. He attended a Wistar Party; he praised the library of the American Philosophical Society; he noted other learned bodies in the city with an "earnest desire to pursue knowledge for its own sake." Because there was much leisure in Philadelphia, scientific and literary pursuits were cultivated successfully and steadily. On making the obligatory visit to Franklin's grave, "the Socrates of modern days," Hall praised his practical wisdom, rather than the scientific contributions. A few pages on, Hall gave a history of the invention of the steamboat. Reflecting on the rival claims, he declared that an inventor who applied science cleverly without having discovered the underlying principles deserved more than the pure experimenter who did not see beyond his work to its application.

Totally at variance with Joseph Henry's position at the same period in Albany, Hall wrote from the security of a society smugly complacent about its role in generating knowledge. Henry and like-minded scientists in the United States could not tolerate such denigration of pure scientists.

[2] James David Forbes was at this time tak-

ing the longest of his numerous trips to the Continent. Forbes left London in May 1837 and spent most of his time traveling throughout Germany and Austria, meeting prominent scientists and conducting meteorological observations. He did not return to Scotland until August 1839. John Campbell Shairp et al., *Life and Letters of James David Forbes* (London, 1873), pp. 230–255.

FROM ALEXANDER DALLAS BACHE

Henry Papers, Smithsonian Archives

[July 16, 1837][1]

Dear Henry,

The results of the oscillation of "Rusty" & "bright" at London were these:[2]

1. Time of ten observed by counting 30.6, 31.0, 31.4, Approx time 31″ for 10 osc'ns

2. Then began.   June 24, 1837 Weather hazy Wind N.E.   2′35″ for 50.

h	,	″	Semi Arc.	Temp.°	Gauge	"Rusty"	{ Watch slow
1, 27,	47.6		6°	77°	2½ Inches		{ loses 27″06 in 1 hour
10—							
	28,	18.4					
10—							
		50.0					
10—							
	29	20.8					
10—							
		52.0					
10—							
	30	23.6					

These five compared with the last five give so many determinations to eliminate the error of observing the beg^g & end.

[1] Henry's file note gives the date as August 1837. However, a letterpress copy of the letter in a chronologically arranged volume of outgoing correspondence in the Bache Papers, Smithsonian Archives, appears before a letter dated July 18, 1837. We are assuming Bache gave this letter to Henry just before Henry left Paris.

[2] While abroad, Bache made a series of ob-

servations on terrestrial magnetism which he reported in "Observations of the Magnetic Intensity at Twenty-one Stations in Europe," *Transactions of the American Philosophical Society*, 1841, n.s. 7:75–100. The needles "Rusty" and "Bright" were used only in the London and Paris observations and then given to Henry to oscillate in the United States.

50	33	00.0				
50	35	36.0	These obs^{ns} are only for the number of oscillations	15	36.4	Time of 10 osc^{ns} at 77°
50	38	12.4			36.8	" 31.23
50	40	48.4			36.4	or
10—						+ .23 corr^n for chr^r rate
	43	24.0			37.2	31.46
10—						
	44	26.4			37.2	
10—						
		58.0			37.0	
10—						
	45	29.2				
10—				15	36.8	at 77° Fah.
	46	00.6	—2°	—77°—		

Place of observation Westbourne Green near London (See a further description). I do not trouble with the details of the subsequent sets 31.44 at 77 in arcs of 6 to 2 was the next determ^n of the time.

"Bright" gave 25.21 at 72½ between 6° & 2°.

and 25.21 at 72¼ " " "

Any points omitted you will find in my memoir a copy of which I give you with this.[3] To get to Westbourne Green the name of a row of houses you go out the Harrow Road pass the first toll gate & go on until you come to a bridge over the Paddington Canal, pass Eastward along the canal until you get behind the gardens of the row called Westbourne green then

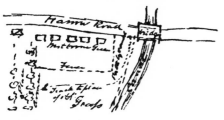

bear off to the South & you find a row of noble trees under the shade of one near the middle of which (row) the ob^{ns} were made. This rude sketch albeit inexact may help you if Capt J. C. Ross should not be in town.[4]

Bache used a vacuum apparatus for these horizontal intensity readings so he included a gauge reading in the list of conditions.

[3] Not found with the letter. Bache may be referring to a draft of his London observations which later appeared in his article, or perhaps to an earlier paper, "On the Relative Horizontal Intensities of Terrestrial Magnetism at Several Places in the United States . . . ," APS *Transactions*, 1837, n.s. 5:427–457, which detailed his methods of observation. Both are in the Henry Library.

[4] According to Bache's article, Ross had formerly lived near Westbourne Green.

I expect you to oscillate at London, at home say at Philadelphia in my lattice observatory in the yard Ches^t Street, or at Girard College, or at your home if these are extremely inconvenient places. Then to send me out the needles. Best perhaps to oscillate then put them together for a month & then oscillate again & put them up to send for they will thus be sure of getting to me safe. Send to Mr Vaughan & not later than June next (to reach London.)[5]

The Holmesburgh visit[6] you will not fail in & to tell me all about the Girard College, Frank. Inst. & Univ^y, and my friends that you can learn in Philad.

Goodbye & may Heaven bless you & return you safe to your family & home usefulness.

Ever truly Yours
A D Bache

P.S. If Watkins' instrument[7] suits you order one for me (without crystals) & refer him for pay to Mr Vaughan & inform Mr P.V. of it. If Soleil's crystals dont fit let me know: & the shape of mounting to suit app^s Whatever Wheatstone has you can take home for me if you wish & keep safe for me in deposit. Urge him to a complete set of app^s on sound for me.

---

[5] Henry did not make the observations until late in September. In a letter to John Locke of August 8, Bache says he fears that Henry neglected to observe before leaving London for the North (outgoing correspondence, Bache Papers, Smithsonian Archives). On August 25 (see below), Locke wrote Henry with further instructions on finding Westbourne Green. Assisted by T. C. Robinson, Henry oscillated "Rusty" and "Bright" along with two other needles, Robinson A and B, at Westbourne Green on September 27, 1837. At Princeton with Stephen Alexander, he used the same needles for observations in January 1838 and the following July and August before sending all four to Bache in London. Both rough notes and a neat copy of the readings are in Box 17 of the Henry Papers, Smith-

sonian Archives.

Bache's article does not mention Henry's observations, which Henry forwarded to him with the needles in a letter of August 9, 1838 (Bache Papers, Smithsonian Archives; printed in Nathan Reingold, ed., *Science in Nineteenth-Century America* [New York, 1964], pp. 81–90). Henry noted in his letter that his observations didn't agree very well with Bache's.

[6] Perhaps a reference to a visit to Bache's mother which Henry had promised to make.

[7] A polarization apparatus. Henry purchased one from Watkins and Hill and also one from Soleil. Folder of Accounts with Various European Instrument- and Apparatus-dealers, Joseph Henry for the College of New Jersey, 1837, Princeton University Archives.

HENRY'S EUROPEAN DIARY

Henry Papers, Smithsonian Archives

July 24 [1837] Returned to London arrived in the steam boat from Antwerp at 12 o'clock. Hastened to Mr Vaughans, received 2 letters from H. dated

1st and 20th of June.[1] Difficulty in getting my bagage through the custom house. Took lodgings with my Friend H James No 65 Albany Street.

[1] Not found.

TO HARRIET HENRY

Mary Henry Copy (in part),[1] Family Correspondence
Henry Papers, Smithsonian Archives

London July [26–31], 1837[2]

I arrived in this city from Antwerp on the 21st after an absence of two months and a half and felt on landing as if I were returning home after a visit to a foreign land. I immediately hastened to no. 70 Fenchurch street, even before my baggage was passed at the custom house and received as I anticipated two letters from you. . . .[3] I had heard nothing from you for a month and these as you may suppose gave me great pleasure.

The last two weeks of my time in Paris was occupied from early in the morning until late at night in arranging and having packed the articles purchased for the college, in settling my bills and in making visits with Bache. The last part of my stay was by far the most important; it was not until I commenced almost to make arrangements to leave the city that certain sources of information and profit as it were suddenly opened to me. About two weeks and a half before I left Bache and his Lady came, just in time to profit by my experience. They were very glad to meet me again and the remaining time not occupied with the apparatus was spent in Bache's company. . . . The water of Paris did not agree with me. . . . Bache was affected in the same way. I left him quite unwell.

It was my intention as you may recollect to make a short excursion through Belgium and Holland, and at the date of my last letter thought I should extend my tour to Geneva but my stay had been so much prolonged in Paris, that I abandoned all thought of Switzerland. I bade good bye to my friends in Paris with the hope of meeting most of them in America and

[1] The first part of this document, up to the words "story and what is stil more . . ." in the description of Antwerp, survives only in longhand and typed Mary Henry copies. The former is the basis of this text. The original survives for the latter portion. The salutation is lacking in the Mary Henry Copy and is omitted here.

[2] As shown in the text, Henry wrote the last part of his letter on July 31. The letter was received by James Henry in Albany who forwarded it to Harriet in Galway, N. Y., on September 4. We are omitting James's note to her appended to the last sheet.

[3] Not found.

took my passage in the Diligence for Brussels. The road passed through a pleasant part of France, much more highly cultivated than the district between Calais and Paris. We passed through a number of fortified towns all nearly of the same sombre appearance, the streets resembling, as I have said of those of Paris fissures in a basaltic rock. . . . I became quite familiar with the plan of fortification of a city, with redoubts, ramparts, ditches, etc etc, a species of knowledge of which before I was quite ignorant. I occupied the middle seat in the coupé, the front division of the Diligence, my companions in this part of the vehicle were two medical students from America who had been in Paris for two years and were now on an excursion previous to their return to the United States. They were both gentlemanly young men from the South[4] and rendered the journey of two days and one night much less tedious. On the morning of the third day we crossed the line between Belgium and France and while the luggage of another diligence was in process of examination we took breakfast. The examination was not a strict one, my clothing was scarcely disturbed and several pairs of gloves which happened to be on top were passed with a smile. There was an opposition line on the route and great strife the whole distance to be foremost. There is a law in France forbidding any diligence to pass any other diligence, except when it is at rest. There was therefore a great bustle at each change of horses since our vehicle was the foremost in order to get the new team harnessed before the other line could come up, and in some cases so closely were we pressed, the start was made before the arrangement was completed, or the passengers all in their places.

After passing the Belgium line a marked difference was observed in the appearance of the villages, the cultivation of the land, the whole country exhibiting a more advanced state of agriculture. We arrived in Brussels, the capital of Belgium, about six o'clock of the evening of our second day, and took lodging at least I did at the Hotel de Flandres a very pleasant house kept by a Flemish dame. The landlady gave me a cordial welcome and entertained me, partly in French, partly in English, with her history. She had lived in the same house all her life; her father had kept the hotel before her. She had witnessed many changes, was first a subject of Austria, next a citizen of France, then a good subject of the King of Holland; by the revolution of 1830 was converted into a republican of Belgium, and after this became a subject of King Leopold. No part of the world has undergone so many political changes within the last fifty years, as the little kingdom of Belgium.[5] Lying as it does between France and the more northern part

---

[4] Unknown to us.
[5] By the terms of the Treaty of Vienna

(1815) the Austrian Netherlands (Belgium) was united with the United Provinces (Holland)

of Europe it has been the arena of battle of nearly all the Nations of Europe and its fields are rendered fertile by the blood of thousands. You may recollect that the Field of Waterloo is but nine miles from [Brussels]. You may suppose I could not pass it by. The two medical students a New York merchant[6] and I hired an open carriage and at nine o'clock in the morning started for the field. Our route lay to the south of Brussels. We passed through the wood, or as it is here called the forest of Soignes, the Ardennes of Byron, whose green leaves wept, if aught inanimate e'er wept for the non-returning braves.[7] After passing out of this wood we came to the village of Waterloo. I should mention that the King of Holland gave a thousand acres of this wood to Lord Wellington. About a mile from the village is a small hamlet called Mount St. Jean and near this was the principal scene of the battle. I purchased a map on the spot and with the assistance of a most interesting guide, we passed several hours in studying the ground. I must defer an account of our investigations until I can spread the map on a table before you and point out in person the spots of interest. Near the centre of the field an immense mound has been erected surmounted by the Belgian Lion in bronze. The whole structure, including the lion is two hundred feet high and from this elevation a fine view of the whole plain may be had. Our guide was quite intelligent, was about seventeen when the battle took place; lived near the spot. He went with a cousin the morning of the battle to see the array of soldiers. The two lads were charmed with the sound of the music, the glitter of arms and thought how glorious it is to be a soldier. But while thus delighted the first charge was made, the attack took place near the spot where they stood and they were obliged to fly for their lives with opinions somewhat changed as to the pleasures of a soldier's life. For three days after the battle he was engaged with his Father

to form the Kingdom of the Netherlands. Power in the new country was divided equally between the Catholic Belgians and the Protestant Dutch. However, since the Belgians outnumbered the Dutch three to two, and since the Dutch dominated the civil service, Belgian opposition to the union quickly developed. In August 1830, in the wake of the Paris revolution of July, fighting broke out and an independent Belgium was established; Prince Leopold of Saxe-Coburg was given the throne. However, only the intercession of the French army prevented the Dutch from reannexing Belgium.

At the time of Henry's European trip an uneasy truce was in effect between the Dutch and Belgians. Technically the Netherlands and Belgium were still in a state of war. William I, the King of the Netherlands, did not recognize the independence of Belgium until March 1838. It was not until April 1839 that a treaty was signed, establishing the independence and neutrality of Belgium under the guarantee of the major European powers. Adrien de Meeüs, *History of the Belgians*, trans. G. Gordon (New York, 1962), pp. 262–284.

[6] Unidentified.

[7] And Ardennes waves above them her green leaves,

Dewy with nature's teardrops as they pass,
Grieving, if aught inanimate e'er grieves,
Over the unreturning brave—alas!

Byron, *Childe Harold's Pilgrimage*, canto III.

in burying the dead and carrying off the wounded; long before the end of this time his heart was sick of war and not for worlds would he have been a soldier. Such was his simple and I have no doubt true story. The principal part of the field remains precisely as it was after the battle. For several years after the spots of the ground where the most blood had been shed were marked by a more luxurious vegetation. The whole space is now covered as far as the eye can see with fields of wheat and since these are not separated by fences as in our country the whole appears as one. The armies occupied two opposite ridges when the fight commenced, were extended parallel to each other and about a mile apart for nearly five miles. Twenty-five thousand men were left dead upon the field, and in four days, in the several battles which took place around the spot and which included the whole campaign, it is said that no less than sixty thousand human beings were swept from the Earth. And for what? To gratify the pride, the lust for power of a few by nature no better than the meanest that fell. I actually grew sick as I stood on the mound which covers the remains of two thousand of the slain and in imagination faintly realized the horror of the battle. We returned towards night to Brussels and the next morning left for Antwerp.

I should state that before leaving Brussels we visited all the places of interest, the observatory,[8] the museum,[9] Repository of Arts,[10] and the palace of the King who with the Queen happened then to be on a visit to Paris. You will recollect that King Leopold married the daughter of Louis Philippe. She is said to be very fond of the French Capital. The Palace is good enough, not however to be compared in grandeur with the royal mansions I saw in France. It contains a number of good pictures by the old masters and is now being filled up, at least one end of it, for the reception of the Duke of Orleans and his young bride who are shortly to visit Belgium. Rather expensive visitors, since one half of a large mansion has to be remodeled for their accommodation. We next visited the palace of the Prince of Orange, a house which was a part of the year occupied by the King before the revolution of 1830 in France. Immediately after that event the Belgians revolted against the Dutch Government and the members of the royal family then at Brussels were obliged to fly. They left the palace without removing the furniture, and as the house was the private property of the King, it has not been disturbed.[11] The new King Leopold was put upon

[8] Founded in 1827 and headed by Adolphe Quetelet.

[9] Probably the predecessor of the present museum of the Institut Royal des Sciences Naturelles de Belgique. It originated in the eighteenth century in the cabinet of curiosities of Charles of Lorraine. In 1837 the collection was the property of the city of Brussels; title passed to the kingdom in 1842 from which date the Institut originates.

[10] Le Musée de l'Industrie, founded in 1832, a predecessor of the present Musées Royaux d'Art et d'Histoire.

[11] Now the Palais des Académies.

the throne of Belgium by England, France, and Austria, has occupied another house fitted up for him as a palace. The palace of the Prince of Orange is a beautiful mansion all the floors of which are inlaid with rose satin and other costly woods. Most of the rooms are without carpets the floors being richer than any covering. We were not allowed to step on the middle of the floor but were desired to keep along the margin and were furnished on entering with socks of cloth to put over our shoes to prevent dust and scratching.

I was not so fortunate as to find M. Quetelet, the philosopher of Brussels, to whom I had letters and to make whose acquaintance I had first concluded to take this route. He was gone on an excursion to Ostend with his family. I was however received with much cordiality by his assistant[12] and shown the apparatus and astronomical instruments of the place.

After three days in Brussels, I started with the same traveling companions for Antwerp and after a pleasant drive of about twenty miles arrived in that city celebrated both for war and commerce. Do you recollect when we lived in Albany, the papers were filled with accounts of the Siege of Antwerp and that Stephen copied a plan of the citadel? I little thought at the time that within six years I would be on the spot personally inspecting the works and viewing the effects of the Siege. At the time of the Belgian revolution the Dutch were driven out of the [?citadel] of Antwerp which adjoins the city and also commands the river. As they would suffer no vessels to ascend the river and thus caused great confusion in the commerce of the world the French and English after many attempts at negotiation commenced the bombardment of the Fort which held out for many weeks. Antwerp in many things reminds me of Albany. The same kind of houses, built of small bricks and with gable ends to the street. The same clamps and little tackles for hoisting articles to upper story and what is stil more striking the same cast of features familiar to me in Albany and Schenectady are here seen. The house of the better class of citizens are furnished with peep glasses which I have often heard of but never before seen. They consist of a looking glass placed on each side of the window on the out side so that a lady can see what is passing up and down the street without putting her head out of the window. It somewhat surprising that the Dutch of Albany did not import this fashion with the many others.

We assended the steeple of the church of Notre dame one of the highest in Europe 500 feet to the top & from there had a good view of the city and the surrounding country. The church itself is one of the largest I have seen and is a fine specimen of the Florid gothic. It was erected more than 400

---

[12] Not identified.

years ago. Contains many interesting pictures amoung the number the celebrated one by Rubens of "descent from the cross." In this city and also in Brussels there are a great many pictures of the old masters particularly of the Flemish School. I forgot to mention that among the number I saw a very queer one—the birth of Eve. Adam was asleep under a tree and Eve in the act of being drawn from his side. After visiting the principal objects of interest in the city I returned to the Hotel where we stoped and then found myself so much fatigued and exhausted that I was obliged to go to bed. Spent a bad night, and was still quite unwell in the morning. I had procured a passport[13] from the Dutch minister in Paris with which I thought to pass from the Kingdom of Belgium into that of Holland but on inspection it was found that I could not get into the latter without going through Prussia. The King of Holland will not acknowledge the independence of Belgium and will permit no person to come from that country directly into his. The Steamboat the same day was to start at 12 o'clock and what with my illness and the difficulty of getting over the lines I concluded [to] start immediatly for London where should I become worse I would be amoung friends. We had a good passage, my disease did not increase and when I got to London I found that Henry James was still in the city. He commenced a course of medicine with me and wether by accident or skill has effected quite a cure.[14] I am to day (July 31) better then I have been for 6 weeks past. I start the day after tomorrow for Edinburgh and hope to reach there by Saturday night (this being Monday). I have been quite home sick for some days past and were it not that I never expect to return and that it would be a foolish affair I would almost start with the Wellington which sails the 10th of next month. I intend however to sail as soon after the middle of September as possible that is after the meeting of the British association as may be which takes place about the middle of the month.

I have partely persuaded Henry James to accompany me to Scotland. He is to make up his mind tomorrow. I hope my dear wife that you will forgive me for not writing often. If you knew how I have longed to see you and the children for some days past, & often of late I have dreamed of you and our dear Dear little ones, you would not think I was unmindful of you. You say you will never part with me again. I will never require you to do so and should I return safely I will have done with wandering and be content to settle down for life in any situation which Providence may designate. I have an engagement this morning which has caused me [to] scribble this

[13] Surviving in the Henry Papers, Smithsonian Archives.
[14] A short diary entry of July 25, 1837, reads, "Quite unwell—continued so for several days —took medicine from H. J. which produced instantly a change."

letter with such haste that I fear you will scarcely be able to read it. Give my Love to all. I regret that I did not get your letter of the 20th of June before I left Paris as I would then have purchased some articles of lace and put them in my box as you and Mrs Shankland wished. I have several times regretted that you did not put into my trunks as you intended one of your old shoes. Mrs Bache says that if I will send a drawing of your foot in a letter to Mr B she will bring you some French slippers when she returns.

Kiss the children for me. I hope William is a good Boy and gives his mother and grandmother but little trouble. Mary I am glad to learn has been a good girl and that little Puss is making good progress in the development of her faculties mental & Physical. I would give thousands did I possess them to see you but for an hour.

> Adieu my Dear Wife
> & believe me until death
> only your
> Husband

TO ALEXANDER DALLAS BACHE
Bache Papers, Smithsonian Archives

London July 28th (Friday) 1837

My Dear Bache

I arrived in London on Monday last and have since then been almost all the time been confined to the house with the same disease with which you were afflicted when I left Paris. I was attacked in Antwerp and as I found that I could not get into Holland without going a long ways round I concluded to make the best of my way to London and then as soon as practical to Edinburgh. I have taken up my Lodging with my Friend Henry James who has undertaken to be Nurse and Physician to me and thus far has succeeded quite well.

I have as yet seen none of our Friends except the Messrs Vaughan[1] and Mr Roberton.[2] The latter gentleman says he has a bone to pick with you for leaving town without calling on him. He intended to offer you any facilities in his power for intercourse with your Friends while on the continent. He is as kind and attentive now as before.

Mr Wheats[t]on[e] is going on quite rapidly with his wires for the tele-

---

[1] William and Petty Vaughan.　　　　[2] John David Roberton.

graph & has as I am informed several miles of wire put down. I have not yet seen him.[3]

Mr Lock[4] arrived in Town the same day with myself. I met him at the custom house. He left me yesterday rather abruptly to find the residence of Mr Bailey.[5] I met Mr De La Reeve[6] at Watkins[7] yesterday. He made many inquiries about you, regretted that I had not gone to Geneva as all his friends would expect me there as he had written to that effect!? I had quite a plesant visit through Belgium but did not see Quetelet. He had

[3] *King*, pp. 289–290, notes that in July 1837 Wheatstone tested his equipment on a 1.4-mile section of the London and Birmingham Railroad between Euston Square and Camden Town. See Henry's account of his visit to Wheatstone in his diary entry of August 2, where he reports that Wheatstone is working with 13 miles of wire.

[4] Like Henry, John Locke (1792–1856) was in Europe to purchase apparatus for his institution, the Medical College of Ohio. Locke had interests in many different branches of science, concentrating on the natural sciences early in his career and the physical sciences later on. He had a medical degree from Yale (1819), where he had assisted Benjamin Silliman in chemistry. He had an early interest in botany, publishing *Outlines of Botany* in 1819 (Boston). Prior to becoming Professor of Chemistry at the Medical College of Ohio in 1835, Locke had conducted his own school for girls, the Lexington Academy in Lexington, Kentucky, apparently a progressive school based partly on the methods of Pestalozzi. During his association with the Medical College of Ohio from 1835 to 1852, with a brief interruption in 1849–1850, Locke's varied interests resulted in publications on electromagnetism, optics, geology, and terrestrial magnetism, most of which appeared in *Silliman's Journal*. *DAB* and Adolph E. Waller, "Dr. John Locke, Early Ohio Scientist (1792–1856)," *The Ohio State Archaeological and Historical Quarterly*, 1946, 55:346–373.

Toward the end of his career, Locke's relationships with other members of the scientific community became increasingly hostile. Waller's account briefly mentions his emotional imbalance but only in connection with political conflicts at the Medical College of Ohio. His chairmanship of the 1844 meeting of the Association of American Geologists and Naturalists was unsuccessful. Already familiar with his "irascible temperament and frontier mannerisms," participants criticized him for joining in debate from the chair. Feeling slighted, Locke boycotted the 1845 session although he was scheduled to give an address as outgoing president. Sally Gregory Kohlstedt, "The Formation of the American Scientific Community: The American Association for the Advancement of Science, 1848–1860" (Ph.D. dissertation, University of Illinois at Urbana-Champaign, 1972), pp. 88–89, 92 (published, without these passages, under the same title, Urbana, Illinois, 1976). Locke's defense of his invention of an automatic time-registering device for astronomical observations managed to alienate a number of people. His monograph on the subject, *On the Invention of the Electro-Chronograph* . . . (Cincinnati, 1850), amply displays his paranoia. Containing specific accusations against O. M. Mitchel, S. C. Walker, A. D. Bache, and others, the monograph alleges a "combined effort, not only to deprive me of absolute honors but at last to destroy my moral reputation. . . ." Locke called Henry "excellent and amiable" but warned of the potential danger of the improper use of the power of the Smithsonian. At about the same time, Locke came into direct conflict with Henry over the delay in the publication of an article by him on terrestrial magnetism. In response to one of Locke's communications, Henry wrote Bache, "I have received a letter from John L. the most repugnant to my feelings of any thing ever addressed to me. . . . The only charitable conclusion is that he is deranged—there is however sufficient venom in the attack to evince the knave as well as the fool" (January 18, 1850, Bache Papers, Smithsonian Archives). Although Henry eventually published the article in question (*Smithsonian Contributions*, 1852, *3*: 3–29), he and Locke had no further correspondence after the dispute.

[5] Probably Francis Baily.

[6] Henry had met De La Rive and his wife in Paris. See Henry's second letter to his wife of July 5, 1837.

[7] The shop of Francis Watkins.

gone on a tour to Ostend. I saw however his assistant. But I must close with a word of business. Mr. Roberton forwarded to me a Package of books care of the French Institute to be sent to Rothschilds. These I never received. The French with their usual good faith took no trouble to forward the articles.

Will you make inquiries concerning them and send them back to Mr Roberton by the same conveyance as the Compt Rondu.[8]

I have put to your credit or ordered it to be done the 500 F I borrowed. Also gave to Mr Vaughan the 15–5 fr pieces borrowed of Mrs Bache.

My respects to Mrs B. In Great Haste

Yours &c
Jos Henry

[8] *Les Comptes Rendus* of the Institut de France. Henry may have purchased a set in Paris, although no volumes survive in his Library. In a letter of December 1, 1837 (APS Archives), from David Bailie Warden to John Vaughan, Warden indicated he was sending eight numbers of the journal for Henry.

TO STEPHEN ALEXANDER

Mary Henry Copy, Family Correspondence,
Henry Papers, Smithsonian Archives

London July 28, 1837

My dear Stephen. I have just forty five minutes to spare and am very conveniently situated at a desk in the rooms of the Royal Society. I will devote them to you and scribble something which may be interesting on account of the place from which it comes if not for the matter. I returned to London last Monday after an absence of nearly two months and a half having passed nearly the whole of that time in Paris. I made a short excursion on my return through Belgium, visited the Field of Waterloo and stopped a little time at Brussels and Antwerp but could not go into Holland without going through Prussia. I was not very well and in view of the difficulty of getting into Holland concluded to return to London and start as soon as possible for Edinburgh. I was much gratified by my tour through Belgium; every thing in that country appears in a thriving condition.

I bought for you in Paris as many of the articles I could of the list you gave me[1] and Bache will look out for a comet seeker[2] in Germany.[3] I have

[1] Not known to us.
[2] A refracting telescope of large aperture, wide field of view, and relatively low magnification, often used, as the name suggests, to search for comets. William A. Norton, *An Elementary Treatise on Astronomy*, 2d ed. (New York, 1845), p. 43.
[3] It was during the 1830s that Americans be-

purchased for the college eight hundred dollars worth of apparatus more than the five hundred given me.[4] My stay in Paris was at first not as profitable as in London in view of the little that is now doing in Paris in the way of original science.[5] I however towards the last began to make up for lost time—made some valuable acquaintances and was shown the methods of experiment of most of the physicists of the present time. One of the most interesting objects I saw in Paris was solid carbonic acid. This is truly a wonderful substance and does not appear to have attracted as much attention as it deserves. It is scarcely known in England. I was commissioned by Mr. Daniell and Faraday to collect all information possible on the subject. I was so fortunate soon after my arrival to see it exhibited by Gay-Lussac.[6] The carbonic acid is first liquified by its own pressure in a vessel and then suffered to expand into vapor in part, the cold thus produced freezes the other part and thus produces a white flow (?)[7] substance which may be

---

gan to recognize the superiority of the scientific apparatus being turned out by German instrument makers, with the result that most American observatories turned to Germany for their major instrumentation. Leading the way in this regard was the Philadelphia High School Observatory. It ordered its equatorial telescope of $6\frac{1}{2}$ inches from the firm of Utzschneider and Fraunhofer in late 1837. The individual primarily responsible for the decision by the Philadelphia High School Observatory to turn to Germany was Sears Cook Walker, America's leading expert on the German astronomical community and the observatory's unofficial director. Walker, Bache, Alexander, and Henry were all members of "the club," a small, Philadelphia-based, informal group of research scientists.

Stephen Alexander would not have needed Walker's advice, however, in deciding on a German comet seeker. He had already sampled the quality of German instrumentation, having used a borrowed $3\frac{1}{2}$-inch Fraunhofer to observe the solar eclipse of November 30, 1834. This Fraunhofer was purchased by Princeton in 1835.

Elias Loomis, *The Recent Progress of Astronomy; Especially in the United States* (New York, 1850), pp. 160–170; Charles H. Mandansky, "The Central High School Observatory from 1838 to 1850," unpublished, copy in Joseph Henry Papers files, pp. 9–13; *Henry Papers*, 2:273n, 283–284, 290n–291n.

[4] See above, Henry to Henry James, May 23, 1837, footnote 13.

[5] This remark was probably not a qualitative

evaluation of French science, but rather, we suspect, a reaction to certain characteristics of the French scientific community, especially when compared to the English. The letters written by Henry while in Paris indicate that he was busy obtaining valuable knowledge. They also indicate, however, that Henry was having trouble communicating in French. But more important than his problem of communicating in French was his difficulty communicating with the French. This seems to be the nub of his complaint. The establishment figures of French science were preoccupied with teaching, politics, and other activities; they had little time for a stranger from America. This was in sharp contrast with the openness of the English. In England Henry had no difficulty meeting the lions of science. His diary entries show that he had a considerable amount of social contact with the leaders of English science. In contrast, the French scientific elite appear only as figures on the lecture stage. It was only when Henry was in Paris for some time, when he had cultivated the acquaintance of some of the younger contributors to French science, that he was able to participate in the scientific give-and-take that was common during his stay in England.

[6] See above, Henry's first entry of the European Diary for [May 1837].

[7] Apparently the copyist could not decipher Henry's writing. Hare describes the substance as "of a perfect whiteness, and of a soft and spongy texture, very like moistened and aggregated snow." Robert Hare, *A Compendium of the Course of Chemical Instruction. . .* , 4th

handled and which possesses the most powerful refrigerating power ever known. I saw by the mixing of about a pound of the solid acid with three or four ounces of [ether] the astonishing quantity of 15 or 20 pounds of mercury frozen in less than one minute of time in an open wedgwood mortar. The mercury thus frozen may be hammered and broken and then shows a beautiful crystalline structure. I have almost concluded to purchase the apparatus although it will cost 200 dollars.[8]

---

ed. (Philadelphia, 1840), p. 230.

In the next sentence, the copyist wrote "earth," although descriptions of the experiment make it clear that Henry meant "ether."

[8] In Henry's letter to Charles Coquerel of October 1, 1837 (see below), he mentions that Bache ordered the carbonic acid apparatus for Henry and would take it for Girard College if Henry was unable to pay for it. We suspect that Bache did in fact end up with the apparatus, for it does not appear in any of the itemized lists that Henry drew up in order to be reimbursed.

HENRY'S EUROPEAN DIARY

Henry Papers, Smithsonian Archives

[July] 28th [1837] visited the Coloceum—Panorama of London,[1] very ingenious desception. Complete Telescopes for vewing the distant parts of the picture which is represented as being taken from the steeple of St Pauls. Raised in a wooden chamber through a cylendrical tube in the middle of the building from the ground flo[or] to the top by a steam engine. For this an additional 6[d] is charged. The expense of seeing the whole is 4/–.

A camera obscura is exhibited in one room, the picture thrown on the floor. A smal railing is placed around the spot to prevent the audience from encroaching on the space. The focus of the glass appears to be about 8 feet.

---

[1] Located in Regent's Park and opened in 1829, the Colosseum was built to display a massive panorama of London painted by the artist E. T. Parris from some 2,000 sketches made by the surveyor Thomas Horner. The painting covered 40,000 square feet of canvas and viewed London from the perspective of the dome of St. Paul's, where Horner had made his drawings. For verisimilitude, spectators could view the scene from an elevated platform and one of the spectacles of the Colosseum was the huge column which contained both a staircase and an elevator for reaching the viewing platform. Originally hand-cranked, the elevator was possibly one of the first public lifts in England. The name "Colosseum" referred to the size but not the design of the edifice, which resembled a combination of the Parthenon and Pantheon. Around the impressive structure were gardens and a Swiss cottage designed by P. F. Robinson.

A place of popular entertainment, the Colosseum also contained an African glen, marine caverns, and reproductions of antique statues. Scientific lectures and concerts were held there. The Colosseum suffered declining fortunes by 1835, was forced to lower entrance fees, and offered less elevated types of entertainment by

Another room is appropriated to optical exhibitions. Nothing of much interest is however contained in it. The telescopic kaleidroscope interested me most. It is described in the Edinburgh Encyclopedia, also the Ency Britannica. When this instrument is presented to the face of a person at a little distance a striking effect is produced.[2]

The grotto and the Swiss cottage are very tastefully got up.

---

the time of Henry's visit. Ann Saunders, *Regent's Park* (Newton Abbot, 1969), pp. 128–129, 144, 150–151.

[2] The kaleidoscope was invented by David Brewster in 1814 as a direct result of his experiments on the polarization of light by multiple reflections. An immediate fad for the device established Brewster's popular reputation. *DSB*. The compound or telescopic kaleidoscope, also Brewster's invention, employed a double convex lens which extended the power of the instrument and permitted it to form symmetrical images of external opaque objects. The *Edinburgh Encyclopaedia*, edited by Brewster, explains in detail the catoptrics of various forms of the kaleidoscope. (In the 1832 Philadelphia edition, which Henry might have found most convenient, the telescopic kaleidoscope appears on pp. 577–578.) Although later editions treat the device fully, the 1823 edition of the *Britannica*—the latest edition accessible to Henry at this date—lacked a "Kaleidoscope" entry, although the device may have been discussed under other rubrics.

HENRY'S EUROPEAN DIARY
Henry Papers, Smithsonian Archives

[July] 31$\underline{st}$ [1837] In the morning attended at Mr Watkins[1] with Dr Lock[2] to see exps on thermoelectricity.[3] Mr W has been engaged on this subject since my departure for Paris. Has succeeded in making powerful magnets by this kind of electricity; one which will lift 100 lbs. He succeeded in showing me about 40 lbs supported by a soft iron magnet excited by a current of thermo electricity. The battery is composed of plates about 2 inches wide 3 long 30 or more in number. Fastened in a tin case by plaster of paris; plates seperated by mica which does not soak the water and will bear great heat.

Hot iron plate put on one surface the other plunged in ice water with oiled silk interposed. Sometimes hot water is only poured on the upper surface; with this quite brilliant sparkes can be obtained. Mr W uses my coil and with the large battery produces a shock through the toung by puting

---

[1] Francis Watkins, identified above, Hare to Henry, February 13, 1837, footnote 3.

[2] John Locke.

[3] For a more detailed discussion of these experiments, see Francis Watkins, "On Thermoelectricity," *Phil. Mag.*, 1837, 3d ser. *11*:305– 308, a copy of which is in the Henry Library. Henry's own interest in thermoelectricity is documented in many places in this volume, especially his diary entries of April 22 and April 26, 1837 (first entry), printed above.

the two opposite sides of two flat handles on each side of the toung. This apparatus may be much improved: long wire for the coil instead of ribbon, perhaps with iron with in.[4] Mr W shows that the effect is increased with a large battery when a core of iron is placed inside ie when the spiral is a long helix.

Spark produced by large battery with very short wire (few feet)?

Visited Mr Solley;[5] busy at Thermo elect. Not very communicative. Stated that he had been trying various compounds of metals—different sulphurettes. Casts his plates in a little copper dish made of a plate of copper turned up at the edges. Has had one of my magnets made for a person in Maddrass—Made by Newman.[6]

Called in the afternoon on Dr Faraday was received very kindly by the Dr & his Lady. Was invited to take an excursion with the Dr on the new rail way which has lately been opened for 25 miles from London towards Bermingham.[7] Started at 5 oclock; passed over the whole distance of 25 miles in a little more than an hour. Sat part of the way on the engine. Passed through 2 tunnels each more than a mile long; total darkness for 2½ minutes, air shafts at intervals which give for an instant an occasional cleam

[4] In his account of these experiments, Watkins credited Henry's flat ribbon coil with achieving the best results in the production of sparks by thermoelectricity, and urged its use by other experimenters in preference to the long wire coil. This seems to agree with Henry's own statement in his first diary entry of April 26, 1837, printed above, in which he argues the advantages of his ribbon coil over Faraday's long wire coil for eliciting thermoelectric sparks. Yet here Henry appears to be suggesting precisely the opposite, and to be taking the curious position of arguing against his own innovation. We suspect that the explanation lies in Henry's evaluation of the particular experimental arrangement used by Watkins, the precise effects desired, and the specific characteristics of the coils involved in each case (e.g., length, width, material).

[5] Edward Solly, Jr., for whom see above, Henry's European Diary, first entry of April 8, 1837, footnote 12.

[6] John Frederick Newman, identified above, Hare to Henry, February 13, 1837, footnote 4. We have not identified Newman's client.

[7] The London and Birmingham Railway was one of the triumphs of British engineering in the first half of the nineteenth century. Contemporary observers, with no admission of hyperbole, compared it to the Pyramids and the Great Wall of China. As the first trunk line to be built out of London, it occupied a significant place in the economic history of England as well. Authorized by Parliament in 1833, construction began in 1836 under the direction of Robert Stephenson (1803–1859, *DNB*), proceeding from each terminus. The first 24½ miles out of London were opened to the public on July 20, 1837, and the entire 112-mile line was completed the following year. In 1846, the London and Birmingham merged with the Liverpool and Manchester and the Grand Junction to form the London and Northwestern Railway, which for three-quarters of a century reigned as the "premier line" of British railroading. Bryan Morgan, *Civil Engineering: Railways* (London, 1971), pp. 42–45. Vernon Sommerfield, *English Railways: Their Beginnings, Development and Personalities* (London, 1937), pp. 94, 104–106. Rixon Bucknall, *Our Railway History* (London, 1970), pp. 21–29. "London and Birmingham Railway," *Railway Magazine and Annals of Science*, 1837, n.s. 3:288.

Henry jotted down a few technical notes on the railway (verso of "Visit to Sir James South," September 20–30, 1837, below).

of light. 2 tracks intended the whole length of the road. Deep cutting on various parts. Whole contemplated to be finished within a year. Cost 36,000 £s per mile.[8] Weight of iron for a single rail 66 lbs per yd. Wheel of the engine 5½ feet diameter; cylinder 6 inches diameter; 18 inches stroke; steam 50 lbs pressure.

Wood used on embankment and will be continued until the ground is perfectly settled. The tye causes all to settle together. At the commencement there is an inclined plane of about a mile in length with a grade of one in 66 and to over come this a stationary engine is erected to be used however only in cases of frost or snow on the rail.[9]

Mr Faraday and myself were accompanied by the residint engineer Mr Fox a young man.[10] He proposes in order to stop the descent of the train at the end without percussion to receive the carriages against the end of a piston of a large cylender filled with air which will be gradually compressed.

Percussion is prevented or converted into pressure by stuffed leather balls which project at each end of each car and these are on the ends of iron piston rods connected with springs across the car. On this trip there were about 450 persons averaging 75 cts each way more than 300 dollars for our trip which occupied about 3 hours.[11]

---

[8] This was average for railway construction during this period. See above, Henry's European Diary, March 24, 1837, footnote 7.

[9] Even a slight grade could present problems for the comparatively weak locomotives used on the earliest railroads. To obviate this difficulty, early railroad designers went to considerable expense to construct a roadbed that was as nearly level as possible. The London and Birmingham Railway, for example, had a ruling gradient of 1 in 330. On those sections where a steeper incline was unavoidable, a variety of methods were employed, including hauling the train by means of cables attached to stationary engines positioned at the top of the ascent. The advent of more powerful locomotives gradually eliminated the need for such expedients, and by the late 1830s grades as steep as 1 in 38 had been mastered by unassisted locomotives.

Nevertheless, stationary engine-operated cableways remained in use longer at certain locations, particularly at termini, where they proved most practicable in overcoming the steep approaches to some stations. The incline which Henry describes (at the approach to Euston Station, the London terminus of the line) was the only one of its kind on the London and Birmingham Railway. It continued in operation for the first eight years of the railway's existence. A similar cableway at Glasgow's Queen Street Station remained in use until 1908. Morgan, *Civil Engineering: Railways*, p. 45. Jack Simmons, *The Railways of Britain: An Historical Introduction* (London, 1961), pp. 58, 225. *Encyclopaedia Britannica*, 8th ed., s.v. "Railways," pp. 793–794. Dionysius Lardner, *The Steam Engine Familiarly Explained and Illustrated. . . ,* 3d American ed. (Philadelphia, 1838), pp. 192–198. Bucknall, *Our Railway History*, p. 22.

[10] Sir Charles Fox (1810–1874), who in 1837 was at the commencement of his career, was constructing engineer for the London and Birmingham Railway. He went on to build railroads in England, Ireland, Denmark, France, and throughout the British Empire. Active in other areas as well, he designed the Berlin Water Works, and in 1851 was knighted for his role in the construction of the Crystal Palace exhibition. *DNB.*

[11] Since the three-hour trip was a round trip the correct total should be double the amount given by Henry, or nearly seven hundred dollars.

There are on this line a number of skew bridges built of brick on a plan invented by Mr Fox, the young gentleman with whom we made the excursion. He has promised to send me a copy of his paper on the subject through Dr Faraday.[12]

---

[12] Skew bridges, built at oblique angles to the streams or roads they crossed, were developed in response to the need of canal and railroad builders to lay out long, straight paths which would not have to curve continually so as to intersect every obstacle to be crossed at right angles, as had all bridges prior to that time. The Henry Library contains a reprint of Fox's article "On the Construction of Skew Arches," *Phil. Mag.*, April 1836, 3d ser. 8:299–305.

HENRY'S EUROPEAN DIARY
Henry Papers, Smithsonian Archives

Aug 1st [1837] Visited Mr Newman[1]—saw Prof Daniels new battery, took drawing of parts. See paper.[2]

---

[1] John Frederick Newman.

[2] Henry is probably referring to J. F. Daniell, "On Voltaic Combinations," *Phil. Trans.*, 1836, pp. 107–124, which has a scale drawing of Daniell's "constant battery" (plate 9). Although Henry had been shown the battery by Daniell earlier (March 23), he evidently wanted a detailed drawing so that he could construct his own. Henry eventually did so, commencing on March 25, 1840.

TO HARRIET HENRY
Family Correspondence, Henry Papers, Smithsonian Archives

London August [1]st 1837.

My Dear Dear Harriet,

I wrote to you a few days since[1] and closed my letter some what in a hurry. I start tomorrow for Edinburgh and as I may not have an opportunity to send a letter in a week or two from this time I have taken time for one by the fore lock and written in advance of the packet. The good ship Wellington starts for the second time on the 10th and I intend this letter to go with her if a chance does not occur before.

I have entirely recovered from my indisposition and now feel much better than I have done in many months past. I have not enjoyed very good

---

[1] Above, July 26–31, 1837.

health since I landed in Europe. At first the smoke of London affected me and when I went to Paris the waters disagreed with me. I returned to London quite in low spirits and was for two or three days not a little homesick. Nearly all my acquaintances had left town and all things appeared to have changed aspect during my absence.

Henry James however has quite revived me and takes no little credit for the cure. I have called since I last wrote on several of my acquaintances and met with the same kind reception as before. Mr Faraday took me yesterday afternoon on an excursion to see the London and Birmingham rail road as far as it is completed. We started at 5 oclock rode 25 miles and back again in about 3 hours. I was delighted with the jaunt, the road, the country & the company. All were plesant. We passed with great rapidity through two tunnels each more than a mile long, during most of the distance through we were moving with the speed of the wind in total darkeness not a ray of light could be seen.

Mr Faraday has given me a letter to his Brotherinlaw an engineer in Edinburgh.[2] I forgot to state in my last that I was much gratified to learn that the litle dresses as well as the scarf pleased you. I intended one for each of the litle girls. I had purchased some toys for Bub but could not put them in the bundle. Mr Roberton of the Royal Society (assistant secretary) packed the articles in a bundle from that Institution to the albany Institute. I informed him yesterday that they had arrived safely. He is quite an amiable youngish man, was pleased with the intelligence and requested as the "packer" to send his respects to Mrs Henry. I must also inform you that old William Vaughan always requests to be remembered to you when I receive a letter from him. I purchased for the old Gentleman a pulse glass and also a palm glass to show the boiling of eather by the heat of the hand[3] while in Paris. They are known in that city by the name of the glasses of Franklin and on this account I though[t] they would be interesting to the old Philosopher nor was I disappointed. He laughed at the idea of my supposing he would be pleased by bubbles, but said they were philosophical ones & that he would try the pulses of all the ladies who came to see him. On the whole he appeared as much tickled as Bub would have been with the same articles.

Henry James has concluded to start for Ireland this week. I have roused him from a lethargy which he has been enjoying for three months past. He

[2] George Buchanan.

[3] The pulse glass, a philosophical toy to show the boiling of fluids by the heat of the hand, is treated in *Henry Papers*, 1:83n. We assume the palm glass is a variation on this instru- ment. Hare's *Compendium of the Course of Chemical Instruction*, 4th ed. (Philadelphia, 1840), p. 38 and index, in fact lists the same item under both designations.

has been living in London much at his ease with his books and a very few acquaintances. The time has passed very quietly and plesantly with him. He has been waiting for a remittance of money from America; times were so bad when he came away that it was impossible for him to raise as much as he wished not for the mere expenses of the voyage but that he might assist his poor relatives in Ireland. He has also been stopping in London a greater part of this long time for the purpose of having a cork leg constructed. He has one now finished which is a very interesting article and adds much to his appearance.[4]

He brought with him a black man[5] from Albany as a waiter who is a very good fellow in the serving line. He attracts much attention and is quite [a] Lion among the lower classes eats with the family with whom we lodge and would find no difficulty were he not married in getting a white wife. I have urged Henry James to start for Ireland that he may get through his business so as to meet me either in Scotland or at the meeting of the British association at Liverpool which takes place on the 11th of next month. I wish to start for home as soon after that as possible and now think it probable that we will come together and sail from London.

A melancholy accident happened in London last week which you have probably seen mentioned in the papers. A man had invented a parachute or article to attache to a balloon and by which he supposed he could desend to the earth from a great height without the danger of the oscillations which had attended the other forms of the apparatus before tried. He ascended from one of the public gardens amid a crowd of many thousand persons suspended from the basket of the balloon in which were two persons and when he attained the altitude of about a mile and a half he cut loose. The balloon released from his weight sprang upwards to an immense height to the eminent danger of the persons in the car. The parachute desended as rapidly towards the Earth broke in its desent and precipitated the unfortunate adventurer head long to the ground, from which he was raised a short time before in helth and high hopes. Mr Faraday happened to go to the garden was called to by the adventurer who had known him many years before. Mr F asked him if he was certain all parts of his apparatus was of sufficient strength and his principles well tested. The answer was there is no fear of me but I have some apprehension for the persons in the balloon above me. Much excitement has prevailed on account of this accident. The owners of the garden have been blamed for permitting him to assend &

---

[4] See Henry to Bache, May 28, 1837, above. Henry James, Sr.'s reminiscences of his trip to Ireland are recalled by his son Henry James in *Notes of a Son and Brother* (New York, 1914), pp. 265–270.

[5] Billy Taylor. Austin Warren, *The Elder Henry James* (New York, 1934), p. 32.

Mr Faraday has been obliged to publish a letter in the Times relative to his knowledge of the affair.[6]

Notwithstanding all this, last night there were two balloons sent up from different parts of London each containing a man and a woman. They ran a race in the air over the whole length of the city much to the delight of the citizens who would rather that many lives should be lost than they deprived of any pleasure. The more barbarus the sport the more highly it is relished by the multitude here and in this respect I think they are more savage than the multitude in America. In some respects we are in advance of any part of Europe I have yet seen particularly in the condition of females in the lower classes. In France women are every where seen working in the fields. In Belgium you will see women on the road with a hand waggon picking up the horse dung as it is droped by the animal. This is sold by the load to the farmer and thus a subsistence is earned by means unheard of with us.

In Paris the streets are swept by women in some quarters, and almost at every little nook in the side of the street you will find a coblers stall and this not unfrequently occupied by a woman. The lighter kind of Ladies slippers are made by females. In London in all the public streets women are arranged along the side walk on the edge of the gutter with large baskets filled with apples cherries and other fruit forming a large load which is supported by a strap around the loins for hours together. During the coldest and wetest weather you will find a female stationed at a cross walk with a birch broom in one hand and the other supporting an infant constantly sweeping the stones asking a penny of every passenger. The greater number of these pass her by unheaded, occassionally one gives her a copper.[7] I have as yet been in company with but few females since I came to Europe

---

[6] The spectacular parachute accident of the landscape painter Cocking received extensive newspaper and magazine coverage in England. Picking up stories from the London papers, the Franklin Institute *Journal* (1837, 20:219–227) analyzed the mishap in an illustrated article. Cocking's fatal parachute experiment was reportedly the second ever attempted in England. The previous descent, done thirty years earlier by Garnerin, was endangered by extreme oscillations, a problem Cocking endeavoured to remedy by reversing aspects of Garnerin's design. In a balloon piloted by two other aeronauts, Cocking began his ascent from Vauxhall on July 24. According to observers, his parachute collapsed shortly after its separation from the balloon at an altitude of 5000 feet. The London *Times* (issue of July 26) reported that Cocking's demise was an oc-

casion for further regret when "the landlord at the inn at which the body lies was guilty of a violation of the ordinary forms of decency, by admitting the public to view the remains of the unfortunate gentleman, as well as the parachute, at 6d. a-head. . . ."

In a letter to the *Times* (August 1, 1837), Michael Faraday defended himself against the charge made by Monck Mason at the Cocking inquest that Faraday encouraged Cocking to ascend against Mason's advice. Faraday claimed he had pointed out to Cocking structural defects in his parachute but, seeing that Cocking was determined to continue, refrained from disturbing his concentration further.

[7] For additional remarks in this vein see Henry's first letter to his wife of July 5, 1837.

except in Paris where I met with several but they were principally Ameri-cans. Most of the English Ladies I have met with have been very intelligent and asked many questions about america particularly <*inquiries*> about the negro population. They cannot understand our prejudices relative to them and cannot see why they should not have all the privaledges of a white man. I was obliged on one occasion to ask a lady if she could ever think of marr[y]ing a black man. She said she certainly would not fancy the colour but that there should be no legal objection to prevent those who pleased from marr[y]ing together.

Miss Martineaus book on America has just appeared and is making some-thing of a sensation here. It is very hard on America in reference to the slave question also our politics religion &c.

I have not as yet seen the book but read to day a review of it. She gives some stories relative to the horors of slavery which are really revolting but which cannot be true. We are surrounded on all sides by men in a savage state and where civilized and savage man come in approximation a semi-barbarism is produced more productive of crime and cruelty than the in-tirely savage state since all the wickedness of civilized man is found in this without the controoling principles. From this class of persons extending along the western side of the Missis[sippi] along the southern coaste in-cluding New orleans & Florida an English tourest may find ample materials to make a book of american atrocities which with a litle colouring and well chosen examples may render us black in the eyes of the world as crime can make us. But these scarcely belong more to the United States than the barbarism of the British East Indian possessions do to this country.[8] There

---

[8] Henry's perception of blacks as a less civilized, if not actually inferior, race was a view common to Northerners of his time. Op-posed to the idea of human slavery, but con-vinced that the varying degrees of black and white civilization would inhibit the peaceful coexistence of the two races, Henry supported the early plans for African recolonization. Like most of his fellow Northerners, Henry was not prepared to endorse the abolition of slavery if it entailed the subsequent entrance of Black people into White society. Instead, he wrote to Asa Gray (May 22, 1862) that he was "warmly in favour of colonization," the con-struction of "an empire in Africa which will be so attractive to the negro that under the repulsive influence of caste in this country he will be voluntarily impelled in that direction." (Historic Letter File, Gray Herbarium Library, Harvard University.) Thus in 1839, Henry pledged three dollars to the Princeton Coloni-zation Society for the furthering of such a plan.

Although Henry was opposed to slavery and dismayed at the condition of blacks in the South, the issue was not one which loomed large in his life. In rejecting an offer of the Chair of Natural Philosophy at the University of Virginia, Henry expressed some distaste at the thought of living in a slave state, but con-ceded that the high salary and other advan-tages of the institution outweighed his re-vulsion and that he would have accepted the offer had other conditions been different. (*Henry Papers*, 2:428). He was, however, ex-tremely sensitive to criticism from outsiders, whose perspectives he believed to be distorted. America could not be held responsible for the inevitable consequences of the close association of two races of such different levels of de-velopment. The United States, he felt, was being taken to task unfairly.

are many things connected with America which are much to be regretted and which every reflecting traveler must feel. When at a distance we see with less predijudice the good and bad qualities of our home and no person can have a proper ide[a] of America who has not viewed it from a distance and in connection or in comparison with other countries. We have too exalted an opinion of our influence and the share of attention we occupy in the minds of Europe. We are too far removed to exert any direct influence and the great mass of people in France and England are too ignorant of our affairs to be much influenced by them. The French have but litle respect for the Americans. They hate the English but do not despise them; they have no more love for the Americans and far less respect. The Americans in Paris receive no attention, they are never admitted into fashionable society. Col Thorns[9] family is the only exception and for this priviledge he has it is said paid very dearly and is not allowed to invite to his table only persons of a certain rank who may have been desig[nated] to him. Very few of the Americans who go to Paris can speak French sufficiently well to enjoy conversation in that Language. The smattering they get before going abroad is like the English spoken by Mr Jager. They soon acquire enough to know that they speak very badly. The result is that they make few attempts to get into French society and these are unsuccessful. Most of our people of wealth who travel on the continent might as well stay at home. They come without an object and[10]

Henry's chauvinism was typical of the reponse of many Americans to European criticism. The second quarter of the nineteenth century brought hundreds of Europeans to the United States to see the "great experiment in action." Scores of travelogues, personal accounts, letters, and articles ensued, stirring up a flurry of nationalistic reaction on both sides. Imbued with a sense of the superiority of their own culture and institutions, European observers were often harsh in their judgement of a young nation that had challenged their cultural and political traditions. Americans eager to be accepted by Europeans as cultural equals were at the same time proud of their differences. They found it difficult to accept any sort of criticism, particularly when the validity of their democratic practices was questioned. The institution of slavery was an especially sensitive issue.

Harriet Martineau, whose book *Society in America* was published in London in 1837, was one of a great wave of Europeans appraising the new nation, and Henry, one of the many Americans who reacted negatively against it. Apt as many of her criticisms were, Martineau, according to her biographer, Robert K. Webb, had a tendency to regard her limited experience in America as representative of the whole, and to expect too much of the country too soon. Likewise, Henry, at the writing of this letter, had not actually read Martineau's work and thus failed to recognize the strong current of respect and admiration that lay beneath her criticisms.

Leon F. Litwack, *North of Slavery: The Negro in the Free States, 1790–1860* (Chicago, 1961), pp. vii, 24. Robert K. Webb, *Harriet Martineau, A Radical Victorian* (London, 1960), p. 134.

[9] Colonel Herman Thorn, an American residing in Paris in the 1830s. Formerly a purser in the navy, Thorn lived in high style at the Hotel Monaco, once the residence of Talleyrand. Foster Rhea Dulles, *Americans Abroad: Two Centuries of European Travel* (Ann Arbor, 1964), p. 77.

[10] The letter breaks off here.

August 2, 1837

TO ELIAS LOOMIS

Loomis Papers, Beinecke Library, Yale University

London Aug 2ⁿᵈ 1837

My Dear Sir

I regret that I did not meet you to day since you sail in so short a time for America. I am glad that you go with the packet of the 10ᵗʰ since I have a great regard for Capt. Chadwick. You will find him a good fellow and I hope you may have a speedy and plesant passage. You will let me hear from you when you get settled in the West and although I am a bad correspondant I will endeavour not to let it be my fault if the acquaintance we have formed in Europe should drop in America.

With Respect and Esteem Yours &c
Joseph Henry

HENRY'S EUROPEAN DIARY

Henry Papers, Smithsonian Archives

Aug 2ⁿᵈ [1837]—Called on Mr Babbage kindly received. Was engaged until my name was sent in. Spent long time with me explaining the new operations of his improved calculating machine. Says he has now brought it to develope the expression of the problem of the three bod[i]es,[1] and to tabulate any function of one or more variables.

He spoke of his new book.[2] Said he did not disagree with Mr Whewell as to the deductive philosopher but he did disagree with him in making all mathematicians deductive philosophers.[3] Deduction is as much used in

[1] Among the most significant astronomical tables are those based upon particular solutions of the three body problem (the calculation of an orbit when the secondary is disturbed by a third body; the lunar orbit is the classical example). Charles Babbage's initial motivation in developing a calculating engine was to lessen the drudgery involved in preparing such tables, and the improved quality of the resulting tables one of the major justifications in his request for governmental aid for his project. Charles Babbage, "Observations on the Application of Machinery to the Computation of Mathematical Tables,"

Charles Babbage and his Calculating Engines, eds. Philip and Emily Morrison (New York, 1961), pp. 311–314; Dionysius Lardner, "Babbage's Calculating Engine," *Edinburgh Review,* 1834, 59:267–284, 323–324; Robert Grant, *History of Physical Astronomy, From the Earliest Ages to the Middle of the Nineteenth Century* (London, 1852), pp. 44–46.

[2] *The Ninth Bridgewater Treatise. A Fragment* (London, 1837).

[3] Babbage probably had in mind William Whewell's Bridgewater Treatise: *Astronomy and General Physics Considered with Reference to Natural Theology* (Philadelphia, 1833),

mathematics as in any other part of knowledge that is when mathematical truths are discovered. But there has been a fashion among mathematical writers which should be reprobated and which results from the custom of ancient chalenges in the way of the solution of problems, of stating principles in a general and very obscure manner entirely different from that in which the mind conceived them thus disguising the method of the discovery. This remark is precisely the same that Priestly made many years since in his history of Electricity on that subject. Most men says he are fond when they make a discovery and are thus raised to an eminence to kick away the ladder of ascent and to present them selves aloft to the envy of the multitude.[4]

Mr B informed me that Brunell the engineer had observed the solidification of carbonic acid when operating with his engine. Spots of the which substance were observed when the liquid was let out into the atmosphere.[5]

Mr B. asks if atmospheric air cannot be condensed and fixed by puting into the condensing apparatus a quantity of alcaly to fix the nitric acid which might be formed by the condensation.[6] He also suggests the use of spongy platina to assist the union of the two gases. I have promised to send Mr B an account of the process of seperating iron by means of the magnetic apparatus.[7] Also send him account of Black machine at Nantucket. Pump-

---

pp. 245–248. There Whewell carefully distinguishes between the very creative and rare process of conceiving general laws through induction and the more common practice of working out the consequences of such laws through mathematical deductions. One could easily interpret Whewell's remarks as a putdown of mathematicians.

[4] We have been unable to locate such language in Priestley. Rather, Priestley limited himself to a comment on the value of a history of science for the further advance of science:

> To whatever height we have arrived in natural science, our beginnings were very low, and our advances have been exceedingly gradual. And to look down from the eminence, and to see, and compare all those gradual advances in the ascent, cannot but give the greatest pleasure to those who are seated on the eminence, and who feel all the advantages of their elevated situation. And considering that we ourselves are, by no means, at the top of human science; that the mountain still ascends beyond our sight, and that we are, in fact, not much above the foot of it, a view of the manner in which the ascent has been made, cannot but animate us in our attempts to advance still higher, and suggest methods and expedients to assist us in our farther progress.

Joseph Priestley, *The History and Present State of Electricity*, 3d ed., 2 vols. (London, 1775), *1*:v–vi.

[5] Isambard Brunel had used liquid carbonic acid as a power source. He found that the cold generated when the liquid rapidly evaporated was sufficient to solidify some of the acid. J. Frederic Daniell, *An Introduction to the Study of Chemical Philosophy*, 2d ed. (London, 1843), p. 161.

[6] The atmospheric gases (oxygen and nitrogen) had resisted all attempts by Henry's contemporaries to condense them. William Allen Miller, *Elements of Chemistry: Theoretical and Practical*, 3d ed., 3 vols. (London, 1860–1863), *1*:331–332.

[7] None of the extant correspondence between the two men contains any accounts of the technological innovations listed here. Nor is there any confirmation that Henry sent any published material. Babbage's interest in the accounts was probably related to his book on manufactures. For Henry's work on magnetic ore separators, see *Henry Papers*, *1*:364–372.

ing machine by wind on the sea coast for salt. Passage down the Susquehanna by General Clinton. Fire for heating manufactory by two stoves. Phila[d] water works. Weighing cotton by cotton to obviate change of density of atmosphere. Magnet around lighting rod for indicating the descent of a discharge. Passage of a river by the oblique action of a keel or rudder attached to a boat connected by a transverse rope. Method of making an extemporaneous carriage in the West.

Mr B gave me a copy of his work on manufactures[8] and promised me a copy of his Bridge water treties[9] as soon as he can procure one. He made some remarks on the difference of mechanical and chemical action possibility of producing mechanical motion by the latter. Immense mechanical forc[e] required to seperate the particles of a mass of iron which by chemical action are disunited without apparent expenditure of much force. To meet Mr B at the Liverpool meeting also Mr Faraday.

Called the same day on Mr Wheatstone has been much engaged with the galvanic telegraph has succeeded thus far beyond his anticipations can ring a bell at the distance of 13 miles and transmit any intelligence through a circuit of that length.[10] Experiments are making at the railway works; 13 miles of wire terminations in different buildings. I am to receive a more detailed account of the whole when I return.[11]

Atempted while in London to see Prof. Daniels to give him an account of the carbonic acid apparatus, but did not suc[ce]ed. He was out of town most of the time I was in the city.

Visited one day collection of old paintings.

[8] The presentation copy of Babbage's *On the Economy of Machinery and Manufactures*, 4th ed. (London, 1835), survives in the Henry Library. The inscription is dated August 1837.
[9] William Vaughan forwarded a copy of Babbage's *Ninth Bridgewater Treatise*. William Vaughan to Joseph Henry, March 3, 1838,

Henry Papers, Smithsonian Archives.
[10] This represents quite an improvement since the last time the two men met to discuss the telegraph. See above, Henry's European Diary, April 1, 1837.
[11] Henry's diary for this period has been lost.

HENRY'S EUROPEAN DIARY
Henry Papers, Smithsonian Archives

[August 4, 1837] Started Aug 2nd at 11½ o'clock P M the night of the day I visited Mr Babbage in the steamboat Clarrence for Edinburgh and arrived in that city at 4 o'clock on the 4th after an unusually quick passage with a strong and fair wind to assist us of 38½ hours. The distance I believe is about 450 miles.

The fare was 3£s including boarding. The boat was crowded with passengers and amoung the number was Sir C Bell author of the Bridgewater volume on the hand & Animal Mechanics, Library of useful knowledge. He is a large but not fleshy fine looking Scotchman now Professor of Surgery in the University of Edinburgh.[1] Was quite seasick had but little conversation with any of the passengers—except one, a queer little Scotchman perhaps not an uncommon character. Gleaned from him quite an account of the state of party feeling in Scotland and the arguments against reform urged there. He was a warm tory. I was much amused at his sophestry, had quite a trate of national prudence displayed in this man who was probably a third rate lawyer. He made an apology for his great coat which was a travelling one. I asked him to inform where a Mrs McPherson kept a boarding house as this was the place where Bache lodged. He said she lived in Lothian Street but made some hesitation in giv[ing] me the information. I informed him that a Friend had lodged with her and had been pleased with the situation. I wanted a comfortable respectable Lodgins but one that was not very extravagant. He said with some [?peculiarity] of manner that I would be quite comfortable there and that it was probably a place which would suit me. After this I observed that he was not quite as ready to converse with me as before and although quite polite and friendly rather avoided my company. He promised however to procure me a coach which would take me to the place. There was some delay in my getting my bagage off the boat. My scotch friend did not wait and left me to find a coach as I could. When I arrived at the house directed and saw its situation and the inhabitants it contained, the conduct of the cautious Scot was explained. When I asked for Mrs McPherson he began to suspect that I must be rather a poor body and not fit company for a writer to the Sygnet[2] & that it would be well to get quit of me as soon as possible. The Mrs M who I inquired for was quite another kind of a person. She lodges in Queen street a part of the new Town.

After considerable difficulty found Mrs M. Lady not at home, rooms all occupied until monday. Got lodgins at one guiney per week at corner of Hanover and George street, plesant situation not good of access.

---

[1] The Scots anatomist Charles Bell (1774–1842, *DSB*) was knighted in 1831 for his scientific accomplishment and, in 1836, became Professor of Surgery at Edinburgh. Bell's *The Hand, Its Mechanism and Vital Endowments, as Evincing Design* (London, 1833) was the fourth Bridgewater Treatise. His *Animal Mechanics or, Proofs of Design in the Animal Frame* was an 1828 contribution to the Library of Useful Knowledge.

[2] Writers to the Signet were considered the highest grade of lawyer in Scotland, being privileged to prepare writs, charters, and other matters for the Crown. *OED.*

HENRY'S EUROPEAN DIARY
Henry Papers, Smithsonian Archives

Sat 5 Aug. [1837] Yesterday it rained when I landed. Saw little of the city. Today clear but quite cold Thermometer at 58° or 59. Salied fourth to view the city took a turn around several blocks of streets in the New town. Monument to George the fourth in the cross street just by my window. Figure of Bronze colosal very spirited by Chantry erected in 1832 to commemorate the visit of the King.[1] On the next cross street statue to Pitt in the same style probably by the same artist.[2]

In the same street (Georges) is a fine monument to Lord Melville. It stands in the centre of St Georges[3] Square & erected principally by the subscription of naval gentlemen. Lord M was during the Reign of George the 3rd the principal Secritary of State and Lord of the Admiralty.[4] Monument a copy of Trajans pillar.[5] Whole height of column and pedestal 136 feet 4 inches. Surmounted by a statue of 14 feet by Robert Forrest[6] a native of Lanarkshire.

[1] On August 14, 1822, George IV (1762–1830) arrived in Edinburgh, the first reigning English monarch to set foot on Scottish soil since Charles I. After much pageantry, arranged primarily by Sir Walter Scott, the King departed on August 29, having won for the monarchy new popularity in Scotland. Another result of the visit was the development of a closer relationship between the Highlands and Lowlands of Scotland. *DNB*; John Buchan, *Sir Walter Scott* (1932; reprint ed., Port Washington, New York, 1967), pp. 240–242.

F. L. Chantrey's Edinburgh statue of George IV was erected in 1831. Its inscription is quite simple: "GEORGE IV VISITED SCOTLAND MDCCCXXII." Margaret Whinney, *Sculpture in Britain, 1530–1830* (Baltimore, 1964), p. 221. A. J. Youngson, *The Making of Classical Edinburgh: 1750–1840* (Edinburgh, 1966), p. 227.

[2] This statue was indeed created by Chantrey. It had been erected in 1833 at a cost of £7,000. Whinney, *Sculpture in Britain*, p. 221.

[3] The monument was actually in St. Andrew's Square. At some later date Mary Henry made the correction.

[4] Henry Dundas, first Viscount Melville (1742–1811), was educated at the Edinburgh High School and University. He was a Member of Parliament from 1774 to 1802, when he was raised to the peerage. Lord Melville first became connected with the Navy in 1782 when he was named Treasurer of the Navy. With one brief interruption in 1783–1784, he held this post until 1800. He became First Lord of the Admiralty in 1804 and held that position for about one year. *DNB*.

The monument to Lord Melville was erected in 1821 at a cost of £8,000. The money came from contributions made by the officers and men of the Royal Navy. James Gowans, *Edinburgh and Its Neighbourhood in the Days of Our Grandfathers* (London, 1886), p. 115.

[5] The Pillar of Trajan was erected in Rome in 113 A.D. by Trajan (53–117; Roman emperor, 98–117) to commemorate his victories over Dacia. Depicted on the pillar are incidents in the two Roman-Dacian Wars. A statue of Trajan was placed on top of the pillar. Basil Kennett, *Romae Antiquae Notitia; or the Antiquities of Rome* (1st American ed.; Philadelphia, 1822), p. 74. This book is in the Henry Library.

Unlike the Pillar of Trajan, the column of the Melville monument is fluted. There is no sculpture ornamenting it. Gowans, *Edinburgh and its Neighbourhood*, p. 115; there is an engraving of the monument facing p. 112.

[6] Robert Forrest (1789?–1852) was a self-taught sculptor. His major commissions—the Melville statue being one of the earliest—were limited to Scottish subjects. Samuel Redgrave, *A Dictionary of Artists of the English School* (1878 ed.; reprint ed., Bath, 1970), p. 157.

Called on Mr Buchanan[7] Mr Faradays brotherinlaw. Mrs. B. is the sister of Mrs. F.

Mr B. is an engineer member of the Phil Society of Edinburgh[8] was a pupil of Playfair[9] and afterwards of Lesley.[10] Took me first to the Royal Institution[11] a greecian building on the mound or bridge which is thrown across the valley which seperates the old and New town. This building is of the doric order but as highly ornamented as this order will bear. Between the trygliphs garlands are placed with wide borders on the frieze and the top ornamented with acroterea.

The Rooms of the Royal society are in this house besides those of several other institutions. We were shown the Library which contains a good collection of scientific books but not better than those (and perhaps not as good) of the American Phil. Society. No provision is made for the admission of strangers to the library unless one of the members accompanies the per-

---

[7] Henry had met George Buchanan in London. See his diary entry of April 18, 1837, above.

[8] Chartered in 1783 as an intellectual assembly embracing both scientific and literary learning, the Royal Society of Edinburgh soon became a scientific society dominated by the professoriate of Edinburgh. Judging by the pages of its *Transactions*, the interests of its members lay primarily in the earth sciences, physics, and chemistry. There was relatively little interest in either technology or medicine. Steven A. Shapin, "The Royal Society of Edinburgh: A Study of the Social Context of Hanoverian Science" (Ph. D. dissertation, University of Pennsylvania, 1971); Steven A. Shapin, "Property, Patronage, and the Politics of Science: The Founding of the Royal Society of Edinburgh," *British Journal for the History of Science*, 1974, 7:1–41.

[9] John Playfair (1748–1819) was educated at the Universities of St. Andrews and Edinburgh. He held the Chair in Mathematics at Edinburgh from 1785 until 1805. In the latter year he became the Professor of Natural Philosophy at the same institution. His forte was geometry, although his presentation of James Hutton's geological thought in *Illustrations of the Huttonian Theory of the Earth* (Edinburgh, 1802) was of more significance to the development of geology than his mathematical work was to mathematics. *DSB*.

[10] John Leslie (1766–1832) studied at the Universities of St. Andrews and Edinburgh. When Playfair changed chairs in 1805, Leslie succeeded him as Professor of Mathematics. Leslie became Professor of Natural Philosophy at Edinburgh upon Playfair's death. Heat radiation was his primary area of research. *DSB*.

The writings of both Playfair and Leslie are represented in the Henry Library.

[11] The Royal Institution grew out of a decision in 1822 to build a public building to house jointly the Royal Society of Edinburgh, the Society of Scottish Antiquaries, the Royal Institution for the Encouragement of the Fine Arts, and the Board of Trustees for Manufactures and Fisheries. The few (a perpetual lease for a fixed rent) was granted to the Board of Trustees for Manufactures and Fisheries, with the other three societies as its tenants. Initially completed in 1826, the Royal Institution quickly proved to be too small. A plan of expansion was approved in the summer of 1832, and the expanded building was completed by the end of 1835. Youngson, *The Making of Classical Edinburgh*, pp. 162–165.

William Henry Playfair (1789–1857) was the architect responsible for both the initial and expanded versions of the Royal Institution. Appointed architect for the New Town of Edinburgh in 1818, Playfair spent the next forty years designing public buildings, primarily in the classical style. Among the institutions designed by him are the National Gallery, Surgeons' Hall, the New Observatory, and the enlarged Edinburgh University. *DNB*; Youngson, *The Making of Classical Edinburgh*, passim.

son admitted. Sillimans journal, the American Almanac, North American Review were observed among the articles.

The meeting room is adjoining the library and contains a number of interesting paintings of the eminent men of the society among these are Watt, Scott, Sir J Hall,[12] Robinson.[13]

There is a small museum in an upper room containing a number of interesting articles of natural history. A collection of organic remains collected and discovered by Dr Hibbert[14] in 1833 in a fresh water deposit of lime stone in a laicarrce[15] near the city called Burdiehouse quarry. These consist of fish and various aquatic plants with a variety of teeth. *Coprolites** were also found.[16]

The rock veins under the marine limestone of the coal formation. Same remains found lately near Glasgow and in Fife.

The museum also contains a drawing of the house in which Sir I Newton was born about one foot square also of the room in the house in which he was born. There is also a panel of the book case used by him. A large microscope, two geological models of islands near Scotland also a cast of the hands and feet of the immense Ourangoutang described in the Edinburgh journal as killed in _____.[17]

I was much interested in a specimen of sulphate of iron crystalized precisely like the crystals of nitrate of mercury noticed by me.[18] The hornes turn over in the same manner and each are also hollow.

---

* petrified feces

[12] Sir James Hall (1761–1832) was one of the first British chemists to accept Lavoisier's views on chemistry. In addition to his work in chemistry, Hall conducted a number of experiments testing Hutton's geological theories. *DSB.*

[13] John Robison, Sr.

[14] Samuel Hibbert-Ware (1782–1848) received a medical degree from the University of Edinburgh in 1817, but his avocation was geology. He published extensively on the geology of the Shetland Islands and other parts of Scotland. Henry had no personal contact with him because Hibbert-Ware had left Edinburgh in 1835. (Hibbert assumed the name of Ware in 1837.) *DNB.*

[15] A rather uncertain reading. We suspect Henry was attempting to form a noun from the word "lacustrine," a geological term applied to freshwater formations. W. T. Brande, ed., *A Dictionary of Science, Literature, and Art* (New York, 1843), p. 637.

[16] Hibbert-Ware published his analysis of these specimens in a paper entitled "On the Fresh-Water Limestone of Burdiehouse in the Neighbourhood of Edinburgh, Belonging to the Carboniferous Group of Rocks. With Supplementary Notes on other Fresh-water Limestone," *Transactions of the Royal Society of Edinburgh,* 1836, *13*:169–282. The paper included a description of the fish fossils by Louis Agassiz.

[17] Henry himself left this line, probably because he had forgotten the site of the kill when he got around to making his diary entry. The article he was thinking of was Clark Abel, "Account of the Capture of a Colossal Orang-Outang in the Island of Sumatra, and Description of its Appearance," *Edinburgh New Philosophical Journal,* October 1826–April 1827, 2:371–375 and April–October, 1827, 3:81–84.

[18] We are uncertain where Henry had viewed the crystallization of nitrate of mercury.

Visited the shop of Mr Adie inventor of the sympisometer.[19] Introduced to Father and son.[20] Was shown a dividing engine of the same dimentions and construction of that made by Troughton.[21] Chart of the weather for the space of 10 years by Mr Adie projected on two large sheets of paper so as to show the curves of the thermometer & the barometer for each year. The middle of the time was 1800.

	inch
The mean of the Barometer was	29.60732
The mean of the Thermometer "	46.49013
The Mean height of rain (annual)	23.232
Prevaling wind	

Was shown a heliostat on the principle mentioned in Dr Youngs natural Philosophy,[22] very simple, moved by a common watch in which a slit is made in one side so that the hour wheel may play into a large wheel which moves the metalic myror. To ease the action of

---

[19] Alexander Adie (1774–1858), a Fellow of the Royal Society of Edinburgh, was an instrument maker in Edinburgh from 1804 until his death. He had been interested in meteorological problems since 1816. When Henry visited him, his shop was at 58 Princess Street in New Town. Nicholas Goodison, *English Barometers, 1680–1860* (New York, 1968), p. 119.

Adie's sympiesometer, patented in 1818, was similar to a modification of the barometer first suggested by Robert Hooke in 1667/8. Atmospheric pressure is measured through its compression of a gas, in Adie's case, hydrogen, with a correction made for the influence of temperature upon the gas. The sympiesometer made an excellent marine barometer. It was compact, relatively free of the oscillations usually created by the motion of the ship, and highly sensitive to the changes in pressure which were warnings of changes in the weather. Alexander Adie, "Description of the Patent Sympiesometer or New Air Barometer," *Edinburgh Philosophical Journal*, 1819, *1*:54–60; W. E. Knowles Middleton, *The History of the Barometer* (Baltimore, 1964), pp. 375–379.

[20] Richard Adie (d. 1881) began his career as an instrument maker about 1835 in Liverpool. In 1837 he returned to Edinburgh to become a partner with his father. E. G. R. Taylor, *The Mathematical Practitioners of Hanoverian England, 1714–1840* (Cambridge, England, 1966), p. 466.

[21] A dividing engine was used to divide circles as finely and precisely as possible. The graduated circles were in turn used as scales, primarily for astronomical instruments; the more precise the graduations of the scale, the more precise the observations made by astronomers.

Edward Troughton's dividing engine impressed G. B. Airy, later to become Astronomer Royal, "as the greatest improvement ever made in the art of instrument-making." It won for its creator the Copley Medal of the Royal Society of London and membership in that organization. Although he first conceived of his method of mechanically dividing circles in 1778, Troughton did not produce the first specimen of his dividing engine until 1785. It was another quarter-century before he described his instrument for the Royal Society. *DSB*; Edward Troughton, "An Account of a Method of Dividing Astronomical and Other Instruments, by Ocular Inspection, in Which the Usual Tools for Graduating are not Employed. . . ," *Phil. Trans.*, 1809, pp. 105–145; G. B. Airy, "Report on the Progress of Astronomy During the Present Century," *BAAS Report, 1831–1832* (1833), p. 132.

[22] Thomas Young, *A Course of Lectures on Natural Philosophy and the Mechanical Arts* (London, 1807), *1*:425–426, discusses the heliostat as a source of light for a microscope. First invented by Willem J. 'sGravesande (1688–1742) about 1720, the heliostat was used to deliver sunlight to one spot for an extended period of time. The mechanism which drove the hour hand of a clock was used to drive a mirror about a spindle placed parallel to the earth's axis. Once pointed at the sun, the mirror would continue to point at it, always reflecting sunlight to the same location.

the watch a spiral watch spring is wound around the axes of the myrror.[23]

Was informed that the Melville Monument had been struck by lightning about 2 weeks since. Some interesting facts relative to the lateral discharge. Man nocked down, structure but little injured. Person saw every part as if on fire rays darting out.

Mr Forbes not in Edinburgh on the continent[24] has been making experiments on temperatures at great depths.[25] Used for some experiments long wires of copper and iron. With these shows a class experiment. Dips the two solders into basins of water of different temperature.

Leslies hygrometer a differential thermometer with one bulb covered with cloth wet with water.[26] Instrument made by an assistant[27] of Leslies who now assists Mr. Forbes.

[23] At some later date Henry added the sentence: "Same article reinvented by Dr Potter of London University."

Richard Potter (1799–1886) began to show an interest in science around 1830. It was not until 1841, however, that he obtained the professorship in natural philosophy and astronomy at University College, London. He held this chair, with the exception of one year, until 1865. *DNB.*

Potter announced what he thought was a new form of the heliostat, with credit to 'sGravesande but not to Young, in "On a New and Simple Heliostat," *Phil. Mag.*, 1833, 3d ser. 2:6–8.

[24] See above, Bache to Basil Hall, July 16, 1837.

[25] For Henry's description of these experiments, see his diary entry of August 7, 1837, below.

[26] The scientific community had been aware of the cooling effect of the evaporation of a liquid as early as the seventeenth century, but it was not until the end of the eighteenth

century that a hygrometer (a device to measure humidity) was constructed based on this principle. James Hutton (1726–1797, *DSB*) is credited with being the first to wet the bulb of a thermometer and observe the decrease in temperature produced by evaporation; the amount of decrease was assumed to be proportional to the humidity. Leslie's contribution was to use a differential thermometer (a U-shaped tube with a bulb at each end) so that the comparison between the wet bulb temperature and the dry bulb could be made more easily. John Leslie, "Description of an Hygrometer and Photometer," *Nicholson's Journal*, 1800, 3:461–467; W. E. Knowles Middleton, *Invention of the Meteorological Instruments* (Baltimore, 1969), pp. 120–126.

Henry had been aware of Leslie's form of the differential thermometer as early as 1830, although at that time he preferred using John Daniell's version of the hygrometer. *Henry Papers*, 1:309–311.

[27] Not identified.

HENRY'S EUROPEAN DIARY
Henry Papers, Smithsonian Archives

Aug 6 [1837] Sunday Weather quite cold to me for the season of the year thermometer in Room 55 about the same as at New York when I left in Feby. At 11 o'clock salied forth to go to church. Followed two ladies resolved to go to church where they went wherever it might be. Crossed the mound entred the old town and passed down high street entred the general door of the church of St Giles.[1]

This is a very ancient structure and is celebrated in the history of Sco[t]-land. It is however much altered and was almost intirely remodeled in 1833. Many however of the old parts remain.

There are at present two churches established in this building besides a small congregation which meet in a room designed for the general assembly. It was something singular for an American to see three congregations coming out of one door all under the same roof and so near that the singing of the one could be herd by the other.[2]

It was in this building that James the 1st of England took leave of his Scotch subjects immediatly after the sermon on Sunday.[3] Here also the circumstance occurred which gave rise to the Porteous mob described in Sir W S Hart of Mid Lothian.[4] Two men had been condemned to death for defrauding the excise. They were guarded to the church as was usual by

[1] Dating primarily from the fourteenth and fifteenth centuries, St. Giles' cathedral was at the time of Henry's visit the most important religious edifice in Edinburgh. During the Reformation, it had become a Presbyterian church, which it remained except for the seventeenth century, when it was made part of the Stuarts's attempt to introduce Episcopacy to Scotland. The restoration of 1829–1833 destroyed many of the most beautiful features, although a subsequent restoration in 1872–1883 returned it more nearly to its medieval appearance. J. Cameron Lees, *St. Giles', Edinburgh* (Edinburgh, 1889).

[2] St. Giles' was not unique in this respect. A number of the larger Scottish town kirks were subdivided into two or more congregations at the time of the Reformation. In part, this was an attempt to adapt the large spaces of the medieval cathedral to the more intimate requirements of Protestant worship. More important perhaps was the economic incentive. The need for additional parish churches created by the growth in the urban population was more easily filled by subdividing existing structures than constructing new ones. In the case of St. Giles', at least, there was also a political motivation. Though some earlier partitioning had occurred, the formal division of St. Giles' into separate parish churches took place in 1598 in conjunction with James VI's attempt to establish his control over church administration in Edinburgh. For more on St. Giles', see below, Henry to Harriet Henry, August 27, 1837, footnote 5.

George Hay, *The Architecture of Scottish Post-Reformation Churches, 1560–1843* (Oxford, 1957), p. 27. James F. White, *Protestant Worship and Church Architecture* (New York, 1964), pp. 82–83. Lees, *St. Giles', Edinburgh*, pp. 191–192.

[3] James VI of Scotland, the Protestant son of Mary Queen of Scots, became James I of England upon the death of Elizabeth I in 1603. On April 3, 1603, he bade farewell to his Scottish subjects at St. Giles'.

[4] The Porteous Riots of September 1736, are described in considerable detail in the opening chapters of Sir Walter Scott's *Heart of Midlothian*, first published in 1818. The riots, which took their name from the victim, Captain John Porteous (d. 1736; *DNB*), followed the basic outline given by Henry. The incident was as much an expression of suppressed Scottish nationalism as it was of admiration for the self-sacrifice of the hanged prisoner. The excises, the target of the condemned men's crime, had been regarded since the Act of Union in 1707 as a symbol of English oppression by much of Scotland, and smugglers were generally viewed as patriots. The Porteous Riots caused great indignation in England and Edinburgh was threatened with a variety of sanctions, though in the end Parliament settled for a £2000 fine levied against the city. Basil Williams, *The Whig Supremacy, 1714–1760* (Oxford, 1962), pp. 278–279. Janet R. Glover, *The Story of Scotland* (London, 1960), pp. 205–206.

three soldiers to hear the *word* before condemnation and execution. One of the[m] a stout fellow seized a sold[i]er by each hand and a third with his teeth then cried to his comrad to escape which was done. The populace were so much pleased with the magninimity of the man that they demanded his release. A part[y] of soldiers were ordered to attend the gallows at the time of execution with guns charged with balls. The capt was one of the city guards by the name of Porteus who in an ill advised moment ordered the soldiers to fire on the people on some appearance of disorder. Many were killed. Porteus was arrested and found guilty of murder but was reprieved for a time by the Queen;[5] the King was absent. The populace arose broke open his prison dragged him fourth and hanged him on a lamp post near the spot where the people were killed. This is also the church in which the celebrated John Knox preached and instigated the public against prelacy.[6]

I happened to get into the smallest part of the building and to listen to the discourse of quite a young man who was not difficcent in eloquence but who will probably preach better after some years of practice.

A large gold plated plate was placed at the door with a gentleman at the side of it for collecting the money for the poor and the expenses of the church.

Returned was quite chilled ordered fire—dinner—tea—reading—bed.

---

[5] Queen Caroline, wife of George II, acted as Regent during her husband's periodic trips to his Hanoverian possessions.

[6] John Knox (1505–1572; *DNB*), religious reformer and father of Scottish Presbyterianism, was minister of St. Giles' from 1559 to 1572.

HENRY'S EUROPEAN DIARY
Henry Papers, Smithsonian Archives

Mond. Aug 7ᵗʰ [1837]. Called by appointment at 8 o'clock to breakfast with Mr Buchannan. Had quite an interesting conversation with him on the subject of steam-boats Locomotives rail ways &c. Mr. B. says that he thinks the maximum effect of a water wheel of the overshot kind is the same in reference to velocity as that of a weight drawing another wight over a pully (See Youngs N P.[1]). Mr B once lectured on natural philosophy before the

---

[1] Thomas Young, *A Course of Lectures on Natural Philosophy and the Mechanical Arts*, 2 vols. (London, 1807). A reading of the sections on the overshot wheel—one where the water flowed from above the wheel—has failed to find an explicit connection between the velocity of the overshot wheel and one weight drawing another over a pulley. However, such

society of arts[2] in this city. He is the translator of the article Electricity by Biot in the suppliment to the Encyclopedia Britanica.[3] His Brother[4] is the writer of the article on america in the Encyclopedia Britanica. Also in the Edinburgh Gasiteer.[5] Called with Mr B at Prof Jamesons[6] not at home. Also on Mr Robeson[7] son of Professor Robeson[8] not at home. Then on Mr Sang[9] teacher of Mathematics a person who has written several articles for

a connection does appear in the work of John Robison, Sr. His concept of equilibrium in a machine in uniform motion was developed using two weights connected over a fixed pulley by a thread. He then used this concept to explain the workings of an overshot wheel and to prove that the performance of such a wheel increased as its velocity decreased. John Robison, *A System of Mechanical Philosophy*, 4 vols. (Edinburgh, 1822), 2:226–231, 601–607.

[2] The Society for Promoting the Useful Arts in Scotland was founded in 1821. Twenty years later it was chartered as the Royal Scottish Society of Arts. The society served as a forum for the exchange of technical ideas and as a means of publicizing inventions and technical improvements. To encourage innovation, prizes were awarded for outstanding inventions and essays. *Transactions of the Royal Scottish Society of Arts*, 1841, *1*:iii–vi.

[3] The *Supplement to the Fourth, Fifth and Sixth Editions*, 6 vols. (Edinburgh, 1815–1824) consisted primarily of original, signed contributions by some of the leading figures in British and French science and the arts. Among the contributors were Thomas Young, Walter Scott, P. M. Roget, François Arago and Thomas R. Malthus.

[4] David Buchanan (1779–1848) was a newspaper editor in Edinburgh from 1808 until his death. In 1814 he brought out an edition of Adam Smith's works, the result of his interest in political economy. Other areas of special study were geography and statistics. He contributed numerous articles to the seventh edition of the *Encyclopaedia Britannica*. *DNB*.

[5] The *Edinburgh Gazetteer, or Geographical Dictionary*, 6 vols. (Edinburgh, 1822), *1*:141–157. The article, which is unsigned, defends the New World against Buffon's charges that the fauna of the Americas is inferior to that of the Old World. It also assumes that the United States will expand westward, displacing the Indians.

[6] Although Robert Jameson (1774–1854) was apprenticed to a surgeon, his enthusiasm for mineralogy and geology led him to give up the idea of a medical career. He became a

student of John Walker, the Professor of Natural History at Edinburgh University, and through Walker obtained charge of the university museum. In 1803, upon the death of Walker, Jameson was given the Regius Chair of Natural History at Edinburgh, a position he held for the next half century.

Jameson was one of the leading figures in Scottish science during the first half of the nineteenth century. He published extensively in support of Abraham Gottlob Werner's Neptunian theory of the creation of the earth's crust, with its assumption of a primeval ocean from which the geological strata precipitated. Under his control the university museum grew from a small number of specimens to the second largest natural history collection in Great Britain. His teaching inspired a large number of naturalists. Henry probably knew him best, however, as the editor of the *Edinburgh Philosophical Journal*. The *Journal* was founded by Jameson and David Brewster in 1819, with Jameson becoming sole editor in 1824. He remained editor for thirty years. *DSB*.

[7] John Robison (1778–1843) was educated at Edinburgh. In 1802 he went to India where he made his fortune as the contractor for the artillery corps of the Nizam of Hyderabad. He was elected a Fellow of the Royal Society of Edinburgh in January 1816, just a few months after his return from India. He was also a founding member of the Royal Scottish Society of Arts. At the time of Henry's visit he was general secretary of the Royal Society of Edinburgh. Knighthood was bestowed the following year. *DNB*.

Robison had the reputation of being hospitable to foreign visitors. Through the offices of George Buchanan, Henry did meet and become friendly with Robison. George Buchanan to Henry, August 8, 1837, Joseph Henry Papers, Library, American Philosophical Society; Henry to Harriet Henry, August 16, 1837, printed below.

[8] John Robison, Sr.

[9] Edward Sang (1805–1890) was educated at the University of Edinburgh, where he was one of John Leslie's prize pupils, as Leslie

Jamesons journal one on the pulleys and ban[d]s of turning lathes[10] another on the proportions between a model and the original.[11]

He appears to possess considerable mechanical ingenuity and was quite willing to exhibit to me any of his articles but is somewhat inclined to claim a little more than is quite proper. He purchased the apparatus which belonged to the late Sir J Leslie and showed me many articles which I have seen described and which now belong to the history of the science.

The original freezing apparatus[12] of Sir John with three plates and a large single acting pump. Mr Sang now puts these plates on his lecture table and conects them to his pump by a tube of lead. Weaving reads to place before the object glass of a telescope to show some of the phenomina of interferances. The consentrater of Lesley (see his philos[13]) simple level with bubble under a plate of glass like Mr Lukins' artificial horizon[14] to determine if a surface is level. Good instrument. Gives the side at once which is too high.

Steel chain with long links for the catenarian curve. String of bullets for the inverted curve. String for the curve of the suspension bridge which is near a parabola.[15] Various balls for whirling one in which the centre can be with drawn. At first it revolves without rising; centre out rises.

---

himself certified in 1822. After a period as a surveyor and civil engineer, Sang earned his living as a mathematics teacher in Edinburgh. From 1841 until 1854 he was Professor of Mechanical Philosophy at Constantinople, the only period in his life when he was away from Edinburgh for any time. Elected a Fellow of the Royal Scottish Society of Arts in 1828, Sang was later Secretary for the Society. He became a Fellow of the Royal Society of Edinburgh in 1849. Sang published extensively in the fields of mechanics, mathematics, and engineering. He was probably best known, however, for his computations of logarithmic and actuarial tables. D. Bruce Peebles, "Edward Sang," *Proceedings of the Royal Society of Edinburgh*, 1895–1897, *21*:xvii–xxvii.

There survive in the Henry Library reprints of four of Sang's early publications. Three are presentation copies.

[10] "On the Adaption of the Fly-wheel and Pulley of the Turning Lathe to a Given Length of Band," *Edinburgh New Philosophical Journal*, 1831, *10*:239–251.

[11] "A Few Remarks on the Relation which Subsists Between a Machine and its Model," *Edinburgh New Philosophical Journal*, 1833,

14:145–155.

[12] Probably the apparatus used in 1810 to achieve very low temperatures by evaporating water under conditions of low pressure in the presence of a desiccant. John Leslie, *Treatises on Various Subjects of Natural and Chemical Philosophy* (Edinburgh, 1838), pp. 362–376.

[13] Leslie's concentrator exhibited the accumulation and transfer of momentum and was used to illustrate lectures. John Leslie, *Elements of Natural Philosophy* (Edinburgh, 1823), *1*:142–152.

[14] Henry's description of Lukens's artificial horizon appears in *Henry Papers*, 2:183–184.

[15] A catenarian curve is formed when a chain of uniform thickness is allowed to hang freely from its two end points. If a string of uniform beads is suspended, then inverted, a catenary arch is formed. It was discovered that such an arch was the best form for structures, such as bridges, which had to support vertical forces, although it left something to be desired if the structure was subjected to lateral forces. Denison Olmsted, *An Introduction to Natural Philosophy*, 2 vols. (New Haven, 1831), *1*:296–297.

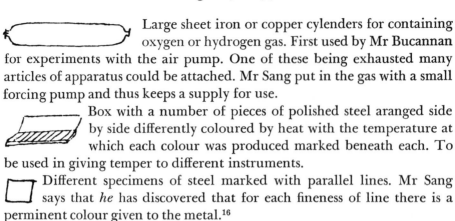 Large sheet iron or copper cylenders for containing oxygen or hydrogen gas. First used by Mr Bucannan for experiments with the air pump. One of these being exhausted many articles of apparatus could be attached. Mr Sang put in the gas with a small forcing pump and thus keeps a supply for use.

 Box with a number of pieces of polished steel aranged side by side differently coloured by heat with the temperature at which each colour was produced marked beneath each. To be used in giving temper to different instruments.

Different specimens of steel marked with parallel lines. Mr Sang says that *he* has discovered that for each fineness of line there is a perminent colour given to the metal.[16]

Two lenses to be achromatic & serve as the eye glasses of tele-scopes by Mr Sang himself.[17]

 A modification of the kalidrophon[18] by Mr Sang. The bead is made of silver wire drawn through a plate. The only improve-ment I could see in the instrument over the original one of Mr Wheatstone is the foot which is formed of heavy cast iron & the several wires screw into it.

Large perfectly smooth slate cost about 3 £s good article for class.

Small iron apparatus for the lime lamp.[19] Made of iron because wood warps with the heat and moisture. The polarizing apparatus consists of two of Nichol's eye pieces.[20] The mica or spar or salts between.

---

[16] An instance where Henry supplies evidence that Sang sometimes claimed "a little more than is quite proper." If we have interpreted Henry correctly, he was referring to a phenomenon first noticed by David Brewster in 1822 and described by Brewster in "On a New Series of Periodical Colours Produced by the Grooved Surfaces of Metallic and Transparent Bodies," *Phil. Trans.*, 1829, pp. 301–316 (a reprint survives in the Henry Library). Brewster was uncertain at the time as to the cause of the colors, although he had discovered that the effect was dependent upon the distance between the grooves. Later he ascribed the colors to a diffraction effect. *Encyclopaedia Britannica*, 8th ed., s.v. "Optics," pp. 613–617.

[17] According to Peebles's obituary (see above, footnote 9), Sang presented a paper before the Royal Society of Edinburgh on January 6, 1837, entitled "On the Construction of a Solid Achromatic Eyepiece." This paper was never published.

[18] For the kaleidophone, invented by Charles Wheatstone in 1825, see above, Henry's diary entry of April 4, 1837, footnote 4.

[19] A version of Drummond's lamp (see above, Henry's second entry of the European Diary for March 23, 1837, footnote 2) which was used in the laboratory when an intense beam of strongly polarized light was required. Faraday, for example, would use the lamp in 1846 while conducting his early experiments on producing electricity from light. Thomas Martin, ed., *Faraday's Diaries*, 8 vols. (London, 1932–1936), *4*:398–399.

[20] Described in "On a Method of so Far Increasing the Divergency of the Two Rays in Calcareous-spar, that only One Image May be Seen at a Time," *Edinburgh New Philosophical Journal*, 1828, *6*:83–84, William Nicol's polarizer (often termed the Nicol eyepiece in the literature) consisted of a rhomboid of

Molecular action shewn by a piece of round steel wire which has probably been left a little hard filed on one side about half away. The wire bends in the form shown in the figure. The tension is relieved on one side and not on the other.

Same thing shewn by turning out the middle of a brass plate. The middle of the thin part will bulge out. (Try these with different metals and different circumstances.)[21]

Diagram with strings to show that the action of 4 fources equal and applied in the direction of the sides of a tetrahedron would be in equilibrium. (See Lesley.)[22] (Agreed to call on Mr Sang tomorrow.)[23]

Went with Mr B to the observatory[24] to meet by appointement Mr Henderson[25] the astronomer royal and professor of astronomy in the University of Edinburgh. Prof H is a person of small stature about 35 years old with a plesant countenance and quite an agreable manner. He was originaly an atorneys clerk but always was pleased with astronomy. He spent one year

---

calcite spar split along a diagonal, with the halves cemented together with Canada balsam. The balsam reflected the ordinary beam of light, but allowed the extraordinary beam to pass almost undeviated. Henry would later receive a first-hand account of Nicol's research. See below, Henry's European Diary, August 9, 1837.

[21] Although Henry would later refer to these demonstrations by Sang in his "Record of Experiments" entry of September 28, 1844 (Henry Papers, Smithsonian Archives), we have failed to uncover any evidence of Henry conducting the systematic investigations of the phenomenon suggested by his parenthetical remark. Even the reference of September 28 was no more than an aside. Henry's concern on that day was chiefly with the molecular cohesion of soap bubbles.

[22] Although the section on statics in Leslie's *Elements of Natural Philosophy*, *1*:37–69, uses similar diagrams, we have been unable to locate a reference to this specific piece of apparatus.

[23] See the next document.

[24] Plans for building an observatory in Edinburgh date back to 1736, although the first Edinburgh Observatory, usually designated the "old" observatory (see below, footnote 28), was not completed until 1792. Construction on a new Edinburgh Observatory was begun in 1818 as part of the program of the Astronomical Institution (founded 1812) to make astron-

omy a viable science in that city. The goals of the Institution were three: to establish a research observatory (the new observatory was to fulfill that function), to establish a popular observatory, and to encourage interest in the other physical sciences by supplying apparatus and books. Under the leadership of Thomas Henderson (see below, footnote 25) and his successor, Charles Piazzi Smyth (1819–1900, *DSB*), Edinburgh Observatory became a respectable center of astronomical research. *Edinburgh Encyclopaedia* (Philadelphia, 1832), s.v. "Observatory."

[25] Although Thomas Henderson (1798–1844) never attended a university, he had the mathematical skills to excel at astronomical computations. He followed a legal career until 1831, at the same time publishing papers which established his credentials in British astronomical circles. In that year he was appointed Royal Astronomer at the Cape of Good Hope, a position he resigned in 1833 due to ill health. The following year he was selected almost simultaneously as the first Astronomer Royal for Scotland, professor of practical astronomy at Edinburgh University, and director of the Calton Hill observatory. Henderson's most important discovery was the annual parallax of α Centauri. His announcement in January 1839 was based on observations made at the Cape of Good Hope and reduced at Edinburgh. He failed by only a couple of months being the first to discover stellar parallax. *DSB*.

447

at the Cape of Good hope where he was sent by the government.

Mr Henderson showed me the different parts of the observatory which is a very convenient and beautiful building with four fronts in the form of a cross with a cupola or rather a hemespherical dome on the intersection. The arm of the cross to the south forms the Entrance that to the North the calculating room. The one to the west contains the mural circle[26] and the opposite one the great transit instrument.[27]

The length of each cross part of the building is 62 feet the projections 28 feet the diameter of the dome 13 feet. The four fronts present doric pediments supported with 6 columns of the same order. To the west of the observatory in the same enclosure is the old observatory[28] which was erected many years since but never furnished with instruments. It is now occupied by the servant of the observatory in the lower story and above by a meeting room for the astronomical society and in the room next the roof is placed a camera obscura for the amusement of the public. This instrument is a tolerable good one and throws the image on a table under neath which has a concave surface and is adjusted to the focus by sliding up and down on a stem which passes into the middle of the stand probably counter poised by weights.

The great transit instrument of the observatory was mounted by Repsold[29] of Hamburgh, the object glass of which was made by Fraunhofer

[26] The astronomical circle was an instrument designed for the measurement of the altitude of a heavenly body at the instant of its arrival on the meridian. For increased accuracy the larger circles had their axes fixed into massive piers, allowing only slight adjustments in the vertical and horizontal directions. Such circles were known as mural circles. They were used to find the latitude of the observatory. Once the latitude was known, the circle could be used to find the declination (analogous to terrestrial latitude) of a star. William A. Norton, *An Elementary Treatise on Astronomy*, 2d ed. (New York, 1845), pp. 32–36.

[27] Such instruments were used in conjunction with clocks to time the passage of celestial objects across the meridian. These observations could be used either to correct a clock or to determine the right ascension (analogous to terrestrial longitude) of a celestial body. Norton, *Elementary Treatise on Astronomy*, pp. 26–32.

The British observatories were atypical in their choice of instruments. The mural circle, which reigned supreme in England, was rarely seen in nineteenth-century Continental observatories, where it was considered too large and awkward. Most European astronomers preferred using the transit circle, an instrument which could do the work of both the transit instrument and the astronomical circle. J. L. E. Dreyer and H. H. Turner, eds., *History of the Royal Astronomical Society, 1820–1920* (London, 1923), pp. 72–73.

[28] Designed by James Craig (d. 1795, *DNB*), the architect responsible for the concept of New Town, the "old" Edinburgh observatory was completed in 1792, sixteen years after the foundation stone was laid. Lacking both instruments and an endowment, the observatory was essentially unused for an additional twenty years. Not until the Astronomical Institution decided on making the old observatory the popular observatory in its grand plan (see above, footnote 24) was there any progress. It was the Astronomical Institution which supplied the camera obscura mentioned by Henry, as well as telescopes and globes. *Edinburgh Encyclopaedia* (Philadelphia, 1832), s.v. "Observatory."

[29] The transit instrument in the Edinburgh

shows signes of decomposition. A drawing of the spots which are in every part of the disc was made about 3 years since and this shows by present comparison that the defect does not increase. Great care is taken to keep the glass from moisture by a wooden cap put on the end of the instrument when not in use. The diameter of this object glass 6 inches and 4/10 the focal length 8 feet 2 inches. The magnifyers are from 120 to 250.

I was shewn the north star near the meridian at about 3 oclock. It appeared very distinct like a brilliant point near one of the cross wires but with considerable motion owing to the unsteadyness of the atmosphere.

The situation proves to be a good one for an observatory. It is above the smoke of the city and the atmosphere of the sea is not found to affict it. The atmosphere of Scotland like that of England is not good for the use of high magnifying power but a few nights in the course of the year will answer for some observations. The power of the great transit is more than sufficient for all purposes of accurate observation and the money which it cost would have been in part at least better employed according to Mr H in purchasing a good telescope for sweeping the heavens. The cost of the object glass was 100 £s and of the mounting about 400 more.

The mural circle is one by Troughton or rather by his parterner and now successor Syms. It is of the same form and size as the one at Greenwich namely 6 feet in diameter has 6 microscopes and as many clamps with two circles of division on the external circumference one of gold for the minutes the other parallel of platina carring the figures of the minutes the degrees are pointed out by an index of brass by the side of the microscope and the seconds are red by the micrometer hed attached to the microscope. A stone is placed parallel to the pier which supports the instrument for placing the basin of mercury on a firm support when the instrument is used for an observation by reflection.

Mr H having determined the latitude does not now use the instrument in this way since it is very inconvenient the slightest wind gives great trouble and not more than one observation out of 10 will answer.

The instruments are so firmly placed that they are not found to alter scarcly at all except the transit which during the summer months appears to raise its eastern gudgeon a second or two.

I should have mentioned that the axis of the transit which are of the form of large truncated cones are supported at the outer ends by a hooked pice of iron which is itself counterpoised at the opposite side of a lever over the

Observatory was installed in 1831 and was one of Adolf Repsold's first commissions. Repsold (1806–1871), the son of a German instrument maker, went on to a distinguished career as a designer and builder of astronomical instruments. The observatories at Oslo, Königsberg, Oxford and Lisbon are among those possessing instruments by Repsold. *DSB*.

pier by weights. On the inner curve of the hooks friction wheels are placed so that the instrument moves very easily and is ballanced so as to remain in any position. The counter weights are of such  a size as just to produce the slightest pressure on the axis without raising them from the Ys. Near the eye glass there are two circles each about 9 inches in diameter and placed one on each side of the tube of the instrument these serve to place the transit to any declination so that a given object may be brought into the field at any time. The two are used so as to be set seperately so that two objects may be brought into the field in rapid succession.

The declination is set on the limb by the index and the instrument is then set to the direction in the heavens by moving it so that the level attatched to the small circle is adjusted to the horizon.

To adjust the transit of course it is necessary to reverse it in its Y's and this with a large instrument of the kind is a difficult matter and one attended with some riske as the opperation is performed at Greenwich. There the whole instrument is piveted out of its place by a tackle and ropes then with the aid of several men is turned around and gradually let down by hand into its seat. To obviate this operation an instrument is here used which was I believe invented in Germany. It operates like a wagon jack and by a crank turns two bevel wheels which raise a large screw carrying on its upper end a pair of Y's. This apparatus is placed on a strong wooden stand and moves on friction roolers on a small rail way directly under the instrument. When placed in the proper position and it is guided to this by the rails the handle is turned the Y's rise to the cones of the instrument and gradually lift it from its place. The whole is then drawn out on the rail way the instrument turned round by turning the central support the car wheeled back and the transit again lowered to its place. This beautiful contrivance[30] is also used at the observatory at Paris and also at Brussels. There is a stone placed a little to the north of the instrument for placing a basin of mercury for observations of the pole star. This is useful in testing the level since the axis must be horizontal if the star seen direct and by reflection are both in the same part of the field of view when the instrument is instantly moved

[30] The superiority of the German method of reversing the transit instrument was self-evident to most astronomers and the reversing stand became a standard item in observatories. There is a fine illustration of the reversing stand on plate V of the *Annals of the Astro-nomical Observatory of Georgetown College, D.C.*, 1852, *1*. By the time Georgetown received its transit from the Munich firm of Ertel & Son (1844), reversing stands came along with the instrument. Ibid., *1*:27–32.

from one to the other. The field of view of the transit with the smaller power occupies about ½ a degree but the whole is not seen at once and there is a movable piece which moves before the end of the tube showing the 5 cross hairs in succession 2 or 3 at a time. The pieres of the transit are of single blocks of stone and rest on the rock of the hill.
The cross hairs in the microscope are of this appearance ((( )((((microscopes of the mural circle. The perpendicular markes represent the degrees on the limb, ✗ the cross hairs.

The cost of the mural circle with its fitting up was about 900 £s. The openings in the roof over the two instruments are formed by sliders of mahogany which is used to prevent warping. They overlap like shingles and are drawn aside laterally by strings passing over pulleys in the manner the skye light in the Phil Hall at Princeton is managed. Several parts move very easily and one or more may be opened as occasion may require. They are each about 2½ feet long, the opening is about one foot wide.

All the observations made at this observatory are sent to London[31] after being reduced and compaired with the places deduced from calculations from the tables. They are then returned and printed in Edinburgh at the expense of the government under the eye of the astronomer. Mr Henderson has but one assistant while there are 5 or 6 at Greenwich.[32] The Astronomer Royal does little himself in the way of observation only directs the whole.[33] At Greenwich observations are made during clear weather through the whole 24 hours, at Edinburgh only through a part. The fixed stars, moon and the planets are regularly observed.

---

[31] It was the practice of the Home Office to consult with the Royal Astronomical Society before allowing any public body to publish astronomical observations. Henderson's observations through 1835 were reviewed by the Council of the Royal Astronomical Society in 1836. The following year the observations made in 1836 were evaluated. Thereafter the practice was discontinued. It was recognized that Henderson did not require that sort of supervision. Dreyer and Turner, eds., *History of the Royal Astronomical Society*, p. 67.

[32] Founded in 1675 by Charles II for the purpose of aiding navigation, the Royal Greenwich Observatory developed over the next century and a half into one of the centers of accurate observational work. This despite difficulties with funding, staff, instruments, administration, and the government's continuing attitude that the observatory's function was to assist navigation.

With the appointment of George B. Airy (1801–1892, *DSB*) in 1835 as the seventh Astronomer Royal, Greenwich underwent a number of changes. Airy was an advocate of efficiency through organization. Greenwich, which had developed a reputation for internal disorder and sloth in publication, became a center for the mass production of astronomical data. Meteorological and magnetic observations became part of the Greenwich routine as well. Graham Smith et al., "Three Hundred Years of Greenwich," *Nature*, 1975, *55*: 581–606.

[33] A reference to the Astronomer Royal at Greenwich. The Astronomer Royal for Scotland did observe regularly.

The reductions much more tedious than the observations. Compare the moons position with Burckharts tables.[34]

The principal error in the tables of the moon appear to be one of the epoch. The moon is about 7 seconds too fast.

The cause of this error is not known.[35] The same exists with Herchel[36] and Saturn not with mars and jupiter.

Perhaps as has been observed by some astronomer of the day some influence is acting other than gravitation.[37]

[34] Johann Karl Burckhardt (1773–1825) was born and educated in Germany, but came to Paris in 1797. In 1799 he became an assistant at the Bureau des Longitudes. Eight years later he was made director of the observatory of the École militaire. His lunar tables, based on the formulae in Laplace's *Mécanique Céleste*, but with certain empirical corrections, were published in 1812. Their superiority to previous tables was quickly recognized. They were adopted as the standard by both the British *Nautical Almanac* and the French *Connaissance des Temps* and remained in use until 1857. *Poggendorff, I*:344; Arthur L. Norberg, "Simon Newcomb and Nineteenth-Century Positional Astronomy" (Ph.D. dissertation, University of Wisconsin, 1974), pp. 273–274.

[35] Some ten years after Henry made this entry, Peter Andreas Hansen (1795–1874, *DSB*) found that the cause of the error in the epoch (the mean longitude of the moon at a given time) was the gravitational influence of Venus, previously thought to be insignificant. It was Hansen's *Tables of the Moon*, published in 1857, which replaced Burckhardt's tables as the standard. Norberg, "Simon Newcomb," p. 274; Robert Grant, *History of Physical Astronomy from the Earliest Ages to the Middle of the Nineteenth Century* (London, 1852), pp. 118–121.

[36] The seventh planet of the solar system was discovered by William Herschel in 1781. Faced with the unprecedented problem of naming a planet, Herschel finally responded in 1782 by calling the celestial body Georgium Sidus, after his patron, George III. Herschel's suggestion, modified to "the Georgian," became the official British usage. However, it was rejected by the rest of the astronomical world. French astronomers, following the lead of Joseph Lalande, chose to honor the discoverer by naming the planet after him. The rest of the Continent adopted the suggestion of Johann Bode that the tradition of mythological names be continued and that the new planet be called Uranus. The confusion and conflict were not ended until the 1840s, when in conjunction with the naming of the eighth planet, the principle of mythological names was finally accepted. Morton Grosser, *The Discovery of Neptune* (Cambridge, Massachusetts, 1962), pp. 22–23, 127.

Henry's decision in this diary entry to call the seventh planet Herschel, and thus to follow the French example, was contrary to the trend in the English speaking astronomical world. A survey of English-language astronomical texts in Henry's Library written by contemporaries—a group which includes Mary Somerville, John Farrar, George Airy, John Herschel, Ferdinand Hassler, and William Norton—shows that American and English scientists rejected both the official British policy and the French view by using the term Uranus.

[37] Probably a reference to the suggestion that an ethereal fluid was resisting the motion of the planets. Such an idea had been presented by Leonhard Euler (1707–1783, *DSB*) in 1772 to explain the secular acceleration of the moon, having argued earlier that this inequality could not be produced by the force of gravity. The ethereal theory went into disfavor, however, when Laplace, in 1787, developed an explanation for secular acceleration which depended solely upon the force of gravity.

It is questionable whether any astronomer of the late 1830s would have been satisfied with an explanation of a planetary orbit which depended upon the existence of an ether. The generally accepted cause of Uranus's unpredictable behavior was a planet beyond its orbit. Grant, *History of Physical Astronomy*, p. 61; Grosser, *Discovery of Neptune*, pp. 46–57.

 Mr H also showed me the thermometers sunk in the ground or rather into the solid rock under the direction of Mr Forbes at the expense of the British association for determining the temperature at different depths[38]—or rather the change of temperature. A hole several inches in diameter was drilled into the rock and 4 thermometers inserted one of 25f 6 inch another of 12f 8 another 6^f 4^{in} & 3f 2 in. These are made of glass and filled with spirits of wine. The bulbs are cylendrical of the deepest 9 inches long and about 1½ inches in diameter.

The bulb of the longes is the largest since the range of temperature is quite small the degrees are required to be large.

They are surrounded with sand in the hole and project about 18 inches above ground. Are enclosed in a box. To test the accuracy of these Mr Forbes let down into the same hole a wire of copper and iron soldered together at the lowest point. These are kept from touching by being wrapped with silk and then bound together. They are put in with the thermometers and the two ends project and entre a small house near by.

To the upper end of the iron wire a small piece of copper wire is soldered *a* and when this point is diped into water of which the temperature is so varied that no current is observed by the galvanometer then the temperature of the water is the same as that of the soldering at the bottom of the pit. And consequently this temperature is known.[39]

---

[38] These experiments represent an attempt to measure the relative conductivity of solar heat through three different types of soil. Begun in early 1837, the observations were continued until the spring of 1842. While made at the suggestion of and under the supervision of Forbes, the observations were usually conducted by other individuals. James D. Forbes, "Account of Some Experiments on the Temperature of the Earth at Different Depths, and in Different Soils, near Edinburgh," *Transactions of the Royal Society of Edinburgh,* 1849, *16*:189–236; *British Association Report, 1836* (1837), pp. xx, 291–293.

[39] The use of a pair of iron and copper wires to measure temperature was a technique shown Forbes by Jean Peltier in 1835. It was based on the fundamental principle of thermoelectricity. If two different metals were joined to form a circuit, and the two junctions were at different temperatures, then a current was created; if, however, the junctions were at the same temperature, as in Forbes's experiments, then no current would flow.

An alternative approach, although one that some of Forbes's contemporaries thought inaccurate, was to measure the intensity of the thermoelectric current created in the circuit when one of the junctions was at a known temperature. Pouillet had found that for certain thermoelectric couples the intensity of the current was directly proportional to the difference in temperature of the couples.

Forbes was not the only scientist to apply the principles of thermoelectricity to the problem of measuring the temperature in a relatively inaccessible location. About the same time that he was carrying out his observations of the temperature of land at great depths, Becquerel was using the same technique to measure the temperature of water at great depths.

James D. Forbes, "Supplementary Report on Meteorology," *British Association Report, 1840* (1841), pp. 47–49; G. K. Burgess and H. Le Chatelier, *The Measurement of High*

This is only used as a check on the thermometers. I should have stated that a correction is made for the expansion of the spirits in the tubes. The minimum temperature of the deepest has taken place this year in June but when the correction is made for the expansion of the tube it will probably be in july.[40]

Besides these thermometers are 2 other sets one in the earth near the city and another in the free stone quarry near Leith. All under the direction of Mr. Forbes.

Before quitting the observatory I must mention the chair used for ob- 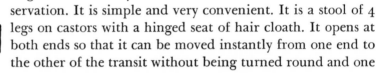 servation. It is simple and very convenient. It is a stool of 4 legs on castors with a hinged seat of hair cloth. It opens at both ends so that it can be moved instantly from one end to the other of the transit without being turned round and one or the other end thrown up for the purpose of resting the head or back.

There is also a station of the trigonometrical survey of Scotland[41] preserved in the building of the observatory. A hole is made in the floor and when the shutter is taken up a brass cone is seen with a marke on the upper face. The survey of Scotland in the subtriangulation has not been completed.

Called in the afternoon on Mr Adie the optician. Was shown his new form of the Sympiesometer for the measuring of heights. It differs from his old instrument in having the bulb of the thermometer and that of the

---

Temperatures, 3d ed. (New York, 1912), pp. 101, 108–109; W. E. Knowles Middleton, *A History of the Thermometer and Its Uses in Meteorology* (Baltimore, 1966), pp. 177–178.

[40] Because of irregularities in the observations, Forbes was unable to determine the epoch of the minimum temperature in 1837. In the following year, however, the minimum did occur in July as predicted. The correction for the expansion of the alcohol in the thermometer was vital for the accuracy of this experiment. The total range of temperature at the depth of twenty-four feet was less than 1° Centigrade. Since a portion of the thermometer was above ground, and therefore sensitive to the heat of a summer day, false readings could occur.

James D. Forbes, "Discussion of One Year's Observations of Thermometers Sunk to Different Depths in Different Localities in the Neighbourhood of Edinburgh," *Proceedings of the Royal Society of Edinburgh, 1832–1844, 1*:224–226; James D. Forbes, "On the Results of the Most Recent Experiments on the Con-

ducting Power for Heat of Different Soils," *Proceedings of the Royal Society of Edinburgh, 1832–1844, 1*:343–345.

[41] Although the Trigonometrical Survey was not formally founded until 1791, its history can be traced back to the military mapping of Scotland which took place in the wake of the Rebellion of 1745. Headquartered in the Tower of London under the command of the Board of Ordnance, the Survey's initial task was to prepare a map of England on a scale of one inch to the mile (the standard scale for military maps of the period). In 1825, with the work only partially done, the Survey shifted its emphasis to the mapping of Ireland. It was not until 1838 that the decision was made to complete England and Scotland. The scale to be used was changed to six inches to the mile. The Survey station that Henry saw at the observatory was established during the period 1810–1820 during the incomplete triangulation of Scotland. Charles Close, *The Early Years of the Ordnance Survey* (Chatham, 1926).

Sympiesometer both covered with wood so that the heat of the hand or the body of the observer may not affect the observation. The part *a* of the instrument is enclosed with wood open below. This instrument depens on the compression of air or gas contained in *b* by a change in the external pressure of the atmosphere. A correction is made for change by change of temperature by a sliding scale—or the scale for measuring the compression has a movable zero for the change of temperature. The instrument is now used for measuring heights. Mr A gave me a table[42] with directions for using the instrument. The art of shooting is carried to much greater perfection in Scotland than in America at least in a Scientific point of view, if not in a practical.

I was shown by Mr A. tellescopes for shooting deer blackened on the out side so as not to alarm the animal. Also shooting spectacles to be fastened to the hat to be screwed on the front part of the hat and capable of adjustment and of being turned up out of the way. Also Mr A informed that he had made instruments for determining the distance of the animal approximately by one observation.

[42] Still preserved in the Henry Library. Unfortunately, the sympiesometer (described in Henry's European Diary, August 5, 1837, footnote 19, above) proved to be a failure as a device to measure heights. Both its portability and its accuracy were inadequate. W. E. Knowles Middleton, *The History of the Barometer* (Baltimore, 1964), p. 379.

HENRY'S EUROPEAN DIARY

Henry Papers, Smithsonian Archives

Aug [8, 1837][1] Called on Mr Sang Mathematical teacher by appointment to see the instruments which belonged to Sir J Leslie[2] or those which he principally used for his original experiments. These were bought by Mr S for the sum of 400 £ (according to Mr Adie). Spent all the forenoon in examining them.

Lamp stand of a convenient form. The screw clamp missing for a number of rings.

[1] The date has been ascertained from Henry's note in the preceding entry that he had agreed to call on Sang the next day.

[2] See the preceding document. There are other very fragmentary notes on these instruments in Box 28, folder 6 "Unsorted Material," Henry Papers, Smithsonian Archives.

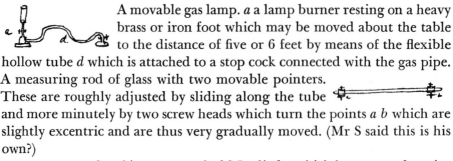 A movable gas lamp. *a* a lamp burner resting on a heavy brass or iron foot which may be moved about the table to the distance of five or 6 feet by means of the flexible hollow tube *d* which is attached to a stop cock connected with the gas pipe. A measuring rod of glass with two movable pointers. These are roughly adjusted by sliding along the tube and more minutely by two screw heads which turn the points *a b* which are slightly excentric and are thus very gradually moved. (Mr S said this is his own?)

Speaking trumpet[3] of S Leslie by which he proposed to give an alarm with a pistol equal to that with a canon by shooting through the trumpet. To be used in case of shipwreck and so forth.

Cards with gold and silver leaf for fusion by battery.

Apparatus with two small glass tubes for transmitting a current of common air into a bell glass filled with hydrogen and then fireing it.

Number of small copper cups to float in water with small hole in bottom so as to permit the cup to sink in a given time. One floats ½ an hour precisely. Serves as a measure of time, ring an alarm &c.   Sir J L

Turkey crop balloons of different sizes to show the influence of surface.

Mr S Orrery[4] on a large plan distances & sizes of the proper dimensions.

To show Lateral pressure negative by blowing through the pipes the water rises in the tower tube.

Standard lb made of stout glass phial partially filled with mercury. Very simple.

---

[3] Leslie treats the speaking trumpet and its acoustical properties in *Treatises on Natural and Chemical Philosophy* (Edinburgh, 1838), pp. 105–107.

[4] The orrery was a common piece of demonstration apparatus showing the relative positions and motions of bodies in the solar system. The balls were moved by a wheelwork.

Large table (18 inches) made of a slate graduated at the edges for showing the composition of forces in a plane. Pulleys slip round in a groove.

 Thermometer graduated on the glass, defended from the board by a piece of Indian rubber around the neck—good.

Indian rubber cloath used with the air pump instead of grease and other purposes.[5]

 Sir J Leslies method of determining the expansion of water for one atmosphere large ball, stem open to the air filled with known weight of water. Expansion noted by the stem when the air pumped out outer vessel.[6] Mr S sais that the graduations of Pixiis instruments on Oersteds plan is not correct?[7]

Enclose iron on the substances in the large tube. The compression will be determined[8]—S.

 Mr Sangs improvement of the goniometer.[9] A fixed mirror placed under measures the angle between the reflected and the direct image like in the sextant.

 Rotascope[10] the common kind. Mr S thinks he can show the motion of the earth by this instrument in a room. Idea ingenious.

Balls for electrometers made of a wood from the East Indies. More light than cork. Botanical name Eschyhomene Palulosa.[11]

---

[5] The rubber cloth functioned as a valve for the air pump in place of the usual oiled silk. See Denison Olmsted, *Introduction to Natural Philosophy*, 2 vols. (New Haven, 1832), 2:4.

[6] Leslie explains this apparatus to show the expansion of water in *Elements of Natural Philosophy* (Edinburgh, 1823), *1*:23.

[7] Henry, however, bought this instrument from Pixii; see the Appendix. See also H. C. Oersted's "Experiment, die Compression des Wassers zu Zeigen," *Journal für Chemie und Physik (Jahrbuch der Chemie und Physik)*, 1822, *36*:332–339.

[8] i.e., the compressibility of iron.

[9] An apparatus for measuring solid angles, as in the faces of crystals.

[10] The instrument seems to have been designed by Walter R. Johnson as an improvement on the usual apparatus for demonstrating the laws of rotary motion, especially those relating to the change in the position of the axes of rotation. See Johnson's "Description of an Apparatus Called the Rotascope, for Exhibiting Several Phenomena and Illustrating Certain Laws of Rotary Motion," *Silliman's Journal*, 1832, *21*:265–280.

[11] Probably Aeschynomene papulosa, a small shrub from Lower Guinea. Courtesy of James White, Department of Botany, Museum of Natural History, Smithsonian Institution.

Tube with chain in the middle for shewing the
different light in different gases by electricity.
Used by Leslie.

 Vase exhausted with vapour in; black patch on oposite side to exclude direct light. Patch with hole in next the eye to show the
hallow.[12]

Troughtons top for nautical purposes[13] did not answer; interesting article. Black glass on the top. Centre of suspense or
rather of support above centre of gravity. Made to revolve by
a drum. Move in a vacuum for 4 hours in air ½ an hour.

 Leslies steamboat—*a* the boiler and furnace. Steam
projected outwards. Behind furnace a number of
candles—shine through the boiler &c.

In the afternoon called on Mr Sanderson Mr Bullions friend.[14]
He is a Lapidary in company with his son. Manufactures Nicol's
eye pece for Watkins and the London market. Also the circular
polarizing apparatus of the form of the figure*

Showed me a number of interesting articles. Amoung others the op[t]icul
difference of structure between Amathyst and quarts. The former is curiously striated in some cases even when perfectly transparent *ie* when vewed
by polarized light through an analyzing plate of tourmaline (see Lib. U. K.
art. Pol. of Light).[15]

---

* Young Mr Sanderson is the inventor of this.

[12] For the optics of coronas or halos, see
Encyclopaedia Britannica, 8th ed., s.v. "Corona," "Chromatics." Leslie's instrument
demonstrated a well-known meteorological
phenomenon.

[13] Edward Troughton attempted to improve
on an earlier unsuccessful nautical instrument. His improved nautical top, preserving
its horizontality when in motion, was used to
establish an artificial horizon from which to
determine the altitude of the sun and other
celestial bodies. See Troughton's "Description
of the Nautical Top, as Constructed by Edward Troughton," *Edinburgh Philosophical
Journal*, 1819, *1*:105–108. At the date of the
article, the Troughton device was still un-
proven and undergoing tests.

[14] John Sanderson, lapidary and mineral
dealer, had his business at 32 St. Andrew's
Square, Edinburgh. *Edinburgh Post Office
Annual Directory*, 1837–1838, p. 94. His marriage date is known (1797), and he was apprenticed to a seal-engraver D. and A. Deu-
char, entering the guild in 1805. F. S. Grant,
ed., *Scottish Record Society, Register of Mar-
riages of the City of Edinburgh, 1751–1800*
(Edinburgh, 1922), p. 687; Charles B. Boog
Watson, ed., *Scottish Record Society, Roll of
Edinburgh Burgesses and Guild Brethren,
1761–1841* (Edinburgh, 1933), p. 140. Sanderson, father and son, have otherwise eluded us.
Peter Bullions was born in Scotland and educated in Edinburgh. *Henry Papers*, *1*:129n.

[15] Authored by Brewster, the article on
"Polarisation of Light" appears in *Natural
Philosophy* (vol. 1) of the Library of Useful
Knowledge (London, 1829), pp. 7–64. Brewster found that amethyst possessed the ability
to polarize the plane of light both to the right
and left, attributable to its being composed

Tourmaline found among the shorls[16] uncullored ones which polarize the strongest best. Colored ones are obliged to be cut down so much to render them transparent that the polarizing property is destroyed or rather weakened.

Showed me the liquids in quartz discovered by Sir D Brewster.[17] Small piece of a cristal cemented on glass, under [view] of a magnefyer of about 30 times. Heat applied by a ring of iron of thick wire (¼) inch with cork handle heated over the gas lamp. The liquid was seen through the hole in the ring. Under the microscope the appearance of the cavity was like this by the heat. The bubble in the centre expanded so as to fill the whole space or the liquid disappeared.

It gradually returned when the heat was withdrawn with much bubling from the sides of the orifice.

I was next shewn the circulation of blood in the foot of a Frog or rather in the web of the foot. A small frog was wraped in a wet cloath with one of his legs projecting. By this arrangement he appeared quite comfortable and remained quite still. The blood was seen moving with great rapidity in small branches and afterwards in larger to and from the hart principally towards the hart.* This is a very interesting object. The microscope is not an achromatic one.

Two slips of glass put together each about one inch wide and 6 inches long with small pieces of mica between them of different thickness for shewing the colours. Good arrangement.

Was shewn several beautiful specimens of fossilized wood cut and polished so as to be analyzed by the microscope. This subject was studied by Mr Nicol and afterwards published on by Mr Witham of Larkington in 1831 & 1832.[18]

---

* The motion is more or less rapid according to the health of the frog.

---

of alternate layers of right- and left-handed quartz (p. 42).

[16] Schorl is now commonly used to designate a black, iron-rich variety of the optically-active mineral tourmaline.

[17] David Brewster, "On the Existence of Two New Fluids in the Cavities of Minerals, which are Immiscible, and Possess Remarkable Physical Properties," *Transactions of the Royal Society of Edinburgh*, 1826, *10*:1–42. Brewster designated the fluids in quartz and other minerals as new fluids, whose properties he proceeded to investigate. William Nicol made similar studies around the same time. "Observations on the Fluids Contained in Crystallized Minerals," *Edinburgh New Philosophical Journal*, 1828, *5*:94–96.

[18] Nicol first invented a slide-making technique for microscopic viewing of the inner structure of thin sections of minerals. He then extended the method to paleontology in the study of fossil woods, finding that the cell structure thus made visible was a clue to classification. Nicol first published these techniques for both minerals and fossils in H. T. M. Witham's *Observations on Fossil Vegetables* (Edinburgh, 1831). This obscure mode of publication cost Nicol full recognition for his discovery. In undated geology lectures (Henry Papers, Smithsonian Archives), Henry praised Nicol's technique as an important invention, while noting that Witham had unjustly taken the credit.

Mr Sanderson senior is the inventor of a little toy which whirls on a plate of window glass. He mounts the article with two little figures which appear as if in the act of waltzing.

Observed on returning home a sign rather peculiar "Long Ladies cooking and paistry school"—good! !

HENRY'S EUROPEAN DIARY
Henry Papers, Smithsonian Archives

Aug. [9, 1837][1] Called on Mr Nicol[2] was shown a great number of interesting articles. Appointed friday morning to breakfast. Canada balsam of great use in cementing glass which will fracture in another place before breaking at the seam. Can easily be seperated by heat. Method of forming the eye piece of Mr Nicol. No advantage in having them large since the field of view is not increased the angle being the same the length is increased in the same ratio as the thickness. Will describe these more in detail after my next meeting with Mr Nicol.[3] Mr N. lives a little on the out skirts of the city has quite a good house and appears in easy circumstances. Said he could and would devote any time to me, that his time was once not his own but that now he could do as he wished.

Went to the observatory.[4] Met the assistant Mr Wallace.[5] Was shewn the

[1] This entry occurs in Henry's diary between those of August 8 and August 10.

[2] William Nicol (1768–1851, *DSB*), best known for his polarizer, the Nicol prism, which is described above in Henry's diary entry of August 7, 1837. Little is known of Nicol's career until 1826 when he published his first scientific article. His early work was on the structure of crystals. He developed a technique for direct microscopic examination of the internal structure of crystals and rocks. See Henry's diary entry of August 8 (immediately above), footnote 18.

[3] Friday, the date of the breakfast appointment, was August 11. The entry of August 10 is the last dated diary entry which survives. On August 12, Nicol wrote to John Torrey, saying that he was expecting Henry at any moment, and also stating:

The Professor has a great interest in the polarisation of Light and it gave me great pleasure to shew him the little matters I have constructed for illustrating that important branch of optical Science.

On his return from Europe, Henry delivered this letter, as well as Nicol's microscopic analyses of tree sections, to Torrey. Torrey Papers, New York Botanical Garden Library.

[4] Henry had previously visited the observatory on August 7. See his diary entry, printed above.

[5] Alexander Wallace, who had an M.A. from the University of Edinburgh, was assistant to the astronomer at the Royal Observatory, Edinburgh, from 1834 until, apparently, sometime in the 1880s. In observations made with Henderson, Wallace manned the transit instrument while Henderson observed with the mural circle. Wallace remained at the observatory when Charles Piazzi Smyth succeeded Henderson in 1845. Smyth comments favorably on Wallace and his work in the introductions to various volumes of the *Astronomical Observations Made at the Royal Observatory, Edinburgh.*

methods of making and registering the observations. Blank books are used and the observation registered in pencil. The book after being filled and all has been copied is put aside but carefully preserved in case any error should be discovered.

At the observatory is a monument to Playfair designed by his Nephew the architect Mr H Playfair.[6] It is a square structure of about 7 or 8 feet on a side with close doric pillars.

Near the observatory but not within the yard is also an other monument erected to the memory of Dugal Stewart. This is very chaste some what similar to the choregic monument at athens.[7]

Was introduced by Mr Wallace to Mr Russell who made a report at two of the British associations on the subject of waves in a canal, the resistance of boats &c. He is quite a precise gentleman and somewhat of a dandy in his appearance, has the look of a young Lawyer but is a married man. Is quite intelligent but does not evince a general acquaintance with science.[8]

[6] William Henry Playfair was the son of James Playfair, a London architect. Moving to Edinburgh in 1794 to live with his uncle John, he remained there the rest of his life.

[7] William Henry Playfair also designed the monument to Dugald Stewart (1753–1828, *DNB*), Professor of Moral Philosophy at the University of Edinburgh. The *Encyclopaedia Britannica*, 8th ed., s.v. "Edinburgh," p. 406, describes the monument as "a reproduction, with some variations, of the choragic monument of Lysicrates. . . ." The article "Athens," p. 164, states that the original monument was "vulgarly called the Lantern of Demosthenes."

[8] Among his fellow engineers, John Scott Russell (1808–1882) was considered one of the most "scientific" engineers because of his reliance on theory and experimental investigation. Born near Glasgow, Russell showed an early interest in mechanics. After attending St. Andrews University and the University of Edinburgh, he graduated from the University of Glasgow at the age of sixteen. Following his graduation, Russell founded and taught at the South Academy in Edinburgh, where he also taught private science classes and conducted experiments on steam engines and boilers. Russell was a successful teacher and in 1832, upon the death of John Leslie, he served briefly as interim Professor of Natural Philosophy at the University of Edinburgh until the election of James David Forbes. In 1833, at the request of a canal company, Russell became involved in ship design. He began by investigating waves and the resistance of fluids, which led him to proposals on the shape of canals and ships. His work was presented to the British Association in a series of papers in 1834, 1835, and 1837. One paper described his experimental ship the *Wave*, built according to his wave-line principle for minimum resistance. Russell's discovery of the wave of translation, or traveling wave, announced in the report on waves commissioned by the British Association (see the next footnote). At this time Russell was employed as manager of a shipbuilding works where he could apply his new design principles.

In 1844 Russell moved to London where he had his own shipyard. His contributions to naval architecture included innovations in form and structural design. He was an ardent advocate of iron ships. His involvement with I. K. Brunel's massive iron ship, the ill-fated *Great Eastern*, eventually cost him his shipyard and he returned to practicing as a consulting engineer. In 1860 he helped design the *Warrior*, the first seagoing armored frigate.

Russell's other engineering accomplishments included steam carriages which ran on roads, a steamer to ferry trains across Lake Constance, and the rotunda of the 1873 Vienna Exhibition.

Russell's institutional affiliations included the Royal Society of Edinburgh from 1837, the Royal Society of London from 1849, and the Institution of Civil Engineers. In addition to his books on naval architecture he published *On the Nature, Properties, and Application of Steam, and on Steam Navigation* (Edinburgh, 1841), *A Treatise on the Steam Engine* (Edinburgh, 1841), and *Systematic*

He is associated with Dr Robeson in the experiments on the waves. I am to meet him tomorrow at 11 o'clock to witness some of his experiments.[9]

I learn from Mr S that Mr Russell is called the interem Professor from having filled the chair of N P for a short time after the death of Leslie.

He has been much engaged in experiments on steam but has not well suceded. He now lectures on Natural philosophy at some medical establishment.

Called on Mr Sanderson after dinner, found the young man in. Receved some information on the art of cutting glass and stones. Use plate of flat lead or brass or tin, powder of emery for pollishing. He uses a circular horizontal wheel.

For slitting quartz or other hard stone use diamond powder, workes very quick. With thin wheel cut an inch in 20 minutes. Very thin gash, some cases as thin as paper.

Lead plate retains the emery powder but is sooner ground out of flat.

Diamond dust is formed by pounding black and irregular diamons in a small steel mortar about 2 inches in diameter with a hole of ½ an inches. The diamonds for the dust at this time is very high. They cost now 30 shillings a carrat or 15 shillings a gram. They however will do a considerable quantity of work.

The dust is put on the circumference of the wheel by the finger and then pressed into the metal with a hard stone.

The best kind of oil for cutting stone is that which is thinest and this is procured by distilling sperm oil at a high temperature. This product is very liquid and according to Mr S possesses great dispersive power so that a small quantity put on the hand will diffuse itself over the skin up the arm.

It would probably posess some peculiar properties on water. A drop put on the cork of a tight bottle in the course of a few hours opens the mouth.

(Try some experiments on this)[10]

Technical Education for the English People (London, 1869).

DNB and *Proceedings of the Institution of Civil Engineers*, 1886, *87*:427–440. George S. Emmerson, *John Scott Russell: A Great Victorian Engineer and Naval Architect* (London, 1977).

Two of Russell's works are in the Henry Library: an 1837 paper, "Researches in Hydrodynamics," *Transactions of the Royal Society of Edinburgh*, 1840, *14*:47–109, and *A Treatise on the Steam Engine*.

[9] At the 1836 British Association meeting, Russell and John Robison were appointed a committee to investigate waves. A preliminary report appeared in *BAAS Report, 1837* (1838), pp. 417–496. For the next few years grants were made for the continuing investigation until the final report by Russell appeared in *BAAS Report, 1844* (1845), pp. 311–390. Robison had recently died and Russell described his role as that of "a valuable counsellor and a respected and cordial cooperator," while crediting himself with conducting the research.

Henry went to see Russell's experiments the next day; see his diary entry of August 10, immediately below.

[10] Henry transferred this information from Sanderson to his commonplace book, Note-

book [10615], page 556:

Oil made by distilling sperm oil at a high temperature possess great diffusive power. A drop put on the hand extends up the arm.

Make experiments on this, in connection with surface action.

We have not located a record of the experiments suggested here.

HENRY'S EUROPEAN DIARY
Henry Papers, Smithsonian Archives

Aug. 10th [1837] B[r]eakfasted this morning with Mr Buchannan in company with Mr Henderson the Ast[r]onomer Royal of Edinburgh. An interesting time. The Astronomer gave us an account of his visit to the cape of good hope where he remained a year engaged under government in observing the stars of the southern hemisphere. He went out in a goverment vessel, 7 week passage, great difficulty in landing. Cape town 30 miles to the north of the cape and north of table mountain. This mountain between 2 and 3000 thousand feet on the perpendicular side in altitude.

The mist settles before a south west wind on the flat surface of the mountain and forms what is called the table cloath. From this it rolls off and is desolved in the air beneath before it reaches the ground.

The stars of the southern hemisphere are very beautiful. The smallest have a peculiar brilliancy. Even the milky way shines with a white light resembling the light of the moon 7 or 8 days old.

The magellanic clouds resemble patches of the milky way broken off. The observatory of the cape is situated 4 or five miles inward from the cape so as to have a horizon unobstructed by the table mountain to the south.[1] Sir J Herschels observatory is at a smaller distance from the city and is obstructed in its horizon to the west by the mountain. This however is of little consequence since his object is merely to sweep the horizon for celestial objects of intrest. Sir J cannot fail to make interesting observations for the same reason that a botanist visiting an unexplored region will be sure to descover some new plants.[2]

Cape town is crowded with people of colour of all nations. The only ones of these who will work are the Mallay population but they are revengefull

[1] The horizon from the west to the southwest was actually partially obstructed by the mountain. David Gill, *A History and Description of the Royal Observatory, Cape of Good Hope* (London, 1913), p. x.
[2] Herschel's work at the Cape, where he arrived after Henderson's departure, was an extension into the southern skies of his father's survey of double stars, clusters, and nebulae. *DSB*. The paraphrase of Henderson makes a connection between natural history and natural philosophy very much in the spirit of the age.

and are not to be depended on.[3] Slavery is now abolished at the cape town.[4]

On the return passage visited St. Helena. Ships scarc[e]ly ever stop going out but almost always on return. They find a difficulty in stopping in the former case on account of the trade wind. The top of the mountan is almost allways covered with mist and the island appears to collect all the fogs of the ocean. The residence of Napoleon was very unhealthy.

The house a mean one and has now gone back to its original use namely a mill house. A new house was commenced by the government for the unfortunate Emperor on a large scale and of fine finish but the prisoner did not live to see it compleeted. It is now ocupied by the governor.

The grave of the Emperor is in a very pretty place—surrounded by treas.[5] Little motion of the ship in the tropical latitudes.

Accompanied Mr Henderson to Mr Russells rooms where the experiments are making on the subject of waves.[6]

---

[3] In his May 1833 letter of resignation, Henderson included among "considerable drawbacks" at the observatory "the state of the bulk of the population from whom servants must be taken and other aid applied for" (quoted in Gill, p. xvii). The Cape Malays, a Muslim population, were valued as skilled artisans and were generally regarded as lawabiding and reserved. I. D. du Plessis, *The Cape Malays* (Cape Town, 1972).

[4] In 1833 the House of Commons had passed an act, effective August 1834, abolishing slavery in the British colonies.

[5] A chronicler of Napoleon's exile at St. Helena termed the location "one of the favored spots of the world" in regard to climate. Henderson evidently stopped there during the windy and rainy winter season.

Napoleon's residence, Longwood, erected in the eighteenth century, was originally a cowshed and barn. The space was later converted into living quarters. Lacking cellars and crawl spaces, almost all of the rooms were very damp. Following Napoleon's death in 1821 the house was abandoned and later restored to farm purposes.

Napoleon's desire to be buried in Paris was frustrated until 1840 when his body was taken from the burial place on St. Helena to Les Invalides.

Norwood Young, *Napoleon in Exile: St. Helena (1815–1821)*, 2 vols. (Philadelphia, 1915), quotation from *1*:153.

[6] A blank space follows this in the diary, perhaps left by Henry with the intention of copying rough notes here at a later time. We have not located any account by Henry of Russell's wave experiments. For a detailed account of the experiments, see "Report of the Committee on Waves, Appointed by the British Association in Bristol in 1836...," *BAAS Report, 1837* (1838), part 1:417–496. No experiments are recorded for the date of Henry's visit; Russell may have taken time out to familiarize Henry with the work in general. In a letter to Lewis R. Gibbes of December 27, 1837 (printed below), Henry mentions witnessing the experiments.

TO HARRIET HENRY

Mary Henry Copy,[1] Family Correspondence,
Henry Papers, Smithsonian Archives

Edinburgh. Aug. 16 1837.

My dear dear little wife—I have been received in this city with much kindness and attention; Mr. Henderson the astronomer royal first took me in tow, then a brother-in-law of Mr. Faraday,[2] next Mr. Robison secretary of the Royal Society of this city and son of the author of Robison's Mechanical Philosophy, a book you have often seen me use.[3] Prof. Forbes is on the continent but I met him in London in the Spring.

A few days after my arrival <*in Edinburgh*> Mr Fresnel[4] of Paris, with whom I had formed an acquaintance in that city came to Edinburgh to visit for the French Government the several scotch light houses, and to make a report on the same.[5] The Commissioners of the Northern Lights, as they are called, to show him due respect and through him to his government ordered

---

[1] Mary Henry and her transcribers made two variant copies of the letter, one in longhand and one in typescript. We have reconstructed Henry's original letter from the more complete longhand copy, with emendations from the typescript.

[2] George Buchanan.

[3] The Robison work in the Henry Library is *A System of Mechanical Philosophy*, 4 vols. (Edinburgh, 1822), edited by David Brewster.

[4] Léonor-François Fresnel, Secretary of the French Lighthouse Commission, identified above, Soleil to Henry, June 21, 1837, footnote 4.

[5] The Scottish lighthouse system under the direction of the Commissioners of Northern Lights—separate from the English and Irish administrations—was modernized in the nineteenth century according to French models. The Fresnels, Léonor and his brother Augustin, dominated French lighthouse technology. Augustin's invention of the dioptric light, utilizing a lens rather than mirrors to focus the beam, revolutionized lighthouse techniques.

Scotland only followed France itself and Holland in adopting the Fresnel improvements. (By mid-century the Americans, too, converted to the Fresnel technology.) Alan Stevenson (1807–1865; *DNB*), of the civil engineering family long-connected with Scottish lighthouses, was instrumental in the introduction of French methods into Scotland. In 1834 Stevenson was dispatched to France by the Commissioners of Northern Lights with "full power to take such steps for acquiring a perfect knowledge of the dioptric system, and forming an opinion on its merits, as he should find necessary" (*Encyclopaedia Britannica*, 8th ed., s.v. "Lighthouses," p. 479). Received generously by Léonor Fresnel, Stevenson wrote a detailed report in favor of the French methods which induced the Scot Commissioners to convert selected lights from catoptric to dioptric, beginning with Inchkeith in 1835. Alan Stevenson's brother Thomas (1818–1887, father of Robert Louis Stevenson; *DNB*) assisted in transferring French instrumentation. The strong influence of the Fresnels on the Northern Lighthouses is plainly seen in Alan Stevenson's excellent article on "Lighthouses" in *Encyclopaedia Britannica*, 8th ed., especially pp. 471, 475, 479. Léonor Fresnel later sent Henry, via David Bailie Warden, some lighthouse literature. Fresnel to Warden, January 23, 1838, Warden Papers, Library of Congress. The Henry Library contains publications presented by Alan Stevenson.

For the introduction of the Fresnel dioptric lamp into American lighthouses, see *United States Light-House Establishment, Public Documents and Extracts Relating to Light-Houses, Light-Vessels, and Illuminating Apparatus . . .* (Washington, 1871), pp. 453, 590.

a steam-boat to be in readiness to convey him to the Bell Rock Light House[6] and the other lights in the neighborhood of Edinburgh at any time he might desire to visit these important objects. It was agreed that the excursion should take place on Friday and I was invited to be one of the party. We started at five o'clock in the morning with the prospect of a very unpleasant day from wind and rain. When we mustered at the steam-boat warf not half the number were present, the greater part of the company which consisted of the most prominent citizens of Edinburgh had been frightened into giving up the excursion by the aspect of the weather. There were but two of the gentle sex present, one the wife of M. Fresnel. I had been introduced to M[dme] Fresnel in Paris and had met her again at Mr. Robison's in this city. She speaks a few words of english and with my bad french I was able to hold rather an interesting conversation with her on our outward passage to the Bell Rock. She has been in America is a daughter of the celebrated Count Real[7] who purchased a large estate on the banks of the St. Lawrence. She has been in Albany. The Bell Rock light house stands on a rock which is entirely covered by the waves at least half of the time. It is forty-five miles from Edinburgh and twelve miles from the nearest point of land. As we advanced into the ocean the weather gave signs of becoming more pleasant and at about ten o'clock as we were approaching the Bell the sun shone through the fog. The light house however could not be seen although anxiously looked for by the captain and several others who had climbed to the top mast of the steamer for the purpose. After some suspense, the sound of a distant bell was heard as if from the bosom of the vasty deep and in a little while after the glazed top of the light house was seen above the fog, a beautiful object like an airy castle resting on the clouds in mid air. As we approached the graceful outline of the structure became visible. Our steamer came as near as safety would permit, we embarked in two boats and were assisted at the foot of a ladder by three light men, dressed in their uniform blue frock coat with buttons stamped with figure of light houses, in honour of the visit and intelligent looking men. . . . We landed on an

[6] The Bell Rock, or Inch Cape, Lighthouse posed extraordinary engineering problems due to its location twelve miles from the nearest land on a reef that was twelve feet under water at high tide. The construction, begun in 1807, was directed by Robert Stevenson (1772–1850, *DNB*), engineer of the Northern Lights Board and father of Alan Stevenson. Smeaton's Eddystone Lighthouse provided the basic model. Alan Stevenson, *A Rudimentary Treatise on Lighthouses* (London, 1850), part I, pp. 12–15. Robert Stevenson, *Account of the Bell Rock Lighthouse* (Edinburgh, 1824). Robert Stevenson, "Account of the Erection of the Bell Rock Lighthouse," *Edinburgh Philosophical Journal*, 1825, *12*:18–38.

[7] Pierre-François Réal (1757–1834) was an important political figure in France during the Revolution and under the Empire. Around 1820, during a brief period of exile, Réal lived on a farm on the Canadian side of the St. Lawrence River. *Nouvelle Biographie Universelle.*

iron grating which extends in different directions around the base of the light house and at low water enables the lone inmates to vary the monotony of their residence by fishing; it serves also as a landing place for necessary stores. The entrance to the structure is on the side about forty feet above the surface of the water and to this we were obliged to climb by means of a long ladder. We were surprised and pleased with the neat and compact arrangement of every article within the house. It is divided into five rooms one above the other. We passed first through the store room where the oil for the great lamps and the provisions for the keepers are deposited. We next passed into the kitchen, where a very cheerful fire of coal was blazing in a small grate. The cupboard and culinary utensils were arranged with a view to the greatest degree of compactness and convenience. The next room to which we ascended was the bed-room; this is divided into two apartments, the floor covered with oil cloth and all the furniture of good material. There are accommodations for six persons for sleeping although only three men at a time are inhabitants of the rock. Provision is made for the inspectors who may chance to be obliged to pass a night on the tower. At the head of each berth in a small case I observed a bible. In the section above the bed-room there is an apartment elegantly furnished with carpet, table, book case &c. called the parlor or Strangers room. This is also provided with a small bed, a well selected library, a telescope and a bust of Mr. Stevenson,[8] the engineer of the Light-house. Above this room is the fifth division the Light chamber. On a large iron frame in the centre of this room are suspended twenty argand lamps arranged so as to form a regular figure or the four sides of a square.[9] Half of these lamps have red glass shades before them and behind each is a bright reflector, and as the whole apparatus is made to revolve by clock machinery it appears at a distance like an ever changing light, alternately red and white. The light room is sometimes called the Lantern and is glazed on all sides by very large panes of glass a quarter of an inch thick. The glass is required to be of this thickness on account of the force of the waves for although the lantern is nearly 150 feet above the usual level of the water, in a great storm the sea has been known to break over the very top and cause the tower strong as it is to tremble to its foundation. The glass is also required to be of great strength to prevent its being broken by thousands of birds which in a storm are blown off from

---

[8] Robert Stevenson.

[9] The Bell Rock light used parabolic reflectors and flame from Argand lamps, named after their inventor Aimé Argand. His lamps were especially favored in Northern Lighthouses. Argand's chief improvements (ca. 1784) were to form the wick into a hollow cylinder, in order to ventilate the flame, and to add a chimney. Alan Stevenson, *Rudimentary Treatise*, part I, pp. 15, 66–70. *Encyclopaedia Britannica*, 8th ed., s.v. "Argand," "Lighthouses."

land towards night. They see the light at a distance, and attempting to fly as it were out of the darkness which surrounds them, they dash against the glass and are often found dead in hundreds in the circular gallery which surrounds the lantern. On one occasion a large wild goose flew with such force against the glass as to break through, breaking at the same time one of the lamps. Every part of the establishment is in the most perfect order. It is not only fitted up with neatness but with an appearance of richness. The railings of the stairs are of polished brass; all the apparatus of the light house and the reservoirs for the oil are of the same material. This gives labor to the light men but is conducive of good order and a certain refinement of mind necessary to the proper discharge of their duty. There are four persons belonging to the establishment, all men of character. Three of these are on the Bell at the same time while one is on shore with his family. They each remain six weeks on the rock and then have two weeks vacation on shore. One of the men informed me that he had lived in this way for upwards of twenty years and that he always grew weary of being on land before the end of the two weeks. How accommodating to varying circumstances are the nature and feelings of man since he can willingly and cheerfully consign himself for nine months of the year to this lone prison. I forgot to mention that an album is kept in the strangers room, in which all visitors are asked to enter their names. These are however not numerous since no one is allowed to enter the light house unless by a permission from some of the Commissioners and from its distant and insulated situation few comparatively have ever been in it. I was probably the first American who had subscribed his name. Sir Walter Scott in 1819 or 20 made a tour around Scotland in the Light house Yacht and thus visited the Bell-Rock. He entered with his name a few lines of poetry in the Album.[10]

Far on the bosom of the deep
O'er the wild waves my watch I keep
A ruddy gem of changeful light
Bound on the dusky brow of night
The Seaman bids my lustre hail
And scorns to strike his timorous sail.[11]
Reef covered at high water to the depth of twelve feet.[12]
Near the south side of the harbor of Arboth there is a handsome signal

---

[10] Scott visited Bell Rock on July 30, 1814, writing the poem *Pharos Loquitur* in the visitor's book. The poem was first publicized by Robert Stevenson. John Lockhart, *Memoirs of the Life of Sir Walter Scott, Bart.*, 7 vols. (Edinburgh, 1837), 3:137. Lockhart includes Scott's diary of the lighthouse tour.

[11] We have omitted some repetitious material inserted by the copyist.

[12] There is an arrow indicating that the transcriber considered shifting this sentence to the end of the following paragraph.

tower about fifty feet high for the purpose of communicating with the Keeper. The light house is about twelve miles from the nearest land, that is Arboth.

Owes its present name to the pious care of an Abbot of Arboth, who placed on a vessel anchored near it, a bell which was rung by the motion of the waves and thus gave warning of the hidden danger.

Tradition of a dutch sailor who wantonly removed the bell and as a retribution was shipwrecked, and perished with all his men on the very spot. This is described beautifully by Southey but the passage lines are too long to quote.[13]

Whole height 115 feet. 13 feet diameter at top, 42 at base, 6 flats floored with stone, 2 store rooms, 1 oil room, 3 kitchens.

We lingered on the "Bell" until the light men warned us that we could stay with safety no longer as the rising waves would soon cover the landing place, and in that case it would be impossible for us to leave the rock until the next low water. As it was we had waited rather too long, the waves at intervals were dashing over the iron platform against the base of the tower. I found however no difficulty in getting into the boat by following a re-tiring wave and springing into the vessel before the surge returned. Not so the person who followed me. He was mounted on the back of one of the light men, when about half the distance from the boat the carrier stumbled and his load fell but fortunately not in the water. The ladies were without ceremony lifted by the Light house men and carried to the boat. We got clear without accident, although one of the boats was nearly capsized by the bad management of the sailors.

We next visited the Light House on the Island of May[14] which is not as interesting being on a large island about twenty miles from Edinburgh. He[re] we dined. A most sumptuous entertainment had been provided at the order and expense of the Commissioners of Northern Lighthouses. After dinner as is customary in Great Britain a number of toasts and speeches were given and among the rest I was called on but as I had antici-pated the affair I was not unprepared, and I gave a sketch of the optical discoveries of the brother of Mr. Fresnel, the inventor of the present system of light houses used in France and now introduced into Scotland. Also the

---

[13] A terror to mariners, the reef inspired a rich mythology. Alan Stevenson, *Rudimentary Treatise*, part I, p. 12. Stevenson mentions Southey's 1802 ballad, *The Inchcape Rock*, re-counting the deeds of the Abbot of Aber-brothok, who attached the warning bell, and Ralph the Rover, who cut loose the Inchcape bell but later perished by his own deed.

[14] The Isle of May light was the first to be converted by Stevenson to the Fresnel dioptric system. In Henry's pamphlet collection is a presentation copy of Alan Stevenson's *Report to a Committee of the Commissioners of the Northern Lighthouses . . . on the New Dioptric Light of the Isle of May* (Edinburgh, 1836).

discoverer of some of the most remarkable properties of light such as that two rays thrown on each other in a certain manner produce instead of more intense light absolute darkness.[15] My address was received apparently with much interest and was not unacceptable to Mr. Fresnel. We left the Island of May after dark in order to witness the operation of the light which was of the new french construction. After a pleasant passage we arrived in the city of Edinburgh about half past twelve at night.

I have been constantly and profitably employed since my arrival in Scotland and regret that I did not curtail my visit in France. . . . There are many things in Scotland like those of Paris. The *cowgate*[16] a street in the old town of Edinburgh is precisely like the *rues* of Paris and it is said that Charles 10[17] during his stay in the north was particularly partial to this dirty passage on account of the similarity. The number of families in different "flats" in the same house, the narrow lanes and enclosed courts are all like Paris.

I have made a hurried visit to Roslyn Castle,[18] was driven there by—

I have just received your letter of July 14. . . . The intelligence that Willy is affected with Shortness of breath has scarcely been out of my mind since reading your letter. I hope he will outgrow the trouble and that you will find him sufficiently strong to receive a few lessons a day. I am not in favor of teaching children things beyond their age but there are some branches of education which if not acquired early can never afterwards be attained in perfection unless at the expense of double the amount of much more valuable time. But the foundation of a good constitution is the most important for without this his mental acquirements will be of little use. While actively engaged in the prosecution of my objects [of] travel I do not feel that I am far from home but the moment my mind is a little relaxed I feel a loneliness and longing for home which would almost induce me to start immediately without going further or waiting for the meeting of the British Association. But now that I have crossed the wide waters and since I am in the way of gathering much knowledge which may be of use to others as well as myself, <*and will in all human probability never again have the same or equal advantages*>, it would be folly not to make the best of my advantages and accomplish as much as possible before my return. I shall leave Edinburgh in a [few] days and then commences as it were my return

[15] Fresnel's experiments on optical interference—the effect referred to by Henry—were the key to his experimental proof and theoretical commitment to the wave theory of light. For a full account, see *DSB*, s.v. "Fresnel."

[16] Cowgate runs from Grassmarket at the southern border of the old city. For a contemporary description of the old city, see John Burford, *Description of a View of the City of Edinburgh* (London, 1825), pp. 4–5.

[17] After being overthrown, Charles X, King of France from 1824 to 1830, retreated to Holyrood Castle in Edinburgh.

[18] Roslin Castle is about seven miles from Edinburgh.

<*towards home*>. I am now at the greatest distance from those I love and every mile will be rendered more pleasant with the thought of an approximation towards home. I intend to return to London after the meeting of the Association which takes place on the tenth of September and will probably sail about the first of October in company with Henry James. . . . DeWitt left me in Paris and intended to sail on the Wellington. God bless you my dear dear Wife. Your own J.H.

One little spot is still left—Tell Willy from Papa that he must study a little every day and learn to read as soon as possible. Papa hopes he will one day be able to assist him in the Hall and read about steam engines and all the other machines.

FROM STEPHEN ALEXANDER

General Manuscript Collection, Firestone Library, Princeton University

Princeton, Aug. 19th, 1837

My dear Brother,

I almost steal an hour this evening to say that I have tried some experiments relative to the continuance of the sensory impression which produces the sensation of touch[1]—and with success.[2]

---

[1] Alexander's interest in the persistence of the sensation of touch was unusual for the day. Compared to vision or hearing, touch was an unexplored sense. The only major study of touch prior to Alexander was produced by Ernst Heinrich Weber (1795–1878, *DSB*). An anatomy professor at Leipzig, Weber had published the results of a number of experiments on touch in his *De pulsu, resorptione, auditu et tactu: annotationes anatomicae et physiologicae* (Leipzig, 1834). This work was read by Alexander and might have been part of the inspiration for the experiments reported in this letter. However, even Weber had ignored the phenomenon of the persistence of tactile sensation after the removal of the stimuli. Not until 1870 did experimentalists generally note its existence.

Alexander's basic premise in his experiments was the existence of a phenomenon for touch analogous to that for sight. Persistence of vision was a well-known phenomenon. There were a number of philosophical toys available to illustrate it. Henry's interest in it dates back to at least 1828, and Alexander was certainly aware of it before he read Weber.

There is no indication that Alexander's work had any impact on the physiologists and experimental psychologists usually awarded the laurels by historians for their work on the sense of touch. No doubt this is due to Alexander's reluctance to publish. The only written version of his work is a brief paper (really no more than an abstract) in the *Proceedings of the American Association for the Advancement of Science*. Moreover, at a time when the trend was toward quantitative work, Alexander's experiments were still qualitative.

Stephen Alexander, "On Some Special Analogies in the Phenomena Presented by the Senses of Sight and Touch," *Proceedings of the American Association for the Advancement of Science*, 1851, 6:365–366; Edwin G. Boring, *Sensation and Perception in the History of Experimental Psychology* (New York, 1942), pp. 465–466, 475–479, 487–509; *Henry Papers*, 2:124–126.

[2] Among the experiments exhibited to the AAAS meeting of 1851 were the four he mentions in this letter.

A small iron pulley with a long axis was connected with a much larger wheel by a band passing around both. The axis had been prepared by filing an iron skewer and was, consequently, in some parts, *flat*; but when made to revolve rapidly appeared throughout to the eye & felt to the hand (when the latter was pressed lightly against it) as would a *round* bar whose diameter was equal to the flat one.

2. When a circular piece of wood was attached to the axis so that the latter penetrated it in the direction of a diameter of a circular section of the wood, and the apparatus was caused to revolve with rapidity, the circular disc appeared and *felt* as if it were of a spherical form, thus presenting both an occular & *tangible* illustration of the mode of describing this solid of revolution. A triangular disc would if treated in the same way, when properly fastened to the axis, have doubtless appeared & *felt* as tho' it were conical & a rectangle as tho' it were cylindrical &c &c.

3. A number of large pins were cut off so as to leave but about ½ inch of the upper end of each and then inserted into the convex circumference of a wooden drum, so as to leave the heads to project. The first was inserted near the edge of the surface; the second the breadth of a pin's-head farther within &c until the series reached the other edge—each being, however, some considerable part of the circumference distant from the other. A second series was then made to pass from the last so as to cross the drum in a contrary direction & to terminate at the place where the first commenced. The whole convex surface of the drum would if developed appear something like this

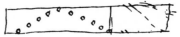

When this was made to revolve with a *moderate* velocity the sensation was that of an oscillation from side to side upon the surface of the drum.

4. Upon the surface of a circular disc, an arrangement of this sort was made. A small circle was described so as to touch the larger & its circumference divided (see figure) into 12 equal parts & through the points of division circles were described, concenric with the edge of the disc: then from a to b was laid off 1/12 of the circumference of the innermost seen in the figure, from a' to b' 2/12 of the second &c &c. When this (having pins driven as before at b, b', &c) was placed at right angles to the axis of the pulley & caused to revolve the sensation was that of a motion similar to the eccentric of a steamboat.

I have not a moment more—hope to write again soon.[3]

Your's as ever
Stephen

[3] There are two later letters from Alexander to Henry on this subject, both dated August 30, 1837 (General Manuscript Collection, Princeton University Library), one being an expanded form of the other. In these Alexander repeated his earlier experiments, described further experiments along the same line, and developed his concept of the analogies between the senses.

"VISIT TO MELROSE ABBEY[1] TO DR BREWSTER"
Pocket Notebook,[2] Henry Papers, Smithsonian Archives

[August 19–21, 1837][3]

Started from Edinburgh Sat 4 oclock. Arrived at the village of Melrose[4] at 9 o'clock. Nothing remarkable on the way except saw coal pitts.

Picture of Melrose Abby. A fellow traveller gave me the price of provisions in this country—Beef 6[d] per lb, Butter 5[d], Bread 8[d] per loaf. A labourer receives from 1/6 to 2/— per day. Put up at village Inn. Bed with slats one of which broke had a bad nights rest. Took up old newspaper which gave an account of the affair of the Little [?Bilt].[5] Started after breakfast for the house of Dr Brewster at a place called Allery.[6] Passed a chain bridge for horse and foot passengers which cost 500£ and pays a total of a ½ penny for each foot passenger.

[1] The Cistercians began construction of an abbey on this spot in 1136. It was destroyed in 1322 and again in 1384, but rebuilt each time. However, after the destruction during the Reformation it was left in ruins, an "exquisite example of medieval Gothic." Sir Walter Scott described the Abbey in the *Lay of the Last Minstrel.* Among those buried on the grounds of the Abbey are many of Scott's historical characters. Also buried here is Sir David Brewster. His tomb sits next to the Abbey wall, right under a window. Brewster himself chose the inscription on the tomb: THE LORD IS MY LIGHT. William S. Crockett, *Scott Country,* 2d ed. (London, 1902), pp. 292–301.

[2] Henry wrote his impressions of his visit to David Brewster in a soft-back book which was small enough to slip into a pocket. Initially, he jotted things down in pencil while the events were fresh in his mind. His remarks are often disjointed and cryptic. At some later date he began to rewrite and expand the account; this time he chose ink, writing right over the original penciled account. For some unknown reason, however, Henry ended the rewrite in the middle of the story. This notebook is identified as 13266 in the Henry Papers control system.

[3] Henry's trip to Melrose Abbey occurred sometime between his letters to Harriet of August 16, 1837 (printed above) and August 27, 1837 (printed below). His departure on Saturday pinpoints the dates of the visit.

[4] In Roxburgh County, approximately thirty miles south-southeast of Edinburgh.

[5] Unidentified; Henry's spelling is unclear.

[6] David Brewster's home from 1827 until his death in 1868. It was on the north side of the River Tweed, across from Melrose Abbey. Crockett, *Scott Country,* pp. 308–309.

Sir D[avid] at home an interesting looking man with young face and hair perfectly white medium size very cordial in manner. Good house with sky light in the middle of the roof and the latter descending each way to the middle of the house. The water drawn off from the valleys by pipes. A number of american books on the table.

Mrs B is the daughter of McPherson the author of Osians poems[7] a very interesting lady friendly and agreeable. Daughter[8] about 16, frank and unaffected.

Mrs B although not young is according to my taste quite handsome. In a conversation on revivals Sir D said he thought they were no more improbable than the discoveries in light had been. He had an accident[9] with nitric acid, a tube of it had broken in his hand and flew over his face hands & he was confined to bed for a 2 weeks. He saw a halo around the candle which indicated that the cornea had been acted upon so as to become rough like a plated of glass sprinkled with dust. He should have washed with alcaly but did not think of it at the time.

Went with the family to the village church. The same which Sir Walter Scott was in the habit of attending. His seat was in the gallery the place of honor in Scotland. The church was very plane but large. On coming out was introduced to the original of Dominy Sampson[10] the tutor of Sir W. S children. He is said to be proud of the distinction although he sat for only half the picture. Homely and is noted for the use of the exclamation prodigious.

[7] In 1760 James Macpherson (1736–1796) published *Fragments of Ancient Poetry.* Two years later he published *Fingal,* an epic poem in six books. *Temora,* another epic poem, was published in 1763. All three works were alleged by Macpherson to be translations of third-century Highland Gaelic poetry originally composed by Ossian, the son of the warrior Fingal. Although highly popular with and influential upon the Romantic writers of Europe, Macpherson's poems were highly controversial. Their authenticity was challenged almost immediately, but it was not until 1797, after Macpherson's death, that the Highland Society of Scotland appointed a committee to investigate his translations. The committee's report, issued in 1805, concluded that Macpherson had edited the original poems rather freely, often inserting his own work where gaps existed in the original. It is now believed that he combined a number of traditional ballads from the sixth century and later epochs into a single epic, adding material as he saw fit, and frequently mistranslating the Gaelic. *DNB*; *Encyclopaedia Britannica*, 1970 ed.

Juliet Macpherson (d. 1850) was one of four illegitimate children fathered by Macpherson. She married Brewster in 1810. *DNB*, s.v. "James Macpherson."

[8] Margaret Maria Brewster Gordon was born in 1823 and was therefore younger than Henry thought. She wrote a biography of her father. Margaret Maria Gordon, *The Home Life of Sir David Brewster*, 2d ed. (Edinburgh, 1870), p. 110.

[9] This incident occurred in the latter part of 1831. Brewster's literary output was adversely affected for some time afterwards. Gordon, *Home Life of Sir David Brewster*, pp. 154–156.

[10] Dominie Sampson is a character in Sir Walter Scott's novel *Guy Mannering.* The man to whom Henry was introduced was George Thomson, the son of the parish minister of Melrose and a tutor in the Scott family. While many of Dominie Sampson's characteristics were borrowed from Thomson, others

Saw a lady with whom I travelled from Antwerp but had in my immagination made her a dutch woman instead of a Scotch one—so much for first impressions.

Every part of this region is made classic by the pen of Sir Walter. Directly in front of the house of Sir D B are three hills said to have been thrown up by Michael Scott[11] the Devil master. A stream of water called the river Tweed is about the size of what we would call a creek flows through the beautiful valley. At Dinner we had thick Scotch broth, butter without salt,[12] preserves from the East Indias made of rice sugar and the otta of roses[13]—sent by the son. Has two sons in the East one in the government and the other in the civil service. A third son[14] in the English army now in Scotland will probably soon visit America.

Sir Davids opinion of Bacons rules for making investigations the same as my own.[15] This is expressed in an article in the Edinburgh review.[16] No

---

were taken from James Sanson, a tutor at the Manse of Earlston (4½ miles from Melrose). Crockett, *Scott Country*, p. 333; John Buchan, *Sir Walter Scott* (1932; reprint ed., Port Washington, N.Y., 1967), pp. 138–139; W. S. Crockett, *Footsteps of Scott* (London, 1908), pp. 110–111.

[11] Michael Scot (died ca. 1235), a "Wizard" renowned for his learning, is supposed to be buried at Melrose Abbey (according to Sir Walter Scott's *Lay of the Last Minstrel*). Among the many legends connected with his name is the cleaving in three of the Eildon Hills, a series of rises south of Melrose. Crockett, *Footsteps of Scott*, pp. 160–161.

Legends aside, Michael has some significance to the history of science because of his astrological activities and his translations of Arabic philosophical and scientific works. Through his efforts, some of Aristotle's writings and those of Ibn Rushd (Averroës) were introduced to the West. *DSB*.

[12] Henry twice mentions that Brewster serves him salt-free butter. Since salt was used to preserve butter, the implication is that Brewster's butter was very fresh. George E. Fussell, *The English Dairy Farmer, 1500–1900* (London, 1966), p. 217.

[13] Otto or attar of roses is the fragrant oil obtained from the petals of the rose. *Oxford English Dictionary*.

[14] Brewster had four sons: James (1812–1852) was in the Bengal civil service; David E. (b. 1815) served with the government in India and married the daughter of a member of Her Majesty's Indian Army; Henry C. (b. 1816)

was the soldier; the fourth son was Charles M. (1813–1828). Gordon, *Home Life of Sir David Brewster*, pp. 82, 108–109, 140, 193, 230, 268.

[15] Brewster argued energetically and often that the philosophy of Francis Bacon (1561–1626, *DSB*) had no influence on either the methodology of scientists or the history of science, although he admitted that nonscientists often thought the contrary. Because Brewster's attacks on Baconianism show a great consistency, we shall cite only two such assaults.

Brewster's concluding chapter to his *Memoirs of the Life, Writings, and Discoveries of Sir Isaac Newton*, 2 vols. (1855; reprint ed., New York, 1965) is partly an attempt to answer those individuals who had characterized Newton as a follower of Bacon. In this chapter Brewster offered the four basic points of his anti-Baconianism (2:400–406). First, he argued that the writings of Bacon were not responsible for the introduction of the inductive method to the scientific community. Brewster cites the philosophies of Tycho Brahe, Copernicus, William Gilbert, Galileo, and Leonardo da Vinci as being characterized by a recognition of the need for both experimental research and the gradual advancement from facts to the determination of causes, two essential elements of Bacon's thought. Secondly, Brewster held that the specific process invented by Bacon to investigate nature was useless for conducting scientific investigations, and in fact had never been used in a successful inquiry. By this he meant the method Bacon laid out in his *Novum Organum*: the gathering of facts, the arrangement of the facts in tables, and the drawing of inductive inferences from those tables. The third point was that the development of science had not in the least been aided by Bacon. Speaking specifically of Newton, Brewster wrote (2:403): "he would have enriched science with the same splendid discoveries if the name and the writings of Bacon had never been heard of." Finally, Brewster argued that the essence of scientific advancement was not the Baconian collecting of facts, avoiding hypotheses, but the ability to imagine all the possible consequences of the discovery of a particular fact, along with the willingness to test those consequences. The great scientist differed from his lesser colleagues "by the excursions of his own fancy into new and fertile paths, far removed from ordinary observation" (2:406). Imagination and speculation were essential parts of the process of scientific discovery, as long as the "wildest conceptions are all subjected to the rigid test of experiment" (2:406). Brewster gave a more succinct rendering of his philosophy in a letter to James Forbes, dated November 13, 1830, and printed in Richard Olson, *Scottish Philosophy and British Physics: A Study in the Foundations of the Victorian Scientific Style* (Princeton, 1975), p. 238. He wrote: "Forget entirely all that you have heard of Lord Bacon's Philosophy. Give full reins to your imagination. Form hypotheses without number." Of course Brewster added the warning that Forbes should put all his hypotheses *"to the test of experiment."*

Henry's position on Bacon can be gathered from the introductory lecture to his course in natural philosophy (Henry's students' notebooks are in the Rare Book and Manuscript Library, Princeton University, and the Henry Papers, Smithsonian Archives) and from his lectures to the Peabody Institute of Baltimore (Henry Papers, Smithsonian Archives). The latter are a much fuller rendering of his views, and while they were delivered in 1866, their similarity to earlier statements of Henry makes us feel confident that the Peabody lectures are a summary of Henry's thought rather than a later evolution.

Of the four elements of Brewster's assault on Bacon, Henry agreed with two. He fully concurred with Brewster's belief that no working scientist used the specific method laid out by Bacon. Indeed, Henry believed that many scientists were unfamiliar with Bacon's method. Henry also accepted Brewster's position that the hypothesis was an indispensable element in the progress of science. The proper

method of scientific investigation was, in Henry's opinion, the adopting of a hypothesis to explain an observed phenomenon, the deduction of the logical consequences of adopting that hypothesis, and the testing of the consequences by experiment or observation. One can easily find illustrations of this method in Henry's work. Where the two men differed was in the role Bacon played in the development of science. Bacon's eloquent appeals to the power of experimentation and observation, as well as his recognition and enumeration of the causes of error (Bacon's four idols), made him, in Henry's eyes, one of the most important pioneers in the use of the inductive philosophy. Bacon's role was that of propagandist or advocate for inductive reasoning.

A comparison of Henry's attitude toward Bacon and scientific methodology with that of contemporary, English-speaking natural philosophers—divided by historians into the Common Sense empiricists, with Brewster representing one wing of that school, and the Idealists, personified during this period by William Whewell—shows he had much in common with the empiricists (samples of the writings of both schools, however, exist in the Henry Library). But the one natural philosopher whose perspective was closest to Henry's was probably John F. W. Herschel (Henry's heavily annotated copy of Herschel's *Preliminary Discourse on the Study of Natural Philosophy* [London, 1830] still survives in the Henry Library), who has been claimed for both schools by intellectual historians. Herschel had an engraving of a bust of Bacon on his title page, as well as much praise for the philosopher, yet he argued that "a facility in framing [hypotheses] . . . is one of the most valuable qualities a philosopher can possess" (p. 204; Henry marked this passage in his personal copy).

Praise of Bacon by the generation of American scientists active from 1815 through 1845 has previously been misinterpreted by historians—George Daniels being one of the primary offenders—to mean that these scientists used a "Baconian" methodology, linked to the prevailing philosophy (Common Sense empiricism) and antitheoretical in thrust. But there is no necessary connection between praising Bacon and restricting one's scientific research to a form of naive empiricism. To praise Bacon was a simple reflex action, a concession to the philosopher's strength as a symbol. Such praise said little, if anything, about the manner in which a scientific investigation was conducted. As Daniels himself ad-

working man of science advocates Bacons method. Whewell of the same opinion.[17] Sir David first discovered the action of a mineral to produce depolarization.[18,19] Next the polarization by transmission[20] happening to look

mitted, allegiance to Baconianism often appeared merely verbal, and Bacon was an umbrella large enough to cover rather diverse approaches to the philosophy of science.

Daniels's greatest failure, however, was not considering the American scientific community within a larger scientific context. American scientists were not isolated from Europe; for example, Henry, Bache, and Elias Loomis were all there in 1837. Viewed from an international perspective, American scientists were not naive empiricists to be put down, but research scientists collecting data in the same manner as their contemporary European colleagues. Their model was not Bacon, but individuals such as John Herschel and Alexander Humboldt. Like some of their colleagues across the Atlantic, they did not exclude hypotheses, but used them, albeit under careful controls. Even Samuel Tyler, Daniels's chief defender of Baconianism in America, believed it legitimate to use hypotheses as *"provisional judgment,"* to be either confirmed or denied by experiment. What the American scientific community meant when it attacked hypotheses was the same thing that some members of the British scientific community meant—an attack on the practice of accepting a theory as the actual description of reality without experimental verification.

Richard Olson, *Scottish Philosophy and British Physics*, pp. 106–111, 252–270; Walter F. Cannon, "John Herschel and the Idea of Science," *Journal of the History of Ideas*, 1961, 22:215–239; Walter F. Cannon, "History in Depth: The Early Victorian Period," *History of Science*, 1964, 3:22–24; Geoffrey Cantor, "The Reception of the Wave Theory of Light in Britain: A Case Study Illustrating the Role of Methodology in Scientific Debate," *Historical Studies in the Physical Sciences*, 1975, 6:109–132; George H. Daniels, *American Science in the Age of Jackson* (New York, 1968), pp. 63–85, 119, 198; Samuel Tyler, *The Progress of Philosophy in the Past and in the Future*, 2d ed. (Philadelphia, 1868), p. 68; Susan Faye Cannon, *Science in Culture: The Early Victorian Period* (New York, 1978), pp. 73–105.

[16] We have been unable to locate an article in the *Edinburgh Review* attributed to Brewster which contains direct remarks on Bacon's

methodology. However, Brewster's review of William Whewell's *History of the Inductive Sciences, from the Earliest to the Present Times* (Edinburgh Review, 1838, 66:110–151), which was forthcoming at the time of Henry's visit, does contain some remarks about scientific methodology which were clearly anti-Baconian.

[17] About the only positive thing Brewster had to say in the above-cited review was to praise Whewell's "just apprehension of the mental process by which discoveries are made" (p. 123). Brewster approved of Whewell's position that the guess, confirmed by experiment, was an essential element in the advancement of science. Although Whewell and Brewster were antagonists over many points of science and philosophy, they did agree on the importance of the hypothesis in the process of scientific discovery and the uselessness of the Baconian method. Of course, Whewell went much further, creating a philosophy of science derived at least partly from Kant, and arguing that the acceptability of a theory was based on extraevidential considerations. *DSB*; Cantor, "The Reception of the Wave Theory of Light in Britain"; Walter F. Cannon, "William Whewell, F.R.S. (1794–1866): Contributions to Science and Learning," *Notes and Records of the Royal Society of London*, 1964, 19:176–191; Olson, *Scottish Philosophy and British Physics*, pp. 177–185; Richard E. Butts, ed., *William Whewell's Theory of Scientific Method* (Pittsburgh, 1968), pp. 3–29.

[18] During experiments conducted in the latter half of 1812, Brewster discovered that many regularly crystallized bodies possessed the power to depolarize light rays; i.e., deprive light of the properties it had obtained upon polarization. Later and more extensive experiments led Brewster to view this phenomenon as the polarization of the light rays in another plane. Brewster would also later concede the priority of the discovery of depolarization to Arago. David Brewster, "Experiments on the Depolarization of Light as Exhibited by Various Mineral, Animal, and Vegetable Bodies, with a Reference of the Phenomena to the General Principles of Polarization," *Phil. Trans.*, 1815, pp. 29–53; David Brewster, *A Treatise on New Philosophical Instruments* (Edinburgh, 1813), pp.

through piec of mica split at one End. Saw a different effet at the two extremities followed this up. In the highlands at the time used pieces of window glass. Sent account to Phil Society. Published in transactions. Young [a]nd Mr Wooliston did not contradict.[21] Afterwards much mortified to find same thing has been done by Malus.[22] Next discovery circular polarization again anticipated by Beot.[23] Disgusted but again attempted. Made

---

xiii–xiv, 335–336.

One interesting sidelight of the subsequent discussion of Brewster's optics in this notebook is Henry's apparent indifference to or unawareness of the great conflict between Brewster, representing the corpuscular theory of light, and the wave theorists. Nor does Henry seem conscious of the connection between Brewster's interest in Newton and his sympathies in optics. For Brewster's position within world optics, see Henry J. Steffens, *The Development of Newtonian Optics in England* (New York, 1977), pp. 137–149. G. N. Cantor offers a reevaluation of the controversy in physical optics in "The Historiography of 'Georgian' Optics," *History of Science*, 1978, *16*:1–21.

[19] It was at this point that Henry ceased his rewrite of his notebook.

[20] Brewster's interest in polarization was initiated by his learning in 1812 of Malus's discovery of polarization by reflection (Malus and his work will be discussed in detail below, footnote 22). After repeating Malus's experiments, Brewster went what he thought was a step further by polarizing light by transmission through a thin plate of agate. Unfortunately for Brewster's pride, Malus had already done this. David Brewster, "On Some Properties of Light," *Phil. Trans.*, 1813, pp. 101–109; David Brewster, "Optics," *Encyclopaedia Britannica*, 8th ed., *16*:539.

[21] At the time of Brewster's experiments Thomas Young was Foreign Secretary of the Royal Society of London, while William Wollaston was its Secretary. Both men were interested in optics. Young in particular monitored activities overseas. He was even in contact with the French, despite the difficulties created by the state of war between France and England. Brewster apparently thought that these two men could have saved him the embarrassment created when he claimed as original discoveries phenomena first described by Arago or Malus. Brewster's own excuse for being unfamilar with the work of the French was his relative isolation in Scotland. "Optics," *Encyclopaedia Britannica*, 8th ed., *16*:539–540.

The humiliation felt by Brewster at being anticipated and the embarrassment at having claimed a discovery as his own which was in fact another's led him to make the following bitter statement upon learning of Malus's publication on polarization by transmission: "If Malus's memoir contains results similar or analogous to these [Brewster's experiments on polarization], I must then consider the labour and anxiety which attended that series of experiments as completely lost." David Brewster, "Account of New Properties of Light," *Annals of Philosophy*, 1814, *3*:190.

[22] Étienne Louis Malus (1775–1812) was one of the first students of the École Polytechnique. On graduation in 1796 he entered the corps of engineers, eventually reaching the rank of major. His military career included participation in Napoleon's Egyptian campaign and garrison duty in Europe. From 1810 until his death he was posted in Paris.

It was during Malus's investigations in response to the Institute's proposal (1808) of a prize for an experimental and theoretical explanation of double refraction that he accidentally discovered polarization by reflection. The discovery was announced in December 1808 and published the following year. In 1811 Malus introduced the term "polarization" for the modification which light had undergone. Also appearing in 1811 was Malus's prize-winning explanation of double refraction.

Malus was recognized by his contemporaries as one of the leading figures in optics. He was elected a member of the first class of the Institute (1810); was accepted into the Société d'Arcueil, an informal group of the leading physicists and chemists in France; and was awarded the Rumford Medal by the Royal Society of London in 1811.

Maurice Crosland, *The Society of Arcueil: A View of French Science at the Time of Napoleon I* (Cambridge, Massachusetts, 1967), pp. 122–125, 301–302, 342–344; *DSB*.

[23] Actually it was Arago who first noticed the phenomenon. In 1811 he used a prism of Iceland spar to observe the two images which

new discoveries. Tea. Introduced to Mr Scott,[24] a young gentleman. No salt on butter. Sir D has now a very valuable collection of papers relative to the life of Newton,[25] collected by a Mr Coduit[26] who married the Niece[27] of Newton lately come in to the hands of Sir D. Conduit and his wife intended to write the life of the uncle death prevailed at 37 of age. Sir D amused us with reading some of the papers. A letter on a law suit.[28] A love letter of Sir Isaac to a widow lady quite philosophical.[29] Correspondence between Newton and Hook in good spirit.[30] Likeness of Mr Babbage[31] by a Lady. Book

resulted when polarized light traversed a plate of quartz cut perpendicularly to the axis of double refraction. He found that the images were of complementary colors; moreover, the colors changed when the prism was rotated. Biot's contribution, presented in papers published in 1812 and 1818, was to generalize Arago's findings and to develop a law of rotary dispersion.

Brewster had first published his account of the phenomenon in 1813, when he acknowledged both the initial discovery by Arago and the more general work of Biot. Later accounts by Brewster sometimes gave credit only to Biot (as in the account to Henry) and sometimes to both Arago and Biot.

Brewster, *Treatise on New Philosophical Instruments*, p. xiii; Brewster, "On Circular Polarization as Exhibited in the Optical Structure of the Amethyst, with Remarks on the Distribution of the Colouring Matter in that Material," *Transactions of the Royal Society of Edinburgh*, 1823, *9*:139–152; *Encyclopaedia Britannica*, 8th ed., *16*:676–677.

[24] Not identified.

[25] This is the famous Portsmouth Collection of Newton's manuscripts and correspondence, which had been the possession of his grandniece, Catherine Conduitt, Lady Lymington. Brewster was the first Newton biographer to have access to these papers, having obtained permission in June 1837 to inspect them. The scientific portion of this collection is now in the University Library, Cambridge. An auction in 1936 dispersed the remainder of the collection. Richard S. Westfall, "Introduction," Brewster, *Memoirs of Sir Isaac Newton* (New York, 1965), *1*:xxxvi; *DSB*, s.v. "Newton, Isaac."

[26] John Conduitt (1688–1737) married Newton's niece in 1717. He succeeded Newton as Master of the Mint upon Newton's death in 1727. His decision to write a biography of his uncle was due to his unhappiness with Bernard de Fontenelle's Eloge of Newton, written for the French Academy of Sciences, for which

Conduitt had supplied much of the material. *DNB*; Brewster, *Memoirs of Sir Isaac Newton*, *1*:viii–x.

[27] Catherine Barton (1679–1740) was the daughter of Newton's half-sister and a country parson. She has become the center of much historical controversy ever since Voltaire claimed that Newton exchanged his niece for an office—to be specific, that Newton allowed his niece to become the mistress of Charles Montagu, Earl of Halifax (1661–1715, *DNB*), in exchange for Halifax's support for the position as head of the mint. Considerable ink has been used in the debate over Barton's relationship to Halifax. She has been called his mistress, his secret wife, or simply his very close, but platonic friend. It is now believed that Halifax, who had known Newton since 1679 when the former had been a student at Trinity College, Cambridge, and the latter Lucasian professor there, gave Newton the post at the mint out of friendship. Barton and Montagu were probably just friends. Brewster, *Memoirs of Sir Isaac Newton*, *2*:270–281; Frank E. Manuel, *A Portrait of Isaac Newton* (Cambridge, Massachusetts, 1968), pp. 248–263; Augustus De Morgan, *Newton: His Friend: and His Niece* (London, 1885).

[28] We have been unable to identify this letter.

[29] This letter is published in Brewster, *Memoirs of Sir Isaac Newton*, *2*:211–212. It was written to Lady Elizabeth Norris in 1703 or 1704. At the time of Newton's letter, Lady Norris had already buried three husbands. Her latest, Sir William Norris (1657–1702, *DNB*), had been a student at Trinity College while Newton was a professor there. Brewster suspected that the two men became acquainted at that time. Brewster, *Memoirs of Sir Isaac Newton*, *2*:212–214.

[30] Most likely the exchange of letters of 1675/6 concerning Newton's theory of light, published in Brewster, *Memoirs of Sir Isaac Newton*, *1*:140–143.

[31] If this is a reference to Charles Babbage,

will be published in the course of a year.[32] Octavo. S W S.[33] the ugliest man Mrs B ever saw yet his pictures are likenesses and all handsom.

The picture of Dr T Young in the National Gallery too much like a dandy[34] somewhat like Sir D knew him. Optical experiments: new property of light interferances from light from the prism passes through a telescope glass across the eye hole fringes but what is remarkable the fringes are only on one side and when the eye glass is inverted no fringes are seen.[35]

we have no idea what it is doing in the middle of a discussion of Newton.

[32] In fact the book was not completed until 1855. We are uncertain as to the cause of the delay. However, the wait was well worthwhile. Both I. B. Cohen in his *DSB* entry on Newton and Richard S. Westfall in his introduction to Brewster's biography of Newton agree that Brewster's work is the best biography of Newton to have been written before or since.

[33] Perhaps a reference to Sir Walter Scott.

[34] Henry is referring to the plate which appears in the second volume of William Jerdan, *National Portrait Gallery of Illustrious and Eminent Personages of the Nineteenth Century,* 5 vols. (London, 1830–1834). The plate was made from the portrait painted by Sir Thomas Lawrence (1769–1830, *DNB*) around 1815. Young appears like a dandy in this portrait because Lawrence's work was characterized by the courtliness and social elegance which he supplied his subjects. Kenneth Garlick, ed., "A Catalogue of the Paintings, Drawings, and Pastels of Sir Thomas Lawrence," *The Walpole Society,* 1964, *39*:206.

[35] Within a month of Henry's visit Brewster reported his findings to the British Association. An expanded series of experiments enabled Brewster to make a fuller presentation before the same body the following year. According to Brewster's accounts, he had been examining homogeneous light from the solar spectrum when he decided to intercept part of the light ray by a glass plate, thus retarding it as compared with the unimpeded part of the ray. Interference fringes resulted. The distinctiveness of the fringes varied according to the orientation of the plate. Further experiments, this time using sulfate of lime instead of glass to intercept the light, led Brewster to conclude that under certain conditions "the different sides of the rays of homogenous light have different properties . . . that is, *these rays have polarity.*" Brewster, an enthusiastic advocate of the emission theory of light, had

found what he thought was new evidence for his beliefs.

Brewster's conclusions were quickly challenged. Baden Powell, as strong a supporter of the wave theory of light as Brewster was of the particulate, delivered a paper at the 1839 meeting of the British Association which argued that all the phenomena attributed to polarity by Brewster could be explained by assuming interference by the two parts of the light ray at the pupil of the eye. Also assumed by Powell in his explanation was the wave theory of light.

Brewster and Powell continued their debate over the true explanation of this phenomenon —and the validity of the wave theory of light —at later meetings of the British Association. Brewster's initial position was that although he was unable to present an entirely satisfactory explanation, he was able to show that the wave theory of light also fell short. He later claimed he could explain the fringes without reference to any theoretical assumptions. Powell, who was joined in 1839 by George Airy in the attempt to reconcile this phenomenon with the wave theory, argued that Brewster either misinterpreted experimental results or simply used incorrect data. Moreover, Powell hammered home the point that whatever the explanation of the fringes, the use of the term "polarity" was improper given the experimental results and the implications of such a term. At the 1848 meeting Powell announced the results of a series of experiments on interference. One particular case produced results analogous to the "polarity" phenomenon discovered by Brewster a decade earlier. Formulas derived from the wave theory accurately predicted the number and character of the bands produced. To Powell the case seemed closed.

Brewster's contributions to this debate include the following papers: "On a New Property of Light," *British Association Report, 1837* (1838), part 2, pp. 12–13; "On a New Kind of

Dr B thinks this a new propery of light. Rays in the spectrum. Common apparatus for throwing in the suns rays; 40 feet distant the prism 2 feet the slit of brass variable with a screw, near prism slit in paste board, telescope near prism with micrometer eye piece.[36] Small telescope.

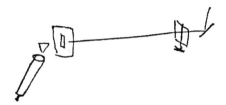

Not necessary that the instrument be achromatic since the light is homogeneous. Prism of plate glass filled with alcohol. Curious substance factitious mother of pearl[37] formed by an incrustation on the sides of the flash wheel in which articles are bleached with clorid of lime. Animal matter the glue in the sizing.

Influence of metals in changing the plain of polarization.[38] The force

---

Polarity in Homogeneous Light," *British Association Report, 1838* (1839), part 2, pp. 13–14; "On a New Polarity of Light, with an Examination of Mr. Airy's Explanation of it on the Undulatory Theory," *British Association Report, 1845* (1846), part 2, pp. 7–8; "On the Diffraction Bands Produced by the Edges of Thin Plates, Whether Solid or Fluid," *British Association Report, 1847* (1848), part 2, p. 33.

Powell's responses appeared in the following: "On the Explanation of Some Optical Phenomena Observed by Sir David Brewster," *British Association Report, 1839* (1840), part 2, pp. 1–2; "On the Bands Formed by Partial Interception of the Prismatic Spectrum," *British Association Report, 1846* (1847), part 2, p. 4; "On a New Case of Interference of Light," *British Association Report, 1848* (1849), part 2, p. 3.

[36] From Brewster's description of the experiment in the *British Association Report* we would have thought that one of the slits would have been placed between the prism and the telescope. Otherwise we see some difficulty in obtaining a homogeneous ray of light.

[37] This substance had been discovered around 1834 on a "Dash-wheel," the piece of apparatus used in rinsing cloth after it had been soaked in the bleaching solution. The discoverer, a cotton manufacturer, believed the artificial mother-of-pearl had resulted from the combination of the lime used to

bleach the cloth and the glue and flour used to stiffen the threads before they were placed in the loom. The lime and stiffener had precipitated out of the rinse water. Brewster had analyzed a sample of the material at the request of the discoverer and found it unique in a number of ways. However, the structure resembled closely that of mother-of-pearl and gave Brewster considerable insight into the causes of certain optical phenomenon created by mother-of-pearl. This was a problem Brewster had been working on for over twenty years. Leonard Horner, "On an Artificial Substance Resembling Shell," *Phil. Trans.*, 1836, pp. 49–51; David Brewster, "With an Account of an Examination of the Same," *Phil. Trans.*, 1836, pp. 52–56.

[38] Brewster had first investigated the action of metals on light in 1815. He was anticipated in the publication of his discoveries by Biot, however, and suppressed the publication of his 1817 paper on the subject. But the work of Fresnel on circular polarization gave him new insight into the problem and led him to renew his investigations. Brewster found that at certain angles of incidence, the plane of polarization of a light ray would change when reflected off metal. Further investigation showed that light reflected off metals and certain metallic ores at the angle at which this change was a maximum had neither the characteristics of plane polarized nor circularly

weaked externally by an other medium put on polarized beam from thick piece of spar fitted into a circle which was once a goniometer.[39] Good method of getting two beams of light polarized at right angles to each other. The ray was received on a surface of metal over which a stratum of oil of casia[40] was spread. Singular changes in the plain of polariza[tion].

Lines in the spectrum made more distinct by holding a tube before the orfice in the slit apparatus in which Nitrus gas is placed.[41] Sir H[42] met with an acident in this. Spilled acid on his hands and face.

Showed me eyes of fish. See his paper.[43] Experiments on thin plates exfoliation from glass. Color by reflection differs from refraction.[44] Remembers Prof Griscom.[45] Mrs B also. Benevolent looking man [. . .].[46]

---

polarized light. Brewster eventually called the phenomenon elliptical polarization. David Brewster, "On the Phenomena and Laws of Elliptic Polarization, as Exhibited in the Action of Metals Upon Light," *Phil. Trans.*, 1830, pp. 287–326.

[39] Invented to provide accurate measurements of crystals, the reflective goniometer consisted of a graduated vertical circle mounted on a horizontal axis and supported by an upright pillar. William Hyde Wollaston, "Description of a Reflective Goniometer," *Phil. Trans.*, 1809, pp. 253–258.

[40] Cassia oil, better known as Chinese cinnamon oil. *Oxford English Dictionary*.

[41] Brewster mapped the spectrum of nitrous acid and compared the map to the one he made of the solar spectrum (the latter was much more detailed than that of Fraunhofer). He also investigated the spectrum created when sunlight was superimposed upon the light from the acid. One of the surprising discoveries during Brewster's experiments was the sharpness and darkness of the lines in the nitrous acid spectrum. David Brewster, "Observations on the Lines of the Solar Spectrum, and on Those Produced by the Earth's Atmosphere, and by the Action of Nitrous Acid Gas," *Transactions of the Royal Society of Edinburgh*, 1834, 12:519–530.

[42] Since this appears to be the same accident mentioned by Henry earlier in this account (see footnote 9), we assume that Henry's "Sir H" at this point was just a slip of the pencil. He must have been referring to Sir David.

[43] Because the structure of the eye was of continuing interest to Brewster, we are un-

certain which of his papers on the subject is being referred to. Two candidates are "On the Structure of the Crystalline Lens in Fishes and Quadrupeds, as Ascertained by its Action on Polarized Light," *Phil. Trans.*, 1816, pp. 311–317; and "On the Anatomical and Optical Structure of the Crystalline Lenses of Animals, Particularly that of the Cod," *Phil. Trans.*, 1833, pp. 323–332. In the first paper Brewster described certain phenomena. The second paper was an attempt to explain the optical phenomena in terms of the anatomical structure of the lens of the eye.

[44] We believe this is Henry's cryptic reference to the research Brewster would present to the British Association in 1838 under the title "On a New Phenomenon of Colour in Certain Specimens of Fluor Spar" (*British Association Report, 1838* [1839], part 2, pp. 10–12). If so, then this is an early indication of Brewster's interest in what became known as fluorescence. A more detailed discussion of this phenomenon in solutions or liquids as opposed to solids will appear in the next volume of the *Henry Papers*.

[45] Although he lacked a college education, John Griscom (1774–1852) had a distinguished career as a science educator and popularizer. He was Professor of Chemistry at Columbia from 1813 to 1820, a member of the faculty of Rutgers's assorted medical schools, and taught in or ran a variety of secondary schools in New Jersey, New York, and Rhode Island. A founder of the New York Mechanic and Scientific Institution and an active member of the Franklin Institute, Griscom was well known for the quality of his popular lectures

on chemistry. He contributed translations and abstracts of foreign scientific articles to *Silliman's Journal* and the *Journal of the Franklin Institute* (he also helped edit the latter for a number of years).

Griscom had breakfasted with the Brewster family in March 1819 during a year-long trip to Europe. His remarks on Brewster are quite favorable, although they emphasize Brewster's literary accomplishments and achievements almost as much as the scientific.

DAB; Bruce Sinclair, *Philadelphia's Philosopher Mechanics: A History of the Franklin Institute, 1824–1865* (Baltimore, 1974), pp. 9, 215–216; John Griscom, *A Year in Europe*, 2 vols. (New York, 1823), 2:342–343, 350–351.

[46] Two illegible words.

FROM JOHN LOCKE
Henry Papers, Smithsonian Archives

London August [25–27],[1] 1837

Dear Sir,

I shall sail on the first in the Sampson. Robinson[2] has made your Intensity apparatus,[3] but both it and mine[4] are faulty in having a wrinkled refracting glass. You will perhaps be obliged to have the graduated circle put on higher up where it is clearer.

If you wish to experiment at Westbourne Green,[5] pass through the "Westbourne Green turnpike gate" and at the first canal bridge beyond turn short to your right through an obscure gate. Pass about 200 yds. along the bank of the canal with a board fence on your right until you come to a *deep hollow* on your right with a double row of elms beyond it. This hollow (like your hat crown) is the place of experiment. Near the upper end of it is now a haystack with an iron rail round it. This you will avoid of course. I have ordered a microscope to be made and left with Mr. Vaughan which I must beg the favour of you to bring along with you to New york and leave with Herman Morris[6] No. 105 Pearl St. New york.

[1] Although Locke dated this letter on the 25th of August, it was not completed, as he himself makes clear, until two days later.

[2] Thomas Charles Robinson.

[3] Henry will later list this apparatus as "Bache's," which we take to mean that it was modeled after Bache's version of a piece of apparatus for measuring magnetic intensity in a vacuum (for Henry's opinion of this apparatus see above, Henry to Bache, June 4, 1836, especially footnote 6). Folder of Accounts with Various Instrument- and Apparatus-Dealers, Joseph Henry for the College of New Jersey, 1837, Princeton University Archives.

[4] Locke's apparatus was definitely modeled after Bache's vacuum apparatus. He would later use it to conduct a series of observations in the United States. John Locke, "Observations Made in the Years 1838, '39, '40, '41, '42, and '43, to Determine the Magnetical Dip and the Intensity of Magnetical Force, in Several Parts of the United States," *Transactions of the American Philosophical Society*, 1846, n.s. 9:283–328.

[5] For Henry's observations at Westbourne Green, see above, Bache to Henry, July 16, 1837, footnote 5.

[6] A merchant by the name of Hermon Mor-

Aug. 27. I have just returned from Greenwich where there is a better place for magnetical experiments than at the green, and it costs only a shilling to get there. I made my experiments for horizontal intensity close to the spot where they are erecting the Magnetical Observatory.[7] I took the dip at the Green and made it 69° 23′3. After you left I saw Daniel[8] and becoming excited about the carbonic acid apparatus, I wrote to Prof. Bache, proposing to pay a part of the cost of it merely to get the model. But I received no answer. I ought not to have made such a request, for he was probably not authorized to make any purchases in such a manner. I am quite contented to do without it. I have succeeded in vibrating a needle in the line of the dip by suspending it with coccoon filaments attached to knife edges: A is the knife edge, B. a bridge pin and C a winding pin there being a similar set on the opposite side. The whole arrangement is a difficult affair but I believe it will give comparative intensity very unexceptionably.

To complete this will be one of my tasks after I return home.[9] Since I returned from Paris I have had made a Melonian galvanometer which in looks and action is so very like one made by Mons. Gourgeon[10] that I do not think you could tell the difference. Mons. Pixii has disappointed me

---

ris was at 205 Pearl Street according to the 1837 city directory.

[7] Greenwich Observatory's expanding role in terrestrial magnetism was a result of the appointment of George B. Airy as Astronomer Royal. When Airy took office in 1835, Greenwich had only a small outbuilding for magnetic observations and no real program. Within a year Airy had proposed the erection of a magnetic observatory, which he himself was to plan. Construction of the cross-shaped structure, located about 230 feet from the astronomical observatory, was completed in the spring of 1838. The final instrumentation was installed three years later. George B. Airy, *Diagrams Representing Diurnal Change in Magnitude and Direction of the Magnetic Forces in the Horizontal Plane, at the Royal Observatory, Greenwich, for Each Month of the Several Years 1841–1876* (London, 1886), p. 1; Royal Observatory, Greenwich, *Magnetical and Meteorological Observations, 1842* (London, 1844), p. i.

[8] John Frederic Daniell.

[9] Locke would later complain that although terrestrial magnetic observations appeared simple to make, "it was not until I had had considerable practice, that I could proceed with confidence and certainty." He had apparently hoped to obtain this practice at London, but the delay in the construction of his apparatus prevented it. Locke, "On the Magnetic Dip . . . ," *Transactions of the American Philosophical Society*, 1839, n.s. 6:268.

[10] F. Gourjon was an important French instrument maker during the years 1834–1845, constructing the apparatus used by Melloni in his thermoelectric experiments and galvanometers used by a variety of institutions and individuals. See, e.g., *The Electrical Magazine*, 1845, *1*:609; also Melloni to Faraday, October 16, 1834, published in L. Pearce Williams, ed., *The Selected Correspondence of Michael Faraday*, 2 vols. (Cambridge, England, 1971), *1*:281. Yet we know little about the man. Henry listed him as T. Gourjon in his address book, but Melloni, who knew him better, gave his first initial as F. in "Nouvelles recherches sur la transmission immédiate de la chaleur rayonnante par différens corps solides et liquides," *Annales de chimie et de physique*, 1833, 55:392.

and informs my agent that my apparatus cannot be made till one month later than he engaged to do it.[11] This is a severe disappointment.

Very cordially your friend

John Locke

[11] Locke was not the only one to be disappointed by the skilled instrument makers of France. A recurring theme in Henry's correspondence in the early months of 1838 will be the nonappearance of the apparatus he ordered.

TO HARRIET HENRY

Mary Henry Copy,[1] Family Correspondence, Henry Papers, Smithsonian Archives

Glasgow Aug. 27, 1837

My dear dear Harriet. I arrived in this city a few days since and have been received with the usual hospitality and kindness which has everywhere met me in this country. In my last letter[2] dated from Edinburgh, I gave you some account of my employment in that city and told you that my time was pleasantly and profitably spent. I lodged in the central part of the city in a street[3] directly in front of the large building which occupies the foreground of the above sketch of the Old Town of Edinburgh. This building is called the Royal Institution and contains the rooms and museum of the Royal Society. All the space in front of the picture is in the New Town, or in other words; the drawing was made from some point in the New Town. The shrubbery seen on either side of the Royal Institution is in a deep valley which separates the two towns. This was once the bed of a lake and is perhaps sixty feet deep. There are two passages across it: one called the mound, a bridge of solid earth, on which the Royal Institution stands; the other, the North Bridge, to the left of but not seen in the picture.[4] I attended the

[1] The only complete copy of this letter is a Mary Henry typescript. A handwritten copy exists for the text up to Henry's mention of Calton Hill; our text up to this point is based on the handwritten copy.

Two fragments of Henry's original text survive; these are on the backs of the two pictures he mentions. Mary Henry evidently clipped out the pictures before discarding the original letter. The first picture is entitled "View From Near the New Club House,

Princes Street, Edinburgh." The second is "View From Princes Gardens, Edinburgh." Both were published by R. Grant & Son, booksellers and stationers in Edinburgh, and were printed on thin sheets of stationery. Henry's writing on the backs has bled through and partially obscured some of the details.

[2] August 16, 1837, printed above.
[3] Hanover Street.
[4] The Earthen Mound was initiated in 1783 as a land-fill project, using the dirt and rub-

church which you see in the distance and which is called St. Giles or the Tolbooth.⁵ It was in this building that John Knox was wont to thunder against papacy and denounce Queen Mary.⁶ There are now three churches in the same building; that is three congregations assemble at the same time and are so near as to be heard by each other while singing. The Old Town as I have stated resembles very much the city of Paris and this resemblance is not extraordinary and by no means accidental since the two cities were once quite closely connected and had frequent intercourse, particularly in the time of the Stuarts. The New Town is one of the most beautiful cities in Europe.⁷ Indeed Edinburgh⁸ as a whole is one of the most pleasant places in the world. The views from the top of the Castle and from Calton Hill are delightful. The Old Town and the New present the most perfect contrast: the one all regularity, the other all picturesque disorder. I was much disappointed at first in the pleasure I anticipated from the study of architecture in the old world. When I arrived in London the whole city seemed so black to me, so defaced by smoke, that I found no pleasure in looking at the buildings. My taste for the science revived however in Paris and has regained its full ascendency over me in Edinburgh. The stone near the city is of a pleasant brownish color and of durable quality; it is easily wrought into any form when newly taken from the quarry but becomes hard by exposure. On the other page you have a view of the New Town, taken from some point on the side hill of the Old Town. In this view you see the rear

ble produced by the construction of the New Town. It was the second passage constructed across the ravine which separates the Old and New Towns. The first was the North Bridge, lying somewhat to the east of the Mound, which had been started twenty years earlier as the first step in the extension of the city to the north. J. Stark, *Picture of Edinburgh . . .* (Edinburgh, 1831), p. 75. *Encyclopaedia Britannica*, 8th ed., s.v. "Edinburgh," p. 394.

⁵ The Tolbooth Church, which derived its name from the prison adjacent to the cathedral, was one of the four parish churches into which St. Giles' was divided at the time of the Reformation. See above, Henry's European Diary, August 6, 1837, footnotes 1 and 2. During the restoration of St. Giles' in 1829–1833, the number of churches was reduced from four to three. Reginald J. W. Hammond, *Edinburgh* (London, 1970), p. 43.

⁶ Mary Stuart, Queen of Scots (1542–1587, *DNB*).

⁷ The New Town of Edinburgh, located across the ravine which forms the northern edge of the Old Town, was begun in 1767 in response to the increasingly crowded and dilapidated condition of the medieval city. Following a plan developed by architect James Craig, the New Town was laid out along three principal east-west axes: Queen Street on the north, George Street in the middle, and Princes Street, built on a terrace facing the Old Town, on the south. Two public squares, Charlotte on the west and St. Andrew's on the east, formed the termini of George Street, while several smaller north-south streets intersected at regular intervals. Even before work on this initial phase was completed in about 1815, however, plans were underway for the extension of the New Town and by the time of Henry's visit it had grown well beyond its original confines. *Encyclopaedia Britannica*, 8th ed., s.v. "Edinburgh," p. 394.

⁸ The copyist omitted these two words which we have taken from the fragments of the original.

of the Royal Institution, and directly in front of it the street in which I reside. Between the margin of the foreground of the picture and the long row of houses is the deep hollow I before mentioned as dividing the two towns. On the extreme right of the picture you will see Calton Hill, on which the Astronomical Observatory is placed. I think it must be one of the most beautiful places in the world. It commands a wide view of the city and surrounding country. The Observatory is a beautiful little building in the form of a cross with four Grecian fronts and a small hemispherical dome on the intersection. The tall tower, near the edge of the picture, is Nelson's monument, an old structure, not in good taste.[9] Near this is a row of large Doric pillars, the commencement of a National Monument, to be erected as an exact model of the Parthenon of Athens. The Committee failed to raise the requisite sum of money and the unfinished structure has remained in its present state for ten or fifteen years. It presents, at a little distance, the appearance of a ruin of an ancient Grecian temple and adds thus a pleasant object to the classic hill.[10] The Observatory is surrounded by a walled enclosure and, at one corner of this, is a small Grecian temple erected to the memory of Playfair. This is after a design by the nephew of the Professor who resides in Edinburgh and has acquired considerable reputation as an architect.[11] In front of the Observatory is a small round columnar structure copied from the Lantern of Demosthenes of Athens, erected as a monument to Dugald Stewart. To the right of the Nelson monument (but not in the picture), and on another eminence, is a beautiful monument to the memory of Burns.[12] It is also a circular structure and is surmounted by a tripod,[13] an instrument sacred to Apollo. The walls are adorned with rows of lyres, an instrument also sacred to poesy. The memory of the Scotch poet is held in great respect here and his reputation is still on the increase. The long street parallel with the front edge of the picture is

---

[9] The 102-foot-high monument to Horatio, Viscount Nelson, British naval hero of the Napoleonic Wars, was erected between 1806 and 1816. Henry was not alone in his estimation of the aesthetic deficiencies of the monument, which has been likened to "a spy glass on a butter churn," and which one modern writer has described as the "only blight on the Calton Hill." L. Russell Muirhead, ed., *Scotland* (London, 1967), p. 75. George Scott-Moncrieff, *Edinburgh* (Edinburgh, 1965), p. 112.

[10] The National Monument, designed to commemorate Scottish soldiers and sailors of the Napoleonic Wars, was begun in 1822. It remains unfinished to this day. Hammond, ed., *Edinburgh*, p. 71. *Encyclopaedia Britannica*, 8th ed., s.v. "Edinburgh," p. 406.

[11] The monument to the Scottish mathematician John Playfair was designed by William Henry Playfair.

[12] The monument to Robert Burns (1759–1796, *DNB*) was designed in 1830 by Thomas Hamilton (1784–1858, *DNB*), who also designed the memorial at Burns's birthplace at Alloway.

[13] The three-legged seat of the priestess at the shrine of Apollo at Delphi, and hence the symbol of the Delphic oracle. *Oxford English Dictionary*.

called Princes street and is the fashionable promenade of the city. Holyrood Palace[14] is not exhibited in either of the views. Of course I did not fail to visit the Palace but as my tour is one of science and not of general and usual sightseeing, I did not pay my respects to this piece of antiquity until the day before my departure. The rooms are, as you have so often been informed, preserved nearly in the same condition as when inhabited by the frail but unfortunate Queen. The bedroom of Mary contains a picture of Darnley[15] and also of the Italian secretary Rizzio,[16] murdered, as you know, in the Queen's presence; the latter is represented as a very good looking young man. The apartments, in the same Palace, occupied by Charles 10th of France, during his visit to Scotland after he was obliged to abdicate the throne are also shown. In the ruins of the chapel which adjoins the Palace is a vault into which, through an iron grated door, may be seen a number of human bones, the largest of which are said to be those of Darnley. From the Palace I went to the Castle[17] and there had a fine view of the city and the adjoining country. Was here shown the Regalia of Scotland: the old crown of Robert Bruce,[18] the sword of state and other Scotch jewels. These articles are exhibited in a round tower, where they were discovered in 1819 after having been lost sight of for more than a hundred and fifty years.[19] It was thought that the crown had been carried to London. The crown room, as it was called, was locked and the keys lost. It could be opened only by a special commission from the King of England. This was not granted until the time above mentioned, when a number of gentlemen of Scotland, among whom was Sir Walter Scott, were appointed to break open the room

[14] The Palace of Holyroodhouse, the principal royal palace of Scotland, was begun in about 1500 by James IV (1473–1513, *DNB*), on a site adjacent to the twelfth-century Holyrood Abbey. Considerably extended and remodeled during the reign of Charles II (1630–1685, *DNB*), the design of the palace reflects the French influence on Edinburgh architecture under the Stuarts. Muirhead, ed., *Scotland*, pp. 53–54, 56.

[15] Henry Stewart, Lord Darnley (1545–1567), the husband of Mary Queen of Scots from 1565 until his assassination. *DNB*.

[16] David Riccio or Rizzio (1533?–1566), secretary and confidant of Mary Queen of Scots from 1564 until his assassination at the hands of Darnley and others jealous of his growing influence. *DNB*.

[17] Dominating the city below it, Edinburgh Castle sits atop Castle Rock, where a fortress of some sort has existed for over one thousand years. St. Margaret's Chapel, the most ancient remaining part of the Castle and the oldest surviving building in Edinburgh, dates from the eleventh century, but most of the Castle is of more recent construction, and additions and alterations to the fortress have continued into modern times. W. Forbes Gray, *A Short History of Edinburgh Castle* (Edinburgh, 1948), pp. 9–25. Scott-Moncrieff, *Edinburgh*, p. 2.

[18] Robert Bruce (1274–1329), the "liberator of Scotland." *DNB*.

[19] In fact, they had not been lost for as long as Henry thought. The "Regalia" or "Honours of Scotland," whose dramatic recovery actually occurred in 1817, had been locked away at the time of the Act of Union in 1707, for fear that they might serve as a dangerous symbol of Scottish nationalism. John Geddie, *Romantic Edinburgh* (London, 1900), p. 85.

and search for the crown. It was thought scarcely possible that it could be in this place after the lapse of so many years. Great interest was excited and, the day appointed, nearly all the inhabitants of the city and surrounding country assembled within sight of the Castle, while the Commissioners proceeded to force open the iron door. It had been understood that if the crown were found the result would be announced to the thousands below by the discharge of the Castle cannon. The event was awaited with breathless expectation and hope had nearly vanished, when the thunder from the Castle announced that the lost jewels were found and that the crown of the Bruce was still in the land of the Scot. The Commissioners, in forcing the door, found the floor of the room covered with dust but entirely empty with the exception of a large oaken chest, secured by iron bands and three large locks. When these were forced, the lid was not immediately raised but suffered to remain closed until the arrival of some of the other Commissioners. It was then raised, with due form, and the crown, wrapped in an old linen cloth, was found resting on a velvet cushion. It was lifted out of the chest by Sir Walter Scott, and, by him, presented from the walls of the Castle to the multitude below. It was received with cheers, waving of handkerchiefs and every demonstration of joy. The old chest still remains in the room and is a curious specimen of the art of other days. I had the above details from the keeper and another person, both of whom were present at the ceremony of opening. The keeper, an interesting intelligent old Scotchman, had been promoted to the office for his valiant conduct at the Battle of Waterloo. He had been a sergeant of the 42nd Regiment and he gave me a detailed account of the battle, which [was] the more interesting on account of my having so lately visited the scene of action. On the top of the Castle, at the highest point, is an old cannon of immense caliber, made before the art of casting guns was in use. It is formed of longitudinal bars of iron hooped, at intervals, with large rings of the same metal. It is several hundred years old and was made to throw balls of stone instead of iron. It is known by the name of "Mons' Meg" and was for a time exhibited in the Tower of London, to which place it was taken many years since, on some threatened invasion, and only returned, by a grant of the king to Edinburgh, in 1827.[20] Its arrival caused almost as great a sensation in "Auld Reekie"[21] as the discovery of the crown and "Mons' Meg" was escorted,

---

[20] "Mons Meg," or "Roaring Meg" as it was also called, was reputedly crafted at Mons in Flanders in 1486, although a native Scottish origin in the district of Galloway has also been claimed for it. The cannon, twelve feet long and weighing five tons, was removed to the Tower of London in 1754 in retribution for the unsuccessful Jacobite rebellion of 1745. It was returned to Edinburgh Castle in 1829 upon the appeal of Sir Walter Scott and others. Hammond, *Edinburgh*, p. 33.

[21] A sobriquet for Edinburgh meaning "Old

from the wharf to the Castle, by hundreds of citizens. In the court leading to the Castle, I saw for the first time a kilted Highland regiment engaged in their exercises. The soldiers of a regiment of the men parade the streets, with girls hanging on their arms, in every part of the city. They seem great favorites with the lower women of the place. Their dress would, in America, be considered a violation of modern propriety. Custom however, in this respect, appears to be arbitrary and absolute. Women here, as elsewhere, are engaged in severe and heavy labor. They are seen carrying baskets on their backs which hold at least two bushels, filled with herring. These they constantly hawk about the streets and they almost crack the ears with the horrid yell "Wha will buy caller[22] herring?" The girls of the lower classes rarely wear shoes and are seen on the streets in short petticoats, exposing thick red legs and dirty feet.

After spending nearly two weeks in Edinburgh and having received much attention from the principal inhabitants of the place, I started for the residence of Sir David Brewster, which is situated about forty miles to the south, within half a mile of Melrose Abbey and two miles from the residence of Walter Scott. The day was pleasant and I arrived at the village of Melrose at about nine at night. The Inn was crowded. I, having only a bag, and for the purpose of seeing the country having taken the top of the coach, was put into a very poor room. The bed was clean if not restful in appearance and I soon fell asleep, to awake near morning with a pain in the back of my neck. The bedstead had given way in the night and the upper part of the bed, with pillows and bolster, had fallen through, leaving my head unsupported. I mention my uncomfortable quarters to show how much attention is paid to apparent wealth in this country. The next day, after some messages had arrived for me from Sir David Brewster, a thousand apologies were made for putting me in such an apartment and my small bag was deposited in a large convenient bedroom, furnished in good style—in short, the bedroom of the establishment. I passed the whole of two days with Sir David and was highly pleased as well as instructed by my visit. Sir David and Lady Brewster received me very kindly and appeared pleased with my visit. I brought with me a letter of introduction but was informed that this was not necessary, that Sir David would welcome me without an introduction. This was the case for he had just published a work (for the Encyclo-

---

Smoky." The name presumably arose on account of the appearance of the hill on which the densely populated Old Town was built, especially at dinner time when the smoke from the city's evening fires could be seen for miles around. Hammond, ed., *Edinburgh*, p. 6. Robert Louis Stevenson, *Edinburgh* (New York, 1908), pp. 50–53.

[22] A Scottish word meaning "fresh." *Oxford English Dictionary*.

paedia Britannica, new edition) on magnetism, in which he devotes a few pages to my experiments and gives a drawing of my apparatus,[23] so that when my name was announced he gave me a cordial recognition and devoted himself during my stay entirely to me. Sir David Brewster is now in the meridian of his mental powers and is one of the most industrious and successful students of Nature now living. He has made a very extensive reputation by his interesting discoveries in light and is still prosecuting, in all his leisure time, the same subject. He highly interested me in the method of repeating some of the more difficult experiments and showed me some discoveries he had lately made, which had not yet been published. He is now occupied with investigating a new phenomenon relative to the dark lines discovered some years since in the solar spectrum. He exhibited these lines to me in a manner I had never before seen and thus introduced me, as it were, to a new world of wonders. The information given me by Sir David was precisely the kind for which I came to this country: the methods of original experimentation and those things which cannot be learned from books. All his discoveries have been made with very simple means. He has a few good instruments and these he takes apart and fits up again in different forms for different uses. Lady Brewster is good looking, appears under forty but must be older since she has been married twenty-six years. She is the daughter of Macpherson, the author of the poems of Ossian. This fact I learned from the Life of Sir David which I procured in Paris.[24] She is quite unaffected and easy in manner with what you would call a slight dash of mischief (or fun) in her composition. She was very kind to me and apparently not unpleased to see someone from America with whom she could converse relative to the books recently published in that county. Sir David, besides his other avocations, is now arranging the materials for a new life of Sir Isaac Newton. These consist of a large collection of papers, containing the correspondence of that Philosopher as well as anecdotes relative to him by his niece and her husband, a Mr. Conduitt, who intended to write a life of Sir Isaac but was prevented by premature death. The papers have been many years unexamined, in the possession of the family, and have lately been given into the charge of Sir David for the purpose of examination and publication. After tea, the first day of my

[23] Presumably the seventh edition, which was completed in stages and published in its entirety in 1842. While we have been unable to obtain a copy of this edition, the article on magnetism in the eighth edition, also written by Brewster, does contain a discussion and illustration of Henry's electromagnetic apparatus. *Encyclopaedia Britannica*, 8th ed., s.v. "Magnetism," p. 75.

[24] *Biographie Universelle et Portative Des Contemporains. . .* , 5 vols. (Paris, 1836), contains a biography of Brewster. The complete set is in the Henry Library.

stay, Sir David favored me with the reading of several of the letters. These were quite amusing and conclusively proved that profound and abstract as were the speculations of this Prince of Philosophers he still belonged to the *genus homo*. One of these letters is addressed to a lady on that very unphilosophical but very natural subject love. An original love letter from Sir Isaac Newton, however ordinary, would be a curiosity at this day but the one in question is interesting still more from its character. It is an address to a widow and clearly proves, by a series of almost mathematical propositions, that it the duty of the lady to forget the memory of her dead husband in the arms of a living one. These letters are in existence on account of the circumstance that Sir Isaac composed with difficulty and always made a rough draft of every letter, which he generally kept. So laborious was he in the production of his works, that it is said he wrote his copies over more than thirty-six times before the manuscript was finished to his taste. Sir David has now but a small family with him; his wife and a daughter of about fifteen constitute the whole. He has however three sons, two of whom are now in the East Indies and the other, an officer in the army, with his regiment in the Highlands. The daughter is a pleasant and pretty Scotch Lass.

I visited Melrose Abbey which is situated in the village of the same name, a few rods from the Inn where I slept. I left Sir David Brewster's family about half past ten and, in company with a young gentleman who had been one of our company at tea and who kindly offered to be my conductor, I made an excursion, late as it was, around the venerable ruin. The moon fortunately had risen some time before and thus gave me an opportunity of viewing the Abbey, according to Sir Walter Scott, in its most proper light.[25] Of this I must speak another time. I returned early the next morning with the intention of visiting Abbotsford[26] with Dr. Brewster. Our horses were saddled immediately after breakfast for the purpose and we were ready to start, when the sun happened to shine out brilliantly, for the first time since my arrival, and this was too favorable an opportunity to lose for an exhibition of some experiments I had not yet seen. One of them having been seen and commented upon, another and another was shown, until the clock struck three, the horses, all the while, waiting for our departure. I had now occupied so much of Sir David's time, I insisted that he should allow me to gallop over alone to Abbotsford, take a hasty glance and

---

[25] Scott's recommendation appears in the opening lines of the second canto of *The Lay of the Last Minstrel*, first published in 1805:

If thou would'st view fair Melrose aright,

Go visit it by the pale moon-light

[26] The home of Sir Walter Scott from 1812 until his death in 1832. *DNB*.

return in time for the stage to Edinburgh. To this he consented. I bade adieu to the family, rode at a rapid pace to the mansion of the departed magician, took a hurried survey, and returned to the Inn just in time for the evening coach to Edinburgh. The next day I started by the canal[27] for Glasgow, passed several villages and, in the distance, Stirling Castle.[28] In Glasgow I have met the same kind attention I have everywhere encountered. Prof. Graham, whom I saw in London, who has just been elected to the chair of chemistry in the London University, first took me in tow. He introduced me to Dr. Thomson, with whose family I made, a few days since, a short visit to Loch Lomond. Dr. Thomson is reputed to be the most surly and rough man of any standing in Glasgow. He was however very kind to me and invited me frequently to his house.[29]

Liverpool, Sep. 11th

I arrived in Liverpool last Saturday without an opportunity of putting this letter in the post. The meeting of the Association took place today and an immense concourse of people are assembling [from] every part of Europe. Almost immediately on my arrival, I met with some of my acquaintances, who were not slow in giving me proper introductions and now I must close this letter. Adieu

[27] The Great Canal, uniting the Firths of Forth and Clyde, a distance of thirty-five miles, was begun in 1768 and completed in 1790. It was connected to Glasgow by an additional three-and-one-half-mile spur. With an average surface width of fifty-six feet, and a depth of ten feet, it was a considerable financial success. In 1822, the Great Canal was joined to Edinburgh by the Union Canal, thirty-one and one-half miles long. In contrast to its predecessor, however, the Union Canal, partly because of the traffic restrictions which its limited depth of five feet imposed, never proved a profitable enterprise. *Encyclopaedia Britannica*, 8th ed., s.v. "Scotland," p. 808.

[28] Stirling Castle, thirty-six miles northwest of Edinburgh and dating from early medieval times, was celebrated in Scottish history by virtue of its strategic position commanding the main route between northern and southern Scotland. Muirhead, ed., *Scotland*, pp. 208, 212–213.

Stirling had an added significance for both Henry and Harriet, since the earldom of Stirling had been in the Alexander family, from which they were both descended, during the seventeenth and eighteenth centuries. See typed notes on Henry's ancestry in Family Correspondence, Henry Papers, Smithsonian Archives.

[29] Thomas Thomson (*Henry Papers*, 1:5) was Regius Professor of Chemistry at Glasgow University at the time of Henry's visit, and the dean of Glasgow's scientific community. Described by the *DSB* as "sometimes arrogant and perpetually sardonic," Thomson was a natural contact for Henry in view of his position as "Glasgow's senior host to distinguished scientific visitors."

HENRY'S EUROPEAN DIARY

Henry Papers, Smithsonian Archives

[August 1837][1] Was introduced today to Mr *Brandes*[2] of Lypesic by Prof Henderson. Mr [B] is an assistant in the observatory of Lypsic. He informes me that there are at least 20 places in Germany Italy and Sweeden where magnetic observations are made at this time under the general direction of Ghouse.[3] The needle is a bar 2 feet long weighs about 4 lbs and of this dimentions. It is supported by a thin wire or a thread of silk 20 feet in length. A mirror of glass is cemented on the end at right angles to the length and before 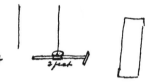 this is placed a telescope very securely placed at the distance of 15 feet. A scale is placed under the end of the tellescope on which divisions corresponding to the distance is drawn. To regulate the telescope which has a cross hair in its focus a mark is placed on the oposite wall. The telescope has a focal length of about 2 feet.

Observations commence the last Saturday in every 2nd month commencing at the end of January. Then last saturday in March. They begin at 12 oclock M and end 12 o'clock on Sunday also at M.

The time is noted by a clock regulated to mean time. The observations are recorded at every 5 minutes for the 24 hours & six single observations are made to determine with greater exactness the declination corresponding to the instant noted. For this purpose the length of one oscillation is determined which for the needle at Lypsic is 22 seconds. The position of the needle is noted at the moment of a given second then at 22 seconds after the second position is noted and so on. It is necessary to commence at a second corresponding to the length of the vibration such that the middle of the 6 vibrations will fall on the minute intend[ed] for the one at which the vibration is registered. This is easily effected by forming a table which is

---

[1] This undated entry appears to be a continuation of that of August 10 where Henry is escorted by Henderson. This is Henry's last formal diary entry.

[2] Carl Wilhelm Theodor Brandes (1814–1843), son of the Leipzig University physicist Heinrich Wilhelm Brandes. *Poggendorff*.

[3] i.e., C. F. Gauss. For the worldwide magnetic network, see Henry's diary entry above, April 21, 1837, footnote 22. The apparatus described below was that of the Leipzig observatory. The large needles were on Gauss's design. See *Henry Papers*, 2:106n–107n, for Gauss's apparatus and for Henry's interest in it.

placed up beside the clock. Suppose the register were to be made for the minute at 12 oclock the needle making vibrations of 22^{sd} thus

	h	m		observ.	middle		
Time	11	59'	5"	−50.2			
					−51.65		
			27	53.1			
					−51.75		
			49	−50.4			
					−51.80	−58.83	} number to be registered
	12	0.	11	53.2			
					−51.85		
			33	50.7			
					−52.10		
			55	53.5			

The needle is enclosed in a box to prevent the agitation of the air and a hole left at the end for viewing the mirror also a small hole at the top for the silk.

The mirror is about 4 inches long by 2 inches wide. A tolerably large mirror is used to expose a greater part of the scale. To prevent still more the approach of a current of air a paper tube is placed around the hole in the front of the box. If the needle does not make the vibration precisely in a [w]hole second it should be loaded with a small piece of copper attached to it and moved backwards and forwards.

To reduce the vibrations as much as possible which is important a large magnetic bar is held in the hand at right angles to the line of the dip and then <*gradually*> suddenly inclined when the needle is near its middle point so as to check it there & then brought back. The bar is held in the hand at the tellescope at the distance of 15 feet from the needle. The needle should be suspended without torsion by means of a weight put into the stirrup at first.

FROM PETTY VAUGHAN

Henry Papers, Smithsonian Archives

London 5th Septr 1837.

My Dear Sir

With shame & confusion of face I have to state that no intelligence of your Parcel at Paris has been rec^d—either from Professor Bache or Mr Roberton.[1]

The former has gone to Germany.

[1] See above, Henry to Bache, July 28, 1837.

I hope you have rec^d the 2 letters I have sent you to Edinburgh. No more yet.[2]

Dr Locke has arrived from Paris & sailed in the Samson on Saturday, with other Boston friends.

Professors Robinson,[3] Parker,[4] McKean,[5] & Goodwin[6] are here. Mr P. proposes going to Lpool & Mr Goodwin may too. Mr R. & D^r M^cK. are for the Continent. Professor Loomis & M^r DeWitt went in the Wellington.

Mr Hamilton[7] writes me from Phil^a 19 July that Mr Saxton had arrived & delivered the Parcels, &c. He also say[s], "Please inform Professor Henry that the Books he requested me to send, are not for sale in this City."[8]

I wish you a very learned & useful meeting; & hope we may soon see you again in London.

If any letters come for you I will send them to Messrs Thornely, Goree.[9] I am Yr's mo. truly

Petty Vaughan

Mr V. sends his Comp^ts

---

[2] We cannot specify the letters forwarded by Vaughan.

[3] The identifications of Robinson and some of the names that follow are rather tenuous. We assume Vaughan is informing Henry of the comings and goings of other American scientists. Robinson may be Horatio Nelson Robinson (1806–1867), mathematician and textbook author, who at this time directed academies in New York State. He may have had some connection with Locke since he later did some teaching in Cincinnati from 1841–1850. Another possibility is Dr. Samuel Robinson, who wrote *Course of Lectures on Medical Botany, Delivered in Cincinnati, Ohio*, which appeared in several editions between 1829 and 1835. He also wrote on mineralogy. *Herringshaw. National Cyclopaedia of American Biography.*

[4] Probably Willard Parker (1800–1884), who received his M.D. from Harvard in 1830 and taught surgery at Cincinnati in 1836–1837, later teaching at the College of Physicians and Surgeons in New York. During his 1837 European tour, Parker spent a year in Paris learning from the French clinicians. As Vaughan will go on to mention, Parker attended the BAAS meetings at Liverpool. Like Henry and some other touring scientists, Parker kept an excellent European diary, published in John Ruhräh, "Willard Parker (1800–84)," *Annals of Medical History*, 1933, 5:205–214, 376–389. *DAB.*

[5] Probably the prominent Maine physician James McKeen (1797–1873), who began his European visit in 1837. Graduated from Bowdoin College, he received his medical degree from Harvard and settled down to practice in Maine. Beginning in 1825, he taught obstetrics at the Medical School of Maine. McKeen was important in the founding of the Maine Medical Association. Howard A. Kelly and Walter L. Burrage, eds., *American Medical Biographies* (Baltimore, 1920).

[6] Possibly James Scammon Goodwin (1793–1884), another Maine physician who took his degree at Dartmouth Medical School in 1814. We cannot verify a European visit. Kelly and Burrage, eds., *American Medical Biographies* (Baltimore, 1920).

Another possibility, because of a documented European tour in 1837, is Daniel Raynes Goodwin (1811–1890), educator and divine, who taught Modern Languages at Bowdoin from 1835 to 1853, when he became President of Trinity College at Hartford, Connecticut. In 1860, he became Provost of the University of Pennsylvania, where he opposed the addition of a science department. *DAB.*

No Goodwin can be found among the lists of foreigners attending British Association meetings in the Association's 1837 *Report.*

[7] William Hamilton, manager of the business affairs of the Franklin Institute. *Henry Papers*, 2:198n.

[8] The parcels and books are unknown to us.

[9] Thomas and John Daniel Thornely were merchants, located at 7 Goree, in Liverpool.

Gore's Directory of Liverpool and its Environs, 1835 (Liverpool, 1835), pp. 12, 374. They were listed, respectively, as Life Member and An- nual Subscriber of the BAAS in the list of members appended to the Association's *Report* for 1837.

FROM HENRY JAMES
Henry Papers, Smithsonian Archives

London 65 Albany St
Sep. 6. 1837

My dear friend:

I am anxious to hear from you of Your intended movements after you get through with Liverpool. I shall hardly be able to get on there during the meeting of the Association, as I wish to see Mr Halsey[1] immediately on his arrival from France, which will not be in much less probably than a fortnight. Otherwise I should be inclined to go on to L. and prepare for starting home as soon as you could pack up. But you will of Course have to return to London. What time shall you be here? I would like amazingly to get off in the packet which leaves Portsmouth the 20th, but this will hardly suit your views, and altogether probably we had better wait for the Westminster the 8th of October. Write to me, to this address, and attribute the brevity of my letter to the great uncertainty I am under of its even reaching you. It would be impolitic to enlarge upon transAtlantic affairs in a document which may very probably fall into the Enemy's hands, and which coming from a man of my widely acknowledged Note, might, pro- vided, of course, they should have gumption enough to decipher it, greatly aggravate the Existing embarrassments between the two countries.[2] Never- theless, I am just as much as tho' I had written a sheet

Yours Ever truly   H. James

[1] Unidentified.
[2] We have no idea of the "transAtlantic af- fairs" the elder Henry James will not put to paper.

FROM HENRY JAMES
Henry Papers, Smithsonian Archives

London   September 8. 1837.

My dear friend:

Another letter so soon upon the heels of my last will surprise you. I have been cogitating as well as I am able upon the properest time for my return, and I do seriously apprehend that I ought not to postpone my sailing beyond the 20th. Only one thing makes me hesitate and that is your society across. I find that a passage to the United States takes about 35 days, which supposing I left in October would bring me up to the commencement of the Seminary term in November, in getting home. I must of course spend some days in Albany, and a few in New York—and all this while, in this latter case, my time will be consuming, without any benefit to my seminary studies. I have had great reason to reproach myself in this and the past year for loss of time in Princeton, and I do most earnestly desire to get back now in season to allow me to accomplish all my talking with my friends, before the term commences.[1] What say you? Shall you be greatly disappointed, in the Event of my going? I ask this question thus plainly, because I feel that it will be a great disappointment to me to go without *you*. & What time do you think you could be ready to go? If you could get off the 20th—as knowing your anxiety to see your family I presume you would gladly do—Can I assist your motions by seeing to the packing up of your affairs at Mr Rich's,[2] or by doing anything else? Write to me by return post—65 Albany St—& believe me Yrs Ever truly & affectionately

H James

[1] Henry James did not renew his studies at Princeton Theological Seminary upon his return to the United States. Instead, since the inheritance from his father's considerable estate guaranteed him a lifetime income of over $10,000 per year, he decided to settle down in New York City to pursue his calling as an independent philosopher. Giles Gunn, *Henry James, Senior: A Selection of His Writings* (Chicago, 1974), p. 18.

[2] Obadiah Rich, the London bookseller.

FROM HENRY JAMES
Henry Papers, Smithsonian Archives

Sep 12. 1837
London

My dear friend:

I have but time to say a word, having rec[eive]d your letter[1] as I was on the point of going out. I am delighted you are disposed to go along in the Ontario. But let me remind you, that as the Ontario leaves *Portsmouth* & not *London* the 20th, we must get away in the mail from London on the *19*, in the afternoon. I will secure seats; so you must try to be here if you can

[1] Not found.

by the morning of the 19ᵗʰ at the latest. You had better get here on the Evening of the 18ᵗʰ, and take a good nights sleep before riding to Portsmouth. We shall have to get our bundles (i.e. our boxes of books &c) on board the Ontario before she leaves the docks here; if you therefore will give me directions what things you want attended to here in any manner or shape—in the way of purchase or packing up—I will see to them, and have them duly stowed away on board.[2] So write & believe me Ever affectionately

Yours

H. J.

[2] Henry did not depart for America until October 2, nor was he accompanied by Henry James. Instead he returned to London from Liverpool to make some more magnetic observations and to purchase some apparatus.

TO JAMES HENRY

Mary Henry Copy, Family Correspondence,
Henry Papers, Smithsonian Archives

Liverpool Sept. 15 1837

To Brother

I arrived in this city from Scotland on Saturday the Ninth: have been constantly occupied in the affairs of the Association. There is a great collection of strangers from every part of the world now in Liverpool and among the number not a few from America. . . . I have taken some part in the proceedings and have met with the same kind reception here as at every other place in Great Britain I have visited.[1] I intended to start for home as

[1] The seventh meeting of the British Association for the Advancement of Science began on Saturday, September 9, 1837, and ended on Saturday, September 16. In later letters Henry comments in greater detail on particular events and the value of the meetings.

For Henry's participation, the best account is the *Athenaeum*, a weekly London journal, which reported the meeting in the issues of September 16 (pp. 665–687), September 23 (pp. 689–707), September 30 (pp. 717–730), and October 7, 1837 (pp. 743–755). The *Athenaeum* gives greater coverage to the minor communications and to discussions than the official *BAAS Report, 1837* (1838).

On Monday, September 11, Henry attended the Mathematical and Physical Science Section, where he participated in a discussion on magnets made of cast iron (p. 667).

On Tuesday, September 12, he addressed the Mechanical Section on the canals and railways of the United States (p. 687). Henry later described the controversy and embarrassment caused by this talk in a letter to Bache of October 1 (see below).

On Thursday, September 14, Henry addressed the Mathematical and Physical Science Section on lateral discharge (p. 717). This paper was printed in the *BAAS Report, 1837* (1838), part 2, pp. 22–24. Henry apparently wrote it in Paris, originally intending it for the French Institut (see above, Henry's second letter to Harriet Henry of July 5, 1837). For comments on the presentation see the *Athe-*

soon after the meeting as possible and to sail from this port but I shall be obliged to return to London, in order to make some magnetic observations[2] and also to purchase some articles in the way of apparatus which I have not yet procured. .[3] I will sail probably on the 24 but may not find it practical to get off before the first of October. I could stay longer in England with great profit to myself but feel anxious to see my family.

---

naeum, pp. 717–718, and Henry to Coquerel, October 1, 1837, printed below.

In 1838 *Silliman's Journal* reprinted excerpts from the *Athenaeum* and other accounts of the meetings (1838, *33*:265–296 and *34*:1–56). The excerpts chosen included both of Henry's presentations (*33*:296 on canals and railways and *34*:16–18 on lateral discharge).

[2] Bache had asked Henry to make readings of the magnetic intensity at Westbourne Green in London, where Bache had previously taken readings himself (Bache to Henry, July 16, 1837, printed above).

[3] It is unclear whether Mary Henry made an omission at this point. Receipts show that Henry's last-minute purchases included a Clarke electrical machine bought from E. M. Clarke on September 25, 1837. The next day he bought several things from John Newman, including a Faraday voltameter and two thermopiles. Folder of Accounts with Various European Instrument- and Apparatus-Dealers, Joseph Henry for the College of New Jersey, 1837, Princeton University Archives.

"NOTES[1] OF OBJECTS AT CAMBRIDGE"
Henry Papers, Smithsonian Archives

[September 18–20, 1837]

Was introduced to Prof Henslow[2] by Dr Faraday. Started for Cambridge at 2 o'clock Monday 18th found myself in the car for Manchester arrived in

---

[1] These notes consist of hasty jottings on legal–size paper. They appear to be the raw material which Henry would later polish and expand as a European Diary entry.

As Henry mentions below, however, he lost the fourth volume of his diary on September 18. These undigested impressions are the only record of his visit to Cambridge.

At some time the two legal-size sheets of this manuscript were separated in the Henry Papers, Smithsonian Archives. The first sheet is in Box 29; the second, beginning with "fine view of the city" in the middle of the second paragraph of our text, is in Box 30.

[2] A graduate of St. John's College, Cambridge (1818), John Stevens Henslow (1796–1861) received the M. A. in 1821. He obtained the Chair of Mineralogy at Cambridge in 1822. Three years later he was elected Professor of Botany at his alma mater. He was more interested in the geographical distribution of plants than in systematics, and led a generation of Cambridge students into the field.

Among those inspired by Henslow was Charles Darwin. In later years Darwin would record that his friendship with Henslow "influenced my career more than any other." It was through Henslow's efforts that Darwin received a berth on the *Beagle*. Nora Barlow, ed., *Darwin and Henslow: The Growth of an Idea* (London, 1967), pp. 221–226.

One of the treasures in the Henry Library, perhaps obtained during the 1837 trip to Europe, is a copy of a rare pamphlet prepared by Henslow in 1835 by extracting portions of the letters written to him by Darwin while on the *Beagle*. The pamphlet was printed solely for private distribution to members of the Cambridge Philosophical Society. Henry later sent Henslow both specimens and publications from the United States.

that city at about ½ pas[t] 3. Called on Mr Daton[3] not at home. Saw lady withwom he lodged. Also his library: Transactions of Amer Academy, Mr Griscombs tour.[4] Quite well at Present has a few pupils. Statue making of him by chantrey[5] not yet finished or at least brought down.

Started from Manchester at 20 minutes before 7 arrived in Birmingham at 11 o'clock a distance of 97 miles. In morning found Prof Henslow who had left Liverpool without me. Plesant ride to Cambridge where we arrived at about 8 o'clock. Horses of troopers made to capre with the sound of the bugle and the tune of the bold dragoon. Passed through coventry. Article in Review writen by Prof Henslow on [. . .].[6] Lost memorandum book in Birmingham. Red flower on the field a popy. Sine of bad culture. Plesant country good roads. Prof invited me to his house Lady from house. Devoted himself to me during the next day. Visited first the observatory introduced to Prof Chales.[7] Short man. Observatory neat building inhabited by astronomer and 2 assistants.[8] Great transit[9] 10 feet focal length small object glass instrument covered with oiled cloath made by Dolland. Supports on friction rooles with counter poises in the stone piers. Large mural circle 8 feet diameter 6 microscopes. Method of oiling the pivots. Anemometer of Mr Wheele[10] on top of the observatory defective on account of the screw. Large building for the large Tellescop.[11] Glass made by gambey[12] of

[3] John Dalton.

[4] John Griscom (for whom see above, "Visit to Melrose Abbey to Dr Brewster," August 19–21, 1837, footnote 45) had visited Dalton in Manchester and found him to be a simple-mannered man highly respected by the community. The two men breakfasted together at William Henry's. Chemistry was the main topic of conversation. John Griscom, *A Year in Europe*, 2 vols. (New York, 1823), *1*:44–45.

[5] Chantrey's life-size statue, eventually placed in the entrance hall of the Manchester Royal Institution, had been paid for through a subscription raised by the citizens of Manchester. Dalton had sat for Chantrey in the Spring of 1834. William Charles Henry, *Memoirs of the Life and Scientific Researches of John Dalton* (London, 1854), pp. 182–186.

[6] Illegible word. The only article published by Henslow in a review journal was a review of De Candolle's *Physiologie Végétale* in *Foreign Quarterly Review*, 1833, *11*:334–382.

[7] Educated at Trinity College, Cambridge, James Challis (1803–1882) became Plumian Professor and Director of the Cambridge Observatory in 1836. Whatever his scientific merits, Challis's reputation, both among contemporaries and historians, has been clouded

by his failure to discover Neptune after he was given the theoretical position of the planet by John C. Adams. Challis exhibited a complete lack of initiative during the episode. *DSB*.

[8] One of the two assistants was John Glaisher (1819–1846), who joined the staff of the Cambridge Observatory in 1836 and remained for nine years. *Poggendorff.* We have not been able to identify the second assistant.

[9] The transit is described in Robert Woodhouse, "Some Account of the Transit Instrument Made by Mr. Dollond, and Lately Put Up at the Cambridge Observatory," *Phil. Trans.*, 1825, pp. 418–428.

[10] William Whewell's self-registering anemometer gave the direction, velocity, and duration of the wind. The one at Cambridge was erected between the British Association meetings of 1835 and 1836. Ultimately, Whewell hoped to establish a network of such devices to obtain insight into the general annual movement of the atmosphere. William Whewell, "On a New Anemometer," *British Association Report, 1835* (1836), part 2, p. 29; *British Association Report, 1836* (1837), part 2, pp. 39–40.

[11] The Northumberland Equatorial—named after Hugh Percy, third Duke of Northumber-

Paris 12 inches in diameter 20 feet focus mounted by Syms.[13] Large stone pier. Cast in iron supports. Wooden tube. Roof of observatory of zinc like the cover of a tent. Turns on balls. Top of observatory on friction rooles. The telescope to be erected like an equatorial instrument. Equatorial instruments only used for measuring the difference of declination of small objects near each other or of objects such as comets and planets from stars difference in right asscension determined by time so that there is only a declination circle. Large room in observatory left open in good weather so that air may get temperature of the external. Observation made on same star by reflection and direct at same transit by different wires (5 in number). Visited round church model of tomb over the Holy sepulchre[14] [?disfigured] by gallery. Kings college chapel[15] beautiful specimen of gothic of the last period cealing great curiosity all of stone. Screen of oak form of a parallelogram. From top had fine view of the city. Saw all the colleges and Halls 19 in number. Dined in the Hall amused with the antiquated ceremonies. [. . .][16] & Silver Urn put on table. Healths drunk cross table from one to the other origin of this.[17] Three classes in the University sophs junior sophs and senior sophs. Members of Kings college selected from Eaton School near winsor 2½ a year.[18] Peculiar privileges not examined for a fellowship. All fellows of course. None selected from Eaton but to fill the vacancies by death or resignation. Some fellows very old; one a short time since dead 76. Do nothing but eat and drink. Cannot be altered. Kings pupils do nothing

land, who donated the funds for both the telescope and its observatory—was not completed until about a year after Henry's visit. With a clear aperture of 11.5 inches, the telescope was at the time one of the world's largest refractors. George B. Airy, *Northumberland Equatorial and Dome* (Cambridge, England, 1844).

[12] Henry was wrong. The glass for the Northumberland Equatorial came from Robert A. Cauchoix (1776–1845), a Parisian optician. The same artisan was also responsible for Sir James South's great lens and the Sheepshanks Equatorial of Greenwich Observatory. *Encyclopaedia Britannica*, 8th ed., s.v. "Telescope;" *Dictionnaire de Biographie Française*.

[13] William Simms.

[14] The Church of the Holy Sepulchre, built in the twelfth century, was one of only four round churches in England. In 1841 it underwent restoration. Thomas D. Atkinson, *Cambridge Described and Illustrated* (Cambridge, England, 1897), pp. 164–167.

[15] Victorian England thought the chapel of King's College, Cambridge, to be one of the finest examples of Tudor Gothic in Europe. The view from the roof was considered one of the highlights of a visit to the University. Frederick Arnold, *Oxford & Cambridge* (London, 1873), pp. 264–269.

[16] Three words unclear.

[17] The dinner ceremony at Cambridge dated back to the Middle Ages. A cup was passed around the table and each person offered a toast to another. Antique cups and urns were used as centerpieces. J. J. Smith, *Cambridge Portfolio*, 2 vols. (London, 1840), *1*:296.

[18] King's College was founded in 1441. About five years later Eton was founded for the purpose of supplying scholars and fellows to King's. In the nineteenth century, King's Scholars at Eton were elected to fill vacancies on the basis of seniority rather than merit. After three years at King's, the Scholars were eligible to become Fellows.

Henry's information was incorrect on one point. The number of Eton students selected for King's averaged 4.5 per year, not 2.5. Smith, *Cambridge Portfolio*, 2:426.

by obligation no recitations or examinations. Fine living. University an encorporation which governs itself and perpetuates its own members. Senate caput.[19] White Hoods and Black hoods. Antiquated customs examinations[20] by writing at Present. First however a disputation in Latin and hours with a father. Mr Wheall[21] has great influence name easier whistled than pronounced. Vain man but of great talents not as amiable as Peacock.[22] Latter writing the life of Thomas Young.[23]

University Professors and College tutors and lecturors Mr W and also Mr P. are tutors. Large incomes. Trinity the best college others not as many celebrated men. Noble men have peculiar privileges.[24] Earl Burlington[25] 1st Wrangler. Statue of Newton by Roubillac.[26] Lock of hair instruments & telescope used by him. Sheets of his Principia, Cote's[27] letters, Miltons pro-

---

[19] The Caput Senatus was a council elected by a select group at Cambridge from a list prepared by the Vice-Chancellor and the proctors. Unanimous approval by the Caput was required before a dispensation from the requirements for a degree could be requested from the University Senate. The Cambridge University Act of 1856 replaced the Caput with a Council of the Senate. T. J. N. Hilken, *Engineering at Cambridge University, 1783–1965* (Cambridge, England, 1967), p. 22.

[20] Students at Cambridge were initially classified according to their performances in Latin disputations. Top students might be required to participate in as many as eight disputations, while less gifted men might be let off with only one; in the latter case the remaining disputations would be "huddled" (handled through a series of pre-arranged questions and answers). Once placed in one of the four classifications—wranglers, senior and junior optimes, and poll men—by the moderators in consultation with the college tutors, it was impossible for a student to move into another group.

The major written examination, which determined one's ranking within the group, was the Senate House Examination. Four days were spent in the examination, which covered mathematics, logic, and moral philosophy (in the middle of the nineteenth century moral philosophy was removed, leaving what became known as the Mathematical Tripos). The actual process of examination varied slightly according to the student's group. The wranglers, for example, had written questions and underwent eight hours of examination per day. In contrast, the questions were dictated to the poll men, who only suffered through a six-hour day. Hilken, *Engineering at Cam-*

bridge, pp. 9–12.

[21] William Whewell.

[22] George Peacock (1791–1858) received his B.A. from Trinity College, Cambridge in 1813. He was a tutor in Trinity from 1823 through 1839. In 1837 he was elected Lowndean Professor of Geometry and Astronomy. A founding member of the Cambridge Analysts, Peacock was influential in overthrowing the fluxional notation and geometric methodology at Cambridge in favor of the notation of Leibniz and analytical techniques. *DSB*.

[23] *Life of Thomas Young* (London, 1855). According to the Preface (p. vi), Peacock began the biography in the early 1830s.

[24] In a continuation of a tradition dating back to the Middle Ages, the undergraduates at Cambridge were divided into four groups according to socioeconomic class. Each group had a different set of privileges and obligations. Noblemen paid higher fees, but were able to dine at the high tables and wear special gowns. They received their M.A. degree without examination after six terms in residence. Hilken, *Engineering at Cambridge*, pp. 8–9.

[25] William Cavendish, for whom see above, Henry's European Diary, April 20, 1837, footnote 2.

[26] Louis François Roubiliac (1695–1762) was born in Lyons. He came to England around 1738. The statue of Newton in the Trinity Library, completed in 1755, inspired Wordsworth to write:

With his prism and silent face,
The marble index of a mind for ever
Voyaging through strange seas of Thought,
    alone—

[27] Roger Cotes (1682–1716) was a graduate

gram of Paradise lost. Museum of Fitzwilliam:[28] good pictures model of Somerset house in cork also an ancient tomb. Anatomical Museum[29] skelaton of fosil elk 100 [?guineas]. Cast Bones of megatherium from South America, cast of old woman who gave herself for dissection also of D^r something. Cast of the leg of vestris or [?tubigera],[30] pictures of Plica Polonica[31] which infests the hair of every part of the body beautifully arranged on mahogany pedestals bones cleaned with soda very white. Instrument for articulating. Lecture table for anatomy on wheels also to turn up. Seats very steep table just filled semi circular spaces curving Laboratory

Prof Henslows drawings to illustrate botany. Use ox gall portfolio made of frame of wood covered with cloath. Exp on colours Scale of colour.[32] Butter by the yd. Rooms finely furnished. Phil Society of Cambridge[33] Prof Henslow and Wheel secretaries Museum cast of head of Herschell not a handsome man. Collection of British Birds.

---

of Trinity College and Plumian Professor of Astronomy. He assisted Newton in the preparation of the second edition of the *Principia*, contributing a short preface defending the book against Cartesian criticism. *DSB*.

[28] Richard Fitzwilliam (1745–1816), seventh Viscount Fitzwilliam of Meryon, Fellow of the Royal Society, Member of Parliament, and graduate of Cambridge, bequeathed his collection of manuscripts, books, drawings, and other material to Cambridge, along with an endowment to maintain the collection. At the time of Henry's visit the collection was exhibited in the Perse Grammar School. Construction of the museum building did not begin until November 1837. *DNB*; Atkinson, *Cambridge Described and Illustrated*, pp. 492–493.

[29] The Museum of Human and Comparative Anatomy served both to help prepare Cambridge students for a career in medicine and to provide specimens for lecture courses in zoology. At the time of Henry's visit a new building had just been erected to house the collection of anatomical preparations and models, as well as to provide space for the lecture hall Henry described below. *The Cambridge University Catalogue* (Cambridge, England, 1836), p. 30.

[30] Unidentified. The readings are extremely tentative.

[31] Otherwise known as the Polish plait.

Studies of this disease had led some physicians to attack the prevailing early nineteenth-century assumption that hair was inorganic. *Encyclopaedia Britannica*, 8th ed., "Anatomy," p. 835.

[32] In an effort to analyze the complex hues of flowers, Henslow devised a chromatometer, which enabled him to estimate the relative quantity of primary and secondary colors in such hues. He described the apparatus and his results in *The Principles of Descriptive and Physiological Botany* (London, 1836). Leonard Jenyns, *Memoir of the Rev. John Stevens Henslow* (London, 1862), pp. 43–45.

[33] Founded in 1819 through the efforts of E. D. Clarke, a mineralogist, the Cambridge Philosophical Society had originated in suggestions of Henslow and Adam Sedgwick, Professor of Geology. It became a major force in the development of science in Britain. Leadership lay in the hands of the Cambridge Network, a group of scientists and other scholars who set the pace during the first half of the nineteenth century when Cambridge was transformed into a modern scholarly institution. Members of the Network included John Herschel, Babbage, Peacock, Whewell, and G. B. Airy. Walter F. Cannon, "Scientists and Broad Churchmen: an Early Victorian Intellectual Network," *The Journal of British Studies*, 1964, *4*:66–72.

"VISIT TO SIR JAMES SOUTH"[1]
Henry Papers, Smithsonian Archives

[ca. September 20–30, 1837]

Was introduced by Dr Robison[2] of Armah dined with Sir James and Lady. Anectdotes of Cambridge observers. Instrument fell in to a pit with which variation in density was to be observed.[3] French observers. Sir James lived more than a year in Paris at Passey. Kept an observatory.[4] Made observations almost every night. This was in 1824. Observatory room for transit. Another for transit circle made by Troughton. Excellent instrument described in Piersons astronomy.[5] A little altered two additional armes with microscopes making 8 in all. Graduation on two limbs or rather on the two circles. Transit about 6 feet not certain. Equatorial instrument mounted like the large one but support convex on the inside quite steady. The method of screwing together the ⟶ globular part of the tellescope very ingenious, a rod with ⟶ a screw cut on each end one larger than the other. This is inserted by screwing it into the smaller screw. The other end is then put into the large screw and the rod turned around so as to screw out of one into the other. In this way the two parts are drawn together.

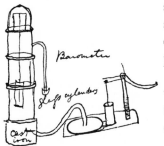

Vibrations of the Pendulum in a vacuum.[6] The whole clock put in under bell glasses. Some interesting results. Large air pump for the vacum, one formerly used for Lesley's exp.

---

[1] The notes printed below appear in a manuscript (in Box 28, folder 6) containing other miscellaneous jottings on Henry's travels in England, on scientific readings and apparatus, and on the London-Birmingham Railway. The notes are undated but internal evidence places this visit to South sometime in late September, after Henry attended the British Association.

[2] Thomas Romney Robinson (1792–1882), the Dublin astronomer and mathematical physicist. Robinson took charge of Armagh Observatory in 1824, after lecturing for several years at Trinity College, Dublin. His first important astronomical publication was *Armagh Observations, 1828–30*. His great work, published in 1859, was *Places of 5,345 Stars Ob-served at Armagh from 1828 to 1854. DNB*. Henry later wrote to Robinson recalling their meeting with South in London.

[3] We have not been able to confirm this anecdote, nor do we know the period to which it refers. At this time Challis was head of the Cambridge Observatory. His predecessor was Airy.

[4] For South's career and astronomical instruments, see Bache's diary above for April 6, 1837.

[5] William Pearson, *An Introduction to Practical Astronomy*, 2 vols. (London, 1829), 2:366–371.

[6] See above, Bache's diary entry for April 6, 1837, footnote 8.

NOTES ON A VISIT TO THE THAMES TUNNEL
Henry Papers, Smithsonian Archives[1]

[September 28, 1837][2]

Visited the Thames Tunnel by special invitation[3] of the author M Brunel the elder. Was first provided with the dress of a miner to keep out water. Was put under the care of one of the assistants and then was admitted into the shield where the excavation was going on.

J.H.

When I was introduced to Brunel at the meeting of the Society of Engineers he asked me as to the part of America I came from. When I replied that I was born in albany state of New York he exclaimed albany! Were you born in albany? Then you can tell me whether the old Dutch church[4] still stands in the middle of state street. Brunel commenced his career as an engineer in this country and among his ferst works was the survey for a canal from the Hudson to Lake Champlaign.[5]

[1] This document (in Box 50) consists of the notes Henry annexed to his copy of the 1837 report of the directors to the proprietors of the Thames Tunnel Company.

[2] The dating of these notes is very problematic. We have somewhat arbitrarily selected the date M. I. Brunel presented Henry with a copy of his *An Explanation of the Works of the Tunnel Under the Thames from Rotherhithe to Wapping* (London, 1837). However, we have no real evidence that Henry visited the construction site on that day. The visit could have occurred any time from April 18, 1837, the date of Henry's initial meeting with Brunel (see above, Henry's European Diary, April 18, 1837), to the 28th of September. It is more likely that the visit was in September,

when Henry was no longer keeping his diary, than earlier, when our knowledge of Henry's activities is more complete.

[3] The invitation was offered at the initial meeting of the two men.

[4] The site of the First Dutch Reformed Church had been sold to the city in 1806 and the church building demolished. At the time of destruction the church building, the second church on that site, was over ninety years old. The congregation of the First Dutch Church traced its history back even further—to 1642. *Howell and Tenney*, pp. 770–771.

[5] For more details of Brunel's work in the United States, see Henry's European Diary entry for April 18, 1837, printed above.

TO ALEXANDER DALLAS BACHE
Bache Papers, Smithsonian Archives

Portsmouth Oct 1st 1837

My Dear Bache

I arrived in this Place last night with the prospect of sailing this morning but the weather has proved very unfavourable and the probability is now that we will not get off until tomorrow. A roughf sea and an angry skey frowns on our departure. I am however anxious to be off and long as you may suppose to see my little Family. I have received almost by every Packet letters from Mrs H. containing the pleasing intelligence that all are well. I made a very plesant visit to Scotland, was politely received by Mr Robeson of the Royal society, Mr Henderson of the Observatory, Mr Russel and several others. At this place I also met with Mr Frenel of Paris on a visit to the Light Houses of Scotland and with him and a party from Edinburgh I visited the Bell rock and the light on the island of May. In Glasgow I met with Graham,[1] Thompson,[2] Mackintosh[3] (the Indian rubber manufacturer) Tenant,[4] Lebig[5] of Germany, Kane[6] and Gregory[7] of Dublin. From Glasgow I passed down the coast through Ayr shire to the line of England and then took a steam boat for Liverpool where I arrived the Saturday preceding the meeting of the Association.

The report of the meeting you will receive in the nos. of the Atheneum[8] which Mr Vaughan will send you as soon as the whole is completed. In reference to myself the whole went off as well as could be expected. I however came to the conclusion that it is rather a hazardous affair for an American to make a communication unless he be well known and his communication addressed to the Section in which his Friends are found. I make this remark on account of the reception with which my communication to the

---

[1] An account of Thomas Graham can be found in Henry's European Diary entry of April 27, 1837, footnote 3.

[2] Thomas Thomson.

[3] Charles Macintosh (1766–1843), chemist and inventor of waterproof fabrics used in garments known by his name. Based in Manchester, Macintosh's manufactory utilized a process depending on the solvent action of naphtha on india rubber. Macintosh's almost accidental association with india rubber obscured his work as a chemist, for which he was elected F. R. S. in 1823. *DNB.*

[4] Charles Tennant (1768–1838), manufacturing chemist, was associated with Charles Macintosh in the establishment of a well-known chemical works for the production of bleaching powder and other alkali products. The firm was located at St. Rollox, near Glasgow. *DNB.* In notebook [7169], p. 241 (Henry Papers, Smithsonian Archives), Henry mentions that he visited Tennant at the chemical works.

[5] Henry gives no earlier account of his encounter with the great German organic chemist Justus von Liebig (1803–1873), *DSB.*

[6] Robert John Kane (1809–1890), chemist, was at this time Professor of Natural Philosophy at the Royal Dublin Society. Kane had studied with Liebig at Giessen for three months in 1836. His *Elements of Chemistry* (1841–1843) was introduced to the United States in an edition by John William Draper. *DSB. DNB.*

[7] William Gregory (1803–1858) was educated for the medical profession in Edinburgh. Having lectured at Anderson College in Glasgow and at Dublin Medical School, Gregory held the chemistry chair at the University of Edinburgh from 1844 until his death. A favorite student of Liebig's at Giessen in 1835 and in 1841, Gregory's main contributions to chemistry were his translations into English of various chemical works by Liebig. *DSB. DNB.*

[8] The issues of the *Athenaeum* pertinent to the events Henry goes on to relate were those of September 16 and 23, 1837, pp. 687, 705.

mechanical section was received.[9] You may reccollect that I had made some preparation to give an account of the Rail ways and canals in America and that I was presented by Mr Tanner of Philadelphia with a map on which all the lines of internal improvements were marked.[10] I concluded after witnessing the hurry of the sections not to give the details which I had intended but merely to present Mr Tanners map, say a few words on the Topography of the United states relative to internal communication and to refer to the authorities for farther information. I had prepared myself a large map of the united states on which all the above mentioned lines were delineated in broad marks. This I had placed on the wall of the room and after presenting Mr Tanners map I occupied the section for about 8 minuts with facts relative to topography collected by myself. The communication was brief and apparently listened to with interest but just as I was stepping from the stage a person named De Butts[11] asked me in rather a roughf manner to give some authentic information relative to the rate of velocity of the American steam boats. Dr Robinson[12] the moderator of the section objected to the question and to the manner. He however stated that I could do as I choosed about the answer. I stated that I was not a professed Engineer and did not expect to be called on for information of the kind but that I would mention one fact from my own observation namely that I had gone from Albany to New York a distance of 150 miles in 9 hours, that the river was wide and a tide from the ocean assisted sometimes the asscent of the boat but that I did not think the velocity on this account was increased more than 2½ miles per hour. Dr Lardner[13] who was one of the Vice Presidents of the mechanical section jumpt up and said the question of Mr De Butts was an important one but that we did not want popular information on the subject, that he did not believe that a velocity as great as I had stated had ever been obtained. On this Dr Robinson the moderator interfered, made some very severe remarks stating that he would not suffer a gentleman and a stranger to be thus questioned and his statements thus commented on. His remarkes made Dr Lardner col[or] to the eyes. I then stated that I re-

[9] Henry's "Friends" were in the section of mathematics and physics. Attending the meetings of that section, the American mathematician A. D. Stanley wrote:

Prof. H[enry] was member of the Committee of the Math. & Phys. Section. He seemed to be on good terms with most of the distinguished scientific men present.

(Stanley to Loomis, October 27, 1837, Loomis Papers, Beinecke Library, Yale University).

[10] For Henry S. Tanner and the maps of internal improvements, see Henry to Torrey, February 13, 1837, above.

[11] Rev. G. De Butts, of Crickhowel, Glamorganshire, is listed in the 1837 *BAAS Report* as one of the Association's annual subscribers.

[12] The astronomer Thomas Romney Robinson, whom Henry had previously met. See Henry's notes of September 20–30, 1837. *BAAS Report, 1837* (1838), p. x.

[13] The scientific encyclopedist Dionysius Lardner (1793–1859), *Henry Papers*, 2:257.

gretted I could give no more definite information, that I wished my communications to receive no favor on account of my being a Foreigner, that truth and Science should know no country—&c &c. These remarkes were received with applause and immediatly after Mr Russel of Edinburgh got up and informed the section who I was and commenced to pronounce a panegyric on me and my labors when as I happened to be near the door I withdrew.[14]

My statement relative to the velocity was correct since the very last time I made the voyage the time was less than 9 hours including several stopings in a new boat called the Swallow.[15] This boat however is so long and narrow

[14] The brief official BAAS report of the meeting of the Mechanical Section passed over these interchanges in silence. A complete though diplomatic account omitting the personal unpleasantries appeared in the *Athenaeum* for September 16 and 23. Lardner, who was due to address the same section on the application of steam power to long voyages, doubted that steamboats could sustain a speed of 15 miles an hour. At Henry's session, a member of the audience, quoting an American engineer, defended Henry's figures for the Albany to New York distance. The discussion carried over to the next day after Lardner painted a rather pessimistic future for speedy and efficient steam navigation. Several commentators again spoke up with American evidence to the contrary. The Hudson steamers were cited several times, clearly corroborating Henry's estimates. An American listener promised to supply the next meeting of the British Association with a full report on American vessels. Until definitive figures could be provided, Lardner declared he would stand by his figures based upon the performance of the most improved British government steamers. In the absence of precise facts, he would not depart from his own examples for "ten thousand miles of Hudson voyages" (*Athenaeum*, September 23, 1837, p. 705).

The attack on Henry created a stir far beyond the meetings. Harsh feelings persisted and the events echoed through the next several years of Henry's career, as later documents in the *Henry Papers* will show. The almost immediate vindication of Henry's facts by events caused Lardner subsequent embarrassment, even humiliation, during an American lecture tour in the early 1840s. Aroused American audiences in Philadelphia reminded Lardner of his ill-founded efforts to embarrass one of their own. Although staying aloof, consciously refraining from applying influence against him in this country, Henry gloated over Lardner's discomfiture. Lardner admitted to a mistake and misunderstanding, but Henry accused him of a moral crime against science and congratulated Philadelphians on their rejection of charlatanism. See J. S. Hart to Henry, March 18, 1842 (Henry Papers, Smithsonian Archives); Henry to Torrey, December 29, 1841 (Torrey Papers, Library, New York Botanical Garden); and Henry to Jesse Buel, the younger, [ca. 1842] (Henry Papers, Smithsonian Archives).

Ostensibly the debate hinged on certain evidence in steam technology. But Henry's pointed appeal to the internationalism of scientific truth brought up chauvinistic undercurrents in Lardner's downgrading of Henry and American evidence. As Henry later indicated to Bache (letter of August 9, 1838, Bache Papers, Smithsonian Archives), he frequently encountered patronizing attitudes toward American culture among the Europeans, especially the English. Adding to Lardner's pretension was his fame as a scientific polymath and encyclopedist. He was the author of a popular book on the steam engine, which also covered steam navigation. Although Henry once respected Lardner's work and made frequent use of his compilations, it is evident that after this encounter he became more suspicious of British experts. While no expert himself on steamboats, Henry knew the Hudson trip intimately. His knowledge of the technological particulars of navigating the river was simply another evidence of a life-long curiosity in technology and a scientist's instinct for fine detail.

[15] The record voyages of the *Swallow* were widely publicized. Built by William Capes of Brooklyn, the *Swallow* displaced 426 tons and its dimensions were 224 x 22 x 8½ feet. Its

that she required two false side keels to steady her. The papers of New York have lately stated that the passage has been made the present season in 8 hours. The conduct of Dr. Larderner was reprobated by the majority of the persons present and during my stay in Liverpool not a day passed afterwards without some persons introducing themselves to me and mentioning the affair.

---

record-setting voyage of 8 hours, 42 minutes was made on October 8, 1836. Henry, who traveled to Albany in October 1836, may have taken the boat at that time. Reynolds, *Alb. Chron.*, pp. 516, 518.

TO CHARLES COQUEREL[1]
Miscellaneous Manuscripts Collection,
Library, American Philosophical Society

Portsmouth Oct 1ˢᵗ 1837

My Dear Sir

I hope you received the numbers of the Library of Useful Knowledge[2] which were sent according to your directions as soon after my arrival in London as possible. I have made a tour in Scotland, attended the meeting of the British Association and have just arrived at this place from London with the prospect of sailing tomorrow for America in the Packet ship Toronto. We would have been off today but the weather has proved unfavourable and the wind contrary.

I directed that a set of the Nos. of the Atheneum containing the account of the proceedings of the Association should be sent to you and also one to Professor Babinet.* I will also direct that a copy of each number be sent to Melloni.

I will forward your articles intrusted to me as soon as possible after my arrival to the Persons to whom they are directed.[4] I leave England well satisfied with my reception and also with the profits I have gained by my tour. The acquaintances I have formed in Europe will I hope be of much service and pleasure to me during life and should I be able to do anything

* I have commenced a letter to our Friend Babinet[3] but the Pilot leaves us before I can finish it. My respects to him. I have also sent a copy of the Atheneum to him.

[1] Henry met Coquerel in Paris. See above, Henry's European Diary, June 28, 1837.
[2] We do not know which numbers were sent.
[3] Henry eventually wrote to Babinet in March 1838.
[4] One of the recipients was Denison Olmsted. Henry to Coquerel, May 28, 1838, Henry Papers, Smithsonian Archives.

more in the way of science I will have an opportunity through my acquaintances in this country and on the continent of making it immediately known.

You will probably find in the reports of the proceedings of the Association many things of interest and also not a few of very puerile communications. But this is to be expected from a meeting of the kind where every person has the liberty of making a communication and where the merest *Sciolist* and the profound *savant* are on the same apparent level. I was on the whole much pleased with the meeting—it gave me an opportunity of seeing together the principal scientific men of the nation and of making the acquaintance of such as I had not before met.

No communication was made to the meeting of much scientific importance and I do not think that the principal men of the nation would bring forward at such a meeting memoirs of much profundity or on which they placed the greatest scientific value. Articles of this kind require to be studied with attention and cannot be appreciated by a large assembly or in the course of the few minutes devoted to any one communication. The chief good of the association appears to be that of forming a kind of festival for men of science for mutual stimulous and to afford an opportunity of those engaged in the same researches of comparing notes and making explanations to each other which cannot so well be done by other than personal communication. Another important advantage of the Association is that from the great number of members a large fund of money is collected and applied to scientific purposes under the direction only of the principal men.[5] Thus Sir David Brewster received a gr[ant] of 100 £s for carrying on

---

[5] While Henry repeatedly voiced his disappointment in the amateurism of the British Association (a complaint that would be echoed in his attitudes toward the American Association for the Advancement of Science), he was greatly impressed by the Association's scheme for supporting original scientific investigation. The influence of the Association plan can be seen in Henry's policies for backing research at the Smithsonian a decade later.

The British Association's grant program was a pioneering effort. There was no other equivalent form of research support in this period in Britain, and probably in the world. It was a grant program very much in the modern mold. Not until the Royal Society of London began to receive the £1000 annual grant from the Government at mid-century did British investigators have a significant alternative to the British Association funds. According to MacLeod (p. 325), the British Association program

"created a visible movement in favour of public support for science."

The BAAS grants are to be contrasted with other types of funds available for science and invention in this period, such as the Board of Longitude's prizes for chronometers and various exclusively mission-oriented projects sponsored by other official and private bodies. The subsidies were also exclusive of those earmarked for scientific publication.

The British Association subventions were originally derived solely from subscriptions of the membership. Not envisioned when the Association was founded in 1831 the program only began in 1833 when annual credit balances began to appear and it was decided the surplus should go to original research. The subsidies were allocated by member scientists through the Association's sectional committees. Some of the subjects were pre-selected by the Association and scientists were solicited to

his experiments on the lines of the solar spectrum produced by the intervension of some gasious medium between the eye and the prism.[6] More than 3000 £'s are now in the treasury to be thus disposed of.

You will find in the Atheneum an abstract of the Paper which I wrote in Paris on the lateral discharge.[7] This was well received by the Section and I intend to prepare a Memoir on the subject as soon as I can find time to extend the experiments. I hope you will let me hear from you when I get home. Reccollect my address—Professor Henry Princeton College New-Jersey United States. Please give my respects to Melloni and inform him that I have sent him a copy of the report of the association. I have herd his name frequently mentioned in England particularly by Mr Faraday and Mr Daniel in terms of the highest commendation.

M Thilorier promised to send me a copy of his discription of his condensing apparatus for carbonic acid with lithographic drawings. Should you see him please to remind him of the promise and say that his descovery of this solidification has produced quite a sensation in England and that I was questioned by almost every Philosopher relative to the details of the process. My Friend Professor Bache ordered for me a set of the apparatus which he was to take for the Girard College provided I would not have money sufficient to pay for it.[8] With much Respect Your Friend

Joseph Henry

carry out the research—a form of mission-oriented research. The largest single portion of funds went to the support of Kew Observatory, which between 1843 and 1872 received £12,300, an allocation which was largely due to the influence of Edward Sabine in Association politics. A long-term project to produce star catalogues was another example of a major allocation. Yet, other funds were widely distributed in small amounts, the intention being to initiate but not wholly fund worthy researches. It appears that in most cases individual investigators would take the initiative in proposing research projects to the Association. A full range of topics was represented, with a decided emphasis on the physical sciences. From 1833 to 1849, almost £15,000 was expended on almost three hundred projects and over fifty investigators. By 1931 some £92,000 had been distributed on almost seven hundred subjects. Although not large, these totals were significant in terms of the lack of alternative funding in the early nineteenth century and certainly as a symbolic gesture in favor of the funding of original research.

O. J. R. Howarth, *The British Association for the Advancement of Science: A Retrospect, 1831–1931* (London, 1931), pp. 146–148, 151–154. R. M. MacLeod, "The Royal Society and the Government Grant: Notes on the Administration of Scientific Research, 1849–1914," *The Historical Journal*, 1971, *14*:323–358. DSB, s.v. "Sabine." The British Association *Reports* give an annual accounting of the grants.

[6] Noted in *British Association Report, 1837* (1838), p. xviii. For the experiment, see Henry's notes on his visit with Brewster, August 19–21, 1837, especially footnote 41.

[7] Henry's communication was reported in the *Athenaeum* of September 30, 1837, p. 717, as well as in the *British Association Report, 1837* (1838), part 2, pp. 22–24. Henry never delivered the paper at the Paris Academy of Sciences as originally planned. The experimental work for this paper is presented above in Henry's "Record of Experiments," beginning on May 6, 1836.

[8] The arrangements with Bache are discussed in Bache to Dearne, August 21, 1837, Bache Papers, Smithsonian Archives.

P.S. I send this to land by the Pilot. We are now under way and will soon be out of sight of the white cliffs of Albion. Adieu.

TO ROBERT BALLANTINE[1]
Retained Copy, Henry Papers, Smithsonian Archives

Ship Toronto[2] off
Portsmouth Oct 2nd [1837]

My Dear Dr

I am just off, the ship is under way. The wind however is adverse a rough sea and an angry sky are before us—Albion appears to frown on our departure, may Columbia smile on our arrival.

The Pilot leaves us in a few moments, I have therefore only time to assure you that I shall allways retain a lively reccollection of my visit to Girvan.

Love to your Good wife & prosperity to you and your's.

In great haste

Your Friend
& Relative
Jos. Henry

P S I have sent a copy of the Atheneum

[1] A resident of Girvan, Ayrshire, Scotland, Ballantine was a relative of Henry's. Since Henry's mother was born in Ayrshire, we assume that Ballantine was connected through Henry's mother and was probably a cousin.

When Charles Scribner (1821–1871, *DAB*), one of Henry's former students at Princeton, went to Europe in the early 1840s, Henry asked Scribner to transmit a bundle to Ballantine as a token of appreciation for the hospitality shown Henry during his visit to Scotland (Henry's Address Book, Henry Papers, Smithsonian Archives). Included in the bundle was a copy of John Stephens, *Incidents of Travel in Yucatan*, 2 vols. (New York, 1843).

Henry inscribed the book: "To Dr Ballantine With the kind regards of his friend and relative Joseph Henry."

We wish to thank Mr. Robert H. Socolow, the present owner of the Stephens volumes, for bringing the inscription to the attention of the Henry Papers.

[2] One of the London packets of the Black Cross Line, the *Toronto* had been in service since 1835. Its port of call was changed to New Orleans in 1849. Two years later the *Toronto* was wrecked off Cuba. Robert G. Albion, *Square-Riggers on Schedule: The New York Sailing Packets to England, France, and the Cotton Ports* (Princeton, 1938), p. 282.

TO HARRIET HENRY

Mary Henry Copy,[1] Family Correspondence,
Henry Papers, Smithsonian Archives

On board Steam-boat W. L. Stephens[2]
Monday Oct. [30],[3] 1837

My dear Harriet. I arrived off the dock on Saturday night last at about eleven o'clock in the packet ship Toronto, Capt. Griswold,[4] after a pleasant passage of twenty-six days.[5] Now that the voyage is over it seems but a day or two since I left England. Time passes on the ocean with few incidents to mark its lapse and the month at sea seems less than one of the crowded days on shore. I was wretchedly ill with sea-sickness during the first seven or eight days. From the crowded state of the cabin I could procure but little attendance but this contributed to my recovery, since I was obliged to make some exertions in the way of assisting myself. Those who have felt the ills of the malady know that it produces the greatest disinclination to action and that any effort tends to diminish the disease.

Few events of importance occurred. A child of Mr. Clay[6] chargé d'affaires of this country to the Court of Russia died a few days after we sailed; the body was put in a cask of spirits for preservation but it would have been much better to consign it to the deep. . . . One night we experienced a violent thunder-storm a very unusual occurrence on the ocean in north latitudes in the month of October. The thunder was loud and the air highly electrified. The ends of spars and tops of the masts were tipped with brushes of electrical light. Several vessels have been struck during the past summer belonging to America but none I believe seriously injured; all risk of this

---

[1] There are two Mary Henry Copies of this letter. Our version is based on the more complete handwritten copy.

[2] Unidentified. The closest we could come was the *R. L. Stevens*, a night steamboat from New York to Albany (New York City Directory, 1837).

[3] The copyist incorrectly gave the date as October 21. From Henry's account of his trip (see his letter to Stephen Alexander of November 2, 1837, below), on Monday, October 30, he took a steam boat from Sandy Hook to New York City.

[4] Robert H. Griswold (ca. 1808–1882) was a captain on the London to New York run from 1833 until 1854. During that twenty-one year stretch he commanded five different ships. He

was the *Toronto's* first captain and remained with that ship until 1845. Robert G. Albion, *Square-Riggers on Schedule: The New York Sailing Packets to England, France, and the Cotton Ports* (Princeton, 1938), p. 336.

[5] Although by no means the record for the *Toronto*, this was a rapid voyage. The average passage from London to New York for this ship was thirty-six days; the shortest was twenty-three. Henry was fortunate not to have been on board during her longest trip: fifty days. Albion, *Square-Riggers on Schedule*, p. 283.

[6] John Randolph Clay (b. 1808) pursued a diplomatic career from 1830 until 1860, holding posts in Austria and Peru, in addition to Russia. *Herringshaw*, p. 224.

kind could be avoided by the use of the lightning rod proposed by Snow Harris[7] and adopted in the government vessels of Great Britain. There is however a strange antipathy to its use among sailors. [They] imagine the vessel is in more danger when it is employed, forgetting that the tall masts serve as attractors without giving protection. Considerable discussion took place among the passengers as to the nature of the light at the mast heads during the storm. One man, who had been more than twenty years a sailor stated that often during a violent storm of wind without lightning a faint light could be observed at the end of masts and spars, and that this on examination was found to proceed from a gelatinous substance of the phosphorescent kind. The phenomena observed by us was undoubtedly an electrical one[8] but that phosphorescent matter should not accumulate at the points of spars[9] I am not prepared to say. The opinion that a substance of the kind does thus accumulate is too common not to have some foundation in truth and is probably connected with some atmospheric phenomena not yet fully investigated. Whoever, says M. Biot, will carefully study for twenty years the facts of popular superstition, will find in them enough true philosophy to repay the labor.[10]

Another circumstance which for a short time relieved the monotony of sea life was a large whale passing close to the ship and crossing obliquely her path. It was one of the largest size. It did not continue on the surface but disappeared at intervals rising again to blow and[11]

[7] For Snow Harris and his lightning rod, see above, Henry's European Diary, March 14–16, 1837.

[8] Henry and his shipmates were observing a display of the brushlike electrical discharge usually called St. Elmo's Fire (a corruption of St. Erasmus, the patron saint of Mediterranean sailors). Recorded since Graeco-Roman times, it was a frequent occurrence during stormy weather. Its electrical nature was well known by Henry's day. Peter Kemp, ed., *The Oxford Companion to Ships and the Sea* (London, 1976), p. 744; William Burney, ed., *Falconer's Marine Dictionary* (London, 1830), p. 107.

[9] Contemporary naturalists had noted a form of phosphorescence due to the decomposition of organic matter in the ocean. Charles Darwin, *Voyage of the Beagle* (New York, 1969), pp. 167–169. Whether there is any connection between this decomposing matter and the gelatinous substance seen by the sailor is uncertain.

[10] We have been unable to identify the source of this quotation. Moreover, the sentiments expressed differ considerably from the elitist views most often expounded by Biot. There is a strong possibility that Henry misattributed the quotation, which Henry will repeat in his "Meteorology in its Connection with Agriculture" (*Scientific Writings of Joseph Henry*, 2 vols. [Washington, D.C., 1886], 2:253). (We wish to thank Dr. Eugene Frankel of the Department of Energy for his assistance in attempting to locate this quotation in Biot's writings.)

[11] The Mary Henry Copy breaks off in midsentence.

FROM JOHN TORREY
Henry Papers, Smithsonian Archives

New York. Nov.ʳ 1st. 1837

My dear friend.

I rejoice that you have returned in safety to your native land. This event I have learned by the public papers—& not by your calling on me—but I won't scold you for this, as I suppose you may have proceeded directly from the vessel to Princeton. But I *do* blame you for not writing to me once while you were absent. I Shall, however, *pump* you well when you come to New York, making you commence at the beginning & so proceeding till you have told me all the queer things you have seen & heard. I see that you were present at the Liverpool meeting of the Br. Ass.ⁿ, & that you made a report to one of the Sections.[1]

So you found the old house standing in the Campus & were not greatly disappointed! Some allowance ought to be made for the unexampled embarrassments of the money market, which have existed ever since you left us—& are not yet greatly abated. When I saw Maclean last week, he said that your house should come down, at all events, within a few days. What do you mean to do while the new building is going up?[2] I wish to see you very

[1] From his letter to Benjamin Silliman of October 17, 1837 (Torrey Papers, New York Botanical Garden Library), we know that Torrey had seen the *Liverpool Chronicle* account of the British Association meetings. The coverage by the *Chronicle*, much briefer than that in the *Athenaeum*, was in the issue of September 16, 1837. Henry had addressed two sections: the Mathematical and Physical Science Section on lateral discharge and the Mechanical Section on the canals and railways of the United States.

[2] The Board of Trustees had met twice during Henry's absence in Europe. At the April 11, 1837, meeting it was resolved "that the building committee proceed as soon as they shall think it expedient, to erect a dwelling house, agreeably to the plan submitted to said Committee, by Professor Henry." The next day the President was authorized to borrow $4,000 or $5,000 to finance the house and the finance committee was authorized to sell stocks if the President failed to raise the money. At the September 27, 1837, meeting of the Board, the Trustees appropriated "a sum not exceeding three hundred dollars" for rental of a house for Henry for a year. The committee on building Henry's house reported that following the April meeting, attempts to find financing both in the Princeton area and in New York had failed and that thus no progress had been made.

At this point, the Trustees' Minutes leave out all mention of an episode documented in the building committee's copy of its report:

> A few days since your committee had the proffer from a member of the board of a loan to enable them to commence the home; at the same time expressing his strong desire that the building should go up this autumn, and sent from N York t[w]o Master Mechanics a Carpenter & Mason. They gave it as their opinion that the work could not be completed this fall, so as to enable Prof Henry to occupy the home before next summer; the walls would be green, would be subject to frost, be weakened thus, and not be in any respect as good as if put up in the spring, nor habitable any sooner. These gentlemen agreed to make out the specification, and hand in their proposals, to the meeting of the board.

Maclean Papers, Building Committee, Trustees' Minutes, Princeton University Archives. Of the three Trustees from New York, Robert

much, but I cannot make a visit to Princeton till about Christmas week, for I am very busy arranging my new laboratory in our Coll. of Phys.[3] You will be pleased, I think, with some of my *traps*. Of course I do not expect to see the laboratory at P. in order for several years yet!

The Expl[g] Exped[n] is not off yet, but there is every reason for believing that it will sail about the end of the month.[4] Many of the scientific gentlemen are here. You must come on & see them before they go.

Prof[r] Daubeny arrived in N. Y. about 6 weeks ago. He has been travelling in Canada lately. I rec[d] a letter from him this morn[g] informing me that he will be here to-night. I went with him to West Point, & ascended the "Crow's Nest" with him & several of the Professors of the Academy. He is a man of considerable talent, & I should be glad to make you acquainted with him. Perhaps he will stop at P. on his way to the South.[5] Present my congratula-

---

Lenox, James Lenox, and William Wirt Phillips, the anonymous donor of money and workmen was probably Robert or James Lenox, who took particular interest in Henry's welfare at Princeton. In September 27, 1837, Trustees' Minutes, the subject is closed with a direction to the committee on Henry's house to "*proceed without delay*, to make arrangements to put up a dwelling house for a professor." Trustees' Minutes, Princeton University Archives.

Construction did not begin until the spring of 1838 and the new house was not ready for occupancy until the following September. Following the dismantling of the old house, the Henrys lived in a rented house near the Theological Seminary.

[3] The College of Physicians and Surgeons had recently moved to a new location further uptown (*Henry Papers*, 2:337).

[4] Torrey was proved wrong within a few days as preparations for the Exploring Expedition suddenly fell apart. On November 9, Dickerson issued sailing directions which Stanton (p. 54) terms "non-sailing directions." Thomas ap Catesby Jones resigned in frustration a few days later. Dickerson offered the command to three candidates in succession. When the last had refused, Secretary of War Joel Poinsett, requested by President Van Buren to "aid" Dickerson, ran through two more candidates before secretly offering the command to Charles Wilkes in April 1838. Following his controversial appointment, Wilkes began to reorganize every aspect of the expedition. He cut down the scientific corps by assigning their duties to Navy officers. Morale in the scientific corps plummeted as

its members received no direct replies to their inquiries as to whether they were still part of the expedition. Although not in danger of being cut himself, Asa Gray resigned in July 1838. Others hung on, despite rumors that a decision had been made to inform them of their dismissal only after the squadron had sailed. James Eights and Walter R. Johnson were among those left off at the last minute. The squadron finally sailed on August 18, 1838. William Stanton, *The Great United States Exploring Expedition of 1838–1842* (Berkeley, 1975), pp. 53–71.

[5] Charles G. B. Daubeny (*Henry Papers*, 2: 194–195), the British chemist, geologist, and botanist, spent almost a year in North America from August 1837 to July 1838. His trip is documented in fascinating detail in *Journal of a Tour Through the United States and Canada, Made During the Years 1837–38* (Oxford, 1843), a work printed in 100 copies for private circulation. Daubeny visited all of the major cities on the east coast of the United States, as well as Montreal, Quebec, and Toronto in Canada. After a trip to Cuba in February, he proceeded from New Orleans on horseback to St. Louis and back to the east coast. An intinerary, accompanied by daily readings of temperature and humidity, appears at the end of the volume. The journal includes observations on the weather, on local flora, and on geology; the latter were presented in greater detail in the separately published *Sketch of the Geology of North America* (Oxford, 1839). Daubeny also comments at great length on modes of transportation, local society, colleges, social institutions, politics, and scientific societies. After witnessing a

tions & my kind regards to Mrs. Henry & to all the members of your family.

> Your faithful friend
> John Torrey

Tear of[f] this Mem.[6] for Prof. Stephen Alexander—for I cannot trust you—

Please send my Settee-bedstead (which I left in the room adjoining the Phil. Hall) to the Canal Basin, to be forwarded to N.Y., & send me a receipt that I may know when to call for it. You would also oblige me by taking out of the case of *Materia Chemica*, in the Hall, a small vial containing *1 gros.* of Potassium. It belongs to me. I purchased it in N.Y. & when I found it was charged twice as much as I can get it for elsewhere, I concluded to pay for it & keep it myself, & get some more for Princeton. Send the vial by any convenient opport[y] to Chilton's.

> J. Torrey

---

poorly attended American Philosophical Society meeting, he observed, "It is too true, that Americans in general interest themselves but little in anything but politics, and what science there is seems broken up into little knots and cabals. Yet there are some good names. . . ." After mentioning Bache, Hare, and others, he continues: "These are men who have risen to eminence without favor or aid from the state, which has no idea of encouraging any kind of knowledge not possessing some

immediate practical bearing" (p. 88).

Daubeny concludes his volume with an evaluation of the strengths and weaknesses of American society and predictions for its future. In a letter to Bache of August 9, 1838 (Bache Papers, Smithsonian Archives), Henry mentions he did not meet Daubeny during his visit to America.

[6] Not done; the memorandum is still attached to the rest of the letter.

TO STEPHEN ALEXANDER

Mary Henry Copy,[1] Family Correspondence,
Henry Papers, Smithsonian Archives

Albany Nov. 2, 1837

My dear Stephen, I arrived off Sandy Hook on Saturday night but owing to the high wind and the want of a pilot did not get within the horse-shoe until Sunday evening and was again detained until Monday afternoon for want of a steam boat. I arrived too late in New York, too late for the evening boat, and therefore took passage the next morning. Near Hudson the machinery gave way and with all these detentions I did [not] reach Albany until eight p. m. Tuesday. I was however compensated for all delay by the

[1] Another Mary Henry Copy, typewritten and less complete, is filed with this one.

meeting with Harriet and the little one. My arrival was published in the morning papers[2] and I had been expected in the day-boat. Harriet had given me up for the night. The boy waited to see me until he could sit up no longer, was with me before I was out of bed and has been with me ever since.

Unfortunately while in Manchester I was robbed of the memorandum book in which I had entered an account of nearly all my observations in Scotland with the names of the persons with whom I had formed acquaintance.[3] During my tour I saw so many places and met with so many persons that unless I can refer to my notes I find it difficult to separate distinctly the different impressions made on my mind. . . . My visit to the west part of Scotland was very hurried. I had remained three weeks or more in Edinburgh and two weeks in Glasgow which left me but few days to spend with my mother's relatives in Ayrshire and to get to Liverpool previous to the meeting of a society which I was obliged to attend. After spending a few days with my relatives on my Mother's side in Ayrshire I started south for Liverpool.

[2] One notice of Henry's return appeared in the *Newark Daily Advertiser*, October 30, 1837, p. 2:

We congratulate the friends of Professor Henry, of Princeton, and the friends of the College of New Jersey generally, upon his safe return from Europe. Professor H. arrived at New York yesterday in the *Toronto* from London, where, and indeed throughout England generally, he has received the attentions due to an individual of distinguished merit.

[3] Henry said earlier that he had lost the memorandum book in Birmingham. He was in both cities on September 18. See above, "Notes of Objects at Cambridge," September 18–20, 1837. Later, he claimed the book had been stolen in Birmingham. Although Henry lost his diary account of his observations in Scotland, there is a short listing of Scottish acquaintances in his Address Book (Box 17, Henry Papers, Smithsonian Archives).

INTRODUCTORY LECTURE
Henry Papers, Smithsonian Archives[1]

[ca. November 11, 1837][2]

Gentlemen

In commencing my course I intend giving this morning a few introductory remarks on the cours intended to be [?given] and definitions in reference to our cours on Natural Philosophy.

[1] This lecture is in Box 18, in a folder entitled "Introductory Remarks and First Lecture."

[2] According to the Minutes of the Faculty of the College of New Jersey, Volume 1835–1845, p. 65, Princeton University Archives, the

I wish if possible to finish the greater part if not my whole course this session. This will give the class more leisure to attend to chemestry &.

In order to accomplish this it will be necessary that I meet the class at least 3 or 4 times a week.

I must request the punctual attendance of the class at the stated hour and also that in no case unless sickness there be an absence from the lecture. This is peculiarly important as time will not permit us to repete the experiments.

I will meet the class onc a week for an [?examination] lecture. This is of great importance as it will be an inducement for the exertion of a closer attention to the subject.

There is no faculty of the mind[3] more under the controll of the volition or more susceptable of being influenced by habit than that of attention.

We can by an effort give strict attention to the subject before us or suffer our thoughs to be drawn aside by every association which may be awaked by the place or the speaker.

Make notes indeavour to write down as many of the facts as can be remembered after lectures.

This will be found an exelent exercise for it often happens that we have a general ide[a] of a subject but no very dis[t]inct knowledge of it that by writing out in full our thoughts we discover our defects & reduce the whole to clearness.

I am anxious to give the class as much information on the subject of my course as possible as time and the extent of our apparatus will admit and I pledge myself to give an experimental illustration of every important principle in Natural Philosophy. In order to accomplish this however considerable labour is necessary in preparation as the apparatus is defective and instead of finding an article for each experimental illustration it is necessary to make one article serve many purposes. Notwithstanding this we hope to shew as many as are given in any college in the country making up by industry what we may be deficient [in] instruments.

---

faculty met on November 11 to distribute the courses among its members. Henry probably delivered his introductory lecture within a few days of this meeting. We know this is the 1837 lecture from the reference to the anticipated arrival of apparatus from Paris.

[3] The goal of higher education in the United States in this period was to train or discipline the various faculties—properties—of the mind.

Each subject exercised only certain faculties, so a broad, balanced curriculum was necessary in order that all the faculties were given attention. Some of the faculties of the mind which concerned American professors were reasoning, demonstration, memory, invention, and, as Henry noted, attention. Stanley M. Guralnick, *Science and the Ante-Bellum American College* (Philadelphia, 1975), pp. 31–32.

A large electrical machine has been ordered from Paris which will probably be received during the winter.

I need not mention the importance of a course of experiments in teaching the truths of science. They give definite ideas which are received with the least labour to the student.

They serve as a system of artificial memory or sensible objects or reference with which to connect a number of particulars otherwise difficult to retain in the mind.

That an experiment should succeed or produce the desired result in most cases requires a favourable condition of many circumstances.

Illustration

Hence persons not in the habit of experimenting do not succeed well particularly before an audience. As in this case the experiment must be performed at once without an opportunity of adjusting the[4]

---

[4] Henry's notes end here. However, by looking at the introductory lectures which Henry delivered in other years we have a fairly good idea of what he then went on to say. The mechanics of the course, including a detailed account of the responsibilities of the students, would have to be taken care of. Then Henry would define the scope of the course. First the purposes, divisions, and methods of science would be discussed. Then natural philosophy would be differentiated from the rest of the physical sciences. At this point Henry could conclude, now ready to introduce the first division of natural philosophy—somatology— to the class at the next lecture. Weiner, "Joseph Henry's Lectures," pp. 68–69.

"RECORD OF EXPERIMENTS"
Henry Papers, Smithsonian Archives

Nov 24 1837[1]

My attention was directed this day to a Phenominon which takes place when a plate of copper is pierced with a small hole and this attempted to be enlarged by a reamer. If the reamer be fore sided and slightly tapering the hole will become a perfect pentagon. If the reamer be a three cornered file the hole becomes square. A perfectly flat reamer tends to form a triangular hole but this is not as well defined as the other two. On a little reflection the following rationally suggested itself to me. The square reamer tends by its

---

[1] Above this entry Henry wrote to himself: "Since last entry, visited Europe." After a long absence from the laboratory, Henry begins again with some miscellaneous observations probably inspired by recent reading. The first, an attempt to explain philosophically the shape of holes reamed in copper plates, deals with the sort of thing Henry might have run across in a magazine like the *Franklin Institute Journal*.

circular motion to produce a round hole but by the pressure given it to make it cut and because it is slightly tapering, it tends by this pressure to form a square hole as it is evident that a hole of this form would be produced were the instrument thrust into the plate without a rotatory motion. The hole which results is therefore intermediate to the circle and the square; a pentagon is this figure. Again when the three cornered reamer is used the pressure tends to form a triangle and the circular motion transformes this into a square, a figure which approximates the circle more than the triangle. On the same principle a flat scewer should form a triangular hole.

Nov 24[th2] Poured a small quantity of alcohol on the surface of sperits of turpentine, singular serpentine action took place over the whole surface. This after about 2 or three minutes ceased. The alcohol then slowly collected into drops and these seperated around the whole basin from the sides as if they were repelled then coalesced and sank to the bottom. In another experiment on the surface of a small glas jar (2 inches in diameter) the alcohol collected all into one large drop which occupied the middle of the glass, always returned when blown to the side as if repelled from the edges.

(Try the effect if the glass is piled or filled above its level with the liquid.)

On spark see some curious experiments described in Phil magazine vol XLVI p 176.[3]

Exp on red hot iron in large coil—make magnet of coil of iron wire round a cylinder of wood or glass, magnetize this by the coil—note the effect.[4]

Make a very long coil, or rather coil of long wire, revolve this in the meridian or on an axis perpendicular to the meridian, see if a spark can be obtained.

Have done so, got currents similar to those by Dr Faraday.[5]

---

[2] Henry initially wrote "Feby" and crossed it out, repeating the November 24th date. We are not sure why.

[3] Henry is mistaken in his citation. The article has not been located.

[4] See *Henry Papers*, 2:145n–146n, 246, for Henry's earlier studies of the effect of heating the cores of electromagnets.

[5] See *Henry Papers*, 2:105.

THOMAS COOPER[1] TO PIERCE MASON BUTLER[2]

Thomas Cooper Papers, South Caroliniana Library,
University of South Carolina[3]

Columbia, Nov. 1837

Sir,

I have to request you to have the goodness to lay before the Board of Trustees the following suggestion. It has been usual for the Board to grant honorary degrees in favor of Citizens of literary eminence. I know of no proposal yet made to the board to confer the same distinction on citizens of the United States whose Scientific discoveries and attainments have contributed to the National reputation. Such an opportunity occurs now.

Professor Joseph Henry of Princetown New Jersey, stands at the head of our scientific men who have suggested and led the way to the very promising discoveries in Electro Magnetism as a moving power of very great expectation & importance. He has just returned from a tour of scientific observation in Europe where his reputation is deservedly established. If the machine of M[r] Davenport of New York should fulfil the public expectation, the original suggestion must be attributed to the very important experiments of Professor Jos. Henry, as I can certify by his descriptions of those experiments to me, ab[t] 3 years ago.[4] I know of no honorary degree conferred by the board of South Carolina, better earned, or that would do more credit to our State than the one now proposed for Professor Henry.[5] I request Sir of the Board of Trustees to take into consideration this proposal of Sir

Your obedient Servant
Thomas Cooper MD

[1] Cooper, political agitator and scientist, first crossed paths with Henry in 1833, when he served as Professor of Chemistry and President of South Carolina College. See *Henry Papers*, 2:122. At the time of this letter he was in retirement, though still politically active.

[2] Butler (1798–1847) was President of the Board of Trustees of South Carolina College and Governor of the state. Butler worked actively in support of education in South Carolina and, as Governor, initiated plans for a public school system. Originally a military man, he died in the Mexican War. *DAB*.

[3] The original is mutilated on the left side and has been reconstructed from a copy of the letter, also in the Thomas Cooper Papers.

[4] For full background on the relations of Cooper, Henry, and Davenport, see *Henry Papers*, 2:122–123, 130–132, 416, 445–448.

[5] On April 17, 1839, Henry wrote Cooper's successor W. H. Ellet, Professor of Chemistry and Mineralogy at South Carolina College, thanking him for an unexpected honor, probably the honorary degree (Henry Papers, Smithsonian Archives). The awarding of the degree was noted in the Columbia, South Carolina, *Telescope* (clipping dated December 12, 1838, among Henry's Honors, Awards, Memberships, 1833–48, Box 39, Henry Papers, Smithsonian Archives).

FROM JOHN P. EMMET[1]

Henry Papers, Smithsonian Archives

University of V^a Decr 4th 1837

Dear Sir

It gives me much pleasure to learn that my enquiry[2] has fallen into your hands;[3] since I am sure it will be both thoroughly and honorably examined. Although I feel a positive conviction of the truth of my main positions,[4] namely the convertibility of elementary colours into each other and the simplicity of white light,[5] still no one will more cheerfully acknowledge any

---

[1] For John Patton Emmet, Professor of Chemistry at the University of Virginia, see *Henry Papers*, 2:388n–389n.

[2] Emmet had submitted a paper to the American Philosophical Society entitled "An Enquiry into the Relation Existing Between Light, Colour, & Shadow, Containing Illustrations Adverse to the Newtonian Doctrine."

[3] At the meeting of the American Philosophical Society of December 1, 1837, a committee consisting of Henry, R. M. Patterson, and Henry Vethake was appointed to evaluate Emmet's paper. We do not have a copy of the committee's report but remarks made by Henry in a letter to Patterson dated January 13, 1838 (Records of the Bureau of the Mint, RG 104, National Archives), lead us to believe that the report was extremely negative. During the meeting of March 16, 1838, it was announced that Emmet wanted to withdraw his paper from consideration. This was undoubtedly a face-saving procedure to avoid having the American Philosophical Society formally reject the paper. Minutes, Archives, American Philosophical Society.

[4] No copy of Emmet's paper has come to light, but from Henry's correspondence—in addition to this letter there is the one from Henry to Patterson, dated January 13, 1838, and one from Patterson to Henry, dated February 9, 1838 (Gratz Collection, State Historical Society of Wisconsin)—and an 1839 version of the paper ("Memoir upon 'Light and Colors,'" Emmet Papers, University Archives, University of Virginia), we have a good idea of its theme. Our knowledge of the details is less certain. Emmet modified his paper even while it was in the hands of the APS committee (Patterson to Henry, February 9, 1838, cited above). Moreover, the version prepared in 1839, to be "submitted to the inspection of Sir J. Herschell or some other distinguished

Philosopher of Europe," clearly differed in many ways from that seen by Henry.

The whole thrust of Emmet's optics was undeniably clear, however: an attack upon Newtonian optics. In this he was not especially original. Throughout the eighteenth and early nineteenth centuries there had been attacks on aspects of Newton's theory of colors. Echoes of at least two appear in Emmet's paper. Johann Wolfgang von Goethe (1749–1832, *DSB*) launched a grand assault upon Newton in his *Zur Farbenlehre*, published in 1810. David Brewster's criticisms of Newton's ideas on colors were expressed in Brewster's *A Treatise on Optics*, 1st American ed. (Philadelphia, 1833), pp. 67–70. We are not arguing that Emmet borrowed ideas from either Goethe or Brewster, although that is a possibility. Rather, we contend only that all three men saw some of the same difficulties in Newton's theory. Emmet was but one in a long line of dissenting natural philosophers. Alternative explanations and theories differed, but all agreed that the experimental evidence did not support all of Newton's contentions. K. T. A. Halbertsma, *A History of the Theory of Color* (Amsterdam, 1949), pp. 53–72.

A comparison of the work of Goethe, Brewster, and Emmet shows clearly that the American was not in the same class as the other two men. He never grasped the importance of understanding the physiology of vision. As a result, a satisfactory explanation of the phenomenon of complementary colors evaded him. As an experimenter, Emmet also proved to be of less quality than either European, not to mention Newton. Unlike Brewster or Goethe, nobody took Emmet's attempt at displacing Newton seriously, especially Henry and his contemporaries.

[5] Emmet's derivation of these two basic tenets is unknown. A possibility is Goethe. He

errour of reasoning or fact which you may point out. Much of my writing I Know is careless from the pressure of other business at the time, and it was my intention to have put the whole subject into a better form for the press. I shall sincerely regret if you should experience any inconvenience from this circumstance; and my principal reason for now addressing you is to request that you will inform me, by mail, of any difficulty which you may experience as to meaning or object. Permit me also to take this occasion to draw your attention to what I view as the main points in most of my experiments, more especially in relation to one experiment which, at our interview,[6] you regarded as consistent with the Newtonian theory.

Hold a piece of white paper before a dark surface and examine it by the prism. One edge will exhibit pure red & yellow and the opposite one pure

 blue. These colors will appear in the same order whether you receive the colored rays into the eye directly or by reflexion. If the refracting angle, m, is shown, as in the fig:,[7] both the edge rays a & b should be resolved by the prism into seven colored rays, each, the red & yellow being next to the angle. Now if any portions of the colored rays, of a, be destroyed by compensation, it must be the *lower* ones, according to the N. theory; and the *blue series* alone should be rendered apparent, see fg:. The *reverse* of this is, however, observed; for only red & yellow will appear: and what then becomes of the violet, indigo

---

had argued that belief in the compound nature of light was absurd. It was obvious to the senses that white light was simple. Colors were created by mixing white light with darkness. The evidence presented for this concept were numerous examples of color being created when light shone through opaque media like the atmosphere. Rudolf Magnus, *Goethe as a Scientist* (New York, 1949), pp. 130–132; George A. Wells, "Goethe's Scientific Method and Aims in the Light of his Studies in Physical Optics," *Publications of the English Goethe Society*, 1967–1968, n.s. *38*:84–87. Whatever the source of these two "main positions," Emmet was unable to sustain the positions under the pressure of the criticism by the committee of the APS. His 1839 paper dropped these points. There, nothing is said about the convertibility of elementary colors, while an explicit denial of the simplicity of white light appears. Emmet instead comes out with a version of the three-color theory; i.e., that all the spectral colors are the result of the combination of portions of the three fundamental colors. Emmet chose red, green, and

blue as his three colors.

The three-color theory was not new. There had been a number of variations offered. The latest was that of Brewster, first presented in 1831. Brewster had chosen red, yellow, and blue as the primary colors. In addition, he argued that the three colors existed over the entire length of the solar spectrum, although with varying intensity. Thus all seven spectral colors are compounds, with red, yellow, and blue simply being those positions on the spectrum where primary red, yellow, and blue are respectively most intense. Brewster, *Treatise on Optics*, pp. 69–70, 315–316.

[6] Perhaps their interview took place at a meeting of the American Philosophical Society.

[7] In Emmet's first figure the diffracted rays exiting the prism are colored. Ray *a* is in three colors: black for green through violet; a sort of brown for the orange and yellow; and red for the red ray. There are only two colors for ray *b*: blue for blue through violet and black for the rest.

& blue? The bottom ray b furnishes the like contradiction, for here the un-compensated rays should be red & yellow and yet the colors *actually* obtained are blue & indigo. Hence I infer that the colored rays are not separated by the prism in consequence of refrangibility. *Secondly*; the blue series is always placed *outside* of the white edge, i e they always appear upon the dark ground, below b,; where as, by their greater refrangibility, they should have the highest position *upon* the white surface. If we say, now, that the eye merely refers them to the position *below* b, I would ask why the same process should not take place with the blue rays of the white ray a? In fact, it is a remarkable feature in my investigations, that this position of the blue *outside* of the white surface entirely, is always shown to exist, since it is apparent that the whole of that white edge is made, by the prism, to change its apparent position in the same direction and nearly to the Same extent as the blue rays.

But it can be shown that there is no ocular deception whatever, by simply using a screen to intercept the rays. Thus, to begin with the ray, a, which only furnishes red & yellow colours, it will be found that the yellow, though *more* refrangible than the red, is actually below it or nearer to the refracting angle, m. Its position, therefore, cannot be represented by the decomposition as shown by the first fig: & which is in accordance with the N. theory.

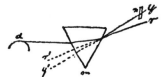

Let us, however, give it the assumed position, i e above the red, as shown in this figure, and then *suppose* that the eye refers it to a place below the red as at y′ of the dotted lines. What should follow from all this? Why, obviously, that when we place the screen in the upper rays which enter the eye, we should cut off the *yellow* rays. Now the reverse of this is found to be the Case; for the screen n, in this position cuts off the red without interfering with the yellow. Nothing surely can be more conclusive, and as the same process is applicable to the blue & indigo rays, which also appear in the inverted order, the conclusion is fully sustained that the colored rays have the same position as that which they exhibit to the eye.[8] I am the more particular in

[8] Emmet's discussion of this phenomenon indicates beyond any doubt that he misunderstood both the geometry and the physiology of the situation. The refraction of the light beams did occur as Newton indicated they would. However, the eye refers the colors in such a way that they appear to have undergone refractions in violation of Newton's theory. Emmet's screening of the red light but not the yellow was not crucial, because it was extremely difficult to screen yellow. The human eye is not sensitive enough to distinguish between pure spectral yellow and a combination of yellow and its spectral neighbors.

From Henry's remarks to Patterson in his letter of January 13, 1838, it seems that Emmet also included an explanation of the converse situation in his paper—a dark patch in front of a light background. Such an inclusion would not be surprising, since Newton's explanation was dependent upon differential refraction, a concept Emmet explicitly rejected. We are un-

mentioning this circumstance now, for two reasons—1ˢᵗ I did not specially notice it in my memoir and 2ⁿᵈ Dᴿ Patterson, who I am told is a member of your Committee, attempted to solve the difficulty of inverted order upon this supposition.[9] Let me beg of you, therefore, to take it fully into consideration.

Another inconsistency, as to the process of compensation, is the following. There should be no pure yellow at all since the red & blue of other white rays would have to fall upon it. Yet the yellow is a pure lemon yellow unalloyed by either red or blue; and in fact, as you will find, the yellow & red *never* appear with the other colors so as to constitute members of the *same* series, there being always an interval of light or shade, no matter how small, between them. If this be true in fact why should we admit the contrary supposition in theory?

But, perhaps, the most difficult matter proposed for your consideration will arise from the generation of new colors, by viewing, through a prism, a black spot or line placed upon a homogeneous color. Select your color where you will & operate with this instrument how you will you shall find no truth in physics better founded. When the contrast in illumination is great, as that between yellow & black, the blue & red colors, thus generated, are uncommonly brilliant. Blue and black are of course less favorable, but blue may be examined upon yellow with entire satisfaction. I entertain such strong confidence in your judgement that I am satisfied you will not regard these striking results as corresponding with any trifling influence of white light. It is evident that we cannot decide the point at issue, if we deny ourselves the aid of *vision* and the mutual support which all my experimental results give to each other cannot fail, I think, to remove any such impression. But if I should be mistaken in my belief, then I beg to refer you to the difficulties, already noticed in this letter, as applicable to white light itself. In fact, you will perceive that the law is a general one for all Kinds of visible luminous matter, both white & Coloured, *that where the deflected ray is bent into light of less illuminating power, it changes to blue & vice versa.*

---

certain what Emmet's alternative explanation was, but we doubt Henry found it at all convincing. Emmet showed little understanding of the phenomenon of refraction. An example of his ignorance was the first proposition of his 1839 paper: "All the colored rays [are] equally refracted within the limits of the prism." Emmet's proposition is based on his theory that only one refraction occurs when light passes through a prism—at the time of emission. No refraction takes place when light enters a prism. The experiments presented as evidence of the theory show that Emmet did not understand something as basic as Snel's law of refraction.

Wells, "Goethe's Scientific Method," pp. 72–77.

[9] We have been unable to locate Patterson's attempt to explain this phenomenon.

Other topics are discussed in My memoir which being of a less elementary character, need not be brought to notice, here.[10]

I have written to you, my dear Sir, a much longer letter than I, at first, intended to do, but my anxiety that you should fully comprehend my views must be my excuse. You have the nursing of my *heir apparent* and I am confident will do it ample justice. All I shall add, therefore, is that I shall be happy to hear from you, upon this or any other subject, whenever you shall have occasion to write.

very truly   John P. Emmet

[10] One of the other topics discussed in Emmet's paper was the creation of colored shadows. Again, it seems that some of Emmet's experiments were not sufficient to prove his contentions. In fact, Emmet himself finally recognized this, as Patterson reported to Henry in his letter of February 9, 1838. Emmet did not accept Goethe's satisfactory explanation of colored shadows as a physiological phenomenon, but rather attempted again to construct a physical explanation. His 1839 paper has a long section in which he attempts to prove that: " 'White rays become colored by crossing colored ones.' The resulting color is the complementary one to the other. In this question I have also discussed the subject of *colored shadows* and shown that this phenomenon is the result of the change which white light undergoes by crossing colored rays." This section, marred by ill-conceived and poorly interpreted experiments, is not convincing. Magnus, *Goethe as a Scientist*, pp. 120–121.

ALEXANDER DALLAS BACHE TO PETTY VAUGHAN
Retained Copy,[1] Bache Papers, Smithsonian Archives

Berlin December 5th 1837

My dear Sir

I am only too much obliged to you for your attention to the sending and divers matters with which I have troubled you from time to time, to complain that Prof Henrys request was not communicated to me.[2] In fact as the matter turned out it made little difference as I had left funds at Paris upon which to draw for the payment. I mentioned it because it seemed carless in my friend Henry to leave me in the dark about his wishes. It only adds one to his many proofs of his *un* worldiness for he actually went to Hottinguers[3] while in Paris to get money on my account & yet has forgotten their adress. The meeting at Liverpool has no doubt has wiped out very many other adresses from his memory for such is his devotion to Physical [science] that

[1] The copy is in what appears to be a juvenile hand and is replete with misspellings; Bache's young sister-in-law Maria may have made the copy for him.

[2] Regarding the purchase of apparatus for solidifying carbonic acid. For the agreement between Bache and Henry, see above, Henry to Coquerel, October 1, 1837.

[3] A major Paris bank.

when once in that stream that he has carried over all ordinary obstacles in the shape of the affairs of common life. The box came safe to hand with the August & Sept no of the Journall Frank. Inst & the numbers of the Atheneum for all them I return my best thanks. To day I have received yours containing a copy of M^r <Snow> Harris's letter: I am very glad to find that he has ordered the articles which he specifies. Please to thank him in my name & to beg him to add the discharging Instruments shown in figs 13 & 16 Philos. Trans for 1834.[4] Be so good as to say to him when the instruments are ready if the artist will forward his account to you which shall be paid. I do not know how it will be best to send the Instruments to Philadelphia, perhaps to send them to London to be shipped direct to Phil. or if the Packets will take them from Portsmouth perhaps it wou[ld] be better to send them there. Of this you will be the best judge. I beg you to decide for me. Adress of the box Girard College for Orphans Phil. A D Bache Prest Care of Wm Hamilton Act^y Frank. Institute Phil. In the case of forwarding such a box besides the Glass with care (and all that) Mr Hamilton out to be apprized of the frail nature of its contents. Excuse my giving you this additional trouble. When you write to your uncle M^r J Vaughan pray give my kindest regards and tell him that I have sent from Hamburgh thro' Bessen, Bessen & Mark[5] & there agents at N York a copy of the Jahrbuch of Shumacker of 1837 and of Rümbers calculations for the Solar Edifice[6] of 1836. Mr Rümber would be much obliged by American observers on that of 15 May 1836 & I hope Mr Vaughan will gratify him by forwarding them which no doubt Philos. Soc. has collected. Neither the sight of the Hamburgh Observatory much less that of Prof Schumacker at Altona would deter the Philos. Soc. from going on in the good work of erecting an Observatory at Philadelphia. Haw Haw[7] The triangle send their

---

[4] Snow Harris's "On Some Elementary Laws of Electricity," *Phil. Trans.*, 1834, pp. 213–246.

[5] Perthes, Besser and Mauke, Hamburg booksellers.

[6] i.e., solar eclipse. In June and July 1838 the Library of the American Philosophical Society recorded Bache's donations of H. C. Schumacher's [*Astronomishes*] *Jahrbuch für 1837* (Stuttgart and Tübingen, 1838) and C. Rümker's *Ueber die Berechnung der Sonnenfinsternisse* (Hamburg, 1837). APS *Proceedings*, 1838–1840, *1*:17, 22. Karl Ludwig Christian Rümker (1788–1862) had been director of the Hamburg Observatory since 1830. Heinrich Christian Schumacher (1780–1850) was Professor of Astronomy at the University of Copenhagen and did his observing at the Royal

facility at Altona. *Poggendorff*.

[7] Bache refers to the continuing problems with the attempts to erect a City Observatory at Rittenhouse Square. Initiated in 1835, the project was jointly sponsored by the City of Philadelphia and the American Philosophical Society. The APS attempted to order equipment through Bache while he was in Europe but Bache never received the order. Difficulty in selecting a site further stalled the project. The City Observatory was never realized, largely because Bache and others felt that existing and planned facilities in Philadelphia, especially the excellent observatory of Central High School, made another observatory unnecessary. (Bache's joking reference to Hamburg and Altona reflects his frustration with those who wanted to proceed anyway.) Whit-

best regards to you and to M^r W Vaughan. Miss Maria observes that by the adittion of my travelling companion[8] it has become a quadrangle. I have already made acquaintainces here which will be both useful & agreable, may communicate to y[ou] therefore continued success in my journey. Has Prof Rogers reached London? I did not know that he intended to visit England this year. He would hardly time his visit so badly as to reach the country after the meeting of the association which must be his principal object in the visit.[9] At the Geological Society he might certainly be heard of. Should Mr Holl[10] call or should you see him give him my reg[ards.]

very truly yours
A D Bache

---

field J. Bell, Jr., "Astronomical Observatories of the American Philosophical Society, 1769–1843," *Proceedings of the American Philosophical Society*, 1969, *108*:7–14.

[8] A Theodore Trewendt translated German materials for Bache during his European trip. A. D. Bache, *Report on Education in Europe* (Philadelphia, 1839), p. 9. Merle M. Odgers, *Alexander Dallas Bache* (Philadelphia, 1947), p. 31. This may be Edward T. Trewendt (1814–1868), bookseller and publisher in Breslau.

Allgemeine Deutsche Biographie.

[9] Probably a reference to Henry Darwin Rogers or William Barton Rogers, although we are unable to verify a London visit at this time by either brother. Henry Darwin Rogers was invited to deliver a paper at the Liverpool meeting but apparently did not attend. *Life and Letters of William Barton Rogers*, 2 vols. (Boston, 1896), *1*:135–136.

[10] See above, Bache to Henry, June 7, 1837, footnote 5.

TO HENRY DARWIN ROGERS[1]
Draft, Henry Papers, Smithsonian Archives

Princeton Dec 5th 1837

My Dear Sir

I regret that I did not again meet you before leaving the city. I wished to have some further conversation on the subject of the casts of the Elgin marbles. We had so short an interview with Mr Biddle on the subject that the matter was not I am afraid perfectly understood.

As the casts of the marbles are presents from the Government and cannot be purchased it is probable that only one set will reach this country. The question then is where should this be placed so that it may be of the greatest public utility.

---

[1] The draft gives no indication of the recipient. In a letter to Bache of August 9, 1838 (Bache Papers, Smithsonian Archives), Henry says he called on Nicholas Biddle with Mr. Rogers. We are assuming he meant Henry Darwin Rogers.

It was concluded by Bache and myself that the copies would be of little use if placed at the city of Washington and that if possible they should be procured for one of our principal cities. Nothing at the time was said about Girard College and the object in placing the affair in the hands of Mr Biddle was not in reference to his connection with that institution but in consideration of his known taste in such matters, his public spirit and the influence of his name in England.

If however it be the intention of the Trustees of Girard College and compatible with the will to make that institution of such a kind that the public can avail themselves of its library of its apparatus of its mechanical models and specimens of the fine arts then it will not be an improper place for the Elgin marbles. But if not then the application should be made in behalf of some more public institution.

The affair however is now before Mr Biddle and I doubt not but he will manage [it] for the best interest of our country.

The following is the information from Mr Children in reference to the copies of the marbles

A set of moldes are now (Oct 1st 1837) making for casting copies of the Elgin marbles for the French Institute. If a proper application were made through the American minister a set of the same might be obtained for the United States.

Or If a number of respectable citizens were to apply in behalf of some public institution seting forth its nature &c and geting the application backed by the government a grant would undoubtedly be made. In the latter case the application should be enclosed in a letter directed to Mr Children one of the curators of the British Museum requesting him to place the same before the Trustees of the museum.

Mr Child[r]en should be made acquainted with the standing of the persons by whom the application is signed inorder to be prepared to answer any questions which might be asked on that head.[2]

---

[2] After seeing the Elgin Marbles in the British Museum in April 1837 (see Henry's diary entry of April 4, 1837, above), Henry and Bache decided to try to get plaster casts for the United States. Failing to interest the American Minister, Andrew Stevenson, Henry approached John George Children just before leaving London. Following Children's instructions outlined in this letter, Henry contacted Nicholas Biddle who was not only a well-known financier but also an admirer of Greek sculpture and architecture. Biddle raised the question at the Girard College Board of Trustees meeting of December 6, 1837, and was authorized to make arrangements to obtain the casts (James Bayard to Nicholas Biddle, December 7, 1837, Biddle Papers, Library of Congress). In the next two years Henry mentioned the subject to Biddle at least twice more (Henry to Bache, August 9, 1838, and July 9, 1839, Bache Papers, Smithsonian Archives). The attempt ultimately failed.

This failure and a later one are described in one of Henry's pocket notebooks ([circa

1848], pp. 115–121, Henry Papers, Smithsonian Archives). In the second attempt, in 1842, Henry worked through a chain of individuals that included in turn Orlando Meads of Albany, Horatio Potter, J. C. Spencer, and Edward Everett, the Minister to London. Everett, not knowing that the source was Henry, questioned the assertion that copies could be had for the asking and requested more definite information (copy, Everett to Spencer, December 17, 1842, Henry Papers, Smithsonian Archives). Henry concluded "that I had not been properly treated in the matter and therefore refused to have anything to do with it."

As Secretary of the Smithsonian, Henry was urged several times to get molds of the Elgin Marbles so that casts could be produced and sold to any academy that wanted them.

In 1873 Henry offered Smithsonian assistance in getting casts of the marbles to W. T. Walters, a fellow Trustee of the Corcoran Gallery of Art who was dispatched to Europe to purchase works of art (Henry to Walters, July 31, 1873, Henry Papers, Smithsonian Archives). Walters was successful; the copies were displayed in the Sculpture Hall of the Corcoran (then in the present Renwick Gallery) when it opened in 1874. Corcoran Gallery of Art, *Catalogue* (Washington, D.C., 1874).

As far as we know, Henry had nothing to do with the copies of part of the Parthenon frieze from the Elgin Marbles in the original Smithsonian building. These were installed in 1902 in a room then known as the Art Room. Although their provenance is unclear, they were probably commercially produced by and purchased from a company dealing in copies of sculpture. Smithsonian Institution, *Annual Report for 1903* (Washington, D.C., 1904), p. 87.

TO JOHN VAUGHAN

Miscellaneous Manuscripts Collection, Library,
American Philosophical Society

Princeton Dec 14ᵗʰ 1837

My Dear Sir

Permit me to introduce to your acquaintance my friend Dr Perrine late American Consul at Campeachy.[1]

Dr P. is much interested in experiments relative to the introduction of Tropical plants into the southern part of the United States. He will exhibit to you a number of specimens of plants which he is confident can be cultivated with success in Florida and which would add much to the wealth of that section of our country.

With much respect
and esteem
Yours &c.
Joseph Henry

[1] Although Henry wrote "Favoured by Dr Perrine" next to the address, a Philadelphia postmark of December 21 indicates Perrine mailed the letter when he reached Philadelphia.

Henry Perrine (1797–1840, *DAB*) had just returned to the United States after serving for ten years as the United States Consul at Campeche, Mexico. A native of New Jersey, Perrine received an M.D. in 1819 from the College of Physicians and Surgeons in New York City (*Columbia Alumni*, p. 198). He practiced medicine in Illinois and Natchez, Mississippi, before his appointment to Mexico, where he collected botanical specimens and gave free medical treatment during a cholera epidemic.

In 1832 Perrine formulated a plan to introduce tropical plants into the United States at a station in southern Florida. His plan was a response to President John Quincy Adams's call to consular officers to suggest foreign plants for cultivation in the United States. In 1838 he received Congressional approval and a grant of land. Unable to occupy the land immediately because of the Seminole War, Perrine and his family moved to a nursery in Florida which he had previously established. In 1840 Perrine was killed by Indians and his house, collections, and records were burned. His family survived.

Perrine received an honorary A.M. from Princeton in 1833. We know nothing of Henry's relationship with him but speculate that they met through John Torrey.

FROM JAMES P. ESPY

Henry Papers, Smithsonian Archives

Phil^a Dec. 24. '37

Dear Sir,

I have received through you Mrs Henry's kind invitation[1] to visit you and her during the holidays and I should be much pleased to do so, but I am now delivering two courses of lectures at the same time, which occupies my whole time.

I think there would be an objection to your mode of trying the permeability of air by aqueous vapour[2] particularly if the tube is placed vertical, for the slightest difference of temperature on the different sides of the tube would cause ascending and descending currents, which would remove the vapour by transportation[3] and not by permeation.

It would be less objectionable to place the tube horizontal or nearly so the water a little the highest. But if the tube was curved as in the annexed

---

[1] Presumably in a letter which has not been located which may also have a description of Henry's method mentioned below.

[2] One of Espy's continuing concerns was whether water vapor could diffuse from a capillary tube, overcoming the resistance of the capillary force without the assistance of air currents. After a series of experiments in the 1830s and 1840s, he concluded that it could not. Henry remained interested in the problem, noting, for example, in a reading note drawn from C. F. Peschel, *Elements of Physics*, 3 vols. (London, 1845), *1*:54, and included in the "Record of Experiments" entry for December 27, 1845:

The same force which elevates a cylinder of water in a fine tube will prevent it from

evaporating. Water in capilliary tubes does not evaporate when hung in the sun for a long time. Mr Espy experiments on this point.

Henry confirmed these statements with experiments of his own. However, when Eben N. Horsford presented contrary results to a meeting of the American Association for the Advancement of Science, Henry modified his stand. He acknowledged that under certain conditions the force of diffusion can be greater than that of surface tension. *Proceedings of the American Association for the Advancement of Science*, 1849, *2*:125–128.

[3] In an undoubted slip of the pen, Espy wrote "pransportation."

figure it would be still better. These curves if numerous I think would retard currents which  might be formed either by unequal heat or unequal moisture if they did not entirely stop them. A mark might be made on the glass at the top of the water which serves the purpose of knowing whether evapouration took place without weighing the acid.

On the 15 Sep I placed a tube as in the ngure on the mantle piece very near the stove in my study having previously merely wet the inside and poured all the water out which would go by turning the mouth downwards. In a short time the moisture disappeared from the inside of the part (B); but during the last 2 months I have seen no diminution of the moisture in the form of little drops in the part (A). The tension of the vapour in that part has always been at least 4 times as great in the atmosphere at the mouth of the tube (B). The tube is about a yard long and $\frac{1}{3}$ of an inch internal diameter and its temperature generally night and day is near 80° sometimes above.

As to Daniells Method of find the height of the clouds by the elasticity of vapour thrusting itself up in a cold atmosphere,[4] if it was true the whole heavens would always be covered with clouds and the base of them would be lower than the base of cumuli as ascertained by my method,[5] and the fact that the heavens are not always covered with clouds is one reason why I suspected that air was not pervious to vapour to any great extent.

As to the whirlwind character of storms I look upon it as too absurd to require refutation. Mr Redfield in Sil. Jour.[6] 20 vol page 46 says that in consequence of the centrifugal force the air spreads out below and is de-

---

[4] Daniell's model of the atmosphere hypothesized a mixture of a dry, permanently-elastic fluid and pure water vapor. The vapor would freely diffuse through the fluid according to Graham's Law, eventually rising to a level where the dew point was low enough to allow condensation (cloud formation). Existing data had, in Daniell's opinion, confirmed the truth of one key component of his model: the dew point did not gradually decrease as the height above sea level increased, but changed abruptly. The atmosphere consisted of distinct strata, with cloud formation confined to certain strata. John Frederic Daniell, *Elements of Meteorology*, 3d ed., 2 vols. (London, 1845), *1*:25, 105–119, 159–167.

[5] Espy rejected the notion that water vapor could diffuse through the rest of the components of the atmosphere, arguing that the vapor could rise only through the agency of air currents. As the air rose it would expand and cool. Clouds would form if the air cooled to the temperature of the dew point. Espy devised the nephelescope, a piece of apparatus which enabled him to measure the drop of temperature when air expanded. Using this information, he was able to develop a formula for the height of cumulus clouds:

$$h = 100\,(t - t')$$

where *h* is the height of the base of the cloud in yards, *t* is the temperature of the air at the earth's surface, and *t'* the dew point at the same location. Temperatures were measured in degrees Fahrenheit. James P. Espy, *The Philosophy of Storms* (Boston, 1841), pp. vii–ix, 27–33.

[6] "Remarks on the Prevailing Storms of the Atlantic Coast, of the North American States," *Silliman's Journal*, 1831, 20:17–51.

pressed in the middle and thus accounts for the fall of the barometer in the middle and for the rain by bringing the cold stratum of the upper atmosphere in contact with the humid stra[tum] of the surface particularly in the more central portions of the storm. And in his essay in the Frank. Jour.[7] Ja Feb '37 He says he has but little objection to My formula on this subject in which I demonstrated that with such a centrifugal force as Mr. Red. supposes the air would move outwards from the centre with a velocity of 280 feet per second and of course downwards with even a greater velocity in the centre. Now in this last essay he also says "it is not my intention to deny an upward movement or tendency at the centre of a whirlwind storm; for of such a movement, apart from theory, I have long since obtained good evidence." It is impossible for me to feel the necessity of making any further comment on such contradictions, than merely to remind you that if air should be depressed in the middle of a storm its capacity for vapour would be increased and no deposition could take place. And that in the central parts of the storm no mixture with the lower atmosphere could take place. This mixture could only be in the borders. I beg of you to study my theory you will be rewarded. Your College will derive vast benefit by its early introduction into it.[8]

If you have a holiday come down and stay at my house.

Yours truly
J. P. Espy

P.S. If you think favourably of my plan of simultaneous observations over the U.S. do write to some member of Congress[9] to advocate the bill as soon as it shall be introduced by J. Sergeant.[10]

---

[7] "In Reply to Mr. Espy, on the Whirlwind Character of Certain Storms," *Journal of the Franklin Institute*, February 1837, n.s. *19*:112–127. For the background of the Espy-Redfield debate on storms, see *Henry Papers*, 2:195–196, 455–456.

[8] Henry did eventually accept Espy's theory of storms, although with some reservations. It is unlikely, however, that that acceptance greatly transformed the life of a Princeton student. Meteorology played a trivial part in the Princeton curriculum during Henry's tenure. There wasn't even a separate section for it in the natural philosophy course. This was in contrast to other colleges—Yale, for example, where Denison Olmsted thought meteorology worthy of an entire course. "Meteorology in its Connection with Agriculture," *Scientific Writings of Joseph Henry*, 2 vols. (Washington, D.C., 1886), 2:293–306; Weiner, "Joseph Henry's Lectures," p. 251; Timothy

Dwight, *Memories of Yale Life and Men, 1845–1899* (New York, 1903), p. 143.

[9] Espy wanted representatives of learned societies and colleges to petition Congress to establish a national system of meteorological observers, "one observer to each 100 miles square, so that we may know when every shower commences and terminates, the course it moves &c. Believing that this is the only information now wanted to predict Rain." (Espy to A. D. Bache, September 18, 1836, Rhees Collection, Henry E. Huntington Library.)

[10] John Sergeant (1779–1852), a graduate of Princeton (1795) and a leading member of the Philadelphia bar, was a member of the House of Representatives from Pennsylvania. He served in the House from 1815 through 1823, again in 1827–1829, and from 1837 until 1841; he was successively a Federalist, a National Republican, and a Whig. In 1832 he was a candidate for Vice President, running with Henry

Clay on the National Republican ticket. Sergeant was an advocate of internal improvements and a strong central government. *DAB*.

Sergeant's motion, introduced on March 26, 1838, was very vague, asking only "that a committee be appointed to inquire into the expediency of encouraging and aiding meteorological observations throughout the United States." *Congressional Globe*, 25th Cong., 2d sess., 1838, *6*:261. It was not approved. It was not until 1842 that Espy's scheme for a national meteorological system received Congressional support. This topic will recur in the *Henry Papers*; after he came to the Smithsonian Institution, Joseph Henry sponsored a national meteorological network.

TO LEWIS R. GIBBES[1]

Lewis R. Gibbes Papers, Library of Congress

Princeton Dec 27th 1837

My Dear Sir

I am happy to learn by our Friend Dr Hun that you have returned in health to your own country ready I presume to commence the practical application of the knowledge obtained by Foreign study.

Agreeably to my promise made in Paris I send you a copy of one of Mr Whewell's papers on the tides.[2] This is the only paper he had on hand relative to the subject. The copies of all the others had been distributed.

After leaving Paris I returned to London *via* Belgium, visited Edinburgh and Glasgow, then went to the meeting of the association at Liverpool, from there to Cambridge and thence to London to sail in the Packet of the 1st of October.

---

[1] Lewis Reeve Gibbes (1810–1894) graduated from South Carolina College in 1829 and received an M.D. from the Medical College of South Carolina in 1836. He then studied in Paris at the Sorbonne and the Jardin des Plantes. He met Henry in Paris probably through their mutual friend Thomas Hun. Gibbes never practiced medicine but rather devoted himself to teaching and research in natural history and several branches of natural philosophy. He taught mathematics at South Carolina College from 1831 to 1835. On his return from Europe, he became a professor at the College of Charleston, where he spent the next fifty years teaching almost every scientific subject including mathematics, physics, chemistry. Although astronomy was said to be his first love, most of his publications were in natural history. A heavy teaching load may have hindered more extensive publication. Yet Gibbes was knowledgeable and competent in the areas he taught. In the 1840s and 1850s,

Henry and Gibbes carried on an extensive correspondence on electricity, on theoretical aspects of natural philosophy and on the philosophy of science. A dedicated teacher, Gibbes also exchanged ideas with Henry on the teaching of natural philosophy. Portions of this highly interesting correspondence will be published in later volumes of this series. Howard A. Kelly, *A Cyclopedia of American Medical Biography*, 2 vols. (London and Philadelphia, 1912); Thomas Carey Johnson, Jr., *Scientific Interests in the Old South* (New York and London, 1936), pp. 133–134. Gibbes was a member of the American Association for the Advancement of Science. Sally Gregory Kohlstedt, *The Formation of the American Scientific Community* (Urbana, Chicago, London, 1976), Appendix.

[2] In the mid-1830s William Whewell authored several papers on tidal phenomena. See above, Henry to Alexander, April 10, 1837, footnote 29.

I was much delighted with this tour and now regret that I stopped so long in Paris. The time would have been much more profitably spent in Great Britain.

I visited Sir David Brewster at his residence near Melrose and was highly delighted with the result. He spent two days principally in instructing me in his methods of experimenting on light.

At Edinburgh I was present at the experiments of Mr Russel[3] on the subject of waves &c. Also made a visit with M. Fresnel (The French commissioner of Light House and Brother of the celebrated Fresnel) to the Bell Rock light House.

On the subject of the resistance of fluids, you gave an exposition of the *new* theory of Prof Wallace[4] in the 55th No of Sillimans Journal.[5]

Now that I know you I of course take more interest in your papers and have looked at the one mentioned. Your directions are simple plain and interesting. I cannot say however that I am fully convinced of the truth of the hypothesis or that it is an accurate expression of the Law of the Phenomina.

As to its orginality you will please refer to the Philosophical Magazine

[3] See Henry's diary for August 10, 1837, footnote 6.

[4] Reverend James Wallace (?–1851), born in Ireland, was first an instructor at the Catholic college in Georgetown and then Professor of Mathematics at South Carolina College from 1820 to 1834, when a reform administration forced him out. After leaving, Wallace retired to a farm near Columbia. He published several articles on mathematics and applied mathematics in the *Southern Review*. Maximilian La Borde, *History of the South Carolina College*, 2d ed. (Charleston, South Carolina, 1874), pp. 184–186.

[5] "On the General Principles of the Resistance of Fluids, in a Notice of the Fifth Article of No. xv of the Southern Review," *Silliman's Journal*, 1835, 27:135–139. Wallace's article, as reported by Gibbes, was a review of William Fairbairn's *Remarks on Canal Navigation* (London, 1831) and Thomas Tredgold, "A Theory of the Resistance of Fluids, Compared with the Best Experiments," *Phil. Mag.*, 1828, n.s. 3:249–262. Both of the authors under review were civil engineers dealing with complicated problems in the theory and application of fluid mechanics. Wallace considered the problem of the resistance of a plane moving in an incompressible fluid. His "new theory" was that "If the inclination of the plane vary, the resistance perpendicularly to the plane will vary as the sine of the angle of inclination." Wallace viewed it as an important corrective to the Newtonian proposition that the resistance varied with the *square* of the sine. However, as Henry will point out below, Thomas Tredgold put forward the same theorem as Wallace in an earlier article, "Researches on the Theory of Hydro-dynamics," *Phil. Mag.*, 1826, 68:11–13, 112–116. Tredgold referred to errors in the demonstration of Proposition xxxiv, Book 2 of Newton's *Principia*.

Although theoretical and mathematical justifications were given for the revision of the Newtonian theorem, the issue seemed to arise from experimental and practical observation that the resistance was greater than the law of the square of the sines predicted. Wallace cites numerous authors who noted the discrepancy between theory and experiment. Fairbairn, for example, pointed out the anomaly with canal boats. This law of fluid resistance remained a problem especially for engineers. In his *Natural Philosophy* (New York, 1842), the engineer Renwick states that, because of problems with the theoretical law, "we are therefore compelled to rely upon experiment for the true laws. . . ." (p. 192).

(not the vol for 1828 but) for 1826 vol 68 page 12 where in a paper by Tredgold you will find the following.

"The demonstration of this Prop in the Principia depends on its being proved that the efficacy of a particle to resist a motion of a surface is as the square of the sine of the angle of inclination of that surface to the direction of its motion. Now I contend that this is not true, but that the real ratio of the resistances is simply as the *sine* of the angle of inclination."

(Here follows the demonstration.)

Let me hear from you as soon as convinient. I will not however promise (for I dare not do so) to be a good correspondant.

In haste Yours Truly
Joseph Henry

P.S. I purchased as you know a lot of articles in Paris of M Pixii. They were to be sent with several boxes of books and other articles by the first of September but most provoking they have not yet arrived. Did you according to promise put into one of my boxes a copy of the book on the art of glass blowing?

Have you seen the report of the meeting of the association at Liverpool? The most correct account you will find in the Nos of the Athineum although there are many mistakes in this. I was on the whole much pleased with the meeting but came to the conclusion that it was only a scientific Jubilee and not a place at which to present important papers. The money given to working men of science for the pursuit of certain experiments is the most important feature of the Institution.

"RECORD OF EXPERIMENTS"
Henry Papers, Smithsonian Archives

Dec 29th 1837

Tried to repeat the exp. of Peltier of the production of cold by the thermo electric pile, and a current of galvanism.[1] The result was an increase

---

[1] Jean Peltier's discovery that cold was produced at the junction of the components of certain thermoelectric couples was announced in "Nouvelles expériences sur la caloricité des courants électriques," *Annales de chimie et de physique*, 1834, 56:371–386. In this particular experiment the couple was bismuth and antimony. Cold was produced when the current traveled from the bismuth to the antimony, and heat when the direction was reversed. This phenomenon is now known as the "Peltier effect."

A presentation copy of Peltier's paper survives in the Henry Library. Unfortunately, Peltier's inscription was partially destroyed when the reprint was bound.

of temperature. The arrangement was not however well made, the conducting wires may have influenced the result.

Try exps on the conduction of magnetic bars for heat and electricity.[2]

Electricity from freezing water.[3] Try electricity from melting sulphur &c Repeat the experiment for determining if the magnitude of a body changes by magnetizing. Enclose soft iron bar in glass tube.[4]

[2] Henry would later conduct experiments on the conductivity of magnetized iron for electricity. "Record of Experiments," April 7, 1838, Henry Papers, Smithsonian Archives.

[3] A change of state could produce static electricity. Henry refers to experiments which illustrate this fact in notebook [23894]; see, for example, the second entry of March 15, 1836, printed above.

[4] This experiment is recorded in Henry's "Record of Experiments," April 10, 1840. It will be discussed in the next volume of the *Henry Papers*.

❦ APPENDIX ❧

BILLS FOR PHILOSOPHICAL APPARATUS

*Folder of Accounts with Various Instrument- and Apparatus-Dealers,
Joseph Henry for the College of New Jersey, 1837,
Princeton University Archives*

The scientific instruments appearing in the following two sets of bills constitute a substantial portion of the philosophical apparaus Henry bought for Princeton while he was abroad. While several important items of equipment were obtained in London—including a magnetoelectric generator from E. M. Clarke and an expensive Dent chronometer—most of the purchases were made in Paris, the home of many superb instrument makers. Of the 151 pieces Henry bought abroad, 132 were from French manufacturers. (Henry's other bills for apparatus are contained in the same folder.) Pixii and Soleil, who presented Henry with the invoices printed below, were among the foremost manufacturers and dealers of philosophical instruments of their day. As the lists reflect, Soleil specialized in optical apparatus while Pixii's forte was electrical equipment. A miscellany of other items came from other Parisian dealers.

The Soleil and Pixii lists are intended to be illustrative of Henry's European buying and of standard instruments commonly available for physical laboratories. As was the case at the Albany Academy, Henry sought to equip his laboratory with both teaching and professional research apparatus. The articles are of varying sophistication. (The truly specialized research instruments Henry generally had to fashion himself.) Some pieces will appear in later lecture and laboratory notes. Many of the articles on the list Henry had seen while touring the laboratories of European scientists like Babinet. While perhaps not fully evident in his diaries, which concentrate on scientific and technological sightseeing, Henry shopped extensively for the apparatus he was commissioned to obtain as well as for other articles requested by scientific friends like Torrey.

In the left column of the Pixii account are catalog numbers specifying items listed in Pixii's *Catalogue des principaux instrumens de physique, chimie, optique, mathématiques* (Paris, 1835), a marked copy of which survives in Henry's Library. The Pixii bill is dated April 14, 1838 (the date of Pixii's delayed shipment to Henry); the Soleil bills are not dated. Henry evidently not only selected items on his visits to their shops but ordered later additions by mail. The story of Henry's financial arrangements for these purchases is a long and entangled

540

one, carefully documented in Allen Shenstone, "Joseph Henry's Bills, 1832–1837–1844–1865," *Princeton University Library Chronicle*, 1967, *28*:150–155. Although initially promised $5000 by the Princeton Alumni Association for the apparatus, due to financial circumstances Henry ended up with a mere $600. He was forced to curtail his purchases and to resort to personal resources as well as to money made available to him by Henry James and others. The European apparatus came to $1410. Henry submitted vouchers for reimbursement for $1143 (unreimbursed expenses of $810 plus $333 interest) to the Princeton Trustees in 1844. (For his accounting Henry used the prevailing rate of 5 francs per dollar.) Unable to pay this and other claims at the time, the Trustees gave Henry a note for payment in one year with interest. However, the note remained unpaid until 1865–a year after Henry himself became a member of the Princeton Board of Trustees.

PIXII

Père et Fils

Catalogue		Francs.	Cˢ
<u>1835</u>			
N<u>os</u> 4	Plan de marbre noir et bille d'ivoire pour l'élasticité.	15	
53	Appareil des tubes capillaires.	18	
65	Areomètre universel pour tous les liquides plus légers ou plus pesants que l'eau.	12	
69	fontaine d'Héron en cristal montée en cuivre. . . .	90	
103	Appareil pour la congélation de l'eau dans le vide composé d'une cloche en cristal d'une capsule en cristal et d'une en métal.	12	
115	Un grand tube pour la chûte des corps.	36	
120	flacon à vaporiser l'éther.	3	
129	Nouvel appareil d'Oerstead pour la commmpressibilité de l'eau.	70	
144	Thermomètre à maxima et minima sur métal. . . .	25	
150	Bouillant de Franklin.	2	50
153	Deux grands miroirs paraboliques concaves en cuivre poli de 18 pouces de diamètre montés sur des guéridons en bois pour la réflexion des rayons calorifiques.	150	
158	Le thermomètre differentiel de Leslie.	15	
159	Le thermoscope de Rumfort.	15	

215	Nouvel appareil de Mr Gay-Lussac pour le dégagement de l'hydrogène servant à remplier le pistolet et la vessie.......................	36	
		499	50
229	Ballon en baudruche de 20 pouces.............	10	
263	Machine electrique de plateau de 36 pouces N° 263 avec conducteur comme pour 30 p^{es} N° 264....................................	750	
278	Tableau magique de Franklin................	8	
297	Carillon à trois timbres pour suspendre à un conducteur..............................	9	
302	Maisonnette pour démontrer les effets de la foudre et la propriété du paratonnerre................	27	
305	Pistolet de Volta en fer blanc vernissé 2 pièces...	5	
314	Le thermomètre électrique de Kinerstley........	18	
323	Appareil a percer la carte dans le vide..........	12	
324	Appareil à percer le verre...................	15	
325	une presse pour la fusion de l'or..............	10	
331	Deux cylindres isolés pour l'électricité par influence..............................	50 50	
337	Grand condensateur pour le développement de l'électricité par contact monté sur un électroscope à feuilles d'or avec disques en zinc et en cuivre isolés...............................	50	
340	Electrophore de 15 pouces avec soufflet........	30	
347	Globe en cristal garni d'un robinet et d'une tige mobile pour faire voir l'effet de l'électricité dans le vide, dans l'air comprimé et à travers les différens gaz............................	36	
351	Grand tube étincellant......................	15	
354	Tableau étincellant monté sur son pied.........	15	
358	Cylindre de verre dépoli d'un bout pour l'électricité par frottement....................	3	
409	Cloche de verre suspendue pour les vibrations....	36	
410	Sonomètre ou monocorde avec règles divisées poids et chevalets mobiles..................	90	
	Un diapason complet.......................	140	
416	Soufflet à pédale avec assortement de tuyaux montés sur un sommier d'après la méthode de Mr Grénier..................................	450	

417	La Sirène acoustique de M<u>e</u> Cagnard Latour.....	100
422	Deux petites cuves carrées en glace avec cloison dans leur diagonale formant double prisme sans garniture en cuivre à 12^f....................	24
		2,382 50

"	Un prisme garni seulement de sa boîte en cuivre..	15
554	Un pied de corde en fer pour echantillon de conducteur de paratonnerre....................	1
556	Un litre de vernis pour le cuivre..............	10
"	4 vases en cristal a pied et à bords renversés......	14
"	3 supports en bois dont 2 tournés et un pour la [?...]....................................	18
"	4 feuilles de cuivre très minces pour imiter le bruit de la pluie..................................	2
"	100 Larmes Bataviques......................	3
"	2 éolipyles en verre........................	2
"	Un petit sceau en cuivre....................	3
"	Une planche noire à deux disques mobiles pour les expériences de la lumière.................	8
"	Batterie électrique de 12 cocaux complette......	100
85	Entonnoir hydraulique......................	4
86	Vases versant deux liquides..................	15
72	Modèle de la vis d'Archimède................	50
106	Plans de glace sans support..................	15
"	4 éprouvettes a pied en cristal—à 2^f...........	8
"	Emballage: 6 grandes caisses, plusieurs caissons pour les objets fragiles fournitures et façon d'en caissage................................	130
	Total	2,780 50

Pour Acquit
Pixii père et fils

SOLEIL Fils, OPTICIEN

N^{os}		Franc.	Cent.
1	appareil polarisation nörremberg..............	50	
2	appareil diffraction de M^{rss} Babinet et geurund..	200	
3	presse a comprimer le verre..................	12	
4	idme a courber le verre....................	12	
5	appareil a chauffer le verre.................	5	

6 analyseur a prisme........................	12	
7 pince a tourmaline........................	30	
8 9 verres trempes a 3 chaques.................	27	
9 un petit support.........................	2	
10 un clivage de spath colle entre deux prismes de glaces.............................	4	
11 plomb carbonaté.........................	6	
12 Appareil savart.........................	10	
13 2 bovase a 2^f chaque......................	4	
14 collection 7 quartz perpendiculaire differante epausseur.......................	28	
15 2 plaque de quartz parallèle.................	10	
16 verre Colore pour les couronnes au soleil.......	5	
17 nitrate de potasse........................	2	
18 sucre.................................	2	
19 tartrate de soude et potasse.................	2	
	423	
20 biscromate de potasse......................	2	
21 tourmaline perpendiculaire..................	4	
22 lentille cilindrique monte sans mouvement.....	18	
23 prisme de flint-glass pour les ray du spectre......	25	
24 5 petits pentins.........................	12	
25 glace noircie encadre......................	6	
26 2 plaques de quartz perpendiculaire rotation inverse...........................	10	
27 quartz enfumé...........................	6	
28 mica a un axe...........................	2	
29 idme a deux axes.........................	2	
30 taffetas gomme..........................		50
31 tourmaline en aiguille.....................	3	
32 un tube...............................		50
Total	514	00

Pour Acquit
Soleil fils

SOLEIL Fils, OPTICIEN

N^{os} des articles	Franc.	Cent.
33 un spath perpendiculaire a 1 axe..............	4	
34 un polariscope de M^r savart (quartz oblique)....	8	

35 Deux verres pour presse a Comprimer a
50^{ct} chaque.............................   1

36 idm ....Courber   1

37 idm ....Chauffer   1^f la piece   2

38 un tube pour la polarisation Circulaire.........   11

39 un prisme de spath.........................   8

40 un lycopode entre deux verre blanc...........   1

41 un quartz et amethyste.....................   5

42 un arragonete de Boheme...................   4

43 un appareil de Monsieur Müller..............   20

44 Scier une plaque de cristal de roche en trois trais   3

45 un appareil pour recevoir la pince à tourmaline
pour les experience au soleil.................   3

46 un prisme ange pour les liquide..............   40

Total   111

Pour Acquit
Soleil fils

Under a name, "letter from" signifies a letter from that person to Henry, while "letter to" indicates a letter from Henry to that person. When Henry is neither sender nor recipient, the names of both parties are given. In the case of Henry, "letters from," followed by a list of names, indicates letters to Henry; "letters to," Henry's letters to various recipients. Subentries are so arranged that letters and documents precede the customary alphabetical listing.